Mission Handbook

U.S. and Canadian Ministries Overseas

2001-2003

(18th edition)

Edited by John A. Siewert and Dotsey Welliver

Evangelism and Missions Information Service

Wheaton College Wheaton, Illinois 60187-5593

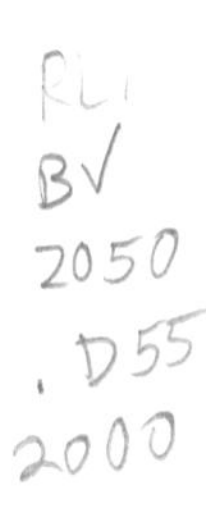

Mission Handbook
U.S. and Canadian Christian Ministries Overseas 2001-2003
(18th edition)

Edited by John A. Siewert and Dotsey Welliver

Published by EMIS, a division of the Billy Graham Center,Wheaton College,Wheaton, IL

Printed in the United States of America. Cover design: Dona Diehl

ISBN 0-9617751-5-7

For information about other publications or resources of EMIS or the Billy Graham Center, phone (630) 752-7158, E-mail: emis@wheaton.edu or visit the website: www.billygrahamcenter.org

Contents

Abbreviations

Admin.	Administrative, administrator
Am.	America, American
Apt.	Apartment
Assoc.	Associate, Association
Ave.	Avenue
Bd.	Board
Blvd.	Boulevard
Cen.	Central
CEO	Chief Executive Officer
Ch(s).	Church(es)
Co.	Company
Comte.	Committee
Comm.	Commission
Conf.	Conference
Cong.	Congregational
Conv.	Convention
COO	Chief Operating Officer
Coord.	Coordinator, Coordination
Ctr.	Center
Dept.	Department
Dev.	Development
Dir.	Director
Div.	Division
Dr.	Doctor, Drive
E.	East
Ed.	Education
Exec.	Executive
Flwshp.	Fellowship
Frgn.	Foreign
Gen.	General
Govt.	Government
Hdq.	Headquarters
Hts.	Heights
Hwy.	Highway
Inc.	Incorporated
Inst.	Institute
Intl.	International
Is(ls).	Island(s)
Lit.	Literature
Mgr.	Manager
Min(s).	Ministry(ies)
Msn.	Mission
Msny(s).	Missionary(ies)
Mtg.	Meeting
N.	North
NA	Not Applicable
NASB	New American Standard Bible
Natl.	National
NE	Northeast
NIV	New International Version
NR	Not reported
NW	Northwest
Ofc.	Office
Org.	Organization
Pres.	President
P.O.	Post Office
Rsch.	Research
Rd.	Road
Rev.	Reverend
Rm.	Room
Rep.	Republic
S.	South
SE	Southeast
Secy.	Secretary
Soc.	Society
St.	Saint, Street
Sta.	Station
Supt.	Superintendent
Ste.	Suite
Svc(s).	Service(s)
SW	Southwest
TEE	Theological Education by Extension
Theol.	Theology, Theological
U., Univ.	University
VP	Vice President
W.	West
Wld.	World

Canada

AB	Alberta
BC	British Columbia
MB	Manitoba
NB	New Brunswick
NF	Newfoundland
NS	Nova Scotia
NT	Northwest Territories
ON	Ontario
PE	Prince Edward Island
PQ	Quebec
SK	Saskatchewan
YT	Yukon Territory

United States

AK	Alaska
AL	Alabama
AR	Arkansas
AZ	Arizona
CA	California
CO	Colorado
CT	Connecticut
DE	Delaware
DC	District of Columbia
FL	Florida
GA	Georgia
HI	Hawaii
IA	Iowa
ID	Idaho
IL	Illinois
IN	Indiana
KS	Kansas
KY	Kentucky
LA	Louisiana
MA	Massachusetts
MD	Maryland
ME	Maine
MI	Michigan
MN	Minnesota
MO	Missouri
MS	Mississippi
MT	Montana
NC	North Carolina
ND	North Dakota
NE	Nebraska
NH	New Hampshire
NJ	New Jersey
NM	New Mexico
NV	Nevada
NY	New York
OH	Ohio
OK	Oklahoma
OR	Oregon
PA	Pennsylvania
PR	Puerto Rico
RI	Rhode Island
SC	South Carolina
SD	South Dakora
TN	Tennessee
TX	Texas
UT	Utah
VA	Virginia
VT	Vermont
WA	Washington
WI	Wisconsin
WV	West Virginia
WY	Wyoming

Other Countries/Areas

BR Virgin Isls	British Virgin Islands
CIS	Commonwealth of Independent States (used when an individual state was not specified or to indicate multiple states/republics)
Equat Guinea	Equatorial Guinea
Fr Polynesia	French Polynesia
Neth Antilles	Netherlands Antilles
Papua New Guin	Papua New Guinea
St. Chris-Nevis	St. Christopher and Nevis
Trinidad & Tobg	Trinidad & Tobago
Turks & Cai Isl	Turks & Caicos Islands
United Arab Emr	United Arab Emirates
Wallis & Fut Is	Wallis & Futuna Islands

Introduction

The purpose of the *Mission Handbook* is to provide the reader with ready access to vital and current information about Christian mission agencies based in the U.S. and Canada that are engaged in overseas (all countries beyond the U. S. and Canada) ministries. As such, it provides the user with the most complete information available in a single publication. The term "agency" is used in the broad sense referring to all denominational boards, nondenominational societies, and other organizations involved in overseas mission.

The United States, Canada, and the Rest of the World

Including only U.S. and Canadian agencies with overseas mission activities has over the years given manageable boundaries to this survey and publication effort. Some of the agencies are also involved in ministries in the U.S. and Canada but home mission data by definition is not included.

Mission agency activity for much of the rest of the world is provided in other publications. For example, non-Western world mission agency information is given in *From Every People: A Handbook of Two-Thirds World Missions* (1989). A continuing series of Christian handbooks with mission sections have been published for Britain and parts of Europe. At various times mission agency information for countries in Africa, Asia, South America, and Oceania has been published in those countries. (See the bibliography for a list of some of these publications.)

The last worldwide publication from the perspective of mission agencies was *The Encyclopedia of Modern Christian Missions: The Agencies* (1967) with Burton L. Goddard as editor. The *World Christian Encyclopedia* (1982) edited by David B. Barrett and *Operation World: The Day-by-Day Guide to Praying For the World* series (latest in 1993) by Patrick Johnstone give overall country totals for missionary sending and receiving.

This Edition of the *Mission Handbook*

The information about the agencies and their fields of service was obtained via a questionnaire shown in the Appendix. In a few cases it was obtained by e-mail, fax, or phone. In the past decade the questionnaire has changed some from survey to survey as the times and mission agencies themselves have changed. Key questions, however, have stayed the same over extended periods of time. For example, questions relating to financial data have used the same definitions since the late 1970s. The countries of service and field personnel questions have remained the same since the early 1990s when the "more than 4 years" definition for long-term personnel was instituted. These definitions were determined in consultation with editors of other mission directories from several countries and the heads of two national mission associations.

The essays for chapters 1–3 have been contributed by Paul Borthwick, John Orme, and Luis Bush, all veterans of the world missions scene. Scott Moreau, who served as a missionary in Africa before taking up his current teaching post at the Wheaton College Graduate School, used his computer expertise to analyze the survey database and come up with a variety of ways to view the data.

Brief History of the *Mission Handbook*

With the Handbook's new home now at the Evangelism and Missions Information Service (EMIS) of the Billy Graham Center at Wheaton College near Chicago, it seems appropriate to briefly review the almost 50-year history of the Handbook and highlight those who have had key roles in providing this unique information resource.

The direct antecedent of the *Mission Handbook* first appeared in 1953 with the title *Foreign Missionary Agencies in the United States: A Check List.* It was compiled and mimeographed by the Missionary Research Library (MRL) in New York under director R. Pierce Beaver. The MRL had been founded in 1914 at the initiative of John R. Mott who chaired the World Missionary Conference at Edinburgh, Scotland, in 1910 and headed its continuation committee.

The 1960 edition was spiral bound and typeset with the title *Directory of North American Protestant Foreign Missionary Agencies* as MRL directors Frank W. Price and Herbert C. Jackson expanded and enhanced the publication.

In 1968 the publication became a cooperative effort of MRL and the Missions Advanced Research and Communication (MARC) Center, a division of World Vision International near Los Angeles. The title became *North American Protestant Ministries Overseas Directory.* Under MARC director Edward R. Dayton, the information was placed in electronic storage and processed by a computer for the first time in 1968.

In 1973 the title included "Mission Handbook" as the publication continued to be enhanced with related articles and expanded analyses of the survey data. For the first time it was published in conventional book size. In 1976 MARC became the sole publisher and in 1979 Samuel Wilson became director of MARC.

The *Mission Handbooks* of the 1990s contained chapters by MARC director Bryant L. Myers which brought together information from various sources displayed as maps, charts, graphs, pictures, and other forms to give a global perspective of evangelism and missions. Also in the 1990s, chapters from the Catholic and Orthodox mission communities were added and "Protestant" in the title was changed to "Christian."

A Word of Caution

Statistics relating to overseas missionary endeavors suffer from the same problems as statistics in general and religious statistics in particular; namely, they may not be comparable because of different interpretation of the questions even though they have been honed to avoid this as much as possible. Even within the same agency some reporting practices may not be consistent from survey to survey because of personnel changes or changes in the agency's practices between surveys.

The reader should exercise caution when comparing statistics between agencies, within the same agency from different years, or combining statistics from different agencies. It can be inaccurate to draw conclusions about a particular agency, group of agencies, or a particular country without being aware of, or securing, additional information that was not in the scope of this survey.

Thanks and Acknowledgments

This 2001–2003 edition of the *Mission Handbook* is possible because of the dedicated efforts of many individuals and organizations. Our special, heartfelt thanks go to those persons in each agency who completed the questionnaires. In larger agencies this may have been a collaborative effort involving executives, accountants, researchers, personnel department staff, and others. In any case, this can be a time-consuming task for busy mission executives, and we deeply appreciate their efforts in the cause of worldwide mission. We cannot say too strongly how grateful we are.

Co-editors John Siewert of MARC in Monrovia, California, and Dotsey Welliver of EMIS in Wheaton, Illinois, kept in close contact by e-mail, phone, fax, and postal mail during the months of the project. Also John spent time in Wheaton, braving snow and cold winds, on several occasions when business brought him to the Chicago area. The team included BGC associate director Ken Gill as executive editor. MARC/World Vision staff members Bryant Myers and Dwayne Sedig were very supportive and helpful throughout the transfer of the project to EMIS.

Others who made a valuable contribution during the early stages of the project through advisory meetings and the sharing of information included Jonathon Bonk, David Broucek, Scott Holste, Grant McClung, Paul McKaughan, Larry Fullerton, and David Mays. We much appreciate their interest and counsel.

Additionally, we acknowledge a great debt of gratitude to the contributors of the first four chapters: Paul Borthwick, John Orme, Luis Bush, and Scott Moreau. And to Geoff Tunnicliffe, Chair of the Task Force for Global Mission for the Evangelical Fellowship of Canada. He furnished valuable insights concerning the section of Canadian analysis in Chapter 4.

Many hours of invaluable aid were provided in the form of technical database assistance by Dr. John Hayward of the Wheaton College Computer Science Department. EMIS staff member Deborah Ferguson provided hours of excellent service with data entry. And EMIS designer Dona Diehl furnished the cover and other help as needed.

We are always grateful to all those people who make special efforts between editions to help us keep the directory updated. To update any of the information in this directory or to suggest a new listing, contact:

EMIS, P.O. Box 794, Wheaton, IL 60189
Phone: (630) 752-7158
Fax: (630) 752-7155
E-mail: EMIS@wheaton.edu

Co-editors John A. Siewert and Dotsey Welliver

CHAPTER 1

Improving Local Ownership of Global Vision

Paul Borthwick

Early editions of what is now the *Mission Handbook* were designed as a useful resource for missions administrators, agency leaders, and the missiological academic community. They purposed to help these readers understand who was doing what with how many people and how much money—and where.

Times have changed in the enterprise of deploying workers into God's harvest field. Local churches now play an increasingly active part in the sending of workers cross-culturally. The 1998-2000 edition of the *Handbook* included a chapter on "Growing Local Church Initiatives" that gave brief case histories of seven local churches and the ways they sent missionaries directly or supported through agencies. Churches with high investments in world missions usually have a professional staff (Missions Pastor or Administrator), multiple missionaries, and "Task Forces" (no longer "committees") dedicated to specific global regions or people groups.

These churches, often involved in groups like ACMC (Advancing Churches in Missions Commitment—www.acmc.org) or the Antioch Network (www.antiochnetwork.org), bring increased expectations into their partnerships with mission agencies. Pastors and church leaders desire to see the global mission of Christ owned by their average congregants. We (I am writing here as a churchman) look to mission agencies to help us—both in strategic global involvement and in the world Christian discipleship of our people.

A Personal Word

Although I now serve as a missions facilitator and teacher, I write these words as a churchman, a minister committed to the local church and the local church's role in world evangelism. I served twenty-two years as a staff member of a large church—Grace Chapel, a nondenominational evangelical church in Lexington, Massachusetts—including fifteen years as the Minister of Missions. In that role, I led a department that supported dozens of missionaries, projects, and national partners through a total annual mission budget of almost $900,000.

I now dedicate my full-time ministry to interacting with churches and leaders—informally in resource sharing, and formally as a speaker or seminar leader. Through travel and teaching, I have probably had the privilege of interacting with leaders from several hundred "missions-minded" churches as well as twenty or more denominations, both small and large.

Through my current role in Development Associates International, I have the privilege of ministering alongside church leaders in countries where the vision for mobilizing others for cross-cultural ministry is quite new. Their questions often reflect their heart for their congregations: "How can I connect the people I am ministering to and with to God's work globally?"

My experiences as a local church leader and now with local church leaders tell me that we approach this *Handbook* differently than a missions executive might. We are asking questions pertaining to the impact of global involvement on our local constituency. As church leaders, pastors, mission committee chairpersons, and missions pastors, we're looking to make the best use of this *Handbook*. Thus, we start with the question, "How can we work with the listed missions and agencies to foster ownership and strategic participation in our local congregations?"

Different Priorities from the Same Command

In Matthew's version of the Great Commission (Matthew 28:18–20), Jesus commands the disciples and the Church to "make disciples of all nations." Steve Hawthorne, who translates this command, "Disciplize the nations," points out that the structure of this Greek imperative creates an interdependency of the words: "make disciples" needs the object—"all nations." The two cannot be separated.

But in reality, the church and sending agency do separate the two—at least in terms of day-to-day practical prioritization. The mission agency generally focuses on "the nations" (or people groups) of the world. The local church focuses on the making of disciples within the congregation. Thus, the agency looks at the church as a source for personnel to go to the nations, and the church looks at global involvement as a means to push people deeper in their understanding of discipleship (more on this later).

In his analysis chapter, Dr. Scott Moreau hints at this two-sided tension. As he analyses the declines and increases in the sending process of the Canadian Church, he observes that the number of full-time Canadian workers has declined but the support of nationals serving elsewhere has increased. If the only goal was "over-there" discipleship of the nations, this observation could still be good news. However, Moreau goes on to comment on the importance of sending in the discipleship life of the Canadian church. "At the same time, there is a crucial need for Canadians themselves to be serving cross-culturally for the long-term health of the Canadian missionary effort" (Moreau, p. 54, Chapter 4 of this *Handbook*).

He implies that long-term health requires the home church of any nation to be mobilizing and sending their own flesh and blood. Discipling the local congregation must be connected to discipling the nations.

Wade Coggins made this connection over a decade ago when he critiqued the trend of North American churches to increase the support of national or indigenous workers—often at the expense or in lieu of sending their own. "If the American church begins to send to missions only its money and not its sons and daughters, the missionary vision will be dead in a generation or less. Substituting money for flesh and blood involvement is a failed policy…Sending dollars to substitute for missionaries would create a misconception that we can fulfill our obligation to the Great Commission with money alone. This would reinforce a dangerous materialism already present in our society." (*OMS Outreach,* January/February 1989).

Partnership

All this points to one basic conclusion. Churches and sending agencies must work together to "disciplize the nations."

This will not be problem-free. A seminar at the Overseas Ministries Study Center (OMSC—www.omsc.org) in New Haven, Connecticut, addressed "The Impatience of the Local Church with Traditional Sending Agencies." We addressed the newfound realities of large local churches sending their own missionaries without the intermediary of agencies like those listed in this *Handbook*.

Groups like the "Antioch Network" seek to push off old paradigms of sending in favor of more church-based programs. They seek to circumvent the bureaucracy and administrative "red-tape" of more staid organizations. (We'll learn over time whether churches operating autonomously as mission agencies will become the very bureaucracies they are rebelling against.)

In addition, the advent of increasingly internationalized mission agencies, with multinational staff and several international offices, certainly intensifies the complexities when it comes to North American churches and agencies partnering together. For the purposes of this article, however, I am writing primarily to North American based agencies and churches working together.

Our Foundations

Before moving into practical questions that churches can ask to foster both strategic partnerships between church and agency as well as local ownership of a global vision, we need to establish our foundations for church-agency relations, the "modality-sodality" model that Ralph Winter identified several decades ago.

As a church leader, my thinking on this subject has been shaped by the cumulative effect of books like A. R. Hay's *The New Testament Order for Church & Missionary,* Michael Griffiths' *Who Really Sends the Missionary?,* and Paul Beals' *A People For His Name.* I believe that strategic partnerships are necessary because:

- The Scriptures illustrate that the local church served as the model for calling, preparing and sending missionaries (Acts 13). In our practical realities, those responsibilities have been split between church and sending agency. If we are to act as the true Church, we must work in partnership.
- The realities of missions demand it philosophically. Referring again to Scott Moreau's analysis in Chapter 4, he summarized that 39.2% of U.S. agencies considered "church establishing/planting" a primary focus of their mission. A missionary sent to establish new congregations will eventually reflect the convictions about the local church that he/she developed in his/her own sending context. If the sent missionary has a poor understanding of and relationship with the local church here, he/she will reproduce those attitudes "over there."
- The realities of missions demand it practically. With increasing amounts of details and expectations from today's candidates, and in light of the increased sense of dysfunctionality in new candidates, agencies and churches must work in partnership so that the most qualified candidates are recruited, trained, and sent out for effective ministry.

Five Questions

Given these foundational considerations, consider five questions church leaders can ask. These questions address the steps that church leaders can take toward mission agencies in an effort to pursue strategic alliances. The answers to these questions will guide church leaders in deciding which agencies will maximize their church's participation in and contribution to the global advancement of the Kingdom of Christ.

Question 1: How can we be involved?

Hands-on involvement leads all other requests that church leaders make of sending agencies. For an agency built on short-term ministries—with the infrastructure to support this—partnerships with churches come easily. For those agencies dedicated to pioneer work in "limited access" locales, where short-term visitors often do more harm than good, partnership will require more work.

Here again we address the issue of different priorities from the same Great Commission command. The function of the mission agency is to get the job done. The organization has a defined task, a stated mission, and a clear-cut vision. The agency sees the local churches as the biblically commissioned partners who can help get the job done through giving, prayer, support, and workers sent. Agencies are asking, "How can the local church help us fulfill the Great Commission?"

The function of local church missions leaders is to educate and mobilize the people in the pew for the Great Commission. With that function in mind, church leaders look for the best avenues possible to get this done. They are committed to the task of the Great Commission, but their first commitment is to life-change in their parishioners. Church mission leaders ask, "How can agencies help us transform our people with a broader, more Christlike worldview?"

When it comes to getting involved, the agency might conclude, "Well, we'd love to involve you, but your hands-on involvement really doesn't help us fulfill our task, mission, and vision." In contrast, local church leaders, who have already discovered that firsthand involvement is their best tool for education, mobilization, recruitment and life-change, conclude: "Well, I guess that agency doesn't want to work with our church."

Cindy Judge, a leader in the International Ministries Department at Willow Creek Community Church in South Barrington, IL, attended the OMSC seminar in December, 1997, referred to earlier, and she wrote an open-letter response to the participants. She illustrated this "hands-on involvement" thrust this way:

> In my present setting at Willow Creek Community Church, we want to help educate our people and provide synergy between home base and field ministry. We try to do this by making the partnerships mutually beneficial. If there is not a demonstrated desire by the mission agency to help guide this process and facilitate the two parties working together, the church will no doubt find some other group that will work with them to work towards a partnership. This includes avenues of service for people to become involved firsthand. This can work out very well, though I think if an agency chooses to detour this kind of involvement, they will miss the opportunity to envision and educate interested laypeople and the future involvement with these people this involvement will produce.

When using this *Handbook* to evaluate maximum partnerships with agencies, church leaders can ask a variety of questions. Some of the answers might be found here, but most will also require correspondence, a phone call, or a trip to the agency's web site.

- How can this agency help build my congregation as "World Christians"? To get this answer, ask for copies of their "mobilization" resources—literature, videos, speakers. Look at the web site to see if there are any instructional introductions to the mission or to the biblical basis for missions.
- In what ways can we be "hands-on" involved—including short-term missions, special projects, intercultural exchanges, etc.? The *Handbook* data on short-termers under each agency can help determine if short-term missions is even part of the agency's mode of operation.
- Does the agency want/desire our church's involvement in the "on-field" care of Christian workers?
- What opportunities are there for pastors/church leaders to serve the mission leadership as board members or in other adjunct positions of leadership? Look over the constituency of the mission's Board of Directors. Are any of these men or women pastors? Church leaders? Active church-based laity?

Question 2: How can we partner together to increase the effectiveness of allocating the limited financial resources we are all dealing with?

Many missions agencies grew within systems which assumed that local churches and individuals would give their monthly support with few questions other than, "How can we pray for you?"

But today's churches and leaders ask a lot more questions. We church leaders often demand that agencies factor in retirement programs, children's education, and healthcare, and then we complain, "How come the missionary's monthly support requirement is so high?"

The advent of big churches sending their own missionaries arose partly as a response to escalating costs. The larger churches desire greater "cost-effectiveness" so they figure that sending their own diminishes the expenses related to missionary support. Some of these cost-cutting measures are illusionary because the administrative costs, home-office costs, and support staff costs get absorbed into the overall church budget.

When dealing with the issue of the strategic allocation of money, churches and mission agencies must be prepared to deal with questions directly. Church leaders' most commonly asked questions might only find a hint of an answer in the data in this *Handbook*. Specific replies will take some investigation.

- Administrative fees: how much is it? Where does that 10 percent or 13 percent or 15 percent go? What does it cover?
- Strategic mergers: wouldn't your small agency be better off if you merged with another so that these administrative costs could be spread out over a larger pool?
- Recruitment: how can we (in local church leadership) work with you to address issues like candidate debt, escalating costs (and expectations) of candidates, and increasing overhead?
- Targets: how much of the money we send really gets to the desired destination? Why should we support the national church through your mission if you take a 10 percent

"service fee" off the top when we can wire the money directly to our overseas partners for a bank charge of $25.00?

- Integrity: do independent auditors endorse your financial practices? Can we be sure of truthfulness in your reports?
- New ideas: if we (local church leaders) have some new ideas about raising support or managing the home office, are you open to hear it? Church leaders who desire to support their own missionaries 100 percent, for example, often get their strongest opposition from agencies; the church leaders interpret the resistance as an unwillingness to change.
- Timing: how long does it take to get answers to basic financial questions? One church initiated a project with a mission agency, but the mission agency took so long in responding with a financial proposal that the church moved on to another agency.

The underlying financial issue relates to change. Church mission leaders ask, "Is the agency at least willing to talk to us about our changing times and the changes in the financial picture?" Let's look at two examples—the first of an agency stuck in an old paradigm; the second of an agency willing to re-evaluate.

A missionary came to our church for support—about $36,000 per year. She worked in the home office writing grant proposals to foundations. I asked her how much money her proposals raised in the previous year. She mentioned an amount over $400,000. I replied with what our church thought was a "no-brainer" question: "Why doesn't your mission set aside for your support 10 percent of the foundation money you raise? I think this is an acceptable practice."

"'Oh, no," she replied. "Everybody in our mission has to live by the same standard of fund-raising—whether on the field or in the office." While I appreciated the spirit of the answer, I told her and her mission that I thought today's donor would think her answer crazy, especially given the amount of time and effort required of the home staff to raise support. Neither the mission nor the missionary wanted to consider re-evaluating a support policy that their founder had set over 100 years ago (when none of their money came from foundations).

In a discussion with the financial team of another agency, we talked about the short attention span of today's givers and how the old $10/month every month for a four-year term did not work so well with the impulse-driven, credit-card, bank-by-computer generation. I suggested that a new model be considered—where a missionary raises all of the support needed for four years right up front. Rather than the full four-year amount (say $200,000), however, the missionary says to supporters, "If you'll help me raise $160,000 up front, we'll put this money in mutual funds and the interest earned will round out our support, saving the Church $40,000 total or $10,000 per year."

The agency financial team agreed to investigate the idea and its implications—financially and as it relates to prayer support. Now the idea may be bogus for a dozen reasons, but at least the agency was willing to think outside the paradigms of support raising that were designed to recruit donors living the economic lifestyle of the 1950s or 1960s.

Question 3: Will agencies join with us in the screening and training of candidates?

If your or your church's goal in approaching this *Handbook* is to discover how to raise up new cross-cultural workers from our congregations, then the first step is to look for the agencies that send North Americans. Then the question becomes, "How can we join together in partnership in selecting, equipping, and sending new workers?" The agency knows how to train candidates to work cross-culturally, but the local church knows the candidates.

As local church mission leaders evaluate which agencies to work with, we should look into the involvement an agency desires. Will they recruit our leadership early in the sending process or will they wait until after a candidate is screened and oriented and started in support-raising?

The local church—especially any local church whose leadership is reading this *Handbook*—usually desires greater input in the screening and sending of candidates. We need agencies to help us think through what this means. We need agencies to say to us, "If you folks won't rise up and help in this process, then we cannot send this candidate." Churches need agencies to force them to take greater responsibility in the sending process.

One church addresses this issue through negotiating three-way covenants between missionary, agency, and home church. In the covenant, each one outlines what is expected in the training and sending process. When the covenant is completed, the candidate knows what he or she must do, the agency outlines what it will do, and the church leadership understands what they must do. Through these covenants, sending becomes a true partnership, and conflict is pro-actively addressed and avoided by outlining expectations from the outset.

The questions we need to be asking agency leadership include:

- How can our knowledge of candidates be better utilized in the sending process?
- What training can we offer so that the burden is taken off the agency?
- How can we offer active ministry training that will serve future cross-cultural ministry?

Question 4: What agencies will allow our involvement in strategic thinking?

The thought of involving churches at the strategic-thinking level might be new to some mission agencies. After all, participation in strategic thinking in partnership with sending churches adds work to the mission agency.

For the agency, it might mean taking the time to train church leaders in areas of missiology. It could mean helping church mission leaders brainstorm realistically on adopting a people group. It often requires agency leaders getting informed enough about churches so that they can involve churches using their areas of expertise, like church planting or small group ministry. Nevertheless, strategic thinking together radically improves the congregation's ability to own a global vision.

Consider this example. Danny Harrell of the historic Park Street Church in Boston pastors their Sunday evening congregation, a congregation of 600 or more, mostly from the "under 30" generation. The congregation sent out a Chinese, Spanish-speaking medical student to Bolivia. Danny and his leadership team met with the leaders of SIM-Bolivia to brainstorm the strategy. The Park Street young adult congregation forced the SIM leadership to "think outside the box," but they successfully negotiated a strategy which would involve more than thirty other Park Street members joining this medical student for short trips over a yearlong period, working with street children in La Paz. Their partnership involved live-link video or computer reports to the church service every Sunday night, and a lot of new paradigm thinking.

Danny said the project had a huge impact on the congregation—informing them, calling them to pray, and recruiting them to give. And he has high praise for the folks at SIM because "they allowed us to think strategically with them about ways we could join together to fulfill the mission to the kids in La Paz, and to enlarge the vision of our people back home."

Strategic thinking for most local church leadership these days means working with national leadership, at least in areas where the church is established. Cindy Judge of Willow Creek Community Church admits that their strategy has focused on Latin America, "where churches seem farther along with indigenous leadership." She writes about the strategic mindset of their laypeople:

> The mission-minded layperson has been hearing for years that missionaries are working themselves out of a job and empowering national leadership. We found that our laypeople expected it to be obvious to be working with nationals rather than missionaries from the U.S.

With this in mind, look over the agencies listed to see who is involved in partnering with national leaders. To do this, you may need to look beyond the *Handbook* data reporting the number of "National Workers" because the numbers listed primarily include those whose financial support comes from the North American church. Many mission agencies do partner strategically with leaders whose support comes from within their own countries.

Some strategic-thinking questions church leaders might want to pursue with mission agencies include:

- If your church has a "people group" that you'd like to adopt, will the agency/can the agency work with you? With regard to such "adoption," will the agency make a way for the church to send a "team" or do they send just individuals to their already established teams?
- Where does the agency focus their efforts? An agency's "country list" cites every location where an agency has staff—but you may need to dig deeper to find out that there are 800 staff members in Nairobi and only two in your target area of the Maldives.
- Where do tasks and geographic foci blend together? If your church wants to focus on evangelism or church planting, there are hundreds of options in this *Handbook,* but many of these efforts might be targeting areas where the church already exists. If your church wants to focus on evangelism or church planting in the "10-40 Window," then the options are fewer. And if you are dedicated to a specific people group in Afghanistan, then there may be very few options listed.
- Does the focus of an organization preclude any involvement in strategic thinking? An agency that serves to raise North American dollars to support indigenous workers often has fewer opportunities for supporting churches to be involved—simply because the strategizing is done by local leadership, and the primary role of the North American church is prayerful and financial support.

Question 5: Will they work with us on communicating vision to the congregation?

It may take some time to answer this question, but it speaks to two basic issues. First, will the agency adjust their language to be understandable even to young or new Christians? And second, will they speak to us honestly about issues related to progress and "success."

In communicating a vision and seeking to recruit new workers, we in the "missionary enterprise" often talk in a secret, encoded language of missions. We try to recruit new workers by blowing what I call our "missiological dog whistles." Only those who are already tuned into the missiological frequency understand the terms, expectations, and ideals. No one else even hears it.

Therefore, talking about "strategic initiatives with indigenous church leadership doing E-3 evangelism through power-encounters and ethno-musicology with the Sundanese unreached people group" might communicate with a professional missions pastor, but what about a lay committee that administers missions?

The senior pastor of one church told me that he said "No" to an agency's presentation simply because he was too embarrassed to admit that he did not understand what the missions presenters were talking about.

But it is not just the complicated missiological words. This linguistic problem hits us strongest with the current use of the terms "mission" and "missions" in the local church. Every church is asking, "What is our mission?" In one church, every pastor is a "mission director" and heads a leadership group called the "mission committee." The word mission in the minds of most of these people pertains to task, vision, or function. "Cross-cultural" or "international" must be inserted to communicate the ideas we are after.

Several times in this chapter I have referred to the "Great Commission" without any explanation because I assume that missiological readers know the term well. We cannot assume the same with the listeners in local churches. I once gave an entire Sunday School class on missions, referring frequently to the Great Commission. After class, I asked a man what he thought the Great Commission was. He was a new believer, a salesman by profession, without any church background or Christian upbringing.

He replied, "What's the Great Commission? I don't know—about 30 percent?" To him, 30 percent would be a GREAT commission. I had spent an entire Sunday School class talking in terms he did not understand! We can wring our hands all we want about the "dumbing down" of missions, but the fact remains: if the average local church attendee does not understand the international world and the language of cross-cultural ministry, their gifts and prayers will dry up. It is our job to work together with mission agencies to make sure that we are mobilizing the local church in terms that local church people understand.

The second issue related to communicating vision to the congregation pertains to speaking honestly about issues related to progress and "success." This is a challenge for both church and agency leaders—especially in the success-driven North American church. One of the saddest observations in the new edition of the *World Christian Encyclopedia* is the statement in their first table: "Some 250 of the 300 largest international Christian organizations regularly mislead the Christian public by publishing demonstrably incorrect or falsified progress statistics" (Table 1-1 "An AD 2000 reality check: 50 new facts and figures about empirical global Christianity today," #47).

Those who give away the missions money of the local church can easily become jaded by the exaggerations, hype, and smooth talking sometimes associated with fund-raising. In an article in *Evangelical Missions Quarterly,* Chuck Bennett of Partners International made the sad observation that the phrase "speaking evangelistically" has become equivalent to lying.

Agencies and churches need to talk honestly about results. We need to agree together to stick with the highest standards of integrity in reporting the impact of ministry. Watch out if the statistics on church attendance use Easter Sunday figures. Be aware that some identify a church as being planted by "their" mission when in reality there are three or four other agencies also taking credit for the same church. Be cautious of sending agencies whose numbers always seem rounded off.

Church leaders committed to world evangelism must demand honesty. When organizations try to sugarcoat some of the harsh realities of survival in the organizational world, savvy business people in the lay leadership of the church wonder if the organization can be trusted. Let's address the challenges and failures openly—without over-spiritualizing or pretending that there is no problem.

Asking the five questions above should help local church leaders broaden and deepen their congregation as "World Christians." This would also help promote the most flexible, creative, and efficient mission agencies as they strive to do their part in fulfilling the Great Commission. And working together in strategic ways, we can all make strides toward bringing about an answer to Christ's moving prayer in John 17 for unity among believers. Let us be found moving in this direction.

CHAPTER 2

Cooperation: Yesterday, Today, Tomorrow

John H. Orme

The two organizations were like oil and water, night and day, cold and hot. They were as different as the Chicago Symphony and the Grateful Dead. But they decided to get together. Buttoned-down, white-shirted, pin-striped corporate IBM got together with Nikes-and-Dockers-clad Apple Computer who made "insanely great" computers for "the rest of us."

For almost 20 years, Apple and IBM had different systems, different software, and competitive worlds. For years, the two watched as personality clashes, shifting technologies, and the success of local upstarts threatened their corner on the market. Then with a slipping grip in a sliding economy, the two began to cooperate.

The world's largest corporations, sometimes former archenemies, now often cooperate through strategic alliances and international partnerships. Such partnerships allow the most effective response to expanding, high-risk, capital-intensive, rapidly changing world markets. The Boeing 777 airplane project, for example, includes three Japanese companies and several European ones with 38,000 suppliers.

Cooperation at the Mission Association Level

With such alliances in the business world, it is sometimes thought that cooperation in the mission world is also new. However, a review of early work in China shows that under Hudson Taylor's leadership, the CIM developed partnerships with other missions.

At one point, at least fifteen missions worked in association with the China Inland Mission (CIM), now the Overseas Missionary Fellowship. Under the arrangement as Associates, each mission retained its separate identity and language, working together as a group. They would agree upon particular areas for ministry (geographic and/or a specialized ministry), working within CIM's goals and strategy for the evangelization of China *(Kingdom Partnerships for Synergy in Missions,* William D. Taylor, editor. Pasadena, CA: William Carey Library, 1994, p. 187).

Partnering is not new. Mission agencies have long been cooperating in evangelism, education, radio, literature, and in medical projects—sometimes by short-term agreement, sometimes by loan of personnel, and sometimes through longer time commitments of joint ministry agreements. All of these arrangements are with those who share basic doctrinal and ministry convictions.

Often these ministries are not in our daily awareness and as time goes by, many of us forget that they exist; we may not even be aware of cooperative efforts that have taken place in the past and by now, have become organizations and ministries themselves. A reminder of some of these activities and projects is helpful as we consider what it means to partner with one another.

I will review a few clear evidences that, at the mission association level, EFMA (Evangelical Fellowship of Mission Agencies) and IFMA (Interdenominational Foreign Missions Association—of which I am Executive Director) do indeed work together now—and have worked together in the past. The following few details were gleaned from the book by Dr. Jack Frizen entitled *75 Years of IFMA: 1917–1992* (Pasadena, CA: William Carey Library, 1992).

Since the founding of the EFMA in 1945, Clyde Taylor, as EFMA's first president (1945–1975), was a catalyst in forging relationships with other evangelical organizations. Throughout the '50s and into the '60s, the EFMA and the IFMA convened many cooperative efforts, meetings, and conferences. In 1960, at the IFMA Annual Meeting, a resolution was passed that "There should be an earnest seeking to work together with those of like precious faith." This led to the first Joint Study Conference (which we now call the Triennial) in 1963 in Winona Lake, Indiana.

A fact known by few today is that in 1962, the EFMA and the IFMA formed the Africa Evangelical Office in Nairobi, Kenya, with Ken Downing of Africa Inland Mission (AIM) as its director. This later became the AEAM (Association of Evangelicals in Africa and Madagascar) and was supported with substantial financial subsidy until 1991. Mr. Eric Maillefer, on loan from the Evangelical Free Church, served the AEAM for eighteen years.

The same group was the initial force in starting BEST (The Bangui Evangelical School of Theology). At least four African congresses were held largely through the support of the EFMA and the IFMA. At the Urbana InterVarsity Student Mission Convention in 1984, Dr. Tokumbo Adeyemo, director of AEAM, expressed his appreciation for all of this and more.

During those years, the IFMA Business Administration Committee published the 1958 Mission Administration Manual. In 1962, a supplement on certain tax issues was published. This became what is known today as the Accounting and Financial Reporting Guide for Christian Ministries published by EJAC, the Evangelical Joint Accounting Committee (1982). EJAC was formed by the EFMA, the IFMA, ECFA (Evangelical Council for Financial Accountability), CMA (Christian Management Association), and CCCC (Canadian Council of Christian Charities). You see, even in money matters, mission agencies and associations can and do work together.

At the 1963 Joint Study Conference (EFMA/IFMA) mentioned earlier, some significant agreements were made providing strong evidence that we indeed do work together. At least seven agreements out of those meetings merit our attention here.

1. All agencies should share mobilization pamphlets under their own logos at the original cost to the originating agency.
2. As mentioned above, this Study Conference was when AEAM was envisioned.
3. Steps were taken to launch EMIS (Evangelical Missions Information Service—now Evangelism and Missions Information Service).
4. The committee that became CAMEO (Committee for Assisting Missionary Education Overseas) was named. This continued until its mission was determined to be completed in 1991.

5. The initial steps were taken that resulted in the Congress on World Mission held in Wheaton in 1965.
6. It was resolved to continue the triennial meetings of the associations.
7. Other joint committee work was begun including the ECLA (Evangelical Committee on Latin America) which functioned from 1957 to 1990.

In 1964 a significant joint effort of the EFMA and the IFMA resulted in the formation of the Evangelical Missions Information Service (EMIS). The EMIS publications, *Evangelical Missions Quarterly* and *World Pulse,* have served the missions community well. A joint committee served until 1997 when it was agreed that to serve the missions community better, another publisher was needed. The Billy Graham Center of Wheaton College (Wheaton, IL) took over admirably. The present boards of EMIS are representative of both the EFMA and the IFMA.

One of the most active and enduring joint efforts of the EFMA and the IFMA was formalized in 1971 as the Personnel & Student Affairs Committee. In 1977, the name was shortened to the IFMA/EFMA Personnel Committee. The dynamic of partnering, however, was the energy that goes back to 1964 when representatives from the EFMA, IVCF (InterVarsity Christian Fellowship), Moody Bible Institute, and the IFMA met in Chicago and later that year at Urbana. The EFMA and the IFMA continued the dialogue until the formal committee was begun. Each December at the IFMA/EFMA Personnel Conference an average of 250 human resource workers from the missions community gather for a major professional conference to study mobilization, management, training, and member care issues in mission. It is the privilege of the IFMA to serve the missions community as facilitator for these conferences.

Without undue further detail, brief mention should be made of other efforts in joint ministries. Through the years, both the EFMA and the IFMA have jointly sponsored conferences on issues relating to China and Islamics. Other joint committees have convened about Bible translations and concerning Asia.

For thirty years, the Summer Institute of Missions was held at Wheaton College. This institute was begun in 1957 as a joint effort and only ceased when it was absorbed into Wheaton's summer program.

Mission evaluation has not been ignored. Through the middle '70s, a joint task force on mission evaluation had meetings, and in 1978 published a fifty-page booklet of guidelines. In 1971, papers from the Green Lake consultation were published under the title, *Missions in Creative Tension.*

We should mention here that the efforts of EFMA and IFMA, along with local church leaders and other organizations, were strong in the formation of the ACMC (Association of Church Mission Committees—now Advancing Churches in Missions Commitment). In 1974, the executive directors of both associations served as special consultants at an early meeting concerning ACMC in Pasadena. Not to be forgotten are efforts with other groups such as WEF (World Evangelical Fellowship), NAE (National Association of Evangelicals), and the Association of Evangelical Professors of Missions, now the Evangelical Missiological Society (EMS).

The most recent cooperative effort became visible in September, 1999, at the Triennial Leadership Conference of the EFMA, the EMS, and the IFMA held in Virginia Beach.

AERDO (Association of Evangelical Relief and Development Organizations) and COSIM (Coalition on Supporting Indigenous Ministries) were also participants in this conference.

Both the EFMA and the IFMA had studied the issue of organizational leadership among its agencies. However strong in doctrine, ministry, and vision an agency might be, organizational leadership skills were too often missing in a significant way from the missionary toolbox. To meet this need, IFMA launched LeaderLink in 1997. At the 1999 Virginia Beach meetings, the EFMA Board adopted LeaderLink as its leadership enhancement program and in cooperative response, the IFMA Board welcomed their partnership. IFMA LeaderLink became simply LeaderLink, the program of leadership enhancement for both the EFMA and the IFMA.

No doubt more could be said about the interaction of the EFMA and the IFMA, and partnering in general. A review of the IFMA library shows shelves and shelves of reports, compendiums, conferences, and committee publications. My regret is that in our (my) activism of today, we write and record very little. As a result, many are simply not aware of the reality of our working together.

Guidelines for Ongoing Cooperation

But to work together in effective partnership, each of our organizations must be permeated by grace, love, forgiveness, and compassion through the Holy Spirit. This will happen only as individuals are permeated by grace, love, forgiveness, and compassion through the Holy Spirit. Organizations are not spiritual. People are spiritual. Only as we each open our hearts to God and then to each other, can we have anything more than structure in our partnering. As personal relationships join, they form that important "inter-organizational relationship" that we all desire.

In his *Biblical Theology of Mission,* George Peters wrote in 1972 that the principle of partnership does not rest in culture, times, or circumstances. It rather "is a relationship which has its roots in our identification with the churches on the deepest levels and in our fellowship in the Spirit, in His suffering and in our mutual burdens, interests, purposes, and goals. Partnership is not circumstantial; it is a matter of life, health, and relationship. It belongs to the nature of Christianity. It is not optional; it is bound up in Christian fellowship and progress" (George W. Peters, *A Biblical Theology of Missions.* Chicago: Moody Press, 1972, p. 239).

John Piper relates a wonderful story about William Carey and Henry Martyn. The two men were among the early missionaries from England to India. Carey was a Particular Baptist and a dissenter from the Anglican Church. He even advocated closed communion. Martyn, on the other hand, was an evangelical Anglican who followed Anglican communion practices.

Nevertheless, Carey wrote, "A young clergyman, Mr. Martyn, is lately arrived, who is possessed of a truly missionary spirit...We take sweet counsel together, and go to the house of God as friends" (John Piper, *Let the Nations Be Glad.* Grand Rapids, MI: Baker Books, 1993, p. 72).

Let us go and do likewise.

CHAPTER 3

Where Do We Go from Here?

Luis Bush

(Editor's Note: Luis Bush presented this speech in its original form at a meeting of the Evangelical Seminary Academic Deans' Meeting, February 3–5, 2000, in Phoenix, Arizona. It has been slightly adapted here for publication.)

Where do we go from here with regard to the Great Commission? Let us briefly raise some issues by considering various perspectives. We should not be surprised to find that we have different perspectives. Not everyone agrees even about where we are in regard to the magnificent millennial moment of this hinge of history. When does or did the twenty-first century officially begin? It's like a tempest in a time clock.

We live in the midst of the great millennium misunderstanding. Global celebrations have already taken place symbolized by the drop of the one-thousand pound ball in New York's Times Square at midnight on December 31, 1999, with its 504 hand-crafted triangular pieces of crystal and nearly 700 lights. However, others were saying, "Wait a minute. The third millennium begins on January 1, 2001."

Whatever the case, the question "Where do we go from here in world evangelization?" is being asked in many places and many settings around the world in these times. This is an important question at a hinge moment of history. Regardless of the precise centennial turn, the year 2000 has served as a giant magnet for all of mankind—a turning point unlike any we have previously known. So for many, the year 2000 instills a sense of urgency spurring on broader thinking.

My thinking here represents one more attempt to coalesce perspectives of many others in addressing the issues, rather than suggesting any specific course of action. I seek to raise some of the necessary questions to be addressed rather than trying to provide a set of answers. We can embark on the journey by considering the following ten aspects.

1. Asking God, who knows the future and holds it in his hands
2. Understanding our changing context of mission
3. Entering into a process that encourages broad global ownership
4. Rediscovering the meaning of the Great Commission
5. Cultivating a set of values
6. Articulating the type of challenges we are facing
7. Identifying the emerging leadership style appropriate for the twenty- first century
8. Training a new generation of Christian leaders

9. Considering the kinds of structures that can best support the push forward
10. Developing an information sharing system in support of a response to the challenges

Asking God, Who Knows the Future and Holds It in His Hands

Perhaps obvious as a first step, yet so easy to forget is that, as Christians, we believe in a God who not only knows the future but also holds the future in his hands. The wise King Solomon poses the question, "Since no man knows the future, who can tell him what is to come?" (Ecclesiastes 8:7, NIV). Since he is writing as a natural man who looks at the cycle of life "under the sun," he has left out the obvious. It is only God who knows the future.

When David learned that Saul was plotting against him, beginning in I Samuel 23:11 (NIV), he asked, "'Will Saul come down, as your servant has heard? O Lord, God of Israel, tell your servant.' And the Lord said, 'He will.'

"Again David asked, 'Will the citizens of Keilah surrender me and my men to Saul?' And the Lord said, 'They will.' So David and his men, about six hundred in number, left Keilah and kept moving from place to place. When Saul was told that David had escaped from Keilah, he did not go there."

Because David was convinced that God knew the future he prayed, and upon receiving his answer, promptly set off in the right direction, escaping calamity that would have come.

Oh, that we as God's people would follow the example of David and pray to God, asking him where we go from here that we may escape the great calamity of missing God's will for his people in the twenty-first century. God not only knows the future. He holds the future. As the apostle Paul reminds us, the future is "...according to the plan of him who works out everything in conformity with the purpose of his will," (Ephesians 1:11, NIV).

Understanding our Changing Context of Mission

Franklin Murphy, former Chancellor of the University of California at Los Angeles, would say of the new generation moving into the twenty-first century that it embraces the philosophy expressed in the three Latin words, Sentio ergo sum–"I feel, therefore I am." We have moved from the so-called Age of Reason in the seventeenth and eighteenth centuries and the statement of Descartes, Cognito ergo sum, "I think, therefore I am," to the nineteenth century and Facio ergo sum, "I do, therefore I am," (in which materialism, the production, possession, and distribution of goods became the guiding principle) to the present day, "I feel, therefore I am."

Upon retiring as Dean of Fuller School of World Mission, Dudley Woodberry presented a vision paper, "Toward the Twenty-first Century: Educating People for God's Mission." He made observations on the following points.

1. *Population explosion in the developing world, stagnation in the developed*
   By 2025 the population will be 8,312 million. Over a billion will need cross-cultural witness to understand the gospel. Most of those are in the 10-40 Window (10 to 40 degrees latitude in Asia and Africa).
2. *Accelerating change*
   Apart from some marginalized pockets, the pace of change is increasing across the board–demographic, technological, economic, political, and social. This leads to

uncertainty, information overload, hesitancy to make long-term commitments, and difficulty in making plans.

3. *Globalization and localism*
   The accelerating change involves the compression of time and space in a shrinking world of rapid communication and travel. National boundaries and oceans are not significant barriers in the global market. At the same time there are centrifugal forces away from globalization to various localisms that seek to retain or forge ethnic or religious boundaries.
4. *Increase in secularization and religious resurgence*
   The religious resurgence has been largely a reaction to the loss of religious and traditional values that have accompanied secularization.
5. *An ethos of pluralism and conflict*
   On the one hand the shrinking of the globe and the migration of peoples have created a pluralistic world—not only in the sense that many religions live side by side, but philosophically that all are to be accepted as different facets of truth. On the other hand, beside this tolerant, accepting attitude is what Samuel P. Huntington has called "the clash of civilizations"—that is, the clash of civilizations or cultures where religion is often the greatest influence.
6. *Multipolar unstable world with end of Cold War*
   The collapse of Communism left only one superpower, but it also reduced the pressures to base political alliances on relationship or nonalliance with the superpowers.
7. *Closing doors becoming revolving doors*
   During the last decade an increasing number of countries have restricted access to missionaries. Yet at the same time such phenomena as the globalization of the economy and the Trojan horse of Hong Kong slipping behind the bamboo curtain have opened the doors for bivocational missionaries.
8. *Postmodern society impacting but not replacing modern and traditional societies*
   The wave of postmodernism has joined modernism and traditionalism. Or from another perspective, the information age has joined the industrial and the agricultural. Yet in each case all three remain with their interacting tensions.
9. *Homogenization and separation of cultures and civilizations*
   Western culture, together with the English language and popular music as communicated through television, is homogenizing particularly the culture of youth in urban settings. At the same time we are experiencing the resurgence of ethnic cultures and the major world civilizations of which Huntington speaks.
10. *Urbanization, involving mixing and fragmentation*
    The world is increasingly becoming urbanized. With urbanization come the problems of the ghettoization and marginalization of the poor and some ethnic groups.
11. *The enlarging and restricting of women's roles*
    Even as women are acquiring increased opportunities and expectations in both the secular and religious world, they are being forced into more restrictive roles in other contexts.
12. *The developing world growing younger while the developed world gets older*
    Currently one-third of the world is under 15 years of age. A global youth culture is

developing non-Christian, united by MTV, rejecting the past, and focusing on the now.

13. *Globalization and regionalization of economies*
    Increasingly economy rather than politics determines alliances, making new bridges for Christian contacts.
14. *Resource relocation with resultant shifting economic strength, chaos, and potential for interrelated collapses*
    The tightening web of interconnection of the global market means that instability in one area can affect the whole.
15. *A widening gap between the wealthy and burgeoning poor*
    The Northern Hemisphere overpowers the Southern in per capita GNP.
16. *Information and communication explosion*
    Most of the world is on the Internet, and much of what remains has E-mail.
17. *Shift in center of gravity for the church*
    A definite shift has occurred in the geographical and vital center of gravity of the church from the West and North to the East and South.
18. *Increased diversity and unity*
    As Western mainline Protestant churches have declined, the more evangelical, charismatic, and independent ones multiply. Among the Evangelicals are growing numbers of postdenominational or "new apostolic" churches.
19. *Indigenization and internationalization of mission*
    As Christianity has globalized, indigenous missions have sprung up around the world. This year the Two-Thirds World will send more cross-cultural Protestant missionaries than the West.
20. *Declining mission interest in some circles while interest increases in others*
    There has been a decline in world mission interest and activity in mainstream Protestantism. At the same time there is increased interest, focus, and optimism concerning mission in other circles.

Broad Global Ownership

Perhaps as important as the vision and values is the strategy process by which these are unveiled. As we prepare to enter the twenty-first century, we need to be wise stewards. We desire to anticipate opportunities as well as problems related to these changes. Today there is a maturing Church in the developing world. The center of gravity for Christianity worldwide in terms of growth, energy, and vision is shifting from the North and West to the South and East. The mission field is fast becoming the mission force. Increasing numbers of leaders for the worldwide Christian movement are emerging from the rapidly growing churches of the non-Western world.

Thus any global vision or strategy-developing process must involve the leaders from the global church. There must be a listening process through such vehicles as forums or working group consultations regionally and/or nationally around the globe. The call is for the church in the West to learn from the church in the non-Western world.

Even as I wrote this paper, the first-ever-nationwide world mission's conference of the Assembly of God denomination in Brazil gathered to coincide with the 500-year discovery of Brazil. Some 7,000 pastors and church leaders came from all over Brazil. I agree with the perspective of Jim Engel in his book, *Rediscovering World Mission,* when he says, "It cannot be denied that the initiative for world mission today is carried more often by Pentecostal churches in Latin America or Independent Churches in Africa than by North America or Europe."

Rediscovering the Meaning of the Great Commission

As we begin the new millennium we need to rediscover the meaning of mission, world missions, world evangelization, and the Great Commission. We have been influenced by modernism. What do these terms mean from a post-modernistic view? We have been influenced in our understanding of mission by a dominant Western church. What do these terms mean as we allow the non-Western world church to take the initiative, and the role of the Western church becomes that of a partner or even a servant? We have been influenced by a dominant male leadership. How can we rediscover the meaning of these terms with our sisters in Christ as full partners at the table? We have been influenced by the dominant role of the older Christian leaders. What will we discover as we invite the emerging, younger leaders to be full partners at the table?

As in the time of the Reformation we are being called back to the Scriptures and the original languages in pursuit of the intent of meaning of the original author. We are also being called to reflect theologically on these terms. The new apostolic reformation churches are making major global initiatives. In large worldwide conferences they are looking at new paradigms for "doing mission."

For a full understanding of what God is saying to us with regard to mission, world missions, world evangelization, and the Great Commission, we need to hear from those embracing this paradigm. Rediscovering the meaning of the Great Commission calls for inviting respected missiologists like the late David Bosch to the table through his writings, particularly the work of the last seven years of his life, entitled *Transforming Mission.* Lesslie Newbigin calls this work a kind of Summa Missiologica. From the first chapter David Bosch seeks to rediscover the meaning of mission and other key terms. He explores an important historical review of the meaning of the Great Commission.

Out of the large meeting convened by Billy Graham in Amsterdam in August 2000, practitioners will be concerned with the work of the evangelist in fulfilling the Great Commission. A Strategy Working Group will deal with two basic criteria: what is being done, and what is left to be done in world evangelization. Their findings need to be brought to the table as we rediscover the meaning of the Great Commission and its implications.

On a small scale the Celebrate Messiah 2000 consultation (12/27/00–1/2/01) is seeking to be a part of this process. Streams representing Christ-activity moving into and through the official millennial change at the end of the year 2000 are being encouraged to reflect through E-mail conferences worldwide—then to bring their conclusions to present at the conference. A team of missiologists led by respected Norwegian theologian-missiologist Tormod Engelsviken is seeking to prepare and present with input from the other streams a Millennial Manifesto that will provide an updated basis of understanding mission, missions, and the Great Commission as we move into the new millennium.

Cultivating a Core Set of Values

In a representative Global Evangelism Roundtable of the World Evangelical Fellowship, the AD2000 and Beyond Movement, and the Lausanne Committee for World Evangelization on March 21–25, 1999, in Hurdal, Norway, several foundational values were agreed to that provide a basis for understanding, moving into the twenty-first century.

"We are a people profoundly committed to biblical, historic, Trinitarian Christianity, with particular appreciation for the Lausanne Covenant, as well as our own Evangelical church heritage. As we consider the future of world evangelization and the life of the global church, we affirm:

1. Our common goal for and passionate commitment to world evangelization
2. Our dedication to a life of prayer and unleashing the entire Church into global intercession
3. The proclamation of a holistic, transforming Gospel, underscoring the centrality of the church for world evangelization
4. The need for a new, global, relational "wineskin" within a context of continuity and not based on position or structure
5. A manifestation of unity grounded in the partnership of equals around the globe
6. The need for a thorough re-examination of a theology of the church
7. Regional and national networks that also have a global focal point
8. The need for a more representative platform in which all members of the Body of Christ are equal partners (for example: charismatics and non-charismatics, male and female, younger and older, academics and practitioners)
9. The need for one cooperative vehicle that supports a plurality of ministries
10. Our obedience to the Holy Spirit for empowerment, guidance, and recognition of leadership
11. Our commitment to a biblical and accountable stewardship of resources
12. Our decision to communicate our unity to every level of our various networks, and to the wider Body of Christ"

Understanding the Types of Challenges We Are Facing

In the context of a rapidly changing world we are faced with many challenges. These challenges are spiritual. They are ideological and they are sociological. They involve advancing the cause of Jesus Christ to the inhabited world and especially the cities and the people groups. This involves a geographical, an urban, and an ethnic challenge. In his book, *The Church is Bigger than You Think,* Patrick Johnstone deals with these challenges, taking one chapter per challenge.

The Urban Challenge. The twenty-first century will be an urban world for the first time. From the present fifty percent urban, by the end of the twenty-first century the world will be eighty percent urban. The twenty-first century will be characterized by the need for pioneer mission in the great cities of the world. The expanding slums and shantytowns in these cities have risen to one billion people, about forty percent of the populations in the cities of the Third-World countries.

The Social Challenge. Christian social responsibility was recognized and affirmed in the last twenty-five years as an essential component of the Great Commission. Among those who particularly call for social responsibility by Christians are the children. Almost one-third of all children conceived are never born due to abortion. An estimated ten million children suffer forced prostitution. Malnutrition kills 35,000 children under five every day. The number of street children has grown to 100 million.

Several other great social problems afflict us as we enter the twenty-first century. AIDS in Africa has grown to alarming proportions with devastating predictions, both for adults becoming afflicted and tens of millions of children becoming orphans in the next ten years. Drug addiction along with the illegal, global drug manufacturing and trading industry engulfs the people in cities and countries today. The diseases of tuberculosis, malaria, and cancers are major causes of death.

The People Challenge. More than 1000 peoples are still without a viable, indigenous church planting movement in their midst with sufficient strength, resources, and commitment to sustain and ensure the continuous multiplication of churches. Various important ministries must be strengthened for this discipline process to be effective and lasting. These include researching, church planting, literature, audio ministries, the Jesus Film, radio, and Scripture translation.

The Ideological Challenge. Islam presents a giant ideological challenge because of a completely different worldview, a social and legal system that makes it almost impossible for a Muslim to become a Christian, and the growth of "fundamentalist" terrorism. Hindus in the world are one of the greatest challenges we face in world evangelization today. Buddhism claims nearly 700 million with a view that there is no God, where salvation is earned by works and life is an endless cycle of reincarnations. Other ideologies include Baha'i, Sikhism, Jainism, and Animism, along with major deviants from mainstream Christianity. All of these constitute significant challenges.

The Spiritual Challenge. We have been involved in spiritual warfare ever since Satan wrested control of the world. Two extremes to avoid are the underemphasis of the spiritual nature of the conflict and too great a preoccupation with the enemy on the other hand. Prayer makes a profound difference in world evangelization. Global networks of prayer have been raised up. "Prayer-fueled advance of the Kingdom of Christ" gives hope for the future.

The Geographic Challenge. The 10-40 Window represents the primary geographic challenge entering the twenty-first century, in that it is the geographical location in which each of the previous five challenges are indisputably and significantly more prominent. An estimated 1.2 to 1.4 billion people have never had the chance to hear the gospel. Over 95 percent of these individuals reside in the Window area. This is where 85 percent of the world's poorest and most deprived live. This region is the residence for over 95 percent of the Muslims, Hindus, and Buddhists in the world.

Identifying the Emerging Leadership Style Appropriate for the Twenty-first Century

From the current trend toward effective organizational development there emerges a picture of a distinct leadership style more appropriate for the new century. The hierarchical view of the leader as superior clouds the truth now being rediscovered that "effective group members all have leadership potential which can be realized as situational demands change."

Leadership style considered appropriate for the future has gone through several dramatic changes of late. The focus of loyalty has shifted from institution to people. The source of energy, rather than coming from stability, comes instead from change and innovation. Instead of leadership being dogmatic and authoritative, it is inspirational, empowering, enabling, and facilitating. The leader, rather than giving orders, coaches and teaches. Instead of the quality depending on the affordable best it calls forth excellence. Expectations for associates are not for security but rather personal growth. Status does not come from title and rank but making a difference. What are considered resources are not so much cash and time but rather equal opportunity information, people, and networks. The flexible leadership style model emphasizes personal relationship over positional relationship. This is the wave of the future beyond 2000.

YWAM leader Tom Bloomer, in a paper titled "Leadership of the Twenty-first Century–Leadership Factors Influencing Innovation in Organizations" writes, "The twenty-first century leader must demonstrate the following characteristics:

1. Visionary: The visionary leader is the one who actualizes shared pictures of the future that result in genuine commitment to results, rather than in expected compliance. A vision that is an attractive, realizable view of the future is one of the greatest unifying and mobilizing dynamics that exists. It is also one of the greatest morale builders and thus a powerful antidote to staff burnout and depression. Failure of vision leads quickly to loss of identity, decision-making becomes capricious, and the organization drifts.
2. Creative: An entrepreneurial orientation, showing higher risk taking and innovativeness. This type of transformational leader seems to be one that would consistently facilitate innovation.
3. Adaptable: The new leader must constantly adapt and re-adapt the organization to rapidly changing environments.
4. Competent: The new leaders must prove their competence.
5. Committed to the goal: Leaders must be totally single-minded in their pursuit of the organization's objectives.
6. Action-oriented: Entrepreneurs and innovators were found, unsurprisingly, to have a strong bias toward action over analysis.
7. Committed to the people: Recent scholarship on charismatic leadership underlines the interplay between vision, commitment of the leader to his people, and results.
8. Motivators: Vision and commitment are powerful motivating forces, indeed some of the most powerful that exist."

Approximately five hundred emerging younger leaders from around the world are gathering as part of the event called Celebrate Messiah 2000. During the six months preceding the event, they will be linked via the Internet, into a global dialogue. They will discuss their vision for the twenty-first century and what God is calling them to be and do as God's key men and women for a new day in history. They will be encouraged to have a vision, to dream, and to put those into practice. The combined dream and vision of the emerging young leader participants will be shared with all who attend Celebrate Messiah 2000 during a key plenary session.

Training Christian Leaders for the Twenty-first Century

Two hundred fifty Presidents and Academic Deans (PAD) representing theological schools from 53 nations gathered at the Doxa Deo Church in Pretoria, South Africa, July 1–3, 1997, to consider ways in which the schools they lead can further the goal of "a church for every people and the gospel for every person." They recognized that theological educators have tremendous potential to bless, but also to damage the church; to enhance but also to hinder the fulfillment of the commission. Looking to the future, they called upon college presidents and academic deans to commit themselves to put the vision of "a church for every people and the gospel for every person" at the heart of ministry training. They resolved to explore together a new paradigm of partnership in theological education–that training schools share their distinctives and resources to accomplish the goal of global evangelization. In considering how to train Christian leaders for the years to come they developed important principles in a PAD Declaration that included the following:

1. The primacy of missiological concern for world evangelism must be recognized and focused in the total curriculum of ministry training.
2. Partnership at all levels and in multiple forms is essential for reaching the unreached people of the world.
3. Formal, non-formal, and relational approaches to learning are to be seen as complementary rather than competitive.
4. The content of ministry training must uphold the uniqueness of Jesus Christ and the necessity of personal faith in him as Lord and Savior. This is especially imperative in the light of the increasing pluralistic environment, which has been brought about by the resurgence of non-Christian religions hostile to the advance of the gospel, by the erosion of historic Christianity in the West, and by the increasing prevalence of secularism almost everywhere.
5. Ministry training must aim to produce practicing supernaturalists who minister effectively in the power of the Holy Spirit, relying on prayer and complete trust in the Word of God.
6. Basic to all ministry training is spiritual and character formation in the life of the student, in part facilitated by the example of teacher.
7. Approaches to ministry training must reflect concern for the whole counsel of God wisely contextualized and sustainable by local and national resources.
8. Academic accreditation may serve to guarantee quality control and encourage institutional effectiveness. At the same time it should not be allowed to impede the spiritual and missiological thrust of theological education. Every effort must be made to assure that accrediting structures affirm and promote commitment to world evangelization.
9. Serious consideration should be given to the training of both husband and wife for their mutual effectiveness in ministry, and accessibility to ministry training broadened to include all who can benefit from it.

A "training in the twenty-first century" checklist–a rough draft of a hypothesis based on interviews of international Christian leaders and observation–involves a set of twenty values which could be alliterated with an "I." The hypothesis is that the more I's, the more effective the training process and outcome.

- Intentional — training with a purpose to fulfill the Great Commission and to serve as a seedbed for leadership development in the Christian world movement
- Individually selective — to faithful people, receiving leaders "in the making"
- Indispensable — using a biblical core of curriculum and a commitment to the Word of God and truth
- Instructional — teaching has happened when the student has learned
- Inspirational — anointing, life giving, enthusiastically delivered
- Intuitive — knowing, perceiving, and relating to Christ. "You search the Scriptures, because you think that in them you have eternal life; and it is these that bear witness of Me; and you are unwilling to come to Me, that you may have life" (John 5:9–40, NASB).

- Incarnational — modeling. "...As the Father has sent me, I am sending you" (John 20:21, NIV). "...Christ...leaving you an example, that you should follow in his steps" (1 Peter 2:21, NIV).
- Impartation — imparting of skills for ministry, mentoring, and using the Jesus-style of leadership development (he practiced it himself, he did it with them, he had them do it).
- Interactive sharing — not only communicating one way, but increasing participation by students
- Information — transmission regarding the world in which they will minister, exegeting the Word and the world; e.g., William Carey and A. T. Pierson
- Interpersonal — emphasizing the importance of relationships, discipleship-oriented implementation, and practical field education
- Intercession — calling upon God for illumination and needs
- Integrative — incorporating missiological studies with other academic disciplines
- Interesting — using methods, processes, and technologies appropriate to the group to enhance interest and student involvement
- Innovative — utilizing tools available today such as electronic libraries and software systems methodology
- Interdependent — participating in exchanges, alliances, and partnerships with others involved in the training process; e.g., the annual fellowship gathering of academic deans of evangelical seminaries
- Internet — using distance learning, E-mail forums, and online delivery systems
- International — calling for high levels of cultural diversity and a cross-cultural community lifestyle because the gifts of the church belong to the whole church
- Inclusive — including women
- Initiative — leading to entrepreneurial risk and spontaneous responsiveness; e.g., YWAM, the largest non-formal training organization and a most significant seedbed for leadership in the Christian movement

The Kinds of Structures That Can Best Support the Push Forward

We live in a networked era, an era that has broken down the ways in which we organize ourselves to get things done. We once were readily defined operational entities that knew who we were and everyone else knew who we were, all within our own operational boundaries. Time and technology has changed all that. In the process of networking, we have discovered the principle that working together across these boundaries had literally exploded as we approached the year 2000. We have discovered that there are a variety of networks, coalitions, partnerships, and movements. Some are embedded in primary unshakable principles and structured partnerships of one sort or other. Some ride the wave of technological advance with E-mail conference networks. Other movements are resource based, seeking to generate and supply greater resources for the task. Some are strategic networks. They seek to advance certain strategic objectives by voluntarily joining together with minimal structure and overhead cost to achieve a multiplying factor toward a common goal.

The role of the local church, the mission agency, and the training institutions as structures to advance the Great Commission is under review as we move into the new millennium.

Discussion with a number of European national leaders, as well as with various church, mission, and school leaders, led to a preliminary consultation on this issue, held at Beatenberg Bible School, Switzerland, June 22–24, 1998. The consultation participants expressed their desire to see closer cooperation and partnership between local congregations, training schools, and mission agencies in the task of world evangelization. They called for the re-examination of the role of the church.

We see the need for a theology that recognizes and affirms the importance of the local church in world evangelization, and the complementary roles of local churches, schools, and mission agencies as integral parts of the Church. We see that local congregations should be the senior partners and potential initiators in world evangelization, and that mission agencies should work in a servant role in consultation, education, and mobilization for world evangelization.

The twenty-first century structure will be a success to the degree that it exhibits authenticity, functionality, and flexibility across generations and gender. Authenticity requires that the organization embody its ideals; functionality requires that the organization work; and flexibility requires that the organization be receptive to the input and suggestions of its members. If these tests are met, the organization will also evidence a high degree of commitment by its members.

Developing an Information Sharing System in Response to the Forward Challenges of the Great Commission

An information sharing system with common categories and codes is needed to respond to the various challenges when considering where we go from here in the Great Commission. These challenges include the ideological/religious, the language, the cultural, the geographical, and the urban. A Harvest Information System (HIS) is in development to meet those challenges by providing information on the harvest field, the harvest force, and the harvest yield.

These registries will be included in the Harvest Information System (HIS):

The Harvest Field
ROG - Registry of Geographic Entities
ROH - Registry of Habitats
ROP - Registry of Peoples
ROL - Registry of Languages
ROR - Registry of Religions

The Harvest Force
ROA - Registry of Agencies
ROM - Registry of Ministries
RON - Registry of Networks
ROS - Registry of Services
RSR - Registry of Scripture Resources

The Harvest Yield
RMA - Registry of Ministry Assessment
RCA - Registry of Church Adoptions

RPM - Registry of Peoples Ministry
RAC - Registry of Access to Churches

Patrick Johnstone says, "I am delighted with the HIS initiative and fully endorse the need for such. We had to simplify and focus for these three to five years. We should bequeath to the Church of the twenty-first century the full challenge. I believe we now have the attention, interest, and concern of many Christians, and we now also have a commonly agreed set of terms and categorizations to make the complicated analysis more practicable."

Common Effort

The coordination of a global effort to collect accurate data regarding all peoples is required so those global, continental, national, and local initiatives can work off the same page.

A Common Information Sharing System

The development of an information sharing system is underway through an alliance of Christian entities committed to the stewardship and maintenance of interlinking information sets related to either the harvest field, harvest force, or harvest yield.

A Common Database

The communication of nonsecured, interrelated, user-friendly information through the preparation of a common information database to be distributed by CD-ROM, hard copy, and computer file transfer as appropriate is being prepared. Security aspects are handled separately.

Conclusion

We are faced with enormous challenges of many kinds as we move into the twenty-first century. The big question is, where do we go from here with the Great Commission. What do we mean by the Great Commission? How can we be effective in the face of a dramatically changing context? What kinds of structures are needed? What leadership style is appropriate? How do we prepare leaders? What process should be followed to ensure that everybody is involved who needs to be? What kind of information system is needed? These are some of the key questions that need to be addressed as we move to fulfill God's purposes.

For the first time in history, the worldwide body and near-instant interconnective resources are in place to permit a major global advance in working together strategically to advance the cause of Christ throughout the world.

Personal witness is undoubtedly the most effective approach to presenting the gospel. However, we have no way effectively to estimate the extent of availability of the gospel through this means. Neither can a meaningful estimate be made of exposure to the gospel through local church outreach worldwide. But there are some means by which access to the gospel can be measured.

The global broadcast of Billy Graham's world television special on April 14, 1996, to nearly every country in the world exposed more people to the gospel than all his combined audiences in 45 years of ministry. Never before in history had so many people heard the gospel message proclaimed in a single day.

By the end of the year 2000, eight out of every ten literate people will have access to the entire Bible in a language they can read. Nine out of ten will have access to a New Testament. Today the acceleration is so remarkable that more than eighteen new language portions per year are being translated compared to just over three per year in 1900.

Audio communication has been an effective way of communicating the gospel, needed because of the continuing high rates of illiteracy. This technology has emerged as a vital mass medium for reaching an estimated two billion people. This includes all radio and recorded Gospel messages as well as other media that do not require reading skills. By the end of 2000 radio broadcasts are expected to cover an estimated 99 percent of the world's population and audio gospel recordings will be available to 96 percent.

One of the most effective means of presenting the gospel in visual and audio form has been the Jesus Film. In January of 2000, Paul Eshleman (who leads the AD2000 saturation evangelism track) reported that the number of viewers had increased to 3.3 billion from the 730 million viewers just four years ago. The number of decisions indicated had risen from 42 to 108 million over that same time period.

None of this is to say that all have yet had access to the gospel. We still have a long way to go. But such global advances represent the heart of God. They are already happening. We have many predecessors for our example and inspiration. Praise God! We must sense and catch this vision to cooperate as never before. We must move forward together.

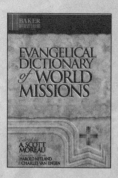

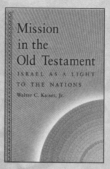

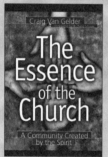

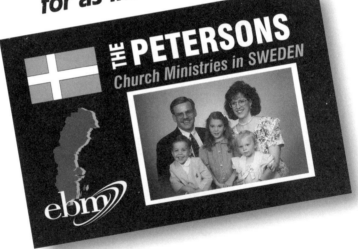

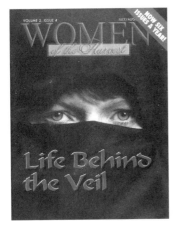

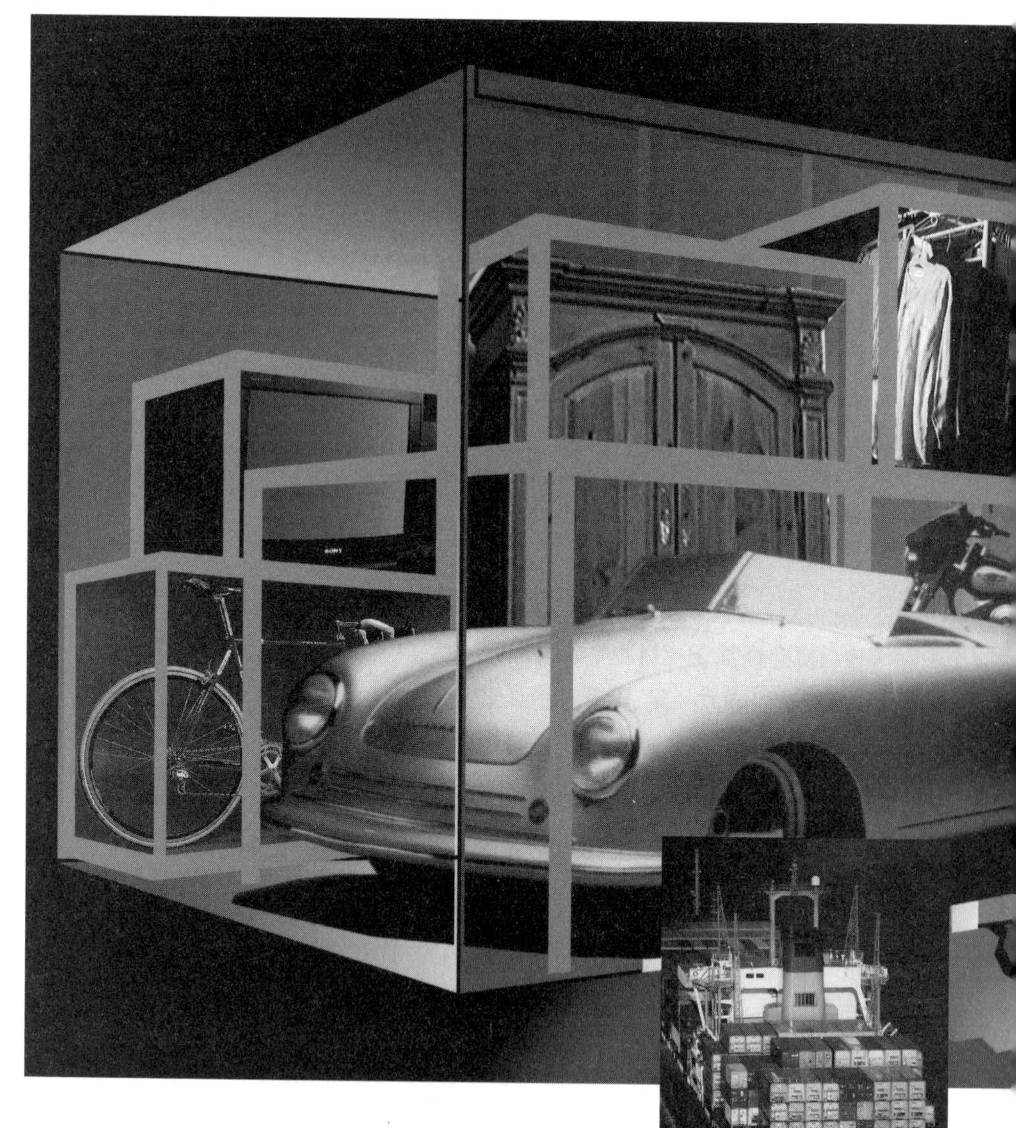

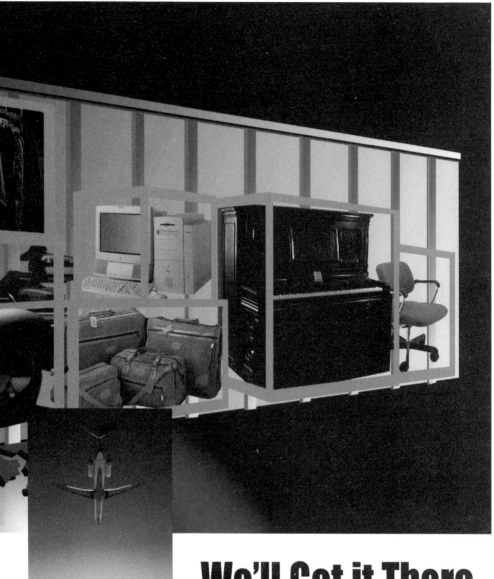

CHAPTER 4

Putting the Survey in Perspective

A. Scott Moreau

Of the 814 agencies listed in the *Handbook*, 693 are in the United States and 121 in Canada. Together[1] they mobilize a reported total on-location missionary force of 119,219[2] full-time[3] people[4] (42,921 North Americans, 3,423 non-North Americans working in a country other than their own, and 72,875 nationals) who are working in a reported 198 countries.[5] The U.S. agencies mobilize a total on-location missionary force of 114,216 (39,887 U.S. citizens, 3,179 non-U.S. citizens working in a country other than their own,[6] and 71,150 nationals) who are working in 197 distinct countries. Thus, roughly speaking, for every four Americans working for U.S. agencies there are seven nationals working in their own country for U.S. agencies, a significant change from the last survey in which there were less than three nationals for every four Americans. When we add in the nonresidential workers, short-term missionaries, tentmakers, U.S. staff and volunteers,[7] 438,065 people are reported to be directly engaged in the missionary task through U.S. agencies listed in this book.

In Table 4.1 we present a summary of several areas of change in the numbers over the past three editions of the *Handbook*. It should be noted that the "Change" column reflects only the difference from the 1996 and 1999[8] surveys. Perhaps the most significant change was in the area of giving: Adjusting for inflation, the total reported income for all U.S. agencies grew an impressive 21.8% from 1996 to 1999. This is discussed in greater detail later in the chapter.

Two other changes may look more significant than they really are. First is the number of non-U.S. personnel serving in their own country. The 1996 survey reported 28,535, while the 1999 survey shows this to have grown by over 149% to 71,150. However, the numbers reported by four agencies magnify this: Christian Aid Mission (18,809), Gospel for Asia (11,286), Campus Crusade for Christ (8,978) and Partners International (4,048). These four comprise 43,121 of the reported national workers (63.7% of the total), compared to 12,272 in 1996 (43.0% of the total). Together they grew by more than 251%. Even if these four are excluded, however, the net gain in reported nationals working for U.S. agencies in their own countries is still an impressive 72.3% and may indicate an increase in the rate of nationalization among U.S. agencies. A possible confirmation of this is the 77.5% increase in non-U.S. personnel serving in countries other than their own.

Second, the number of reported volunteers increased by 231% from the 1996 to the 1999 survey. However, this was dominated by one organization. Campus Crusade reported

42,175 volunteers in 1996; in 1999 this jumped to 171,506. Their gain of 129,331 is more than 94% of the total increase. However, the gain in volunteers for all other organizations combined from 1996 to 1999 was still impressive at 45.8%.

While every other statistical measure went up between the 1996 to 1999 surveys, the number of long-term (four or more years) missionaries actually decreased slightly. This may be an early indicator of a trend to watch closely in the future. It should be noted that the decrease of 117 long-term personnel is more than compensated for by an increase in the number of bi-vocational or tentmaker missionaries (up 1,884 or 141%) and the significant increase in fully supported non-residential missionaries (1,308, or 258%).

Table 4.1: Summary of Changes in U.S. Missions Statistics, 1992-1999

Personnel from the U.S.	1992	1996	1999	Change (1996-99)
FULLY SUPPORTED U.S. PERSONNEL SERVING OVERSEAS				
Long-Term (Overseas more than 4 years)	32,634	33,074	32,957	-0.35%
Short-Term (Overseas from 1 to 4 years)	5,115	6,562	6,930	5.6%
Nonresidential fully supported	626	507	1,815	258.0%
Total fully supported U.S. personnel serving overseas	*38,375*	*40,143*	*41,702*	3.9%
OTHER U.S. PERSONNEL SERVING OVERSEAS				
Short-term of 2 weeks up to 1 year (1996 and 1999)	NA [9]	63,995	97,272	52.0%
Bivocational associates sponsored or supervised	1,040	1,336	3,220	141.0%
Nonresidential partially supported	80	215	310	44.2%
NON- U.S. PERSONNEL PARTIALLY OR FULLY SUPPORTED				
Those serving in their home country	NA	28,535	71,150	149.3%
Those serving in a country other than their home country	1,898	1,791	3,179	77.5%
U.S. MINISTRY AND HOME OFFICE STAFF				
Full-time paid staff	14,694	19,399	21,758	12.2%
Part-time staff/associates	1,742	2,850	2,946	3.4%
Volunteer (ongoing) helpers	37,452	59,332	196,528	231%
FINANCIAL SUPPORT RAISED IN THE U.S.				
Income for overseas ministries [10]	$2,371,537,874	$2,407,284,964	$2,932,779,966	21.8%

Where Are the U.S. Agency Headquarters Located?

The American organizations are found in 435 cities across 41 states. The states which serve as home to the most mission agency headquarters are California (107; 15.5% of the U.S. agencies), Pennsylvania (48; 6.9%), Texas (45; 6.5%), Colorado and Illinois (42 or 6.1% each), Indiana and Florida (34 or 4.9% each), Virginia (28; 4.1%), Georgia (26; 3.8%) and Washington and Ohio (25 or 3.6% each). Not including the sparsely populated Northwest, the most underrepresented section of the United States is New England, with only 2 agencies headquartered in the six-state region (1 each in Massachusetts and Connecticut). In light of the rich heritage of Protestant Christianity in this area of the United States, this is surprising.[11]

Figure 4.1: Distribution of U.S. Mission Agency Headquarters

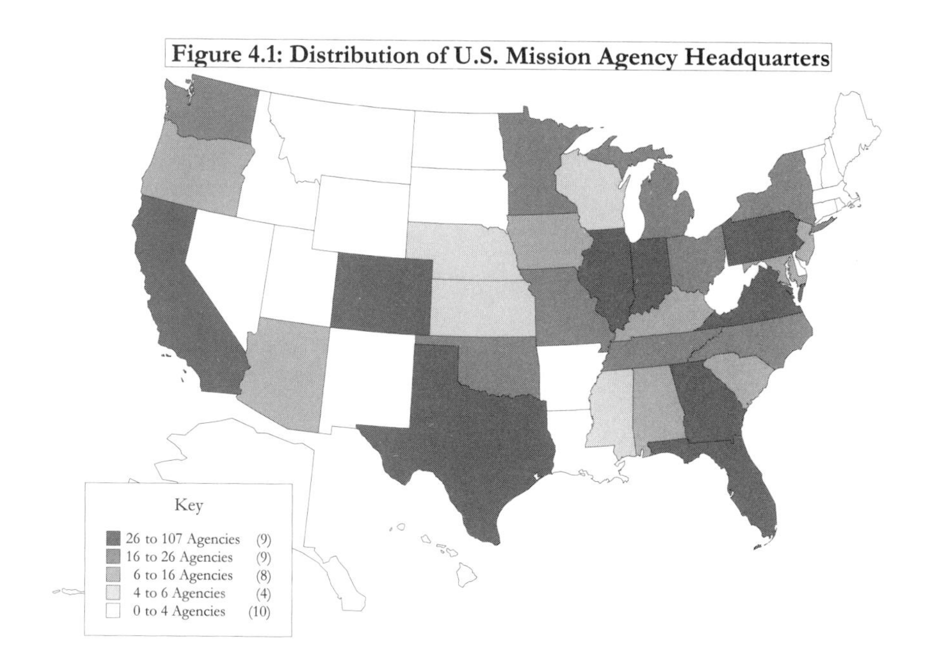

The location of the agency headquarters between surveys was relatively stable. In relation to the 1996 survey the states that lost the most ground were California, New York and Florida (3 less agencies each) and Arizona (2 less agencies). Those that gained the most net ground were Ohio (3 more agencies) and Colorado,[12] Oklahoma, Virginia, and Washington (2 more agencies each). The recent shift of Christian organizations to Colorado Springs (26; in the previous *Handbook* it was 22) has resulted in that city being the home to more mission agencies than any other in North America. It has almost twice as many agencies as Pasadena (14), followed by Wheaton (13), Tulsa (11), New York (10), Dallas and Indianapolis (9 each). Cities that experienced the greatest increase in mission agency headquarters were Colorado Springs (4) and Cincinnati, Indianapolis, Littleton, and Norcross (2 each).

When Were the U.S. Agencies Founded?

Fifty-six of the 693 U.S. agencies listed were founded prior to 1900. The 20th century growth trends are portrayed in Figures 4.2, 4.3 and 4.5. From the 1940s, in which 55 agencies were started, through the 1980s, when 141 agencies were formed, in each decade more agencies were founded than in the previous one. While it looks as though there has been a decline in new agency founding during the 1990s, the full data for the decade are not yet available. It can be seen that the growth of denominational agencies over this time has been slow but steady (see Figure 4.5), while the growth of agencies not tied to specific denominations virtually exploded from the 1930s on (see Figure 4.3 and 4.5).

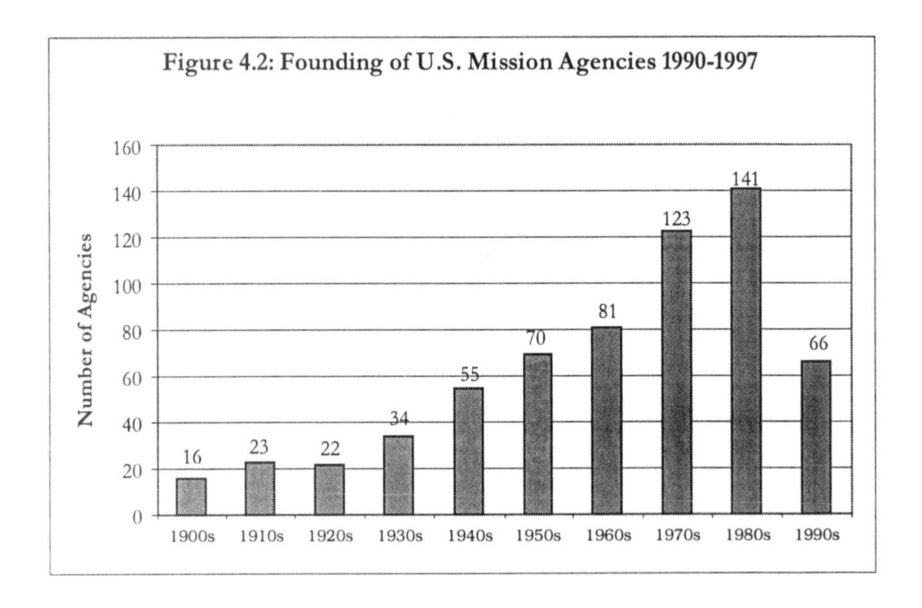

Though further historical studies are necessary to help shed light on this six-decade growth surge, several possible causes may be mentioned. Certainly the well-documented post-World War II boom added to the surge in agency development. Perhaps another factor was the gradual decline through the course of the century in mainline denominational commitment to traditional evangelism and church planting missions. While this was happening, there was a corresponding rise in evangelical commitment and a surge in the formation of new agencies free from denominational control. The rise of Pentecostalism and the Charismatic movement helped sustain the overall surge in growth rate through the 1980s (see Figure 4.3). Contradicting the widely-perceived orientation of the 1980s as the "me" decade in larger U.S. culture, more mission agencies were formed during that decade than any other.

It is helpful to examine the growth of Pentecostal/Charismatic, Baptist and Evangelical mission agencies when plotted separately over the course of the 20th century (Figure 4.3). The Baptist agencies experienced steady growth throughout the century and the graph of the rise of Baptist agencies is fairly straight. The Evangelical and Pentecostal/Charismatic agencies, however, display marked upturns. The Evangelical agencies began their surge in the late 1930s. This sharp rise continued through the 1980s. The Pentecostal/Charismatic surge started in the late 1960s, though flattening off from the mid-1980s on.

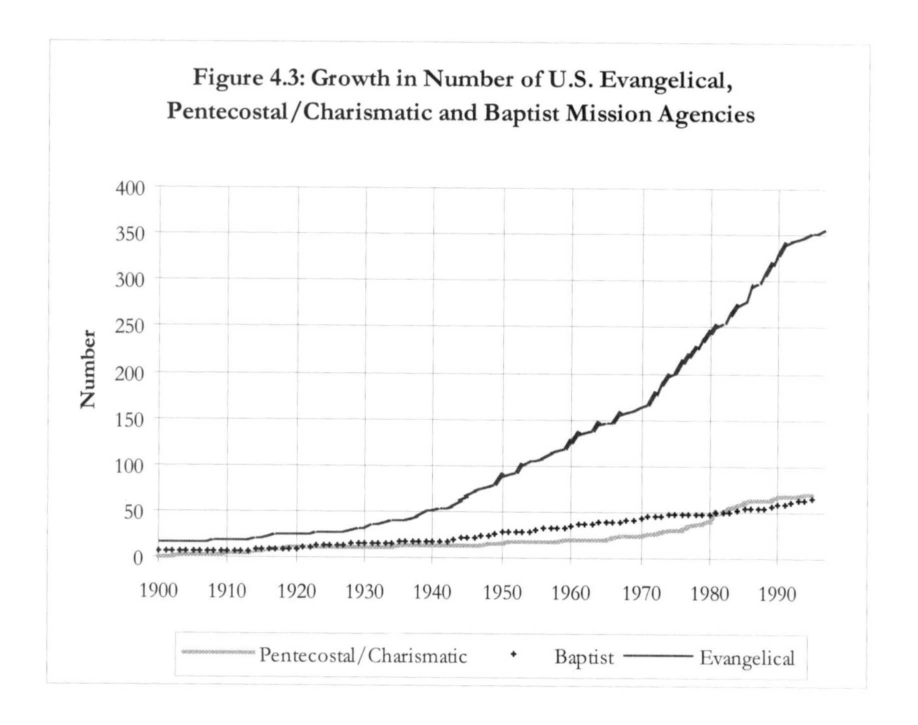

Denominationalism, Stances and Activities

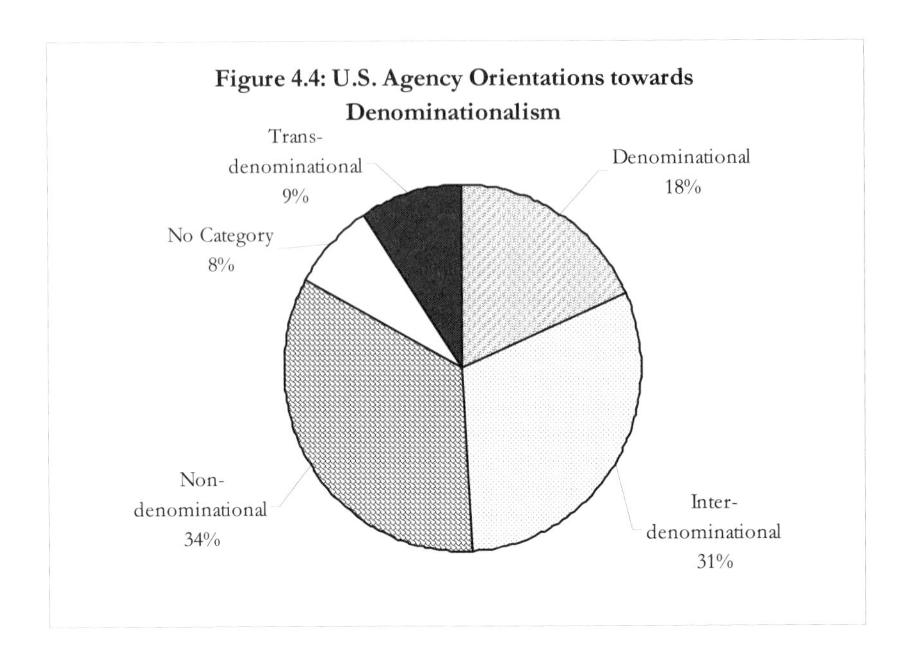

Agencies described their orientation towards denominationalism from among six categories: denominational, interdenominational, non-denominational, transdenominational, prefer that no orientation be used, and other. The frequency of responses is shown in Figure 4.4, which combines the last two categories as "No Category." Overall, less than one in five U.S. agencies describe themselves as "denominational." Some are very intentional in distinguishing nondenominational from interdenominational, while others change from edition to edition of the *Handbook*. Despite the nomenclature, the most significant issue is whether an agency considers itself to be a denominationally-related one or not. To distinguish the latter from the category "nondenominational," in the following discussion we refer to them as *"not-denominational"* agencies.

The 20th century shift from denominational agencies to not-denominational agencies is illustrated in Figure 4.5, which shows the total number of each type of agency listed in the *Handbook* over the course of the century. As the graph clearly shows, denominational agencies were far more numerous in 1900 (when there were 2.8 denominational agencies for every 1 not-denominational agency), they were roughly even by 1940, and the ratio was reversed by 1980 (1 denominational agency for every 2.83 not-denominational agencies). The trend of proliferation of not-denominational agencies continued through the 1990s, and the present ratio is 4.48 not-denominational agencies for every denominational one.

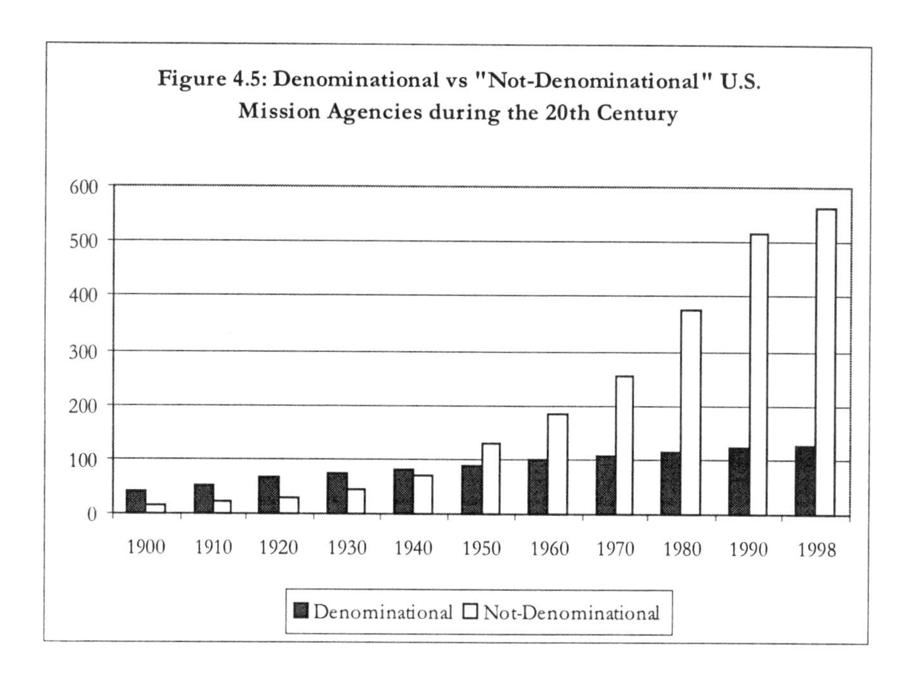
Figure 4.5: Denominational vs "Not-Denominational" U.S. Mission Agencies during the 20th Century
600
500
400
300
200
100
0
1900
1910
1920
1930
1940
1950
1960
1970
1980
1990
1998
Denominational
Not-Denominational

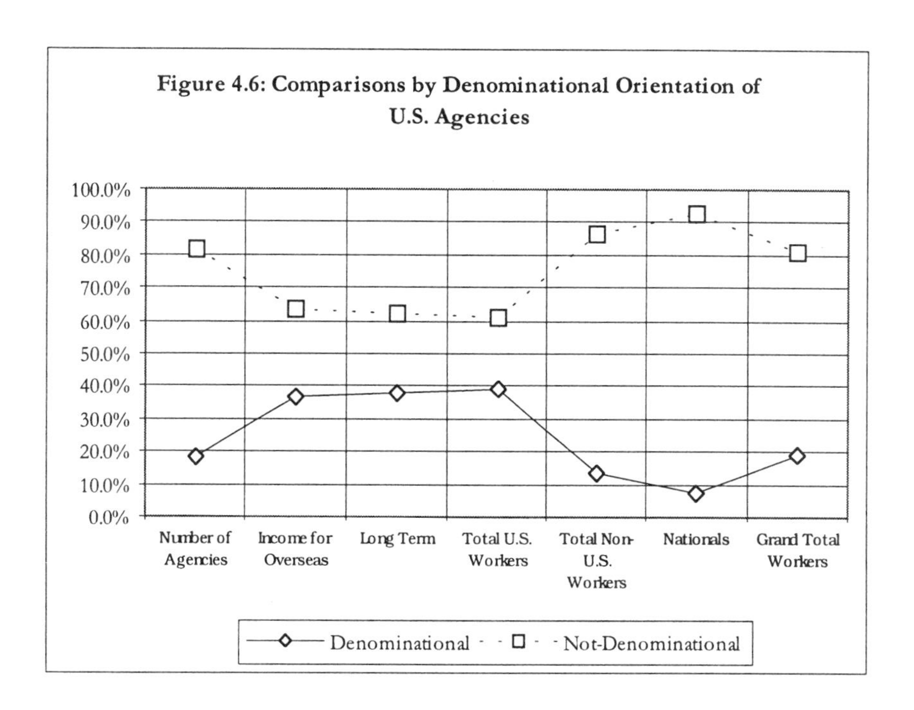
Figure 4.6: Comparisons by Denominational Orientation of U.S. Agencies
100.0%
90.0%
80.0%
70.0%
60.0%
50.0%
40.0%
30.0%
20.0%
10.0%
0.0%
Number of Agencies
Income for Overseas
Long Term
Total U.S. Workers
Total Non-U.S. Workers
Nationals
Grand Total Workers
Denominational
Not-Denominational

Figures 4.6 and 4.7 display several statistics for denominational and not-denominational agencies. From 4.6 we can see that denominational agencies reported proportionately greater overseas income, long-term U.S. missionaries and U.S. full-time missionaries than the not-denominational agencies. The not-denominational agencies, on the other hand, reported relatively more non-U.S. workers in a country other than their own and nationals working in their own country. From 4.7 we see that denominational agencies reported relatively more non-residential missionaries and short-term missionaries. The not-denominational agencies reported relatively more tentmakers and U.S. full-time staff.

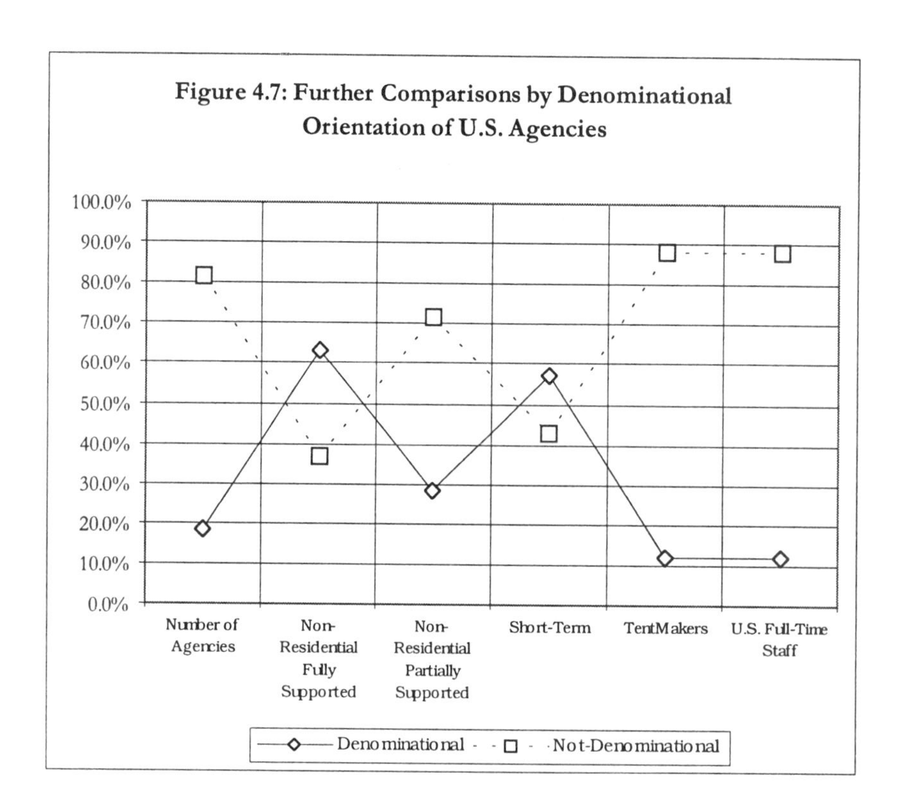

Agencies were also asked to indicate which of twenty-four categories described their doctrinal or ecclesiastical stance. Table 4.2 shows the stances and the number of corresponding agencies, sorted by the number from greatest to least. The vast bulk of the agencies simply choose "evangelical" to describe themselves (51.7%). Of the 357 agencies that chose the term evangelical, only 35 (9.8%) chose a second term. Thirty-seven agencies chose a different primary term but evangelical as a secondary doctrinal/ecclesiastical stance.

Table 4.2: Doctrinal/Ecclesiastical Stance and Associated Numbers for U.S. Agencies

Doctrinal/ Ecclesiastical Stance	*# of Agencies*	*# of Countries*[13]	*Income for Overseas Missions*	*U.S. Long Term*	*Total U.S. Missionaries*	*# of Non-National Workers*	*# of National Workers*	*Total Missionary Force*
Evangelical	357	177	$1,229,658,219	13960	17453	1807	58056	77316
Baptist	65	133	$471,323,951	8046	9239	95	1834	11168
Charismatic	40	71	$32,813,275	415	534	160	814	1508
Pentecostal	28	135	$182,010,076	2126	2528	80	2182	4790
Independent	25	102	$28,474,007	644	672	140	1971	2783
Ecumenical	23	74	$265,737,553	47	512	45	748	1305
Chr/Plym Breth	18	54	$38,109,645	2416	2507	116	15	2702
Lutheran	17	80	$71,822,353	621	864	14	160	1038
Fundamental	15	47	$29,765,551	1742	1840	315	648	2803
Presbyterian	15	91	$73,391,987	1037	1578	6	387	1971
Wesleyan	13	69	$52,562,464	568	614	31	268	913
Mennonite	12	67	$137,443,128	569	704	71	708	1483
Other	10	14	$37,082,989	35	55	6	19	81
Holiness	9	75	$57,201,340	727	840	233	16	1089
Reformed	9	29	$10,616,303	128	137	0	506	643
Methodist	8	17	$86,505,653	610	652	2	13	667
Christian (RM)	6	71	$13,350,713	359	385	28	79	428
Episcopal	6	23	$12,039,113	86	121	9	7	137
Brethren	5	24	$5,756,791	107	178	1	525	704
Friends	4	14	$2,692,324	33	45	12	0	57
Adventist	3	90	$94,240,432	486	542	0	493	1035
Congregational	2	9	$582,805	2	4	0	22	26
Anglican	1	4	$150,000	8	8	13	0	21

Table 4.2 also provides the totals on selected data for each self-identified doctrinal/ ecclesiastical stance. It includes the number of agencies of that stance, the number of countries those agencies are working in,[14] the number of U.S. and non-U.S. expatriate missionaries, and the number of nationals supported by the denominational/doctrinal type. For example, sixty-five agencies describe their primary stance as Baptist. These agencies have personnel or projects in 133 countries, employ 8,046 long-term U.S. missionaries,[15] 9,239 total U.S. missionaries, 95 non-U.S. expatriates, 1,834 nationals working in their own countries. The total missionary full-time missionary force of these agencies is 11,168 people.

Table 4.3: Percent Indicators of U.S. Agencies by Doctrinal/Ecclesiastical Stance

Doctrinal/ Ecclesiastical Stance	*# of Agencies*	*Income for Overseas Missions*	*Overseas Income per Missionary (Total Force)*	*U.S. Long Term*	*Total U.S. Missionaries*	*# of Non-National Workers*	*# of National Workers*	*Total Missionary Force*
Evangelical	51.7%	41.9%	$ 15,904	40.1%	41.5%	56.8%	83.6%	67.4%
Baptist	9.4%	16.1%	$ 42,203	23.1%	22.0%	3.0%	2.6%	9.7%
Charismatic	5.8%	1.1%	$ 21,759	1.2%	1.3%	5.0%	1.2%	1.3%
Pentecostal	4.1%	6.2%	$ 37,998	6.1%	6.0%	2.5%	3.1%	4.2%
Independent	3.6%	1.0%	$ 10,231	1.9%	1.6%	4.4%	2.8%	2.4%
Ecumenical	3.3%	9.1%	$203,630	0.1%	1.2%	1.4%	1.1%	1.1%
Chr/Plym Breth	2.6%	1.3%	$ 14,104	6.9%	6.0%	3.6%	0.1%	2.4%
Lutheran	2.5%	2.4%	$ 69,193	1.8%	2.1%	0.4%	0.2%	0.9%
Fundamental	2.2%	1.0%	$ 10,619	5.0%	4.4%	9.9%	0.9%	2.4%
Presbyterian	2.2%	2.5%	$ 37,236	3.0%	3.8%	0.2%	0.6%	1.7%
Wesleyan	1.9%	1.8%	$ 57,571	1.6%	1.5%	1.0%	0.4%	0.8%
Mennonite	1.7%	4.7%	$ 92,679	1.6%	1.7%	2.2%	1.0%	1.3%
Holiness	1.3%	2.0%	$ 52,526	2.1%	2.0%	7.3%	0.0%	0.9%
Reformed	1.3%	0.4%	$ 16,511	0.4%	0.3%	0.0%	0.7%	0.6%
Methodist	1.2%	2.9%	$129,694	1.8%	1.6%	0.1%	0.0%	0.6%
Christian (RM)	0.9%	0.5%	$ 31,193	1.0%	0.9%	0.9%	0.0%	0.4%
Episcopal	0.9%	0.4%	$ 87,877	0.2%	0.3%	0.3%	0.0%	0.1%
Brethren	0.7%	0.2%	$ 8,177	0.3%	0.4%	<0.1%	0.8%	0.6%
Friends	0.6%	0.1%	$ 47,234	0.1%	0.1%	0.4%	0.0%	<0.1%
Adventist	0.4%	3.2%	$ 91,054	1.4%	1.3%	0.0%	0.7%	0.9%
Congregational	0.3%	<0.1%	$ 22,416	<0.1%	<0.1%	0.0%	<0.1%	<0.1%
Anglican	0.1%	<0.1%	$ 7,143	<0.1%	<0.1%	0.4%	0.0%	<0.1%

In Table 4.3 we show the rankings of the agencies in relation to these two areas by doctrinal/ecclesiastical stance. The percent figures in all categories are the percent for each doctrinal/ecclesiastical type of the total numbers. For example, the fifty-seven agencies that describe themselves primarily as Baptist represent 9.4% of U.S. agencies. They received 16.1% of the income for overseas missions and had an income for overseas ministry of $42,203 per missionary worker. They supplied 23.1% of the U.S. long-term missionaries, 22.0% of the total U.S. missionaries, 3.0% of the non-national workers, 2.6% of the national workers, and 9.7% of the total missionary force. Thus, Baptist-type U.S. agencies report greater focus on U.S. than national workers and receive almost double the average overseas income per worker of other U.S. agencies. However, care should be taken not to simplistically draw conclusions based solely on comparing these numbers. In this case, for example, agencies have different policies on how they count non-U.S. missionaries. In addition, per capita numbers do not necessarily reflect relative missionary salary scales. Some agencies, for example, focus on funding large projects involving few salaried personnel and therefore show disproportionate per capita overseas income (e.g., the ecumenical agencies).

From Tables 4.2 and 4.3 we may also deduce certain general trends as well as see interesting differences among the agencies by their doctrinal/ecclesiastical stance. Among the general trends is that 82.8% of the U.S. missionaries are long-term. Further, 60.6% of the total missionary workforce employed by U.S. agencies is comprised of national workers serving in their own countries, though, as discussed above, this number is largely the result of four organizations.

Interesting differences include the reality that agencies that identified themselves as evangelical tend to report smaller budgets and numbers of missionaries supported than those identified as Baptist, and they report more national workers as part of their missionary force than the Baptist agencies do. Christian/Plymouth Brethren agencies report spending proportionately less per missionary, and more long-term missionaries with less national workers per agency. Ecumenical agencies report greater income per capita than other agencies, with fewer long-term workers. Fundamentalist agencies report spending proportionately less per missionary, more long-term missionaries, and more national workers than the average. Holiness agencies, with only 1.3% of the total number of agencies, report 7.3% of the total non-national missionaries working in countries other than their own.

What Were the Activities of U.S. Agencies?

Table 4.4: Ranking of Primary Activities for U.S. Agencies

1	Church establishing/planting (158; 22.9%)
2	Evangelism, personal and small group (60; 8.7%)
3	National church nurture/support (40; 5.8%)
4	Leadership development (30; 4.3%)
5	Support of national workers (26; 3.8%)
6	Funds transmission (22; 3.2%)
7,8	Evangelism, mass Training/Orientation, missionary (20 each; 2.9%)
9	Development, community and/or other Short-term programs coordination Medicine, incl. dental and public health Training, other (18 each; 2.6%)

From a list of fifty-two options, agencies chose up to six of what they considered their main activities. They also indicated which one they considered their primary activity. Church planting/establishing was by far the most frequently chosen primary activity (158, or 22.9% of U.S. agencies) followed by personal and small group evangelism (60; 8.7%). Table 4.4 depicts the ranking for the primary activities.

Table 4.5: All Activities of Mission Agencies Categorized

Evangelism/Discipleship Activities	
Activity	*Percent*
Church establishing/planting	39.20%
Evangelism, personal & small group	38.20%
Leadership development	24.50%
National church nurture/support	23.00%
Literature distribution	17.90%
Support of national workers	16.40%
Evangelism, mass	15.10%
Bible distribution	11.40%
Literature production	10.10%
Broadcasting, radio and/or TV	9.30%
Camping programs	7.50%
Youth programs	6.70%
Church construction	6.40%
Evangelism, student	5.90%
Children's programs	5.60%
Video/Film production/distribution	5.40%
Audio recording/distribution	4.60%
Translation, Bible	3.20%
Literacy	2.70%
Translation, other	2.30%
Linguistics	1.70%

Education/Training Activities	
Activity	*Percent*
Education, theological	17.40%
Training, Other	11.60%
Education, church/school gen. Christian	10.60%
Education, theological by extension	6.40%
Correspondence courses	4.50%
Education, extension (other)	2.70%
Education, missionary (certificate/degree)	2.20%

Mission Agency Support Activities	
Activity	*Percent*
Training/Orientation, missionary	13.00%
Short-term programs coord.	12.60%
Recruiting/Mobilizing	9.40%
Services for other agencies	6.80%
Technical assistance	5.20%
Information services	4.80%
Management consulting/training	3.50%
Aviation services	1.60%
Furloughed missionary support	1.60%
Purchasing services	0.70%
Association of Missions	0.60%
Psychological counseling	0.60%
Member Care	0.30%
Partnership development	0.10%

Relief and Development Activities	
Activity	*Percent*
Medicine, incl. dental and public health	14.30%
Development, community or other	11.90%
Relief and/or rehabilitation	10.90%
Childcare/orphanage	9.60%
Medical supplies	5.60%
Agricultural programs	4.30%
Supplying equipment	2.90%
Disability assistance programs	1.70%

Other Activities	
Activity	*Percent*
Funds transmission	8.70%
Research	5.40%
Other	1.70%

In Table 4.5, we give the more detailed picture by sorting the 52 activities into four major groups and including primary and secondary activities: evangelistic and discipleship-oriented activities, mission agency support activities, educational and training activities, relief and development activities, and other.[16] To simplify comparisons, rather than giving the number of agencies, we list the activities in ranked order and give the percent of all U.S. agencies that reported they are engaged in each activity.

Overseas Income for U.S. Agencies

The total reported income for the 1999 survey for all U.S. agencies was $2,932,779,966.[17] Adjusting for inflation, this represents a 21.8% increase over the 1996 survey results, which parallels the robust growth in the U.S. economy over the same period and is the greatest increase ever seen from one edition of the *Handbook* to the next.[18] Table 4.6 lists the U.S. agencies whose reported overseas income was $10,000,000 or more. The previous edition of the *Handbook* listed the top 100 agencies, with the 100th having an inflation-adjusted income of $3,583,300. In contrast, this edition's 100th agency had an income of $4,791,154 (a 33.7% increase). Further, in the previous edition of the *Handbook* only 26 agencies reported overseas income at $10,000,000 or above in contrast to the 58 in this edition. Together these give clear evidence that the jump in income for overseas mission work is a broad-based one among the U.S. agencies.

Table 4.6: U.S. Agencies with $10,000,000 or More Income for Overseas Ministries

Rank	U.S. Agency	Overseas Income
1	Southern Baptist Convention International Mission Board	$270,562,000
2	World Vision Inc.	$233,391,000
3	MAP International	$148,197,924
4	Assemblies of God, Gen. Council	$126,470,484
5	Seventh-day Adventists General Conference	$92,828,000
6	Wycliffe Bible Translators USA	$83,591,000
7	United Methodist Church, General Board	$78,240,936
8	Christian Aid Ministries	$73,940,211
9	Compassion International, Inc.	$73,110,343
10	Campus Crusade for Christ, Intl.	$65,739,000
11	Samaritan's Purse	$58,715,127
12	Mennonite Central Committee Intl.	$48,444,000
13	Church World Service & Witness	$48,000,000
14	Food for the Hungry, Inc.	$45,497,314
15	Larry Jones International Ministries (Feed the Children)	$45,178,413
16	Presbyterian Church (USA), Worldwide Ministries	$40,107,046
17	Church of the Nazarene, World Mission Division	$38,602,240
18	TEAM (The Evangelical Alliance Mission)	$28,418,000
19	ABWE (Association of Baptists for World Evangelism)	$28,000,000
20	Mission to the World (PCA), Inc.	$26,591,547
21	Baptist International Missions	$26,400,000
22	New Tribes Mission	$24,822,164
23	Christian Churches / Churches of Christ	$24,000,000
24	Lutheran World Relief	$22,598,621
25	Baptist Bible Fellowship Intl.	$22,531,653
26	SIM USA	$21,812,357
27	Evangelical Lutheran Church in America	$20,709,455
28	Salvation Army, U.S.A.	$20,000,000
29	Bible League, The	$19,880,121

30	Mercy Ships	$19,682,881
31	World Concern	$19,339,518
32	Christian and Missionary Alliance	$19,215,697
33	CBInternational	$18,955,637
34	Church of God (Cleveland, TN) World Missions	$18,308,916
35	Mission Aviation Fellowship	$18,127,895
36	United Pentecostal Church Intl.,	$18,061,036
37	Baptist Mid-Missions	$17,600,000
38	Lutheran Church—Missouri Synod, Board for Mission	$17,432,620
39	Navigators, U.S. International Ministries Group	$17,343,709
40	Habitat for Humanity International	$17,081,351
41	American Bible Society	$16,676,371
42	American Baptist Churches in the U.S.A.	$16,024,902
43	Trans World Radio	$15,430,221
44	Interchurch Medical Assistance	$14,717,252
45	Evangelical Free Church Mission	$13,676,320
46	United Church Board for World Ministries	$13,379,044
47	World Gospel Mission	$13,287,519
48	Opportunity International	$13,000,000
49	Christian Missions in Many Lands	$12,800,000
50	Africa Inland Mission International	$12,694,000
51	Christian Broadcasting Network	$12,688,500
52	Blessings International	$12,375,826
53	Operation Blessing International	$11,461,175
54	OMS International, Inc.	$10,813,795
55	Christian Reformed World Missions	$10,400,000
56	Episcopal Church, Domestic & Foreign Missionary Society	$10,322,549
57	Gospel for Asia	$10,220,539
58	Childcare International	$10,000,000

Where Are the U.S. Agencies and Missionaries Active?

The map in Figure 4.8 graphically displays the broad distribution of U.S. agencies in every country of the world. This is followed by several graphs depicting the distribution of U.S. agencies and missionaries. Figure 4.9 shows the distribution of U.S. agencies by region, Figure 4.10 the U.S. missionaries by region,[19] and Figure 4.11 the total missionary force working for U.S. agencies.[20] While there are more U.S. missionaries in Latin America[21] than anywhere else, the greatest number of total workers deployed by U.S. mission agencies was in Asia (more than double that of Latin America).

Figure 4.8: Distribution of U.S. Mission Agencies

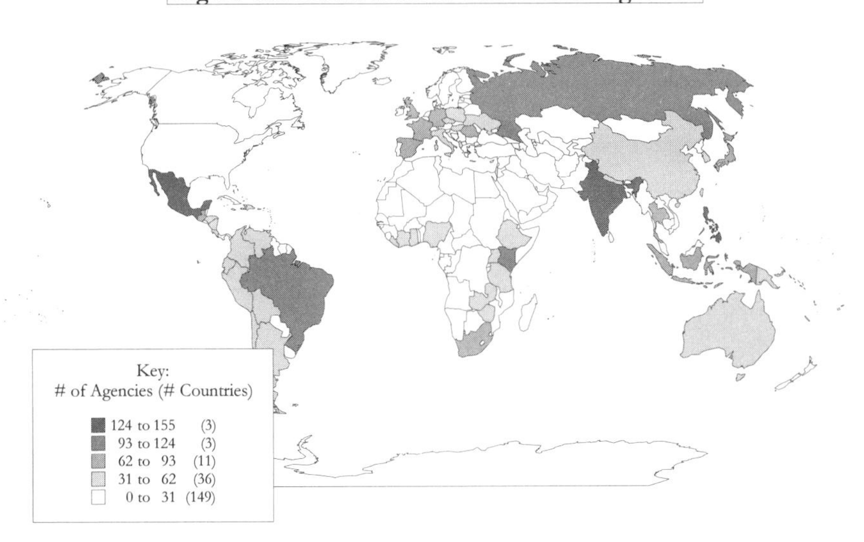

This can be primarily accounted for by the reported deployment of nationals of four agencies, namely Gospel for Asia (11,286), Christian Aid Mission (9,883), Campus Crusade (6,617) and Partners International (3,060). Together these four represent over 71% of the reported Asian nationals working for U.S. agencies.

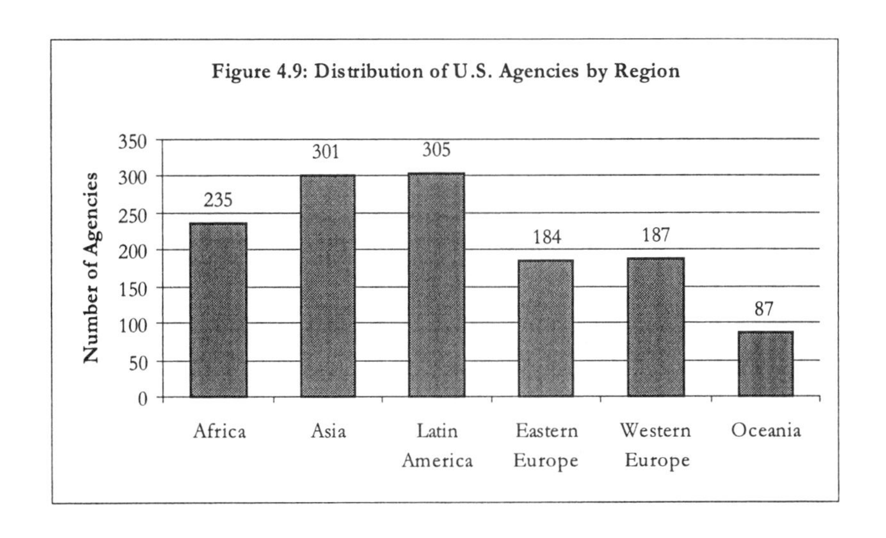

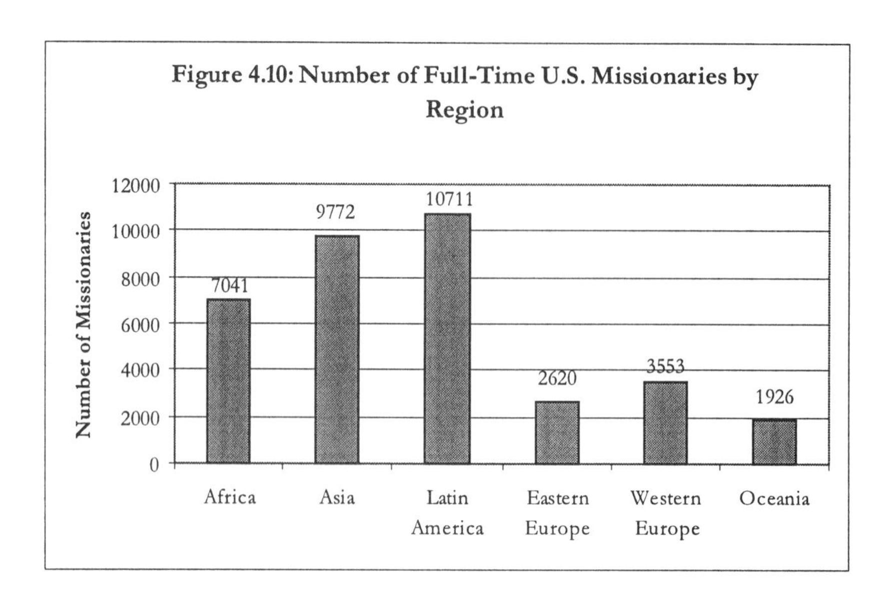
Figure 4.10: Number of Full-Time U.S. Missionaries by Region
Number of Missionaries
12000
10000
8000
6000
4000
2000
0
7041
9772
10711
2620
3553
1926
Africa
Asia
Latin America
Eastern Europe
Western Europe
Oceania

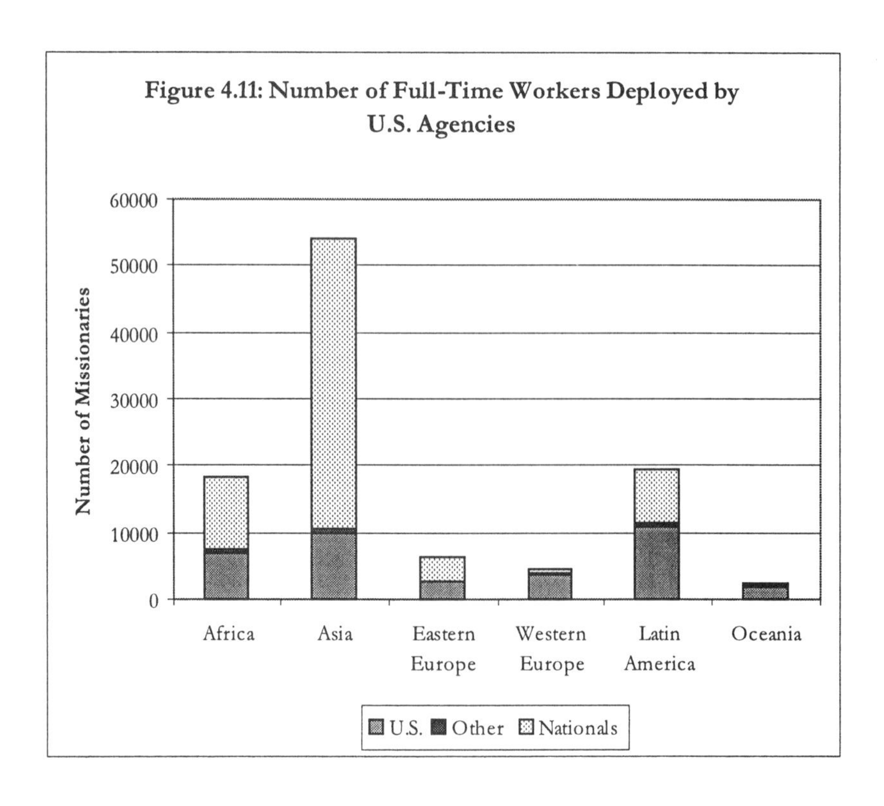
Figure 4.11: Number of Full-Time Workers Deployed by U.S. Agencies
Number of Missionaries
60000
50000
40000
30000
20000
10000
0
Africa
Asia
Eastern Europe
Western Europe
Latin America
Oceania
U.S.
Other
Nationals

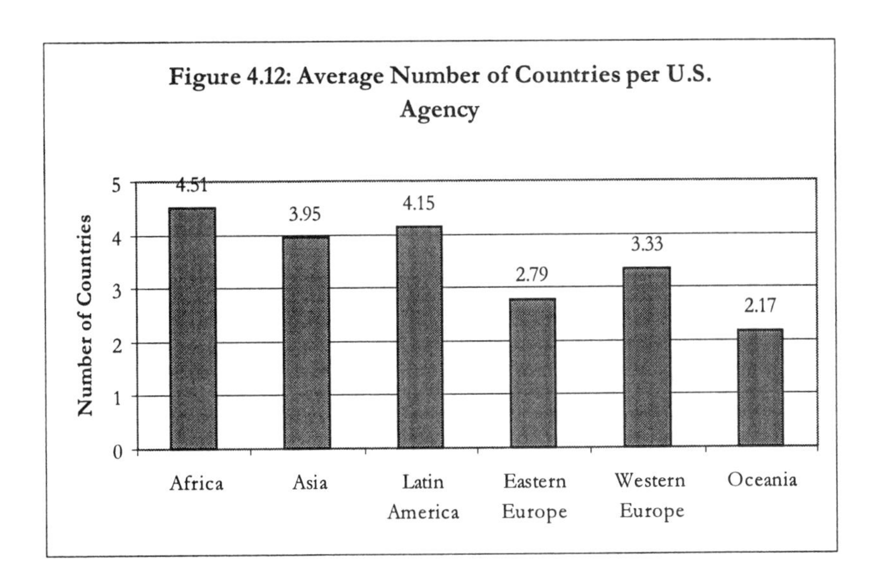

In the tables that follow, we present the countries of the world in which more than fifty U.S. agencies are present (Table 4.7), the U.S. agencies with more than 500 total full-time personnel (including non-U.S.; Table 4.8), and the U.S. agencies with more than 500 U.S. personnel (Table 4.9). The rounded averages per country are 27 U.S. agencies, 203 U.S. missionaries (of which 168 are long-term), 16 non-U.S. expatriates, and 336 national workers.[22]

Table 4.7: Countries with More than 50 U.S. Agencies

Country	# Agencies[23]
Mexico	176
India	153
Philippines	142
Brazil	131
Kenya	116
Russian Federation	111
Japan	102
France	97
Germany	92
United Kingdom	91
Spain	86
South Africa	81
Indonesia	81

Country	# Agencies[23]
Guatemala	81
Haiti	79
Thailand	78
Colombia	73
Peru	72
Romania	69
Ukraine	67
Nigeria	65
Honduras	65
Ghana	63
Argentina	63
Taiwan, Republic of China	61
Bolivia	61
Ecuador	60
Uganda	58
China, Peoples Republic	55
Hungary	55
Costa Rica	55
Cote d'Ivoire	54
Hong Kong	54
Italy	54
Chile	51
Australia	50

Table 4.8: U.S. Agencies with More than 500 Total Workers

Agency	# Countries	U.S. Workers	Non-U.S. Workers	National Workers[24]	Total
Christian Aid Mission	89	0	0	18809	18809
Gospel for Asia	8	0	0	11286	11286
Campus Crusade for Christ, Intl.	111	973	287	8978	10238
Southern Baptist Convention Intl Bd	N/A[25]	4562	0	0	4562
Partners International	37	5	5	4048	4058
Wycliffe Bible Translators USA	37	2930	0	0	2930
Youth With A Mission (YWAM)	77	1817	0	0	1817
Christian Church of N. Am. Missions	8	14	0	1720	1734
New Tribes Mission	23	1514	137	21	1672
Assemblies of God, Gen. Council	105	1543	0	0	1543
Walk Thru the Bible Ministries	50	0	2	1520	1522
AMG International	15	45	0	1265	1310
Every Home for Christ	60	0	61	1156	1217
Food for the Hungry, Inc.	25	81	47	1041	1169
Christian Churches/Churches Christ	67	1154	0	0	1154
SIM USA	52	569	0	501	1070
Churches of Christ	N/A[26]	1014	0	0	1014
Seventh-day Adventists Gen. Conf.	85	514	0	410	924
OMF International	10	156	0	736	892
Presbyterian Church (USA)	66	772	0	0	772
Baptist Bible Fellowship Intl.	70	755	0	0	755
Final Frontiers Foundation	32	0	0	734	734
Christian and Missionary Alliance	41	726	0	0	726
Mennonite Central Committee Intl.	N/A[27]	200	0	520	720
ABWE	38	716	0	0	716
World Concern	21	34	3	647	684
Church of the Nazarene, Wld Mission	72	487	193	0	680
Word of Life Fellowship	N/A[28]	118	48	495	661
Habitat for Humanity International	43	119	29	509	657
TEAM	34	638	9	4	651
Baptist Mid-Missions	44	612	4	6	622
Global Fellowship	13	0	20	583	603
Lott Carey Baptist Mission Conv.	7	0	0	595	595
Mission to the World (PCA), Inc.	46	579	0	0	579
Holt International Children's Services.	10	6	3	549	558
Far East Broadcasting Company, Inc.	7	31	0	525	556
CBInternational	46	550	0	0	550
Frontiers	3	311	231	0	542
India Evangelical Mission, Inc.	1	0	0	525	525

Table 4.9: Agencies with More than 500 U.S. Workers

Agency	# Countries	U.S. Workers
Southern Baptist Convention IMB	N/A[25]	4562
Wycliffe Bible Translators USA	37	2930
Youth With A Mission (YWAM)	77	1817
Assemblies of God, Gen. Council	105	1543
New Tribes Mission	23	1514
Christian Churches/Chs. of Christ	67	1154
Churches of Christ	N/A[26]	1014
Campus Crusade for Christ, Intl.	111	973
Presbyterian Church (USA)	66	772
Baptist Bible Fellowship Intl.	70	755
Christian and Missionary Alliance	41	726
ABWE	38	716
TEAM (The Evangelical Alliance Miss.)	34	638
Baptist Mid-Missions	44	612
Mission to the World (PCA)	46	579
SIM USA	52	569
CBInternational	46	550
Seventh-day Adventists Gen. Conf.	85	514

Short-Term Activity

United States mission agencies reported a total of 97,309 short-term workers (two weeks to one year) sent out during 1998, a 52% increase over the previous edition of the *Handbook*. It is assumed that this represents only a small fraction of the total U.S. short-term workers, since it does not include those who went under the auspices of local churches or on their own. Figure 4.13 shows the number of people whose job to some extent involves support of short-term efforts from the U.S. agencies, and offers comparison with the 1996 survey results. To handle the 52% increase in short-term workers, 34.8% full-time staff, 87.3% half-time or more staff, and 80.9% part-time staff were added. The growth in personnel devoted to servicing short-term missions work indicates a need for further research into the total cost of such work for mission agencies and the benefits that accrue from short-term missions projects.

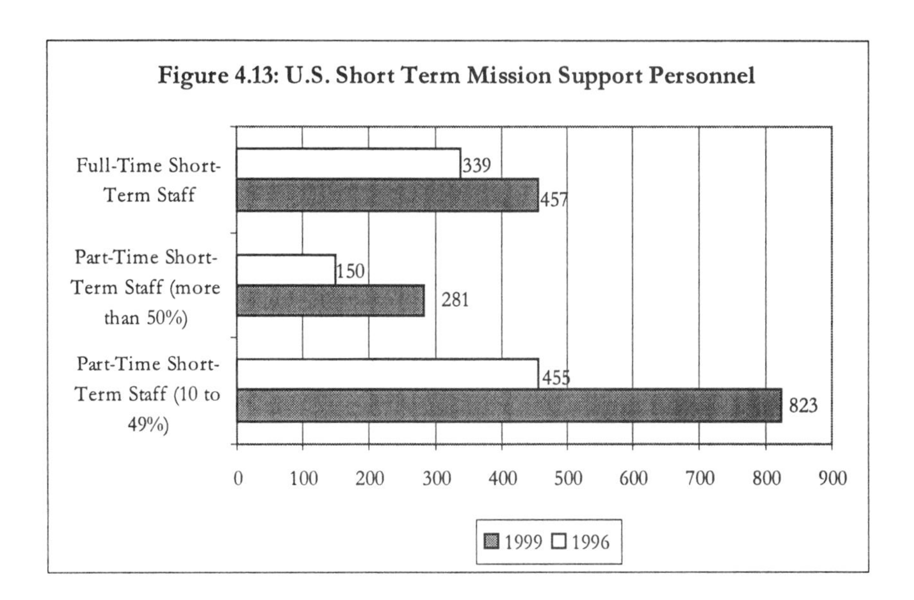

How did the agencies find people for their short-term projects? Figure 4.14 depicts the primary methods on initial contact as well as the changes from 1996 to 1999. It should be noted that the category "school" was added in the 1999 survey, and thus no number is available for 1996.

The largest relative increase in the initial contacts for short-term missions was through conferences (89.8% increase), though initial contacts through churches (47.8%) and individuals (49.6%) also saw significant increases.

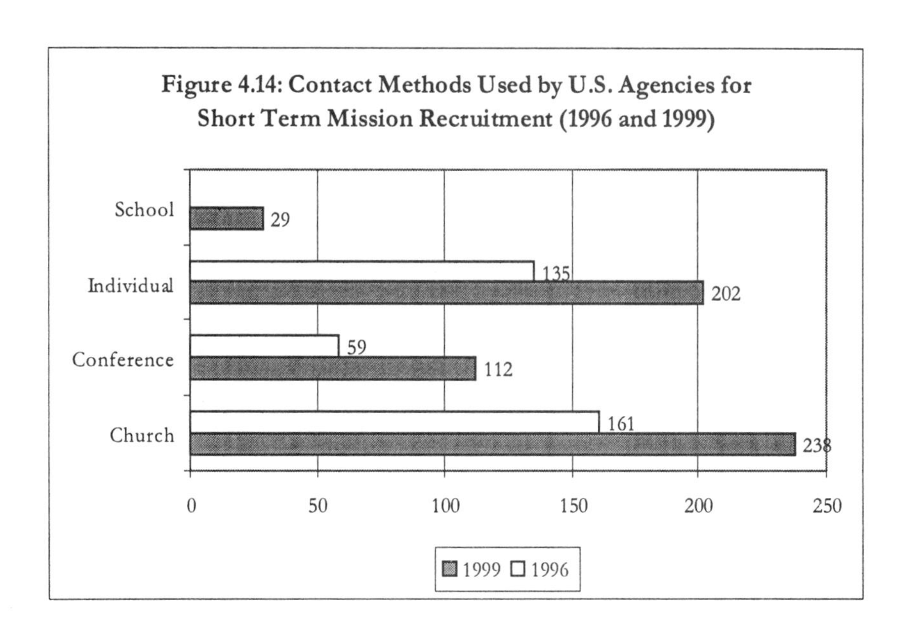

U. S. Home Staff

Figure 4.15 depicts those who make it possible for the field missionaries to work. The full-time home staff workforce increased by 12.2% and the part-time home staff by 3.4%. The ongoing volunteers reported increased by over 232%, but, as discussed at the beginning of the chapter, that increase was largely due to Campus Crusade for Christ's large increase in reported volunteers.

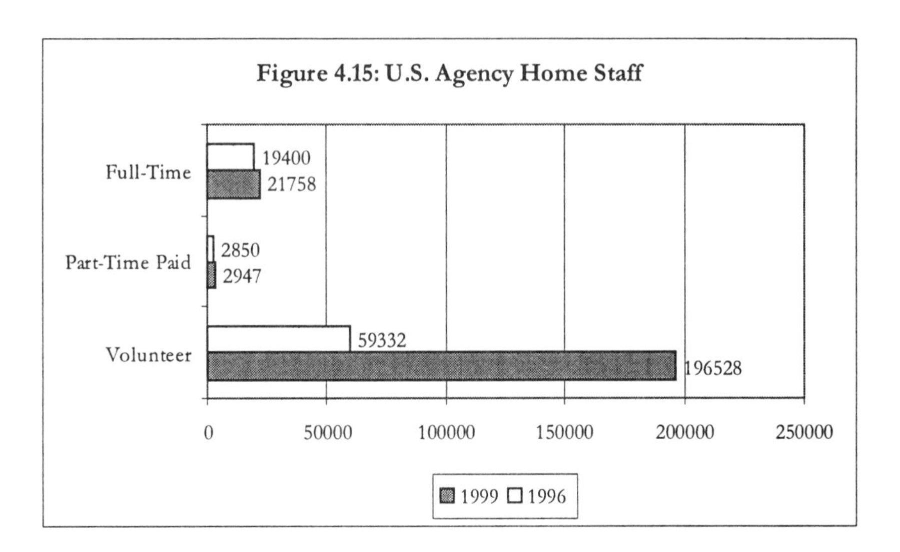

Canadian Agencies

(Editorial Note: Portions of the following Canadian analysis, particularly concerning the ministry of the Evangelical Fellowship of Canada (EFC), were furnished by Geoff Tunnicliffe, Chair of the Task Force for Global Mission of the EFC.)

In Table 4.10 we present a summary of several areas of change in the numbers over the past three editions of the *Handbook*. The Canadian agencies mobilize a total on-location missionary force of 5,003 (3,034 Canadians, 244 non-Canadians working in a country other than their own,[29] and 1,725 nationals) in 115 countries. Roughly speaking, for every four Canadians working there are two nationals working in their own country for Canadian agencies.

Perhaps the most sobering statistic is that the 3.7% decline in long-term Canadian workers seen from 1992 to 1996 accelerated to almost 11.8% from 1996 to 1999. This equates to an overall decline in long-term missionaries of 15% from 1992 to 1999. This reality should give Christian leaders pause as they consider seeking renewal in the Canadian global mission endeavor.

Additionally sobering is the 24.7% decline in volunteers working in agency home offices. On the positive side, these losses are somewhat offset by the significant increases in nonresidential fully supported missionaries (145%[30]), non-Canadian personnel serving in a country other than their own (217%) and nationals serving in their own countries (144%). At the same time, there is a crucial need for Canadians themselves to be serving cross-culturally for the long-term health of the Canadian missionary effort. The adjusted-for-inflation gain in giving of 37.34% is impressive, but, as discussed below, was not evenly distributed among the Canadian agencies.

In Canada, many Canadian mission organizations and church groups find themselves so consumed by the challenge of surviving in the present that envisioning a bold missionary future is not something they feel they can even dare dream. Still others ask whether there will even be an effective role for missions in the twenty-first century.

Within the present uncertain environment—where serious doubts facing the future of mission collide with the committed and generous support offered for missionary enterprises by tens of thousands of Canadian evangelical Christians every year—the Evangelical Fellowship of Canada (EFC) established a Task Force for Global Mission in 1997 to bring together evangelical church and mission leaders from across Canada under one umbrella to shape the Canadian church's mission future.

The task force provides a common focus for evangelicals from many diverse denominational, social, and cultural backgrounds to work together. The many completed and planned projects are evidence that the leaders of mission organizations, denominations, churches, and individuals with a heart for mission are coming together as never before to see God's work among unreached people in Canada and around the world continue to bear future fruit.

Canada's many mission organizations are justifiably proud of their history and uniqueness. Their devotion to their work is strong and admirable. Some organizations are on solid financial ground while others are uncertain about their future. However, most Canadian mission leaders agree that mission organizations need to find new ways to share resources, ideas, and strategies as well as to foster better communication and support if they are to continue to be successful in bringing God's Word to unreached peoples.

Where Are the Canadian Agency Headquarters Located?

The Canadian agencies are found in 49 cities across 7 provinces (Figure 4.16). Ontario is home to more agencies (70) than any other province, followed by British Columbia (21), Alberta (15), and Manitoba (10). Mississauga, Ontario is home to more agencies (13) than any other Canadian city, followed by Winnipeg (9), Calgary (8), Toronto (8) and Vancouver (7).

When Were the Canadian Agencies Founded?

The 20th century growth trends are shown in Figure 4.17. Canadian agencies saw a boom in growth following WW2, slowing after the 1970s. As seen in Figure 4.18, the boom in the 1960s and 1970s was fueled by the increase of new Evangelical agencies (17 were founded in the 1960s and 24 in the 1970s; see Figure 4.20 for comparison between denominational and not-denominational growth). While in the U.S. the growth continued through the 1980s, in Canada it dramatically slowed during that decade.

There are probably several reasons for the decline in the number of new agencies. First of all, economics may have played a significant factor. The economic downturn in the 1980s and early '90s seemed to impact Canada more than the U. S. Secondly, in the past U.S.-based organizations sought to establish a structure in Canada as well. In recent years, U.S.-based organizations have either formed a partnership with existing Canadian ministries or have chosen not to set up Canadian operations. Thirdly, a growing partnership (particularly under the auspices of EFC) has developed among agencies. As a result, new wineskins (as opposed to new organizations) have been created for new missions endeavors.

Table 4.10: Summary of Changes in Canadian Missions Statistics, 1992-1999

Personnel from Canada	1992	1996	1999	Change (1996-99)
FULLY SUPPORTED CANADIAN PERSONNEL SERVING OVERSEAS				
Long-Term (Overseas more than 4 years)	3,075	2,961	2,613	-11.76%
Short-Term (Overseas from 1 to 4 years)	304	416	421	1.20%
Nonresidential fully supported	72	120	294	145.00%
Total fully supported Canadian personnel serving overseas	3,451	3,497	3,328	-4.83%
OTHER CANADIAN PERSONNEL SERVING OVERSEAS				
Short-term of 2 weeks up to 1 year (1996 and 1999)	NA	2,470	3,186	28.99%
Bivocational associates sponsored or supervised	84	140	144	2.86%
Nonresidential partially supported	13	17	38	123.53%
NON-CANADIAN PERSONNEL PARTIALLY OR FULLY SUPPORTED				
Those serving in their home country	NA	707	1,725	143.99%
Those serving in a country other than their home country	36	77	244	216.88%
CANADIAN MINISTRY AND HOME OFFICE STAFF				
Full-time paid staff	1,412	1,622	1,838	13.32%
Part-time staff/associates	249	389	496	27.51%
Volunteer (ongoing) helpers	2,124	3,154	2,374	-24.73%
FINANCIAL SUPPORT RAISED IN CANADA				
Income for overseas ministries [31]	$246,110,734	$245,029,578	$336,533,193	37.34%

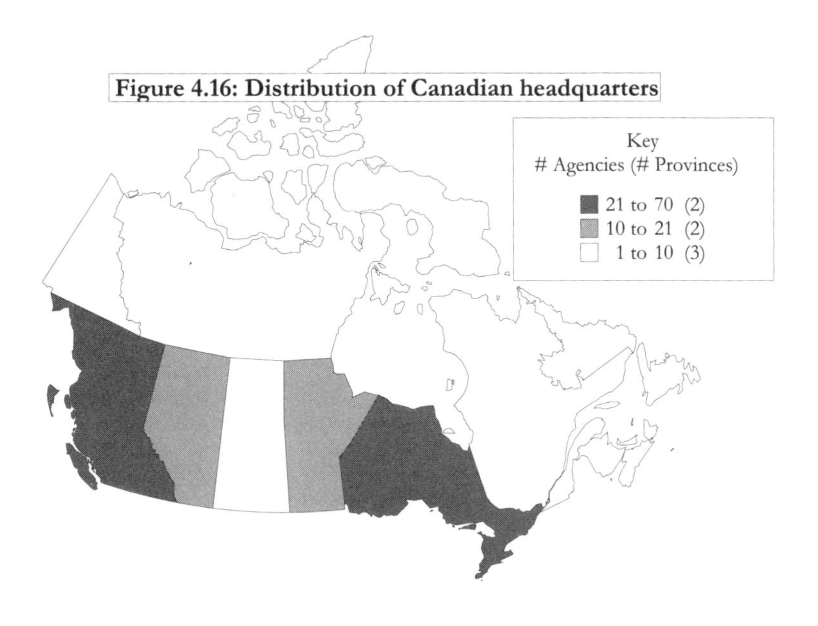

Figure 4.16: Distribution of Canadian headquarters

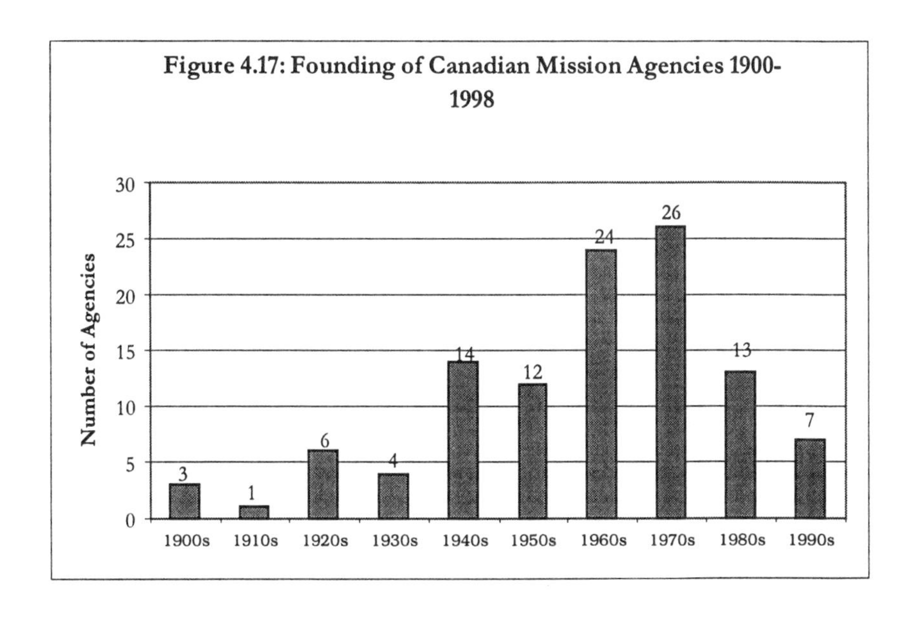

Figure 4.17: Founding of Canadian Mission Agencies 1900-1998

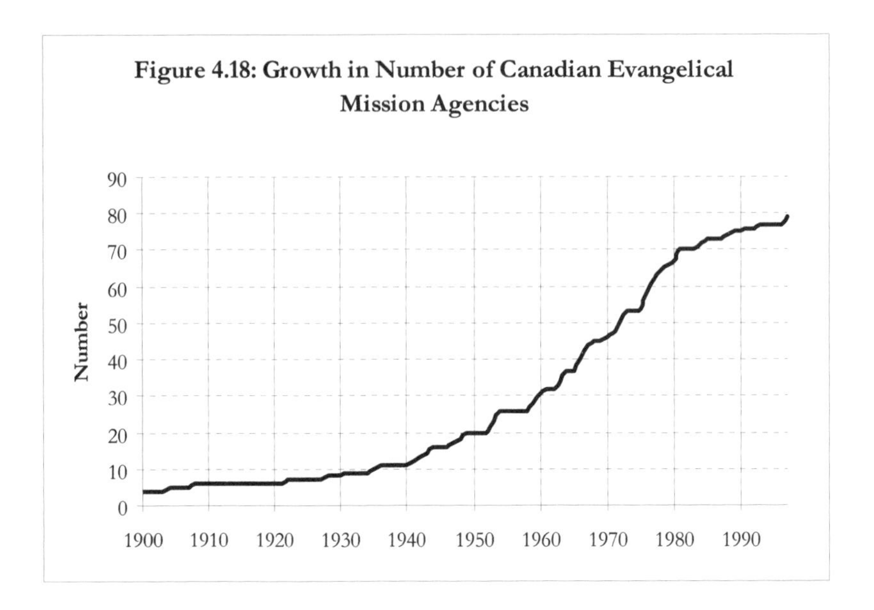

What Are the Canadian Agencies Orientations toward Denominationalism?

Fewer than one in four Canadian agencies describe themselves as denominational (Figure 4.19). Again, though, the most significant divide is between the denominational agencies and the rest ("not-denominational"). While the growth in denominational agencies has been steady over the century, the shift from denominational agencies to not-denominational ones during the century is illustrated in Figure 4.20. Canadian agencies never had the denominational vs. not-denominational ratio of 2:1 seen in the U.S., though the proliferation of agencies that are not-denominational parallels the shift in the U.S. In 1930 the ratio was 1:1, but by 1999 it had shifted to 1:3.3 in favor of the not-denominational agencies.

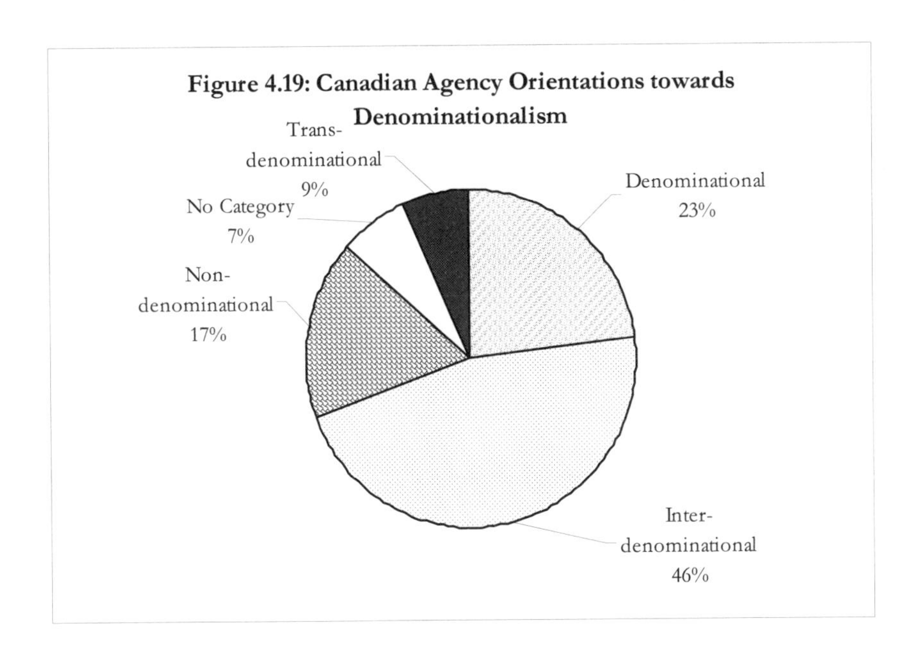
Figure 4.19: Canadian Agency Orientations towards Denominationalism
Trans-denominational 9%
No Category 7%
Non-denominational 17%
Denominational 23%
Inter-denominational 46%

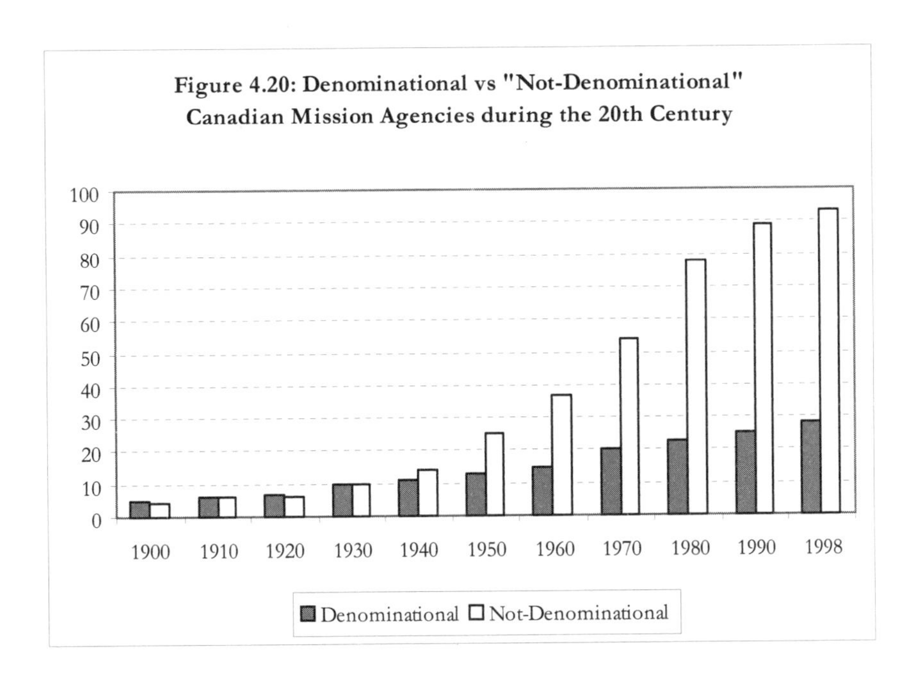
Figure 4.20: Denominational vs "Not-Denominational" Canadian Mission Agencies during the 20th Century
100
90
80
70
60
50
40
30
20
10
0
1900 1910 1920 1930 1940 1950 1960 1970 1980 1990 1998
Denominational
Not-Denominational

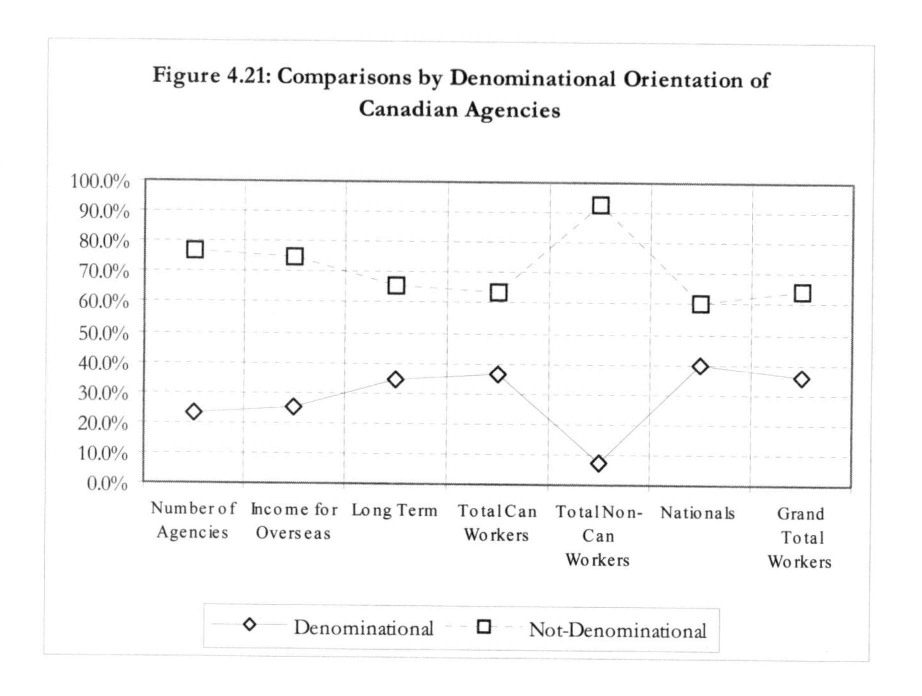
Figure 4.21: Comparisons by Denominational Orientation of Canadian Agencies
100.0%
90.0%
80.0%
70.0%
60.0%
50.0%
40.0%
30.0%
20.0%
10.0%
0.0%
Number of Agencies
Income for Overseas
Long Term
Total Can Workers
Total Non-Can Workers
Nationals
Grand Total Workers
Denominational
Not-Denominational

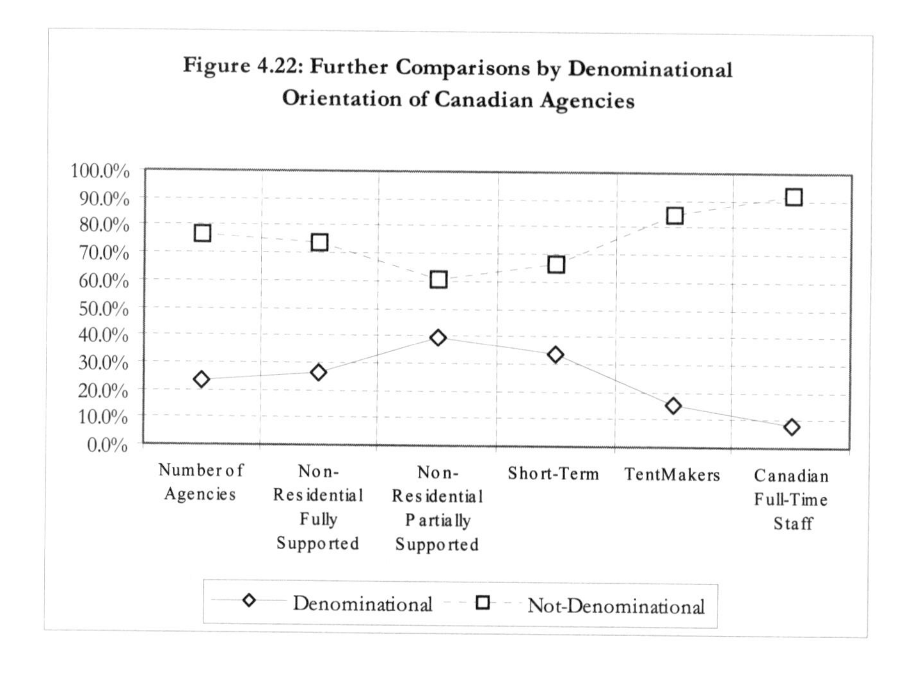
Figure 4.22: Further Comparisons by Denominational Orientation of Canadian Agencies
100.0%
90.0%
80.0%
70.0%
60.0%
50.0%
40.0%
30.0%
20.0%
10.0%
0.0%
Number of Agencies
Non-Residential Fully Supported
Non-Residential Partially Supported
Short-Term
TentMakers
Canadian Full-Time Staff
Denominational
Not-Denominational

For all Canadian agencies, Figures 4.21 and 4.22 depict differences in denominational orientation. Denominational agencies reported relatively more long-term, total Canadian, and national personnel (4.21) as well as more partially supported non-residential personnel and short-term missionaries (4.22). Not-denominational agencies reported more non-Canadian workers in a country other than their own (4.21), as well as more tentmakers and full-time Canadian staff (4.22).

Table 4.11 indicates the primary doctrinal or ecclesiastical stances of the Canadian agencies and provides the total for various data for each stance. As with the U.S. agencies, it is obvious from the table that most agencies simply consider themselves evangelical. Table 4.12 takes the same data and presents it in percentage form to enable comparisons to be made.

Table 4.11: Doctrinal/Ecclesiastical Stance and Associated Numbers for Canadian Agencies

Doctrinal/ Ecclesiastical Stance	*# of Agencies*	*In # of Countries*	*Income for Overseas Missions*	*Canadian Long Term*	*Total Canadian Missionaries*	*# of Non-National Workers*	*# of National Workers*	*Total Missionary Force*
Evangelical	79	117	$237,662,698	1556	1791	222	1009	3022
Baptist	8	35	$9,570,055	138	184	1	6	191
Pentecostal	6	40	$14,452,720	171	197	3	23	223
Mennonite	5	23	$23,669,533	37	65	4	635	704
Fundamental	3	17	$4,246,001	192	192	0	0	192
Lutheran	3	10	$808,433	11	18	8	0	26
Anglican	2	3	$6,293,925	2	8	0	2	10
Charismatic	2	32	$1,433,619	134	134	0	0	134
Chr/Plym Breth	2	45	$4,573,211	192	192	0	0	192
Ecumenical	2	1	$9,000,000	96	96	0	0	96
Independent	2	6	$9,560,000	6	14	0	0	14
Wesleyan	2	0	$28,966	0	0	0	47	47
Holiness	1	3	$240,857	0	0	6	0	6
Methodist	1	28	$4,000,000	35	92	0	0	92
Other:	1	0	$3,909,000	0	0	0	0	0
Presbyterian	1	16	$1,400,000	23	31	0	3	34
Reformed	1	11	$5,684,175	20	20	0	0	20

Table 4.12: Percent Indicators of Canadian Agencies by Doctrinal/Ecclesiastical Stance

Doctrinal/ Ecclesiastical Stance	*# of Agencies*	*Income for Overseas Missions*	*Income per worker (tot. msny. force)*	*Canadian Long Term*	*Total Canadian Msnys.*	*# of Non-National Workers*	*# of National Workers*	*Total Missionary Force*
Evangelical	65.3%	70.6%	$ 78,644	59.5%	59.0%	91.0%	58.5%	60.4%
Baptist	6.6%	2.8%	$ 50,105	5.3%	6.1%	0.4%	0.3%	3.8%
Pentecostal	5.0%	4.3%	$ 64,810	6.5%	6.5%	1.2%	1.3%	4.5%
Mennonite	4.1%	7.0%	$ 33,621	1.4%	2.1%	1.6%	36.8%	14.1%
Fundamental	2.5%	1.3%	$ 22,115	7.3%	6.3%	0.0%	0.0%	3.8%
Lutheran	2.5%	0.2%	$ 31,094	0.4%	0.6%	3.3%	0.0%	0.5%
Anglican	1.7%	1.9%	$629,393	0.1%	0.3%	0.0%	0.1%	0.2%
Charismatic	1.7%	0.4%	$ 10,699	5.1%	4.4%	0.0%	0.0%	2.7%
Chr/Plym Breth	1.7%	1.4%	$ 10,465	7.3%	6.3%	0.0%	0.0%	3.8%
Ecumenical	1.7%	2.7%	$ 93,750	3.7%	3.2%	0.0%	0.0%	1.9%
Independent	1.7%	2.8%	$682,857	0.2%	0.5%	0.0%	0.0%	0.3%
Wesleyan	1.7%	0.0%	N/A	0.0%	0.0%	0.0%	2.7%	0.9%
Holiness	0.8%	0.1%	$ 40,143	0.0%	0.0%	2.5%	0.0%	0.1%
Methodist	0.8%	1.2%	$ 43,478	1.3%	3.0%	0.0%	0.0%	1.8%
Other	0.8%	1.2%	N/A	0.0%	0.0%	0.0%	0.0%	0.0%
Presbyterian	0.8%	0.4%	$ 41,176	0.9%	1.0%	0.0%	0.2%	0.7%
Reformed	0.8%	1.7%	$284,209	0.8%	0.7%	0.0%	0.0%	0.4%

What Were the Activities of Canadian Protestant Agencies?

As with the U.S. agencies, the Canadian agencies were given the opportunity to indicate up to six of what they considered their main activities from a list of 52, as well as indicating which of the six they would consider their primary activity.[32] Church planting/establishing was by far the most frequently chosen primary activity (31, or 25.6% of all agencies) followed by personal and small group evangelism (14, or 11.6%).

Table 4.13: Ranking of Activities for Canadian Agencies

Rank	Activity
1	Church establishing/planting (31; 25.6%)
2	Evangelism, personal and small group (14; 11.6%)
3	Development, community and/or other (9; 7.4%)
4, 5	Support of national workers Literature distribution (6 or 5.0% each)
6, 7, 8	Evangelism, mass Childcare/orphanage Bible distribution (5 or 4.1% each)
9	Funds transmission (4, 3.3%)
10	National church nurture/support Education, theological Broadcasting, radio and/or TV Relief and/or rehabilitation (3 or 2.5% each)

Table 4.13 depicts the ranking for the primary activities. More Canadian agencies are involved in church establishing and planting than any other activity, with personal and small group evangelism a distant second. Community or other development plays a more significant primary role for Canadian agencies (8.2%, rank 3) than US agencies (1.3%, rank 9).

If you consider how Canadians are investing their financial resources, relief and development agencies are at the top of the list. In fact, out of the top (by income level) 24 agencies, 64% of the giving went to relief and development organizations. In addition to this, other agencies received considerable financial support for relief and development projects.

These factors combined with the significant decline in long-term missionaries are major developments to consider and may be reflective of contemporary trends in Canadian evangelicalism. These trends include: (1) The growing impact of the privatization of faith, secularism, pluralism, and post-modernity are all influencing how Canadians engage in global mission. (2) Canadian evangelicals tend to reflect Canadian society as a whole in their concern for poverty and injustice around the world. (3) The trend to support nationals from other countries and also relief and development agencies could be seen as a more strategic use of resources and a commitment to holistic ministry. However, it could also be a growing disengagement with sending Canadian missionaries for the purposes of propagating faith, and sending money instead. (4) There has been an increasing recognition that Canada needs to be evangelized. Research conducted by the EFC is showing that a growing number of churches are placing greater emphasis on reaching Canada than the rest of the world.

In Table 4.14, we give the more detailed picture by including primary and secondary activities and sorting them into four major groups: evangelistic and church oriented activities, relief and development oriented activities, mission agency support activities, and other activities. Within each group we list them by rank and give the percent of agencies engaged in each activity.

Table 4.14: Categorized Activities of Canadian Mission Agencies

Evangelism/Discipleship Activities	
Activity	*Percent*
Evangelism, personal & small group	47.9%
Church establishing/planting	35.5%
National church nurture/support	28.1%
Leadership development	20.7%
Literature distribution	19.0%
Evangelism, mass	14.0%
Support of national workers	14.0%
Literature production	12.4%
Broadcasting, radio and/or TV	9.9%
Children's programs	8.3%
Bible distribution	7.4%
Youth programs	7.4%
Camping programs	6.6%
Translation, Bible	6.6%
Literacy	4.1%
Evangelism, student	3.3%
Linguistics	3.3%
Church construction	2.5%
Audio recording/distribution	1.7%
Video/Film production/distribution	0.8%

Mission Agency Support Activities	
Activity	*Percent*
Training/Orientation, missionary	9.9%
Recruiting/Mobilizing	9.1%
Technical assistance	8.3%
Short-term programs coord.	6.6%
Information services	5.0%
Management consulting/training	2.5%
Furloughed missionary support	1.7%
Aviation services	0.8%
Services for other agencies	0.8%

Relief and Development Activities	
Activity	*Percent*
Development, community or other	22.3%
Medicine, incl. dental & public	18.2%
Relief and/or rehabilitation	17.4%
Agricultural programs	8.3%
Childcare/orphanage	5.8%
Medical supplies	3.3%
Disability assistance programs	1.7%
Supplying equipment	1.7%

Education/Training Activities	
Activity	*Percent*
Education, theological	19.0%
Education (TEE)	10.7%
Education, church/school gen. Christ.	7.4%
Training, other	6.6%
Correspondence courses	5.8%
Education, extension (other)	2.5%
Education, missionary (cert./degree)	0.8%

Other Activities	
Activity	*Percent*
Funds transmission	10.7%
Research	2.5%
Other:	1.7%

Overseas Income for Canadian Agencies

The total reported income for all Canadian agencies was $336,533,193.[33] This is an inflation adjusted increase of 37.3%, the highest ever seen from one edition of the *Handbook* to the next, and significantly higher than the U.S. percent increase of 21.8%. Sixty-one (just over 50%) of the Canadian agencies reported an income gain for overseas ministries, seventeen of which had an increase of greater than $1,000,000. Of those agencies that reported an increase in income for overseas mission work, the ten with the greatest gains accounted for 81% of the total increase. When these ten are factored out, the net gain between editions of the *Handbook* for all Canadian agencies in income for overseas mission work was less than $12.3 million dollars. In contrast to the gains, twenty-four agencies (almost 20%) reported lower income, with four reporting a loss of greater than $1,000,000 each. Therefore, unlike the U.S. increase, which was spread broadly among the agencies, the Canadian growth was limited to a handful of agencies (many of them relief and development agencies) that experienced spectacular overseas income growth. Table 4.15 gives the reported income for overseas mission work for all Canadian agencies with $3,000,000 or more. In the previous edition of the *Handbook*, this list included 22 agencies; in this edition it includes 24.

Table 4.15: Canadian Agencies with Income of $3 Million or More

Rank	Canadian Agency	Overseas Income
1	World Vision Canada	$94,167,000
2	Canadian Food for the Hungry	$20,934,835
3	Samaritan's Purse - Canada	$18,721,623
4	Mennonite Central Committee Canada	$17,645,500
5	Christian and Missionary Alliance in Canada	$12,430,005
6	Pentecostal Assemblies Canada/Les Assemblees	$12,057,000
7	Wycliffe Bible Translators of Canada	$11,000,000
8	HOPE International Development Agency	$9,060,000
9	United Church of Canada, Div. World Outreach	$9,000,000
10	SIM Canada	$8,257,568
11	Campus Crusade for Christ of Canada	$7,329,055
12	Christian Blind Mission International (Canada)	$6,527,419
13	Compassion Canada	$6,500,000
14	Anglican Church of Canada, Partners in Mission	$6,000,000
15	Christian Reformed World Relief Comte. Canada	$5,684,175
16	Canadian Baptist Ministries	$5,400,000
17	MSC Canada	$4,573,211
18	MBMS International	$4,097,862
19	Salvation Army, The	$4,000,000
20	New Tribes Mission of Canada	$3,943,909
21	Canadian Bible Soc./La Societe Biblique Canadienne	$3,909,000
22	World Relief Canada	$3,689,000
23	Bible League of Canada, The	$3,500,000
24	FEBInternational	$3,000,000

Where are the Canadian Agencies and Missionaries Active?

Figure 4.23 maps the distribution of Canadian agencies around the world,[34] Figure 4.24 indicates the distribution of Canadian agencies by region,[35] Figure 4.25 the Canadian missionaries by region,[36] and Figure 4.26 the total missionary force working for Canadian agencies.[37] Parallel to the U.S., though more Canadians served in Latin America than any other region, the greatest number of total workers deployed by Canadian mission agencies was in Asia.

Figure 4.23: Distribution of Canadian Mission Agencies

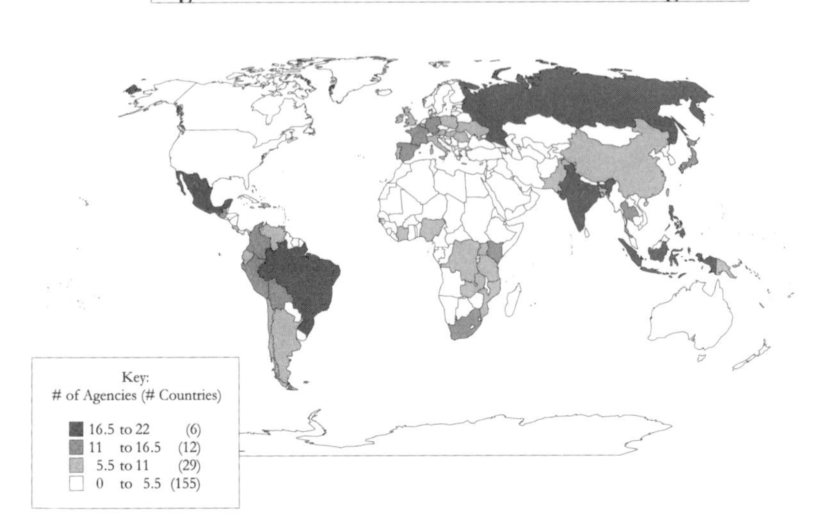

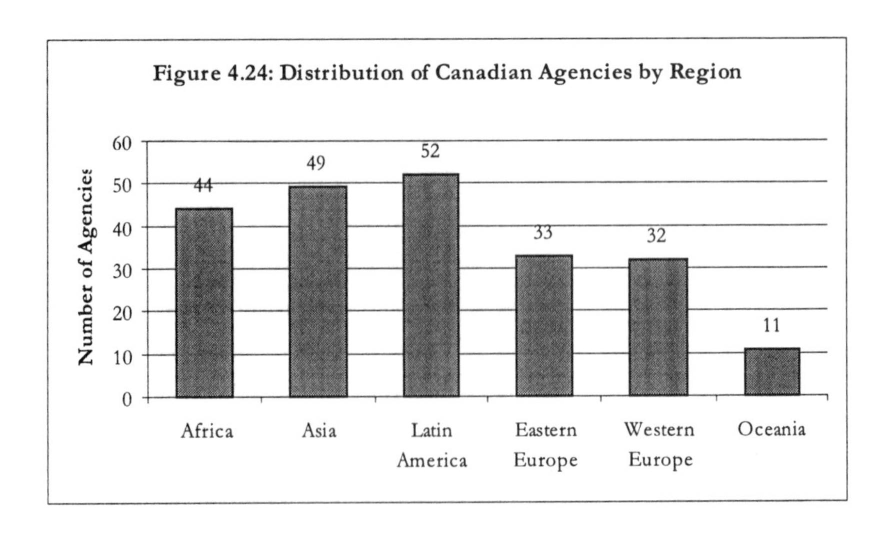

Figure 4.24: Distribution of Canadian Agencies by Region

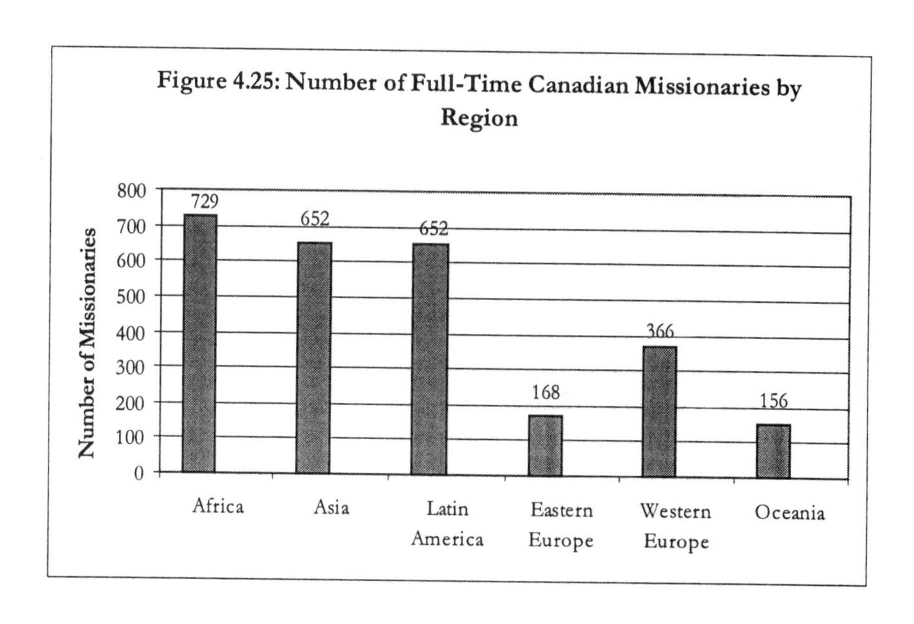
Figure 4.25: Number of Full-Time Canadian Missionaries by Region
Number of Missionaries
800
700
600
500
400
300
200
100
0
729
652
652
168
366
156
Africa
Asia
Latin America
Eastern Europe
Western Europe
Oceania

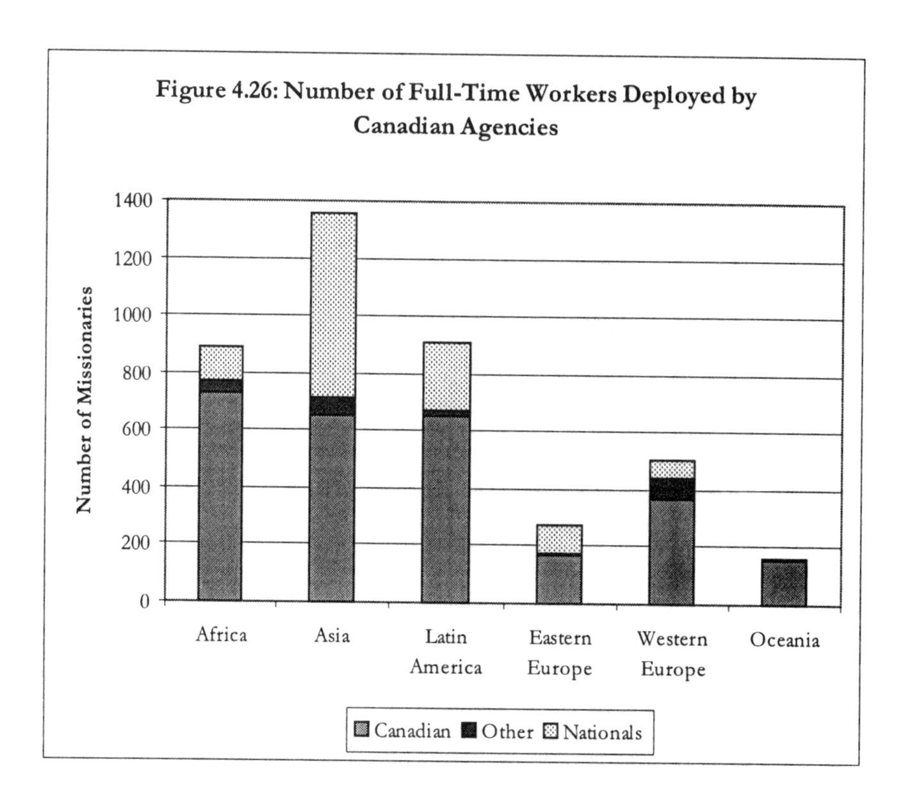
Figure 4.26: Number of Full-Time Workers Deployed by Canadian Agencies
Number of Missionaries
1400
1200
1000
800
600
400
200
0
Africa
Asia
Latin America
Eastern Europe
Western Europe
Oceania
Canadian
Other
Nationals

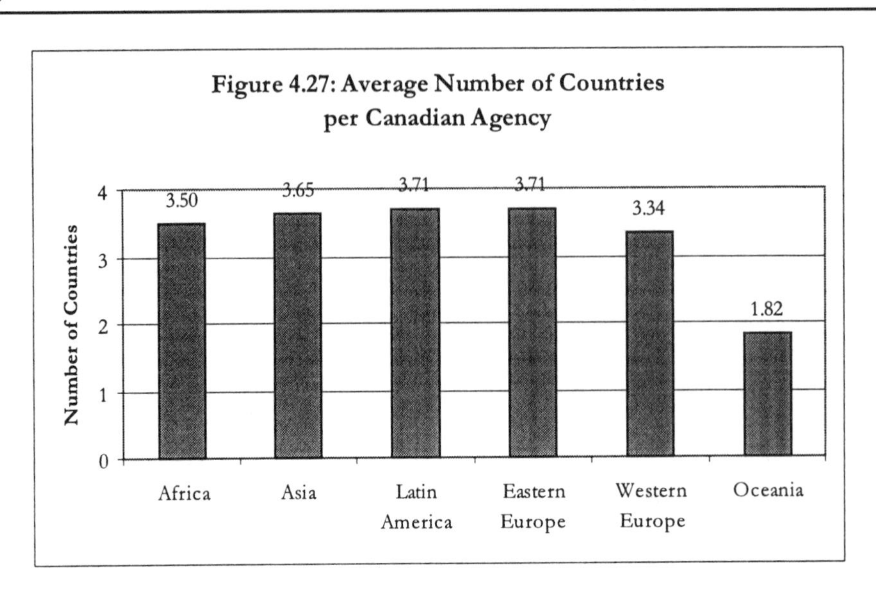

In the tables that follow, we present the countries of the world in which more than 9 Canadian agencies are present (Table 4.16), the Canadian agencies with more than 50 total full-time personnel (including non-Canadian; Table 4.17), and the Canadian agencies with more than 50 Canadian personnel (Table 4.18).

Table 4.16: Countries with More than 9 Canadian Agencies

Country	# Agencies [37]
Brazil	22
Mexico	21
India	19
Philippines	18
Indonesia	17
Russian Federation	17
Kenya	14
Japan	14
Colombia	13
France	13
Spain	13
Guatemala	12
South Africa	12
Germany	12
Peru	11
Hong Kong	11
Bolivia	11
Thailand	11
United Kingdom	10
Italy	10

Table 4.17: Canadian Agencies with More than 50 Total Reported Workers

Agency	#Countries	Can. Workers	Non-Can Workers	Natl. Workers	Total
MBMS International	15	25	0	627	652
Christian Aid Mission	NA	0	0	500	500
Wycliffe Bible Translators Canada	33	415	0	0	415
Operation Mobilization - Canada	34	76	153	88	317
Brethren Assemblies (Canada)	38	192	0	0	192
Christian & Missionary Alliance Can.	40	210	0	0	210
New Tribes Mission of Canada	16	187	0	0	187
Pentecostal Assemblies of Canada/ Les Assemblees	34	165	2	0	167
Youth With A Mission (Canada)	34	134	0	0	134
SIM Canada	23	131	17	0	148
Salvation Army, The	28	92	0	0	92
WEC International (Canada)	19	89	0	0	89
International Christian Aid Can.	4	0	0	99	99
Africa Inland Mission (Canada)	7	95	0	0	95
Leprosy Mission Canada, The	2	0	0	100	100
TEAM - The Evangelical Alliance Mission of Canada	19	66	0	15	81
United Church of Canada, Division World Outreach	NA	96	0	0	96
Gospel Missionary Union Canada	13	78	4	1	83
Canadian Baptist Ministries	18	77	0	0	77
FEBInternational	15	72	1	6	79
OMF International - Canada	9	76	0	0	76
Global Outreach Mission	14	29	0	38	67
Janz Team Ministries	6	51	18	2	71
International Needs - Canada	NA	0	0	53	53

Table 4.18: Canadian Agencies with More than 50 Canadian Workers

Agency	# Countries	Can. Workers
Wycliffe Bible Translators of Canada	33	415
Christian and Missionary Alliance in Canada	40	210
Brethren Assemblies (Canada)	38	192
New Tribes Mission of Canada	16	187
Pentecostal Assemblies Canada/Les Assemblees	34	165
Youth With A Mission (Canada)	34	134
SIM Canada	23	131
United Church of Canada, Div. World Outreach	NA	96
Africa Inland Mission (Canada)	7	95
Salvation Army, The	28	92
WEC International (Canada)	19	89
Gospel Missionary Union of Canada	13	78
Canadian Baptist Ministries	18	77
OMF International - Canada	9	76
Operation Mobilization - Canada	34	76
FEBInternational	15	72
TEAM-The Evangelical Alliance Mission Canada	19	66
Janz Team Ministries	6	51

Short-Term Activity

Canadian mission agencies reported a total of 3,186 short-term workers (two weeks to one year), an increase of 29% over the previous *Handbook*. This can only be assumed to cover a small fraction of the total number of Canadians who went on short-term projects, since it does not include those who went out under the auspices of local churches or on their own. Figure 4.28 shows the number of people whose job to some extent involves support for short-term efforts from Canada, and offers comparison with the 1996 survey results. To handle the 29% increase in short-term workers, 100% full-time staff and 387% half-time or more staff were added, though the less than half-time short-term staff dropped by 3.6%.

In 1999, the EFC researched more than 5,000 churches to determine the factors contributing to the health of global mission programs in the local church. This research determined that there is a direct correlation between a growing missions involvement in the local church and the sending out of short-term teams, both directly from the church and/or with mission agencies. The research determined that if a church is not sending out short-term missionaries it is not sending out long-term missionaries.

Being aware of the critical role that short-term mission is playing in motivating and equipping people in mission, the EFC has worked with hundreds of leaders across Canada to develop a code of best practice for short-term mission (launched in 2000), with the hope of raising the overall effectiveness of this important strategy.

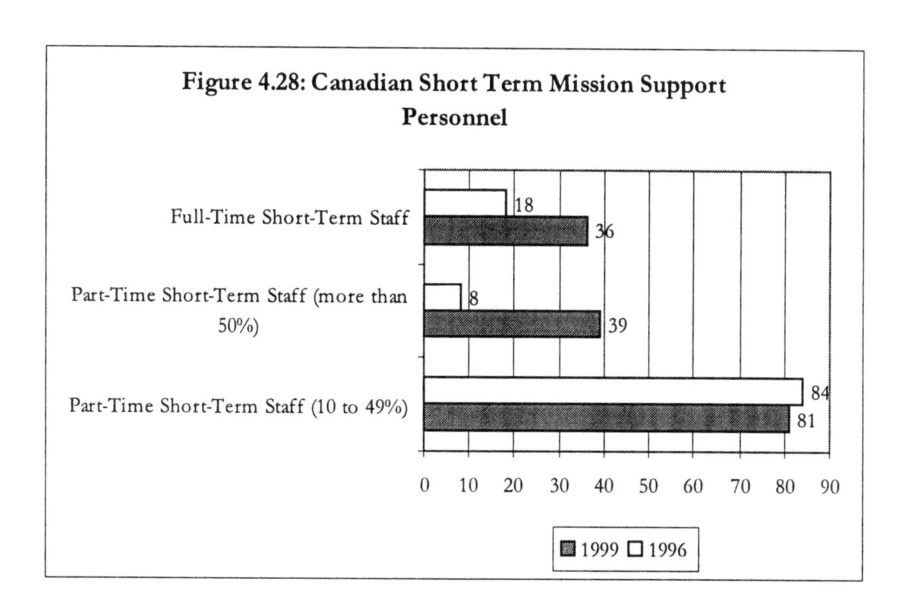

How did the agencies find people for their short-term projects? Figure 4.29 depicts the primary methods on initial contact as well as the changes from 1996 to 1999. It should be noted that the category "school" was added in the 1999 survey, and thus no number is available for 1996. The largest relative increase in the initial contacts for short-term missions was through individuals (54.5%) though initial contacts through churches also rose impressively (51.9%).

Canadian Home Staff

Figure 4.30 depicts those who make it possible for the field missionaries to work and compares the 1996 data with the 1999 data. The full-time home staff workforce increased by 13.3%. The part-time home staff increased by 27.5%, while the volunteers decreased by 24.7%.

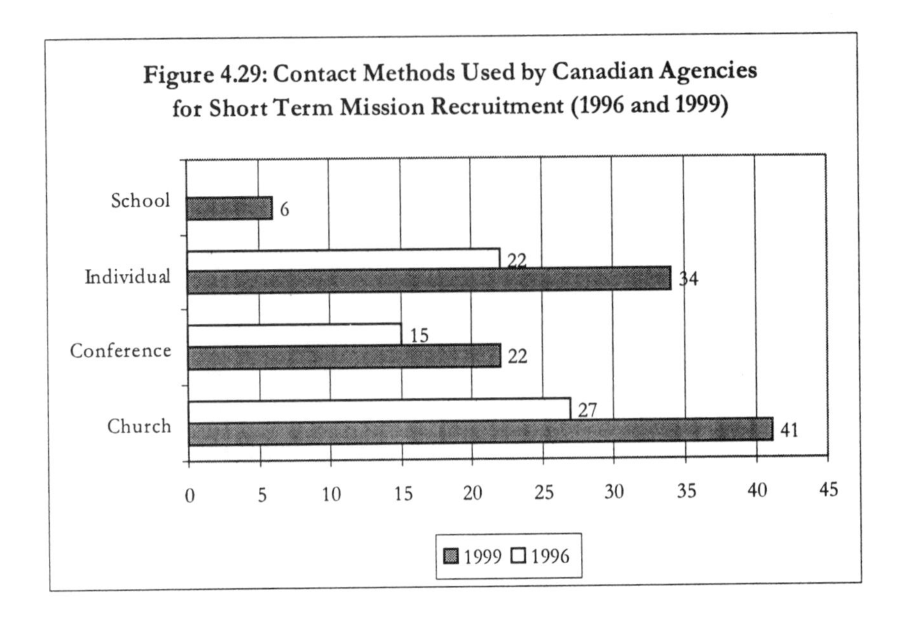

Figure 4.29: Contact Methods Used by Canadian Agencies for Short Term Mission Recruitment (1996 and 1999)

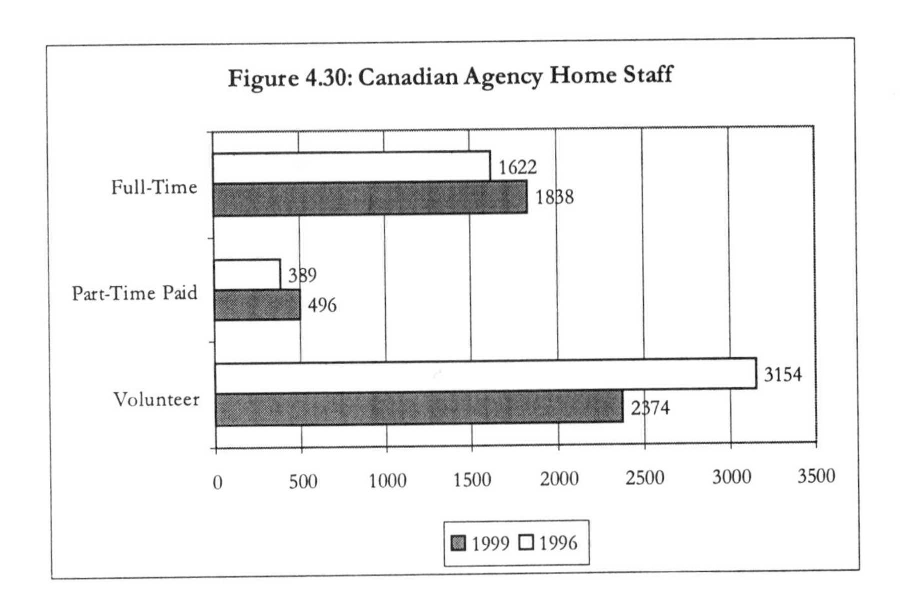

Figure 4.30: Canadian Agency Home Staff

Table 4.19: U.S. and Canadian Agencies No Longer Listed

Name of Agency	Reason No Longer Listed
All Peoples Baptist Mission	Disbanded
Anglican Orthodox Church	Overseas data not available
Association of Regular Baptist Churches (Canada)	Overseas data not available
Bethany Home, Inc.	Overseas data not available
Billy Graham Evangelistic Association, Intl.	Non-mission
Canadian Friends Service Committee	Non-mission
Children International	Not religiously affiliated
Chinese Christian Mission, Inc.	Overseas data not available
Christ for India Ministries	Overseas data not available
Christian Life Missions	Overseas data not available
Christian Literature & Bible Center	Overseas data not available
Christian Literature International	Overseas relationship unknown
Christian Methodist Episcopal Church, Board of Missions	Overseas data not available
Christian Printing Mission	Overseas data not available
Dorcas Aid International USA	Overseas data not available
East West Missionary Service	Overseas data not available
Everyday Publications, Inc.	Overseas relationship unknown
French International Mission	Overseas data not available
Friends for Missions, Inc.	Overseas data not available
Fundamental Bible Missions	Overseas data not available
Global Reach	Overseas data not available
Haiti Gospel Mission	Overseas data not available
Harvestime International Network	Overseas data not available
Hinduism International Ministries	Overseas data not available
His Word To The Nations	Overseas relationship unknown
Icthus International	Overseas data not available
IDEA/PROLADES	Overseas data not available
Independent Board Presbyterian Foreign Missions	Overseas data not available
Inter-Mission International	Overseas data not available
International Films, Inc.	Overseas data not available
Japan Evangelistic Band (Canada)	Disbanded
John Milton Society for the Blind	Overseas relationship unknown
Korea Gospel Mission	Overseas relationship unknown
Liberty Baptist Mission	Overseas data not available
Lutheran Braille Workers, Inc.	Overseas data not available
Metropolitan Church Association	Overseas data not available
Mission Connection, The	Overseas data not available
Missionary Action, Inc.	Overseas data not available
Missionary Crusader, Inc.	Overseas relationship unknown
Missionary Information Exchange	Overseas relationship unknown
New Missions	Overseas data not available
Next Towns Crusade, Inc.	Overseas relationship unknown
Prison Fellowship International	Non-mission
Schwenkfelder Church in USA, Board of Missions	Overseas data not available
Student Mission Advance	Disbanded
Tele-Missions International, Inc.	Overseas data not available
Trinity Intl. Baptist Mission	Overseas data not available
UIM International	No overseas ministries at present
Voice of China and Asia Missionary Society	Overseas data not available
World Salt Foundation, Inc.	Overseas data not available

The Top 50 Agencies Compared 1984 to 1999

MARC conducted surveys of Protestant mission agencies with overseas ministries in 1984, 1988, 1992 and 1996. EMIS conducted the survey with assistance from MARC in 1999. See the Appendix for the 1999 survey questionnaire.

The historical data collected from the fifty largest agencies in the U.S. introduced in the previous version of the *Handbook* continues to facilitate analyses of trends, now stretching from 1984 to 1999. In the 1999 survey, these agencies accounted for approximately 63% of the long-term mission overseas personnel in those years. *Handbook* users refer most often to the information about long-term mission personnel and income for overseas ministries from among the approximately thirty key statistical items gathered in each of these surveys.

The following six figures show the number of long-term overseas mission personnel and income for overseas ministries in relation to three different characteristics of mission agencies.[38] These basic charts indicate the occurrence of some definite trends. Most are gradual, however, and in only two places is there a shift between the categories displayed in the charts.

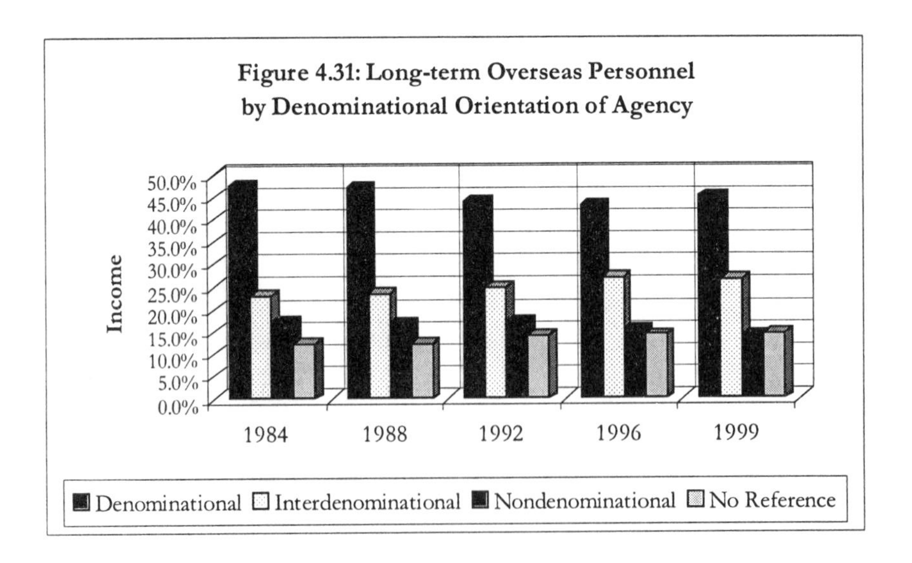

Figures 4.31 and 4.32 show long-term personnel and financial support for overseas ministries in terms of the denominational orientation of the sending agency. The category "No Reference" shows agencies that preferred not to use the term denomination as a reference in describing themselves. In recent years the survey questionnaire also included "transdenominational" as a category, but none of the larger agencies used that term to describe their denominational orientation.

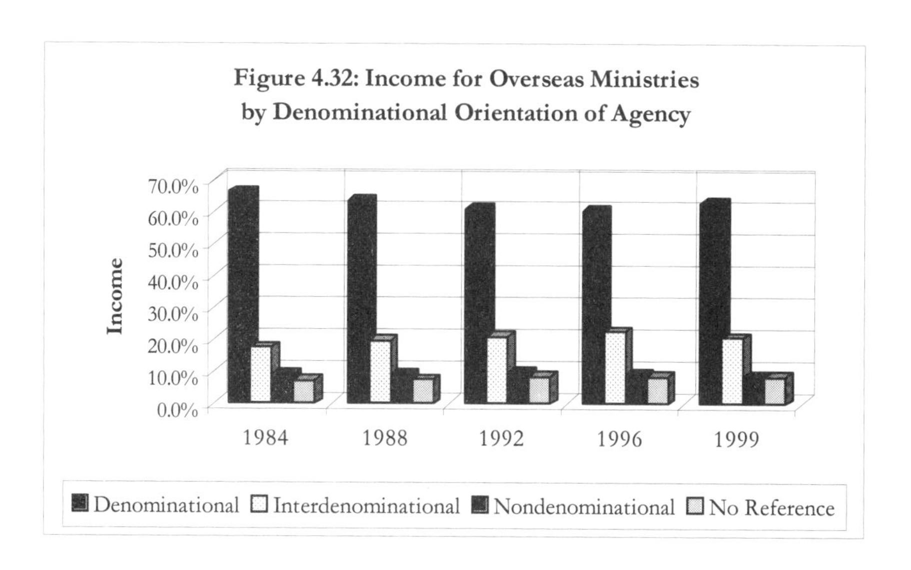

Figure 4.32: Income for Overseas Ministries by Denominational Orientation of Agency

The two figures show small changes in the percentages for this period, but no shifts between the given categories. A slight trend across the 14 years is a 2.9% decrease in the proportion of long-term personnel and a 3.8% decrease in the proportion of income for overseas ministries for those agencies describing themselves as denominational.[39] The agencies describing themselves as interdenominational picked up the corresponding percentage increases for the most part. However, in 1999 the denominational agencies still led in income for overseas ministries, with 62.7% to the combined 37.3% for the other three categories, a slight increase from the 1996 split of 60.2% and 39.8%.

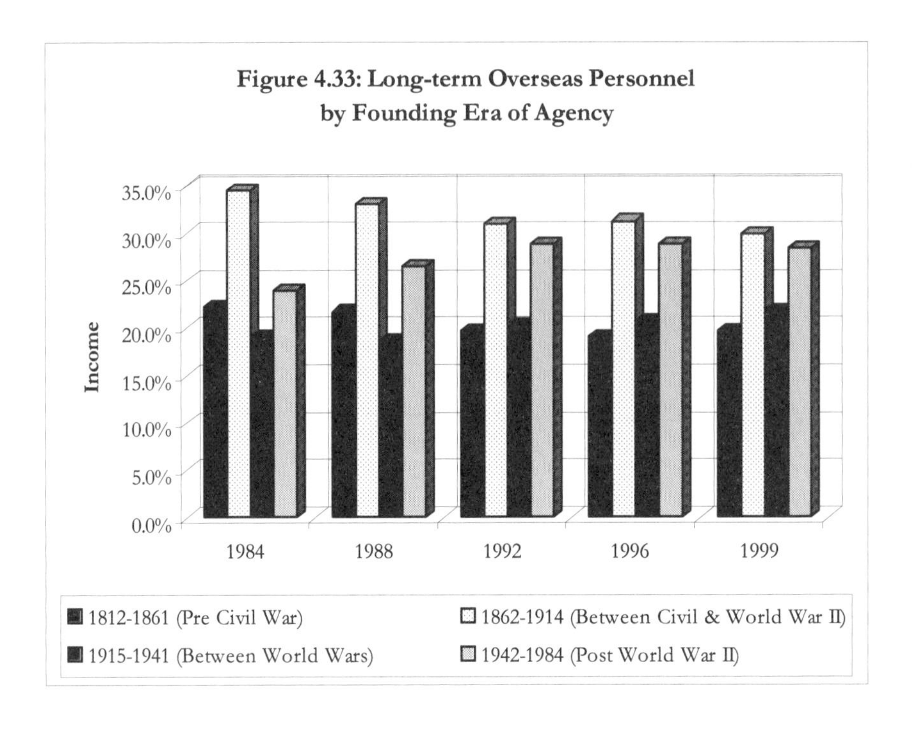

Figures 4.33 and 4.34 show long-term personnel and financial support for overseas ministries in terms of the era in which the agency was founded in the U.S. For agencies that are the result of mergers, the founding date of the oldest agency was used. In a few cases where mergers took place during the 14-year period covered by the figure, combined totals of the previously separate agencies were used for the years before the merger. For denominations that may have been formed before their overseas mission program was in operation, the date used was the first year that missionaries were sent overseas. All of these agencies were founded before 1984 so that statistics were available for all of the survey years for each agency.

The eras used in the charts are those that social historians have noted were times when basic changes took place in U.S. history. These periods are bounded by the U.S. Civil War of the 1860s and the World Wars of the twentieth century. Overseas mission work for the most part stood still or stopped during those wars. After the wars much of the world experienced some basic change and the mission agencies founded after those times of transition tended to reflect the new realities more quickly than those established earlier.

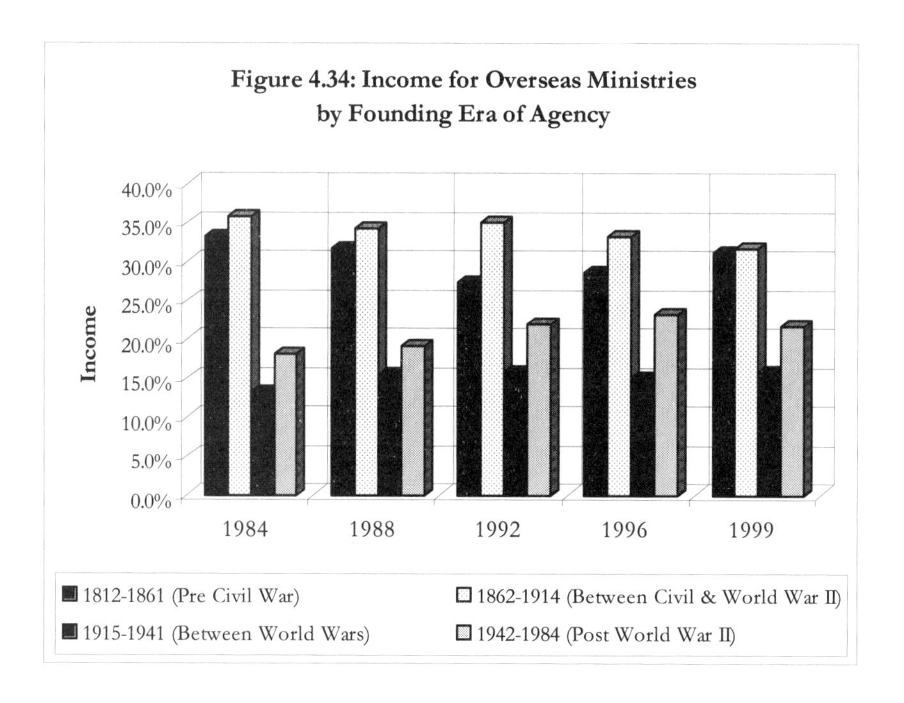

The trends for missionary sending and financial support in Figures 4.33 and 4.34 are identifiable but not markedly distinct. One might expect that the "older" agencies (founded before 1915) might show decreases in the percentage of personnel and financial support compared to the "newer" agencies (founded after 1915). This is the case, but not by great amounts. There was a 6.9% shift between 1984 and 1999 to the newer agencies in both personnel and financial support. But while the older agencies and newer agencies each had roughly 50% of the long-term personnel in 1999, the older agencies still had a distinct lead in the amount of financial support by 62.7% to 47.3%.

Figure 4.33 reveals one of the instances where a basic shift (although small) has taken place. For long-term personnel, the percentage from agencies founded between the World Wars (1915-1941) surpassed the percentage from agencies founded in the pre-Civil War era (1812-1861) by 1% in 1992, increasing to 1.9% in 1996 and 2.1% in 1999.

Figures 4.35 and 4.36 show long-term personnel and financial support for overseas ministries in terms of the doctrinal and/or ecclesiastical stance of the agency. Five categories are shown with the remaining summarized under "other." The 1999 survey questionnaire lists the twenty-two doctrinal/ecclesiastical groups used in the survey. This list has been refined over time with the core categories remaining the same. There are five generic categories (ecumenical, evangelical, etc.) and seventeen denominational families (Adventist, Baptist, etc.). In cases where agencies indicated more than one category, their primary historical group is used.

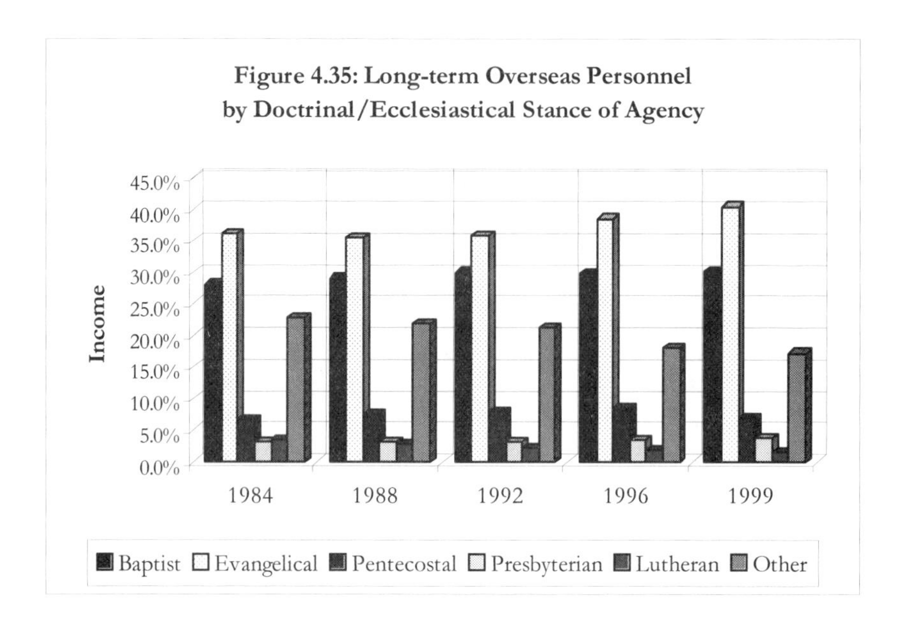

The trends for missionary sending and financial support in Figures 4.35 and 4.36 are also identifiable, but not markedly distinct. Figure 4.36 reveals another instance where a basic shift has taken place. Income for overseas ministries among agencies that use the generic term "evangelical" as their primary term moved into first place for income in 1992, passing the Baptist denominational family. By 1999, however, the Baptist family had moved back into first place. These evangelical agencies already had the largest percentage of long-term personnel in 1984 at 35.8%, and increased this to 40.4% by 1999.

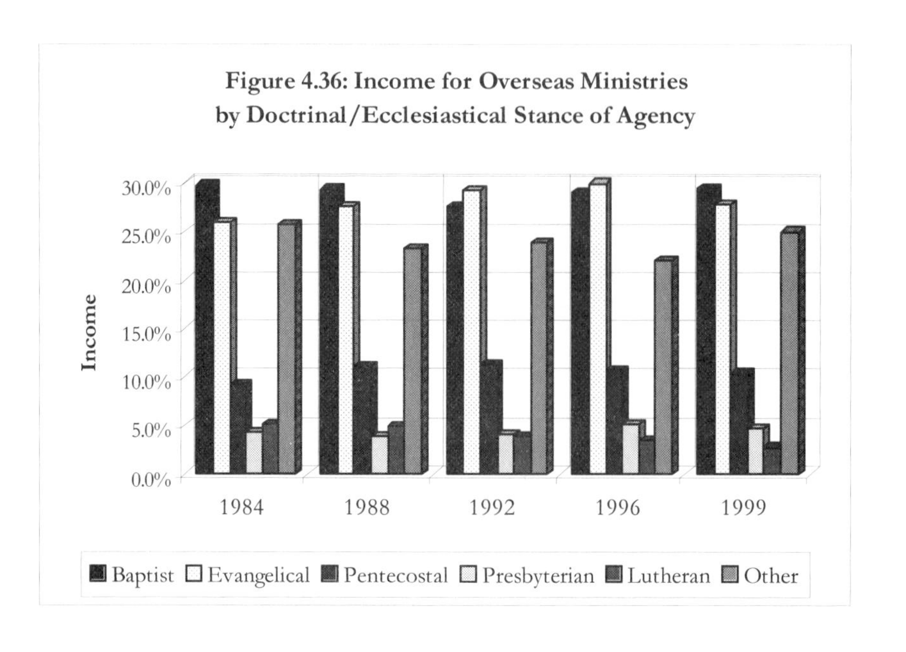

Endnotes

[1] World Harvest Now, Inc., Evangelical Greenhouse Ministries, Crisis Consulting International, and the Christian Reformed World Relief Committee are listed in the *Handbook*, though their numbers are not included in this survey, since we received information from them too late in the data analysis period to include.

[2] Throughout the analysis we refer to "reported" totals, since they are only as valid as the numbers received from each agency. Several factors contribute a certain "softness" to the numbers, including 1) the real numbers fluctuate during the year, 2) agencies use different methods for counting their personnel, 3) some report painstakingly exact numbers for the month the survey is completed, while others provide either highs or averages for the year, and some provide estimates, especially for soft-categories such as volunteers and nationals.

[3] By full-time we mean those who are in service for one year or longer.

[4] Throughout this chapter we will use the terms missionary, worker, and personnel interchangeably.

[5] The numbers reported on country totals will always be the minimum confirmable number. Two factors are involved. First, this does not include countries of nonresidential personnel, short-term workers, tentmakers, or where agencies have ongoing programs they support financially but without personnel. Second, several agencies report a general region but not specific countries for their missionary personnel. For example, 73 agencies indicated they had missionaries in Asia but did not specify which countries. Also, Southern Baptist Convention IMB indicated only regions rather than countries for all 4,562 of their U.S. overseas personnel.

[6] This number includes Canadians working for U.S. agencies.

[7] The reported 1,600,000 volunteers of the Salvation Army are excluded because it so skews the total numbers.

[8] The survey was sent out in April of 1999, requesting 1998 data.

[9] The way the data was reported changed from 1992 to 1996, thus the numbers for 1992 are not directly comparable to those of later years.

[10] Data for 1992 and 1996 adjusted for equivalence to 1999 dollars from Consumer Price Index information.

[11] In some Evangelical circles New England has a reputation of being spiritually cold, but this data should not be read as a confirmation of this perception. However, further research into reasons behind the dearth of agency headquarters in New England is warranted.

[12] Though the city of Colorado Springs gained four agencies, the state as a whole gained only two.

[13] This is a minimum number; see note 5 above.

[14] This is a minimum number; see the explanation in note 5 above.

[15] Includes non-residential fully supported missionaries.

[16] Of course there are semantic issues not only with the categorizations but also with the terms themselves. Our intention is to provide a broad brush-stroke for comparison from the data rather than divide the missionary task into these categories.

[17] Financial data were not received from eighty-eight of the U.S. agencies.

[18] It is possible that an important part of this increase was due to the rise of foundations during the same period and the greater use of foundations for funding by the agencies. Further research would be needed to verify this.

[19] Does not include 4,264 U.S. missionaries whose regions of service were undisclosed (sixty-two U.S. agencies reported at least some of their missionaries as working in unspecified countries).

[20] This number includes U.S. workers, non-U.S. workers in a country other than their own, and national workers. It does not include 4,264 U.S. workers, 262 non-U.S. workers in a country other than their own, and 2,731 national workers whose region was not disclosed.

[21] "Latin America" includes South and Central America and the Caribbean.

[22] These standard deviations on these averages are very large (e.g., the STD on the number of agencies per country is 30.38, larger than the average), indicating a big spread with many agencies at the bottom and few agencies at the top end of the spectrum, skewing the data.

[23] This is a minimum number; see note 5 above.

[24] A "0" in this category does not necessarily mean that there are no nationals for this agency; it may rather indicate a difference in reporting styles across the agencies.

[25] Southern Baptist Convention IMB reported the number of missionaries by region rather than by country.

[26] Churches of Christ provided the number of missionaries by region rather than by country.

[27] The MCC did not specify the countries in which its missionaries are present.

[28] Word of Life Fellowship did not specify the countries in which its missionaries are present.

[29] This number includes U.S citizens working for Canadian agencies.

[30] While this looks impressive, almost all of the growth took place among five agencies: MBMS International (from 0 to 627), Christian Aid Mission (from 316 to 500), The Leprosy Mission Canada (from 0 to 100), International Christian Aid Canada (from 0 to 99), and Operation Mobilization Canada (from 2 to 88). The net effect of the rest of the agencies reporting was a loss of personnel.

[31] Adjusted for inflation.

[32] Five activities from the list of fifty-two were not indicated by any of the Canadian agencies.

[33] Data were not received from twelve of the listed agencies.

[34] "Latin America" includes South and Central America and the Caribbean.

[35] Does not include 317 Canadian missionaries whose regions of service were undisclosed. There are ten Canadian agencies that reported at least some of their missionaries as working in "unspecified" areas of the world.

[36] This number includes Canadian workers, non-Canadian workers in a country other than their own, and national workers. It does not include 317 Canadian workers, 39 non-Canadian workers in a country other than their own, and 553 national workers whose country or region was not disclosed.

[37] This is a minimum number; see note 5 above.

[38] "Long-term" is defined as fully supported personnel with length of service expected to be more than 4 years.

[39] It should be noted that these are not absolute decreases, but decreases in the share of the total personnel and giving by agencies which identified themselves as denominational. In real terms, denominational personnel decreased by 5.9% and giving increased by 93.2% (not adjusted for inflation) over the period. *In relation to what happened in the other agencies*, the percent of those long-term missionaries employed by denominational agencies decreased by 2.9% and the percent of overseas income decreased by 3.8%.

Our Vision

- To evangelize, disciple and mobilize Chinese people for Christ.

Our Mission

- Evangelize and disciple Chinese students at U.S. universities
- Publish and distribute Chinese literature and resources in simplified and traditional Chinese text
- Publish and distribute bi-monthly AFC's Ambassadors Magazine
- Sponsor a tri-annual Chinese missions conference to mobilize Chinese Christians as an emerging missionary force
- Sponsor a Chinese singles and family ministries to strengthen and empower each community

Visit our website:
www.afcinc.org

Executive Director: David T. Chow
Address: 21A Leaman Rd., P.O. Box 280, Paradise, PA 17562
Office Telephone: 717-687-8564
Bookstore Telephone: 800-624-3504
Mainland Chinese Literature Telephone: 888-462-5481
E-Mail: afcinc.org

ARAB WORLD
MINISTRIES

adidas

ARISE International

Awake
Renew
Intercede
Send
Equip

VISION

****to proclaim the Gospel of the Kingdom to the least evangelized world.***
****to encourage, train and equip Christian leaders in the regions where they face persecutions.***
****to help those who are in the midst of disaster around the world.***

ARISE International
P.O. Box 3221
Silver Spring
Maryland 20918

E-mail:
mission@arise-intl.org
Web site:
www.arise-intl.org

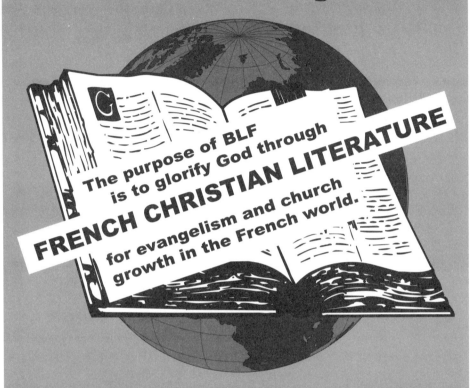

The Great Commission
Are you ready for the challenge?
CALVARY
INTERNATIONAL

The Fellowship of Missions

FOM provides fundamentalist mission agencies with a forum for mutual encouragement, discussion of vital issues in missiology, and the affirmation of the truths of historic Christianity as propagated through the Great Commission.

FOM member agencies extend the ministries of thousands of local churches through its more than 3,000 missionaries serving in 70 countries. Information about these ministries may be obtained by contacting the FOM office or the FOM web site www.fellowshipofmissions.org. Its publications, *Focus On Missions,* and *FOMenter,* are provided without charge to individuals/churches who would like to keep abreast of mission news.

FOM membership is open to all fiscally responsible agencies holding to the premillennial return of Christ and who are committed to the biblical principles of personal and ecclesiastical separation. For further information contact...

Rev. Leigh E. Adams, President
140 Jacqueline Drive, Berea, OH 44017-2730
Phone 440-243-0156 • Email ladamsfom@earthlink.net

Biblical • Fundamental • Premillennial • Separatist

GLOBAL OUTREACH MISSION

over 50 years of missionary evangelism

* is an interdenominational foreign missionary organization

* was founded in 1943 as the European Evangelistic Crusade by evangelist James Stewart

* is dedicated to carrying out the Great Commission

* has over 346 missionaries serving in 39 countries

* each missionary is free to follow the Lord's leading in determining methods of ministry

YOU ARE INVITED . . .

. . . to join us in reaching the world for Christ!

Global Outreach Mission is very diverse in its ministry . . . church planting, aviation, radio, medical, community development, camping, literature distribution and other forms of evangelism.

You can experience missions for a summer - from three to eight weeks; for short term - 3-36 months or career for as long as the Lord directs. We maintain no age limit for service. We will not turn you down because of age.

GLOBAL OUTREACH MISSION

USA
Box 2010 - Buffalo, NY 14231-2010
Tel. (716) 688-5048 FAX (716) 688-5049
E-Mail: GLmiss@aol.com

CANADA
Box 1210 - St. Catharines, ON L2R 7A7
Tel. (905) 684-1401
Website: globaloutreachmission.com

Other Personnel:
Non-USA serving in own/other country 2
Short-Term less than 1 year from USA 6
Home ministry & office staff in USA 10
Countries: Brazil 4, Colombia 4, India 4, Mexico 1, Philippines 27, Ukraine 2

ACTS International Ministries

(719)282-1247 **Fax: (719)282-1139**
E-Mail: AlvinLow98@yahoo.com
P.O. Box 62725, Colorado Springs, CO 80962
Dr. Alvin Low, President

An interdenominational support agency of evangelical tradition engaged in theological education, evangelism, leadership development, literature distribution, literature production and support of national churches.
Purpose: "...equipping national Christian leaders in the least evangelized, economically deprived and restricted countries of the world..."
Year Founded in USA 1991
Income for Overseas Mins $60,000
Fully Supported USA Personnel Overseas:
Expecting to serve more than 4 years 1
Other Personnel:
Home ministry & office staff in USA 1
Countries: Unspecified 1

AD2000 & Beyond Movement

(719)576-2000 **Fax: (719)576-2685**
E-Mail: Info@ad2000.org
Web: www.ad2000.org
2860 S. Circle Dr. #2112, Colorado Springs, CO 80906
Dr. Luis Bush, President

A transdenominational support network of evangelical tradition engaged in mobilization for mission and providing information services to churches and others involved in world evangelization. This office plans to close in 2001.
Purpose: "...to encourage, motivate and network men and women church leaders by inspiring them with the vision of reaching the unreached by AD2000 through consultations, prayer efforts and communication materials..."
Year Founded in USA 1989
Income for Overseas Mins $401,558
Personnel:
Home ministry & office staff in USA 8

Adopt-A-People Clearinghouse

(719)574-7001 **Fax: (719)574-7005**
E-Mail: AAPC@xc.org
Web: www.aapc.net
P.O. Box 63600, Colorado Springs, CO 80962-3600
Mr. Dick Bashta, Exec. Director

A nondenominational service agency of evangelical tradition engaged in providing people group information services to churches and others involved in world evangelization.
Purpose: "…to envision, impassion and equip local churches and mission organizations worldwide to spiritually adopt all remaining unreached people groups through prayer, partnership, provision and personnel for the purpose of planting churches."
Year Founded in USA 1989
Income for Overseas Mins .... NA
Personnel:
Home ministry & office staff in USA 4

Advancing Indigenous Missions

(830)367-3513 **Fax: (210)734-7620**
E-Mail: coth@a-omega.net
P.O. Box 690042, San Antonio, TX 78269
James W. Colley, Exec. Director

A transdenominational support agency of evangelical and charismatic tradition engaged in support of national churches.
Year Founded in USA 1990
Income for Overseas Mins .... NR
Personnel:
Home ministry & office staff in USA 2

Advancing Native Missions

(804)293-8829 **Fax: (804)293-7586**
E-Mail: ANM@adnamis.org
Web: www.adnamis.org
P.O. Box 5303, Charlottesville, VA 22905
Mr. Carl A. Gordon, President

A transdenominational support agency of evangelical tradition engaged in support of national churches, Bible distribution, funds transmission, leadership development and mission-related research.

Purpose: "...to seek out, evaluate and support native missions groups who have a clear and defined evangelical statement of faith, who are open and transparent in their finances and who are working among unreached people groups."

Year Founded in USA 1990

Income for Overseas Mins $2,362,000

Personnel:

Short-Term less than 1 year from USA 50

Home ministry & office staff in USA 24

Advancing Renewal Ministries

(704)846-9355 **Fax: (704)846-9356**

E-Mail: ARM_INC@compuserve.com

11616 Sir Francis Drake Dr., Charlotte, NC 28277

Dr. Arthur M. Vincent, Director

A nondenominational support agency of Lutheran tradition engaged in support of national workers, Bible distribution and literature distribution.

Year Founded in USA 1982

Income for Overseas Mins $48,600

Personnel:

Non-USA serving in own/other country 15

Home ministry & office staff in USA 4

Advent Christian General Conf., Dept. of World Missions

(704)545-6161 **Fax: (704)573-0412**

E-Mail: worldmissions@adventchristian.org

Web: www.adventchristian.org

P.O. Box 23152, Charlotte, NC 28227

Rev. David Ross, Exec. Director

A denominational sending agency of Adventist tradition engaged in church planting, theological education, TEE, evangelism, literature distribution and support of national workers.

Year Founded in USA 1865

Income for Overseas Mins $511,328

Gifts-in-Kind $5,000

Fully Supported USA Personnel Overseas:

Expecting to serve more than 4 years 12

Other Personnel:

Non-USA serving in own/other country 83

Short-Term less than 1 year from USA 28

Home ministry & office staff in USA 2

Countries: India 4, Japan 2, Mexico 1, New Zealand 2, Philippines 3

Africa Evangelical Fellowship See: SIM USA

Africa Inland Mission Intl.

(914)735-4014 **Fax: (914)735-1814**

E-Mail: AIM_Info@aimint.org

Web: www.aim-us.org

P.O. Box 178, Pearl River, NY 10965

Dr. W. Ted Barnett, U.S. Director

An interdenominational sending agency of evangelical tradition engaged in church planting, Christian education, theological education, evangelism, leadership development and medical work.

Purpose: "...to plant maturing churches...through the evangelization of unreached people groups and the effective preparation of church leaders."

Year Founded in USA 1895

Income for Overseas Mins $12,694,000

Gifts-in-Kind $215,909

Fully Supported USA Personnel Overseas:

Expecting to serve more than 4 years 433

Expecting to serve 1 to 4 years 50

Nonresidential mission personnel 4

Other Personnel:

Short-Term less than 1 year from USA 103

Home ministry & office staff in USA 76

Countries: Cen Africa Rep 2, Chad 3, Comoros Isls 6, Congo 5, France 2, Germany 2, Guatemala 1, Kenya 333, Lesotho 5, Mozambique 26, Namibia 4, S Africa 1, Sudan 1, Tanzania 81, Uganda 11

Africa Inter-Mennonite Mission

(219)875-5552 **Fax: (219)875-6567**

E-Mail: AIMM@sprynet.com

Web: home.sprynet.com/sprynet/aimm

59466 County Rd. 113, Elkhart, IN 46517-3644

Rev. Garry Prieb, Exec. Secretary

A denominational sending agency of Mennonite tradition engaged in church planting, evangelism, leadership development, linguistics, support of national churches and Bible translation.

Purpose: "...to make known the love of God in Jesus Christ to the people of Africa in ministries of word and deed, witness and service that God's people be brought to full stature in Christ."
Year Founded in USA 1912
Income for Overseas Mins $849,198
Fully Supported USA Personnel Overseas:
Expecting to serve more than 4 years 16
Expecting to serve 1 to 4 years 8
Other Personnel:
Non-USA serving in own/other country 12
Short-Term less than 1 year from USA 6
Home ministry & office staff in USA 6
Countries: Botswana 5, Burkina Faso 9, Congo/ Zaire 2, Cote d'Ivoire 2, Senegal 4, S Africa 2

African Bible Colleges, Inc.

(601)923-1679 **Fax: (601)924-6353**
E-Mail: BuckABC@netdoor.com
P.O. Box 103, Jackson, MS 39060
Rev. William L. Mosal, U.S. Director
An interdenominational sending agency of evangelical tradition engaged in leadership development, Bible distribution, broadcasting, correspondence courses, Christian education and evangelism.
Purpose: "...to further evangelical Christian education through establishment and funding of Bible colleges in Africa and the acquisition of Christian teachers for African schools and colleges."
Year Founded in USA 1977
Income for Overseas Mins $709,378
Fully Supported USA Personnel Overseas:
Expecting to serve more than 4 years 16
Expecting to serve 1 to 4 years 6
Other Personnel:
Home ministry & office staff in USA 1
Countries: Malawi 22

African Christian Mission
See: ACM International

African Enterprise, Inc.

(626)357-8811 **Fax: (626)359-2069**
E-Mail: AEUSA@compuserve.com
Web: www.africanenterprise.org
P.O. Box 727, Monrovia, CA 91017
Mr. Malcolm Graham, Exec. Director
A nondenominational support agency of evangelical tradition engaged in evangelism, leadership development, relief and/or rehabilitation and missionary training.
Purpose: "To evangelise the cities of Africa through Word & Deed in partnership with the Church."
Year Founded in USA 1962
Income for Overseas Mins $1,303,758
Personnel:
Non-USA serving in own/other country 131
Short-Term less than 1 year from USA 3
Home ministry & office staff in USA 6
Countries: Congo, Ethiopia, Ghana, Kenya, Malawi, Rwanda, S Africa, Tanzania, Uganda, Zimbabwe

African Leadership

(615)595-8238 **Fax: (615)595-7906**
E-Mail: lcwarren@sprynet.com
P.O. Box 682444, Franklin, TN 37068-2444
Mr. Larry Warren, Exec. Director
A transdenominational support agency of evangelical tradition engaged in leadership development, church construction, Christian education, theological education and TEE. Personnel information from 1996.
Year Founded in USA 1990
Income for Overseas Mins $217,686
Personnel:
Home ministry & office staff in USA 12

African Methodist Episcopal Church, Dept. of Missions

(202)371-8700 **Fax: (202)371-8735**
1134 11th St. NW, Washington, DC 20001
A denominational support agency of Methodist tradition engaged in Bible distribution, childrens programs and church construction. Statistical information from 1996.
Year Founded in USA 1844
Income for Overseas Mins $500,000
Personnel:
Short-Term less than 1 year from USA 275

African Methodist Episcopal Zion Church, Dept. of Overseas Missions

(212)870-2952 Fax: (212)870-2808
E-Mail: domkd5@aol.com
475 Riverside Dr. Rm. 1935, New York, NY 10115
Rev. K. J. Degraffenreidt, Sec./Treasurer

A denominational sending agency of Methodist tradition engaged in support of national workers, evangelism and literature distribution. Statistical information from 1992.

Year Founded in USA 1876
Income for Overseas Mins $251,000
Fully Supported USA Personnel Overseas:
Expecting to serve more than 4 years 4
Countries: Ghana 1, Guyana 1, Jamaica 1, Liberia 1

African Mission Evangelism

(423)579-1467 Fax: (423)579-2337
E-Mail: cbridges@jbc.edu
Web: www.ame-gccs.org
2313 Bell Dr., Knoxville, TN 37998
Dr. Carl Bridges, President

A nondenominational sending agency of Christian (Restoration Movement) tradition engaged in theological education, church planting and support of national churches.

Year Founded in USA 1968
Income for Overseas Mins $129,969
Fully Supported USA Personnel Overseas:
Expecting to serve more than 4 years 11
Expecting to serve 1 to 4 years 1
Other Personnel:
Non-USA serving in own/other country 12
Short-Term less than 1 year from USA 6
Countries: Ghana 12

Agape Gospel Mission

(540)562-4753 Fax: (540)562-4753
E-Mail: 104072.747@compuserve.com
P.O. Box 11785, Roanoke, VA 24022-1785
Rev. Rick Whitcomb, Intl. Director

An interdenominational support agency of charismatic tradition engaged in church planting, evangelism and training. Statistical information from 1992.

Year Founded in USA 1983
Income for Overseas Mins $60,000
Personnel:
Non-USA serving in own/other country 33
Short-Term less than 1 year from USA 1
Home ministry & office staff in USA 1

AIMS (Accelerating International Mission Strategies)

(757)226-5850 Fax: (757)226-5851
E-Mail: aims@aims-usa.org
P.O. Box 64534, Virginia Beach, VA 23464
Dr. Howard Foltz, President

An agency of missions-focused churches, agencies, training institutions, vendors, and individuals working cooperatively to make a worldwide impact for Christ. Name changed from Association of International Mission Services in 1999.

Year Founded in USA 1985
Income for Overseas Mins $190,870
Gifts-in-Kind $48,000
Personnel:
Short-Term less than 1 year from USA 10
Home ministry & office staff in USA 12

Alberto Mottesi Evangelistic Association

(714)375-0110
E-Mail: mottesi@flash.net
Web: www.albertomottesi.org
P.O. Box 2478, Huntington Bch., CA 92647
Mr. Alberto H. Mottesi, President

An interdenominational service agency of evangelical tradition engaged in evangelism, broadcasting, leadership development and family restoration in 19 Spanish-speaking countries.

Year Founded in USA 1977
Income for Overseas Mins .... NA
Fully Supported USA Personnel Overseas:
Nonresidential mission personnel 2
Other Personnel:
Home ministry & office staff in USA 5

All God's Children International

(503)282-7652 Fax: (503)282-2582
E-Mail: agci@usa.net

Web: www.allgodschildren.org
4114 NE Fremont St., Portland, OR 97212
Mr. Ron Beazely, President
A nondenominational service agency of Pentecostal tradition engaged in childcare/ orphanage programs, literature distribution, providing medical supplies and relief and/or rehabilitation. Statistical information from 1996.
Year Founded in USA 1991
Income for Overseas Mins $568,000
Fully Supported USA Personnel Overseas:
Nonresidential mission personnel 2
Other Personnel:
Non-USA serving in own/other country 5
Short-Term less than 1 year from USA 4
Countries: Bulgaria, China, Romania

Allegheny Wesleyan Methodist Missions

(330)332-5271 **Fax: (330)337-9700**
E-Mail: AWMC@juno.com
P.O. Box 357, Salem, OH 44460
Rev. William M. Cope, Director
A denominational sending agency of Wesleyan-Arminian and Holiness tradition engaged in evangelism, Bible and literature distribution, church planting and Christian education.
Year Founded in USA 1969
Income for Overseas Mins $377,333
Fully Supported USA Personnel Overseas:
Expecting to serve more than 4 years 14
Other Personnel:
Short-Term less than 1 year from USA 12
Home ministry & office staff in USA 2
Countries: Haiti 9, Peru 2, Ukraine 3

ALM International
See: American Leprosy Missions, Inc.

Ambassadors for Christ Intl.

(770)980-2020 **Fax: (980)956-8144**
E-Mail: afci-isc@mindspring.com
Web: www.afcinternational.org
1355 Terrell Mill Rd. #1484, Marietta, GA 30067
Rev. Allan Gardner, Intl. Director
A nondenominational support agency of evangelical tradition engaged in training and support of national workers.
Purpose: "...to support spiritually gifted preachers and Bible teachers to reach their homelands for Jesus Christ."
Year Founded in USA 1972
Income for Overseas Mins $621,445
Personnel:
Home ministry & office staff in USA 6

Ambassadors for Christ, Inc.

(717)687-8564 **Fax: (717)687-8891**
E-Mail: AFC@afcinc.org
Web: www.idsonline.com/afc
P.O. Box 280, Paradise, PA 17562
Mr. Jerry Murray, Business Mngr.
An interdenominational support agency of evangelical tradition engaged in evangelism and mobilization for mission. Statistical information from 1996.
Year Founded in USA 1963
Income for Overseas Mins .... NA
Personnel:
Home ministry & office staff in USA 22

American Association of Lutheran Churches - Comm. for World Missions

(520)287-7042
E-Mail: Esco3229@aol.com
801 W. 106th St., #203, Bloomington, MN 55420-5603
Pastor Joel Midthun, Chair
A denominational support agency of Lutheran tradition engaged in funds transmission, church planting, relief and/or rehabilitation and Bible translation.
Year Founded in USA 1987
Income for Overseas Mins $35,000
Personnel:
Non-USA serving in own/other country 3
Short-Term less than 1 year from USA 1

American Baptist Association Missionary Committee

(903)792-2312 **Fax: (903)794-1290**
Web: www.abaptist.org

P.O. Box 1050, Texarkana, TX 75504
Randy Cloud, Secretary/Treasurer
A denominational support agency of Baptist tradition engaged in church planting, theological education and evangelism. Statistical information from 1992.
Year Founded in USA 1924
Income for Overseas Mins $450,000
Fully Supported USA Personnel Overseas:
Expecting to serve more than 4 years 16
Countries: Am Samoa 2, Australia 1, Colombia 1, Costa Rica 3, France 1, Germany 1, Japan 1, Kenya 3, New Zealand 2, Solomon Isls 1

American Baptist Churches in the U.S.A., Intl. Ministries

(610)768-2201 Fax: (610)768-2115
E-Mail: Janet.Medrow@abc-usa.org
Web: www.abc-im.org
P.O. Box 851, Valley Forge, PA 19482-0851
Dr. John A. Sundquist, Exec. Director
A denominational sending agency of Baptist tradition engaged in support of national churches, development, theological education, evangelism and mobilization for mission.
Purpose: "To further evangelism...strengthen national churches...foster world mission consciousness in USA churches...assist in the internationalization of mission...meet human need."
Year Founded in USA 1814
Income for Overseas Mins $16,024,902
Fully Supported USA Personnel Overseas:
Expecting to serve more than 4 years 120
Expecting to serve 1 to 4 years 3
Nonresidential mission personnel 3
Other Personnel:
Non-USA serving in own/other country 12
Short-Term less than 1 year from USA 375
Home ministry & office staff in USA 44
Countries: Bangladesh 1, Bolivia 2, Cambodia 2, Chile 4, China (PRC) 3, Congo/Zaire 19, Costa Rica 3, Cuba 1, Czech Rep 6, Dominican Rep 6, El Salvador 2, Ghana 1, Haiti 7, Hong Kong 4, India 4, Japan 11, Mexico 8, Nicaragua 6, Philippines 7, Russia 4, S Africa 5, Thailand 17

American Bible Society

(212)408-1200 Fax: (212)408-1512
E-Mail: webmaster@americanbible.org
Web: www.americanbible.org
1865 Broadway, New York, NY 10023
Dr. Eugene B. Habecker, President
An interdenominational specialized service agency engaged in Scripture translation, publication and distribution in fellowship with 135 members of the United Bible Societies and other Bible Society offices, operating in some 200 countries and territories.
Purpose: "...to provide the Holy Scriptures to every man, woman and child in a language and form each can readily understand, and at a price each can easily afford."
Year Founded in USA 1816
Income for Overseas Mins $16,676,371

American Leprosy Missions, Inc.

(864)271-7040 Fax: (864)271-7062
E-Mail: AmLep@leprosy.org
Web: www.leprosy.org
1 ALM Way, Greenville, SC 29601
Mr. Christopher J. Doyle, Pres./CEO
A nondenominational specialized agency of evangelical tradition engaged in funds transmission, disability assistance programs and providing medical supplies.
Purpose: "To serve as a channel of the love of Christ to persons with Hansen's disease (leprosy)...helping them to be healed in body and spirit and to be restored to lives of dignity and usefulness."
Year Founded in USA 1917
Income for Overseas Mins $3,933,747
Personnel:
Home ministry & office staff in USA 30

American Missionary Fellowship

(610)527-4439 Fax: (610)527-4720
E-Mail: AMFInfo@aol.com
Web: www.americanmissionary.org
P.O. Box 370, Villanova, PA 19085
Dr. Donald C. Palmer, Gen. Director
A nondenominational support agency of evangelical tradition engaged in church

planting and cross-cultural ministry in USA leading to overseas missions.

Purpose: "...to evangelize, disciple and congregate the yet-unreached peoples of the United States for Jesus Christ."

Year Founded in USA 1817
Income for Overseas Mins .... NA
Personnel:
Bivocational/Tentmaker from USA 400
Home ministry & office staff in USA 16

American Scripture Gift Mission

(321)255-7774 Fax: (321)255-8986
E-Mail: asgm@flash.net
Web: www.asgm.org
P.O. Box 410280, Melbourne, FL 32941-0280
Gary & Linda Powell, Ministry Adminstrators

A nondenominational support agency of evangelical tradition distributing all-Scripture booklets and tracts in more than 400 languages, primarily for evangelism. The USA branch of SGM International, London, England.

Year Founded in USA 1933
Income for Overseas Mins .... NA
Personnel:
Home ministry & office staff in USA 3

American Tract Society

(972)276-9408 Fax: (972)272-9642
E-Mail: ats@atstracts.org
Web: www.atstracts.org
P.O. Box 462008, Garland, TX 75046
Mr. Daniel Southern, President
Mr. Kent Barnard, Vice-President

An interdenominational support agency of independent tradition engaged in literature production/distribution. Personnel information from 1996.

Year Founded in USA 1825
Income for Overseas Mins .... NA
Personnel:
Home ministry & office staff in USA 28

American Waldensian Society

(610)317-8870 Fax: (610)317-8874
E-Mail: Waldensi@ptd.net
3083 Altonah Rd., Bethlehem, PA 18017-2503
Revs. Ruth & Edward Santana-Grace, Co-Dirs.

An interdenominational support agency of ecumenical tradition engaged in support of national churches and literature production. Statistical information from 1996.

Year Founded in USA 1906
Income for Overseas Mins $407,444
Personnel:
Short-Term less than 1 year from USA 30
Home ministry & office staff in USA 3

AmeriTribes

(520)670-9400 Fax: (520)670-9444
E-Mail: info@ameritribes.org
Web: www.ameritribes.org
3710 S. Park Ave., Ste. 708, Tucson, AZ 85713-5045
Mr. Timothy C. Brown, Exec. Director

A nondenominational sending agency of evangelical tradition engaged in community development and church planting among tribal peoples of the Americas. Financial information from 1996.

Purpose: "...facilitating the development of reproducing indigenous churches among tribal peoples of the Americas."

Year Founded in USA 1944
Income for Overseas Mins $15,750
Fully Supported USA Personnel Overseas:
Expecting to serve more than 4 years 6
Nonresidential mission personnel 2
Other Personnel:
Home ministry & office staff in USA 4
Countries: Mexico 6

AMF International

(708)418-0020 Fax: (708)418-0132
E-Mail: amfi@iname.com
Web: www.amfi.org
P.O. Box 5470, Lansing, IL 60438
Mr. Wesley N. Taber, Exec. Director

An interdenominational sending agency of evangelical tradition engaged in evangelism, literature distribution, mobilization for mission, short-term programs and training focused on Jewish outreach.

Purpose: "Building bridges of understanding between Jewish and Christian communities for over 100 years."

Year Founded in USA 1887
Income for Overseas Mins $86,160
Fully Supported USA Personnel Overseas:
Expecting to serve more than 4 years 2
Expecting to serve 1 to 4 years 1
Other Personnel:
Bivocational/Tentmaker from USA 12
Short-Term less than 1 year from USA 20
Home ministry & office staff in USA 20
Countries: Israel 3

AMG International

(423)894-6060 **Fax: (423)894-6863**
E-Mail: missions@amginternational.org
Web: www.amginternational.org
P.O. Box 22000, Chattanooga, TN 37422
Dr. Spiros Zodhiates, President
Dr. Paul Jenks, CEO
An interdenominational sending agency of evangelical tradition engaged in Bible distribution, childcare/orphanage programs, church planting, theological education, relief and/or rehabilitation and support of national workers.
Year Founded in USA 1942
Income for Overseas Mins $4,508,705
Fully Supported USA Personnel Overseas:
Expecting to serve more than 4 years 45
Nonresidential mission personnel 1
Other Personnel:
Non-USA serving in own/other country .. 1265
Bivocational/Tentmaker from USA 1
Short-Term less than 1 year from USA 30
Home ministry & office staff in USA 21
Countries: Albania 2, Bulgaria, Cyprus 2, Greece 16, Guatemala 2, India 2, Indonesia, Mexico 3, Philippines 2, Romania, Spain 10, Thailand 2, Turkey, Uganda 2, Unspecified 2

AMOR Ministries

(619)662-1200 **Fax: (619)662-1295**
E-Mail: mtsc@amor.org
Web: www.amor.org
1664 Precision Park Lane, San Diego, CA 92713
Scott & Gayla Congdon, Presidents/Founders
A nondenominational sending agency of Christian (Restoration Movement) tradition engaged in relief and/or rehabilitation, support of national churches, short-term programs, missionary training and youth programs.
Year Founded in USA 1980
Income for Overseas Mins $2,500,000
Gifts-in-Kind $40,000
Fully Supported USA Personnel Overseas:
Expecting to serve more than 4 years 12
Expecting to serve 1 to 4 years 13
Nonresidential mission personnel 1
Other Personnel:
Non-USA serving in own/other country 6
Short-Term less than 1 year from USA 36
Home ministry & office staff in USA 15
Countries: Mexico 25

Anglican Frontier Missions

(804)355-8468 **Fax: (804)355-8260**
E-Mail: AFM@xc.org
Web: www.afm-25.org
P.O. Box 18038, Richmond, VA 23226-8038
Rev. E. A. de Bordenave, Director
A denominational sending agency of Episcopal and evangelical tradition engaged in church planting, Bible distribution, literacy work and video/film production and distribution.
Purpose: "...planting indigenous churches among the 25 largest and least evangelized people groups of World A."
Year Founded in USA 1993
Income for Overseas Mins $271,356
Fully Supported USA Personnel Overseas:
Expecting to serve more than 4 years 14
Other Personnel:
Home ministry & office staff in USA 4
Countries: Algeria 2, China (PRC) 4, India 1, Iran 2, Nepal 2, Tibet 1, Yemen 2

Anis Shorrosh Evangelistic Association, Inc.

(334)626-1124 **Fax: (334)621-0507**
Web: www.islamexpose.com
P.O. Box 7577, Spanish Fort, AL 36577-0577
Dr. Anis Shorrosh, Evangelist
An interdenominational support agency of Baptist and evangelical tradition engaged in evangelism, audio recording/distribution, broadcasting, literature distribution, translation work and video/film production and

distribution with special emphasis on Muslims.

Year Founded in USA 1970
Income for Overseas Mins $25,000
Personnel:
Non-USA serving in own/other country 1
Short-Term less than 1 year from USA 2
Home ministry & office staff in USA 1

Apostolic Christian Church Foundation, Inc.

(309)925-9040 Fax: (309)925-9040
12666 Locust Rd., Tremont, IL 61568
Mr. Jim Hodges, Exec. Director
Mr. Steve Meyer, Missionary Committee Chair

A denominational sending agency of Anabaptist tradition engaged in funds transmission, church construction, relief and/or rehabilitation and support of national workers.

Purpose: "...exists to help fulfill Christ's Commission by sending out members of the AC Church who are called by God to become foreign missionaries."

Year Founded in USA 1953
Income for Overseas Mins $1,010,529
Fully Supported USA Personnel Overseas:
Expecting to serve more than 4 years 31
Other Personnel:
Non-USA serving in own/other country 24
Short-Term less than 1 year from USA 10
Home ministry & office staff in USA 2
Countries: Argentina 1, Australia 2, Brazil 17, Czech Rep 1, Indonesia 2, Japan 2, Mexico 1, Papua New Guin 2, Paraguay 1, Puerto Rico 2

Apostolic Team Ministries, Intl.

(419)841-8033 Fax: (419)843-9318
E-Mail: ATMRKing@aol.com
6109 W. Bancroft St., Toledo, OH 43615
Mr. Ronald G. King, Admin. Director

A nondenominational support agency of charismatic tradition engaged in church planting and missionary training.

Year Founded in USA 1980
Income for Overseas Mins $200,000
Fully Supported USA Personnel Overseas:
Expecting to serve more than 4 years 15
Other Personnel:
Non-USA serving in own/other country 8
Home ministry & office staff in USA 8
Countries: Albania 5, Bolivia 2, Brazil 2, France 4, UK 2

Arab World Ministries

(800)447-3566 Fax: (610)352-2652
E-Mail: awmusa@awm.org
Web: www.awm.com
P.O. Box 96, Upper Darby, PA 19082
Mr. Robert Sayer, U.S. Director

A nondenominational sending agency of evangelical tradition engaged in church planting, broadcasting, TEE and evangelism.

Year Founded in USA 1952
Income for Overseas Mins $4,257,192
Fully Supported USA Personnel Overseas:
Expecting to serve more than 4 years 139
Other Personnel:
Non-USA serving in own/other country 97
Short-Term less than 1 year from USA 29
Home ministry & office staff in USA 17
Countries: Bahrain 2, Belgium 2, Egypt 10, France 36, Germany 4, Israel 3, Jordan 14, Kuwait 2, Lebanon 7, Morocco 11, Netherlands 6, Oman 2, Spain 6, Tunisia 11, United Arab Emr 4, UK 13, Yemen 6

Arabic Communication Center

(626)291-2866 Fax: (626)291-2159
E-Mail: ACCKAMEL@juno.com
Web: www.ACCWORLD.org
P.O. Box 1124, Temple City, CA 91780
Dr. Hisham S. Kamel, President

A denominational specialized agency of Presbyterian tradition engaged in translation work, Bible distribution, theological education, evangelism, literature distribution and video/film production and distribution.

Year Founded in USA 1992
Income for Overseas Mins $30,000
Gifts-in-Kind $10,000
Fully Supported USA Personnel Overseas:
Nonresidential mission personnel 5
Other Personnel:
Short-Term less than 1 year from USA 7
Home ministry & office staff in USA 4

ARISE International

(301)613-2180 Fax: (301)549-0921
E-Mail: mission@arise-intl.org
Web: www.arise-intl.org

P.O. Box 3221, Silver Spring, MD 20918
Rev. C. Daniel Kim, Director
A nondenominational support agency of evangelical tradition engaged in mobilization for mission and support of national workers.
Year Founded in USA 1990
Income for Overseas Mins $50,000
Gifts-in-Kind $8,000
Personnel:
Non-USA serving in own/other country 14
Short-Term less than 1 year from USA 3
Home ministry & office staff in USA 3

Armenian Missionary Association of America, Inc.

(201)265-2607 Fax: (201)265-6015
E-Mail: amaainc@aol.com
31 West Century Rd., Paramus, NJ 07652
The Rev. Dr. Moses B. Janbazian, Exec. Director
A nondenominational service agency of evangelical and Congregational tradition engaged in Christian education, childcare/orphanage programs, church planting, evangelism, medical work and relief and/or rehabilitation.
Year Founded in USA 1918
Income for Overseas Mins $3,000,000
Fully Supported USA Personnel Overseas:
Expecting to serve more than 4 years 4
Expecting to serve 1 to 4 years 1
Nonresidential mission personnel 4
Other Personnel:
Non-USA serving in own/other country 6
Short-Term less than 1 year from USA 32
Home ministry & office staff in USA 14
Countries: Armenia 2, Lebanon 3

Artists In Christian Testimony

(615)591-2598 Fax: (615)591-2599
E-Mail: ACTnashville@actinternational.org
Web: www.actinternational.org
Box 395, Franklin, TN 37065-0395
Rev. Byron L. Spradlin, Director
A support agency of evangelical tradition engaged in training, evangelism, and management consulting/training.
Purpose: "...to release an army of arts ministry specialists into church, missions and market place ministries around the world...in the process helping better mobilize and equip them for the world evangelization movement."
Year Founded in USA 1973
Income for Overseas Mins $50,000
Fully Supported USA Personnel Overseas:
Expecting to serve more than 4 years 6
Expecting to serve 1 to 4 years 2
Nonresidential mission personnel 2
Other Personnel:
Non-USA serving in own/other country 8
Short-Term less than 1 year from USA 1
Home ministry & office staff in USA 4
Countries: Central Asia 2, France 2, Japan 2, Philippines 2

Asian Outreach U.S.A.

(714)557-9160 Fax: (714)557-2742
E-Mail: AOUSA@earthlink.net
Web: www.asianoutreach.org
3941 S. Bristol St. #67, Santa Ana, CA 92704
Rev. James R. Swanson, Exec. Director
An interdenominational support agency of evangelical tradition engaged in Bible distribution, broadcasting, leadership development, literature production, support of national churches and training in Asia.
Year Founded in USA 1960
Income for Overseas Mins $1,615,000
Personnel:
Home ministry & office staff in USA 2

Assemblies of God, General Council, Div. Foreign Missions

(417)862-2781 Fax: (417)862-0978
E-Mail: DFM@ag.org
Web: www.ag.org
1445 Boonville Ave., Springfield, MO 65802
Rev. John Bueno, Exec. Director
A denominational sending agency of Pentecostal tradition engaged in church planting, correspondence courses, theological education, leadership development, literature production /distribution, missionary training and video/film production and distribution.
Purpose: "...proclaiming the message of Jesus Christ to the spiritually lost...establishing churches, following the New Testament pattern...training leaders to proclaim the message of Jesus Christ to their own people and to other nations...touching poor and suffering people with the compassion of Jesus Christ..."

Year Founded in USA 1914
Income for Overseas Mins $126,470,484
Fully Supported USA Personnel Overseas:
Expecting to serve more than 4 years 1253
Expecting to serve 1 to 4 years 290
Nonresidential mission personnel...................40
Other Personnel:
Short-Term less than 1 year from USA ... 12403
Home ministry & office staff in USA 261
Countries: Albania 11, Am Samoa 2, Angola 2, Argentina 25, Austria 8, Bahamas 9, Belarus 9, Belau(Palau) 4, Belgium 54, Belize 8, Benin 2, Bolivia 14, Botswana 2, Brazil 13, Burkina Faso 9, Cambodia 33, Cameroon 6, Canary Isls 4, Chile 23, Colombia 31, Congo 2, Congo/Zaire 4, Costa Rica 25, Cote d'Ivoire 2, Croatia 2, Czech Rep 5, Dominican Rep 14, Ecuador 31, El Salvador 40, Equat Guinea 8, Eritrea 6, Ethiopia 23, Europe 4, Fiji 6, France 16, Georgia 5, Germany 29, Ghana 2, Guam 13, Guatemala 18, Guinea Bissau 4, Haiti 8, Honduras 18, Hungary 8, Iceland 2, Indonesia 30, Ireland 8, Italy 4, Jamaica 14, Japan 44, Kenya 34, Kiribati 2, Korea-S 2, Laos 1, Latin America 60, Latvia 7, Lesotho 2, Liberia 2, Lithuania 6, Luxembourg 4, Madagascar 9, Malawi 9, Mali 6, Malta 2, Marshall Isls 2, Mexico 74, Mongolia 17, Mozambique 5, Namibia 4, Netherlands 4, Neth Antilles 2, New Caledonia 2, Nicaragua 17, Niger 4, Nigeria 8, Oceania 2, Panama 14, Paraguay 26, Peru 18, Philippines 88, Poland 4, Portugal 9, Romania 28, Russia 110, Rwanda 4, Senegal 9, Sierra Leone 2, Singapore 15, Slovakia 4, Slovenia 4, Solomon Isls 2, S Africa 35, Spain 45, Suriname 2, Swaziland 6, Taiwan (ROC) 12, Tanzania 4, Thailand 20, Togo 11, Tonga 6, Ukraine 12, Unspecified 67, Uruguay 10, Vanuatu 4, Venezuela 21

ASSIST - Aid to Special Saints in Strategic Times

(714)530-6598 Fax: (714)636-7351
E-Mail: assistcomm@cs.com
Web: www.rwcc.com/assist.htm
P.O. Box 2126, Garden Grove, CA 92642
Mr. Dan Wooding, President

A support agency of evangelical tradition engaged in a Pen Pal ministry, Bible distribution, evangelism, and literature distribution.

Purpose: "...encourages and supports believers who, for religious, political or economic reasons, are unable to worship and witness freely for their faith."

Year Founded in USA 1989
Income for Overseas Mins $70,000

Associate Reformed Presbyterian Church
See: World Witness, the Foreign Mission Board of the Associate Reformed Presbyterian Church

Association of Baptists for World Evangelism
See: ABWE

Association of Free Lutheran Congregations World Missions

(612)545-5631 Fax: (612)545-0079
E-Mail: HQmail@aflc.org
Web: www.aflc.org
3110 E. Medicine Lk. Blvd, Minneapolis, MN 55441
Rev. Eugene Enderlein, Missions Director

A denominational sending agency of Lutheran tradition engaged in church planting, childcare/orphanage programs, theological education, evangelism, medical work and support of national workers.

Year Founded in USA 1963
Income for Overseas Mins $676,302
Fully Supported USA Personnel Overseas:
Expecting to serve more than 4 years 12
Expecting to serve 1 to 4 years 1
Other Personnel:
Non-USA serving in own/other country 52
Short-Term less than 1 year from USA 9
Home ministry & office staff in USA 2
Countries: Brazil 9, Mexico 4

Association of International Mission Services
See: AIMS (Accelerating International Mission Strategies)

Audio Scripture Ministries

(616)396-5291 Fax: (616)396-5294
E-Mail: ASM@audioscriptures.org
760 Waverly Rd., Holland, MI 49423

Mr. Ron Beery, President

A nondenominational specialized agency of evangelical tradition engaged in audio recording/distribution in more than 150 languages. Statistical information from 1996.

Year Founded in USA 1989
Income for Overseas Mins .... NR
Personnel:
Home ministry & office staff in USA 2

Aurora Ministries

(941)746-2572 Fax: (941)748-2625
Web: www.auroraministries.org
P.O. Box 1549, Bradenton, FL 34206
Rev. James E. Pike, Director of Missions

A nondenominational support agency of independent tradition engaged in church planting, Bible distribution, evangelism and literature distribution. Formerly Bible Alliance Mission, Inc.

Year Founded in USA 1978
Income for Overseas Mins $277,600
Fully Supported USA Personnel Overseas:
Expecting to serve more than 4 years 4
Other Personnel:
Non-USA serving in own/other country 6
Home ministry & office staff in USA 2
Countries: Italy 4

Awana Clubs International

(630)213-2000 Fax: (630)213-5986
Web: www.awana.org
One E. Bode Rd., Streamwood, IL 60107-6658
Rev. Jack D. Eggar, President/CEO
Larry Fowler, International Missions Dir.

A nondenominational ministry of evangelical tradition providing Bible-based, Christ-centered weekly club programs and leadership training for local churches around the world. There are 57,000 AWANA clubs worldwide with 200,000 leaders serving 104 countries.

Purpose: "…to reach children and teens with the gospel of Jesus Christ and to train them for Christian service."

Year Founded in USA 1950
Income for Overseas Mins $5,000,000
Fully Supported USA Personnel Overseas:
Expecting to serve more than 4 years 30
Other Personnel:
Non-USA serving in own/other country 140
Home ministry & office staff in USA 425
Countries: Africa 2, Asia 4, Australia 2, Europe 6, Latin America 16

Back to the Bible International

(402)464-7200 Fax: (402)464-7474
E-Mail: info@backtothebible.org
Web: www.backtothebible.org
P.O. Box 82808, Lincoln, NE 68501
Dr. Woodrow Kroll, President

A nondenominational service agency of evangelical tradition engaged in broadcasting, audio recording/distribution, literature production, support of national workers and video/film production and distribution.

Purpose: "To lead believers into spiritual maturity and active service for Christ in the local church and the world. To reach unbelievers with the Gospel of Christ by teaching the Bible through media."

Year Founded in USA 1939
Income for Overseas Mins $1,793,094
Personnel:
Non-USA serving in own/other country 142
Home ministry & office staff in USA 118
Countries: Australia, China, Ecuador, Egypt, India, Italy, Jamaica, Philippines, Poland, Russia, Sri Lanka, UK

BALL World Missions
See: Children of Promise Intl.

Baptist Bible Fellowship Intl.

(417)862-5001 Fax: (417)865-0794
E-Mail: Bobbaird@bbfi-missionoffice.org
Web: http://www.bbfi.org/
P.O. Box 191, Springfield, MO 65801
Dr. Bob Baird, Mission Director

An independent sending agency of Baptist tradition engaged in church planting, theological education, evangelism, support of national churches and missionary training.

Year Founded in USA 1950
Income for Overseas Mins $31,855,155
Fully Supported USA Personnel Overseas:
Expecting to serve more than 4 years 822
Other Personnel:
Home ministry & office staff in USA 68

Countries: Albania 2, Argentina 31, Australia 31, Austria 2, Azores 2, Bahamas 2, Belgium 9, Belize 6, Bolivia 6, Brazil 38, Bulgaria 2, Burkina Faso 2, Cambodia 8, Chile 11, China (PRC) 4, Colombia 4, Congo/Zaire 6, Costa Rica 13, Cote d'Ivoire 2, Croatia 2, Cuba 4, Denmark 2, Dominican Rep 4, Ecuador 12, Ethiopia 8, Fiji 6, France 10, Fr Polynesia 4, Germany 25, Greece 2, Haiti 4, Honduras 3, Hong Kong 7, Hungary 12, Iceland 2, India 4, Indonesia 4, Ireland 5, Jamaica 10, Japan 26, Kenya 44, Korea-S 19, Lebanon 6, Lithuania 4, Malta 2, Mexico 72, Netherlands 2, New Zealand 16, Nicaragua 6, Nigeria 4, Pakistan 4, Panama 10, Papua New Guin 16, Paraguay 4, Peru 11, Philippines 56, Portugal 6, Puerto Rico 5, Romania 16, Russia 18, Singapore 6, S Africa 17, Spain 16, Sri Lanka 4, Taiwan (ROC) 14, Tanzania 15, Thailand 8, Trinidad & Tobg 2, Uganda 2, Ukraine 2, UK 50, Uruguay 2, Vanuatu 2, Venezuela 6, W Samoa 2, Zambia 16

Baptist Faith Missions

(606)223-8374
E-Mail: grace2u@aol.com
3985 Boston Rd., Lexington, KY 40514
Pastor David Parks, Exec. Secretary

A denominational sending agency of Baptist tradition engaged in church planting, camping programs, Christian education and evangelism. Income information from 1992. Personnel information from 1996.

Year Founded in USA 1923
Income for Overseas Mins $535,000
Fully Supported USA Personnel Overseas:
Expecting to serve more than 4 years 20
Expecting to serve 1 to 4 years 2
Countries: Brazil 18, Kenya 2, Peru 2

Baptist General Conference World Missions

(847)228-0200 **Fax: (847)228-5376**
Web: www.bgc.bethel.edu
2002 S. Arlington Hts. Rd, Arlington Hts., IL 60005
Dr. Robert S. Ricker, President

A denominational sending agency of Baptist tradition engaged in church planting, theological education, TEE, leadership development and mobilization for mission.

Purpose: "...helping member churches fulfill Christ's mission for His church in all communities God calls them to serve."

Year Founded in USA 1944
Income for Overseas Mins $7,500,000
Fully Supported USA Personnel Overseas:
Expecting to serve more than 4 years 111
Expecting to serve 1 to 4 years 2
Nonresidential mission personnel 2
Other Personnel:
Non-USA serving in own/other country 1
Home ministry & office staff in USA 7
Countries: Argentina 14, Asia 2, Brazil 8, Bulgaria 1, Cameroon 6, Central Asia 4, Cote d'Ivoire 8, Estonia 2, Ethiopia 8, France 6, Japan 19, Mexico 7, Philippines 20, Thailand 6, Uruguay 2

Baptist International Missions

(423)344-5050 **Fax: (423)344-4774**
E-Mail: INFO@bimi.org
Web: www.bimi.org
P.O. Box 9215, Chattanooga, TN 37412
Dr. Don Sisk, President/Gen. Director

An independent Baptist sending agency of fundamental tradition engaged in church planting, broadcasting, theological education, funds transmission, literature distribution and training.

Purpose: "...to provide logistical assistance to independent Baptist churches and missionaries."

Year Founded in USA 1960
Income for Overseas Mins $26,400,000
Fully Supported USA Personnel Overseas:
Expecting to serve more than 4 years 485
Expecting to serve 1 to 4 years 2
Nonresidential mission personnel 42
Other Personnel:
Short-Term less than 1 year from USA 180
Home ministry & office staff in USA 35
Countries: Africa 11, Albania 1, Argentina 10, Australia 30, Austria 2, Belarus 1, Belgium 1, Bolivia 10, Brazil 43, Cambodia 5, Chile 2, Colombia 2, Costa Rica 14, Cote d'Ivoire 3, Czech Rep 1, Ecuador 8, Fiji 4, Finland 2, France 4, Germany 5, Ghana 2, Guatemala 6, Guyana 4, Honduras 10, Hungary 2, India 6, Indonesia 2, Ireland 6, Italy 1, Japan 35, Kenya 2, Latvia 2, Mexico 63, Moldava 1, Nepal 2, New Caledonia 2, New Zealand 4, Nicaragua 5, Niger 1, Nigeria 3, N Mariana Isls 4, Norway 1, Panama 2, Papua New Guin 17, Peru 14, Philippines 35, Poland 1, Romania 8, Russia 11, Singapore 4, Slovakia 1, S Africa 7, Switzerland 1, Taiwan (ROC) 1, Tanzania

1, Thailand 4, Togo 1, Uganda 7, Ukraine 9, UK 18, Uruguay 2, Venezuela 17, Zambia 3

Baptist International Outreach

(423)992-0999 Fax: (423)992-4999
E-Mail: 75143.3626@compuserve.com
P.O. Box 639, Maynardville, TN 37807
Dr. William R. Vick, President/Director

A sending agency of independent Baptist and fundamental tradition engaged in church planting, disability assistance programs, theological education, evangelism and providing medical supplies.

Year Founded in USA 1985
Income for Overseas Mins $1,150,000
Fully Supported USA Personnel Overseas:
Expecting to serve more than 4 years 31
Expecting to serve 1 to 4 years 5
Other Personnel:
Non-USA serving in own/other country 56
Home ministry & office staff in USA 6
Countries: Belarus 4, Brazil 3, China (PRC) 4, Kenya 2, Mexico 3, Peru 6, Philippines 2, S Africa 8, Zambia 4

Baptist Medical & Dental Mission International

(601)544-3586 Fax: (601)544-6508
E-Mail: operations@bmdmi.org
Web: www.bmdmi.org
P.O. Box 608, Petal, MS 39465-0608
Mr. Dwight Carr, Executive

A specialized agency of Baptist tradition engaged in medical work, childcare/orphanage programs, church construction, church planting, theological education and evangelism.

Purpose: "...to carry the message of salvation through the free grace of Jesus Christ."

Year Founded in USA 1974
Income for Overseas Mins $7,577,434
Gifts-in-Kind $6,001,290
Fully Supported USA Personnel Overseas:
Nonresidential mission personnel 14
Other Personnel:
Non-USA serving in own/other country 59
Home ministry & office staff in USA 7

Baptist Mid-Missions

(440)826-3930 Fax: (440)826-4457
E-Mail: info@bmm.org
Web: www.bmm.org
P.O. Box 308011, Cleveland, OH 44130
Dr. Gary L. Anderson, President

A sending agency of independent Baptist and fundamental tradition engaged in church planting, theological education, literature production, medical work, relief and/or rehabilitation and Bible translation.

Year Founded in USA 1920
Income for Overseas Mins $17,600,000
Fully Supported USA Personnel Overseas:
Expecting to serve more than 4 years 522
Expecting to serve 1 to 4 years 90
Other Personnel:
Non-USA serving in own/other country 10
Home ministry & office staff in USA 449
Countries: Argentina 5, Australia 28, Austria 3, Bangladesh 3, Belarus 2, Botswana 2, Brazil 155, Cambodia 2, Cen Africa Rep 19, Chile 8, Cote d'Ivoire 28, Ecuador 26, Ethiopia 5, Finland 2, France 25, Germany 26, Ghana 21, Guyana 4, Haiti 6, Honduras 9, India 13, Ireland 5, Italy 2, Jamaica 1, Japan 26, Mexico 18, Micronesia 9, Netherlands 6, New Zealand 7, Peru 38, Poland 2, Puerto Rico 6, Romania 2, Russia 7, Slovakia 4, Spain 6, St Vincent 9, Taiwan (ROC) 2, Thailand 3, UK 22, Unspecified 18, Venezuela 7, Zambia 20

Baptist Missionary Association of America

(501)455-4977 Fax: (501)455-3636
P.O. Box 193920, Little Rock, AR 72219
Rev. Don Collins, Exec. Director

A denominational sending agency of Baptist tradition engaged in church planting, Bible distribution, theological education and evangelism. Statistical information from 1992.

Year Founded in USA 1950
Income for Overseas Mins $2,100,000
Fully Supported USA Personnel Overseas:
Expecting to serve more than 4 years 28
Countries: Bolivia 3, Brazil 2, Costa Rica 2, Czech Rep 1, Guatemala 3, Honduras 4, Japan 1, Mexico 5, Philippines 5, Taiwan (ROC) 1, Uruguay 1

Baptist Missions to Forgotten Peoples

(904)783-4007 Fax: (904)783-0402
E-Mail: bmfp@compuserve.com
Web: www.bmfp.org
P.O. Box 37043, Jacksonville, FL 32236-7043
Dr. Gene Burge, President

A nondenominational sending agency of Baptist tradition engaged in church planting and evangelism. Statistical information from 1996.

Purpose: "...to serve the local church by providing a faith-missions ministry committed to strategic church planting...among the unevangelized people groups of the world."

Income for Overseas Mins .... NA
Fully Supported USA Personnel Overseas:
Expecting to serve more than 4 years 44
Countries: Azores 2, Colombia 2, Europe-E 4, Germany 11, Grenada 2, Iceland 2, Italy 2, Mexico 2, Nigeria 2, Philippines 2, Romania 2, Russia 3, S Africa 2, Trinidad & Tobg 2, Ukraine 2, UK 2

Baptist World Mission

(256)353-2221 Fax: (256)353-2266
E-Mail:
office@mail.baptistworldmission.org
Web: www.baptistworldmission.org
P.O. Box 2149, Decatur, AL 35602-2149
Dr. Fred Moritz, Exec. Director

A sending agency of independent Baptist and fundamental tradition engaged in church planting and theological education.

Year Founded in USA 1961
Income for Overseas Mins $6,800,000
Fully Supported USA Personnel Overseas:
Expecting to serve more than 4 years 256
Other Personnel:
Non-USA serving in own/other country 4
Short-Term less than 1 year from USA 15
Home ministry & office staff in USA 23
Countries: Albania 4, Argentina 4, Asia 4, Australia 4, Belarus 4, Benin 5, Brazil 22, Cambodia 8, Cuba 4, France 20, Germany 13, Ghana 2, Haiti 2, Hong Kong 2, Hungary 4, Ireland 20, Italy 6, Japan 16, Kenya 5, Korea-S 2, Mexico 12, Myanmar/Burma 2, Netherlands 2, New Zealand 15, Papua New Guin 2, Peru 2, Philippines 4, Poland 1, Portugal 2, Puerto Rico 3, Romania 8, Russia 13, Singapore 2, S Africa 7, Spain 9, Thailand 2, UK 10, Uruguay 9

Barnabas International

(815)395-1335 Fax: (815)395-1385
E-Mail: Barnabas@barnabas.org
Web: www.barnabas.org
P.O. Box 11211, Rockford, IL 61126
Dr. Lareau Lindquist, Exec. Director

An interdenominational support agency of evangelical tradition engaged in member care, leadership development, support of national churches and psychological counseling.

Purpose: "...to edify, enrich, encourage, and strengthen missionaries, pastors, national church leaders and their families...through personal, small group and conference ministries."

Year Founded in USA 1986
Income for Overseas Mins $604,673
Fully Supported USA Personnel Overseas:
Nonresidential mission personnel 22
Other Personnel:
Home ministry & office staff in USA 1

Barnabas Ministries, Inc.

(520)466-6600
E-Mail: LANSON@casagrande.com
P.O. Box 1354, Arizona City, AZ 85223-1354
Mr. Lanson C. Ross, President

An interdenominational support agency of Baptist and independent tradition engaged in Christian education, childcare/orphanage programs, evangelism, providing medical supplies and support of national workers.

Year Founded in USA 1993
Income for Overseas Mins $19,735
Personnel:
Non-USA serving in own/other country 16
Home ministry & office staff in USA 4

BCM International

(610)352-7177 Fax: (610)352-5561
E-Mail: bcmintl@csi.com
237 Fairfield Ave., Upper Darby, PA 19082-2299
Rev. Robert T. Evans, President

An interdenominational sending agency of independent tradition engaged in children's programs, camping programs, church planting, correspondence courses, evangelism and training.

Purpose: "...making disciples of all age groups...so that churches may be strengthened and/or established."

Year Founded in USA 1936
Income for Overseas Mins $4,912,843
Fully Supported USA Personnel Overseas:
Expecting to serve more than 4 years 31
Other Personnel:
Non-USA serving in own/other country 157
Short-Term less than 1 year from USA 8
Home ministry & office staff in USA 36

Countries: Austria 1, Belize, Brazil, Cuba 1, Dominican Rep., Finland, France 2, Germany 3, Ghana, Greece, Guyana, Hungary, India, Ireland 2, Italy 6, Jamaica, Mexico, Nepal, Netherlands 1, Peru, Philippines, Portugal, Russia 1, Spain 2, Sri Lanka 2, St Lucia, St Vincent, Suriname 1, Tanzania 1, Trinidad & Tobg, Ukraine 2, UK 5, Zimbabwe 1

Berean Mission, Inc.

(314)773-0110 Fax: (314)773-7062
E-Mail: berean@compuserve.com
Web: www.bereanmission.org
3536 Russell Blvd., St. Louis, MO 63104
Dr. Kenneth A. Epp, Gen. Director

A nondenominational sending agency of fundamental and independent tradition engaged in church planting, camping programs, theological education, evangelism, mobilization for mission and short-term programs. Merged with UFM International in June, 2000.

Purpose: "...presenting the Gospel of Jesus Christ to non-Christian and spiritually neglected peoples both in the United States and abroad."

Year Founded in USA 1937
Income for Overseas Mins $1,005,773
Fully Supported USA Personnel Overseas:
Expecting to serve more than 4 years 46
Other Personnel:
Non-USA serving in own/other country 4
Short-Term less than 1 year from USA 72
Home ministry & office staff in USA 16

Countries: Brazil 9, Congo/Zaire 9, Dominica 1, Ecuador 19, Grenada 2, Philippines 2, UK 4

Bethany Fellowship Missions

(952)829-2492 Fax: (952)829-2767
E-Mail: BFM@bethfel.org
Web: www.bethfel.org
6820 Auto Club Rd., Suite D, Bloomington, MN 55438
Rev. Tim Freeman, Director

An interdenominational sending agency of evangelical tradition engaged in missionary training, church planting, theological education, evangelism, leadership development and literature production.

Purpose: "...to witness, to train and send missionaries, to plant churches, to publish Christian literature, and to establish creative resource ventures for the expansion of Christ's Kingdom."

Year Founded in USA 1963
Income for Overseas Mins $1,302,466
Fully Supported USA Personnel Overseas:
Expecting to serve more than 4 years 75
Expecting to serve 1 to 4 years 4
Other Personnel:
Non-USA serving in own/other country 14
Bivocational/Tentmaker from USA 2
Short-Term less than 1 year from USA 5
Home ministry & office staff in USA 14

Countries: Africa 2, Albania 3, Asia 9, Brazil 22, Dominican Rep 2, France 4, Ghana 2, Indonesia 3, Japan 3, Mexico 15, Paraguay 2, Philippines 6, Slovenia 4, Thailand 2

Bethany Missionary Association

(562)433-5771 Fax: (562)433-1462
2209 E. 6th St., Long Beach, CA 90814
Pastor David Copp, Director

An interdenominational sending agency of independent tradition engaged in Christian education and missionary training. Statistical information from 1992.

Year Founded in USA 1953
Income for Overseas Mins $72,000
Fully Supported USA Personnel Overseas:
Expecting to serve more than 4 years 9
Other Personnel:
Short-Term less than 1 year from USA 2
Home ministry & office staff in USA 5

Countries: Denmark 1, Japan 4, Mexico 4

Bethel Christian Ministries

(206)441-0444 Fax: (206)441-5995
E-Mail: bethelministry@w-link.net
2033 Second Ave., Seattle, WA 98121
Rev. Daniel W. Peterson, Senior Pastor

A nondenominational sending agency of Pentecostal and charismatic tradition engaged in church planting, Bible distribution and evangelism. Previously known as Bethel Pentecostal Temple.

Year Founded in USA 1914
Income for Overseas Mins $70,000
Fully Supported USA Personnel Overseas:
Expecting to serve more than 4 years 8
Expecting to serve 1 to 4 years 2
Other Personnel:
Short-Term less than 1 year from USA 2
Countries: Indonesia 2, Japan 6, Mexico 2

Bethel Pentecostal Temple
See: Bethel Christian Ministries

Bezalel World Outreach
See: Galcom International (U.S.)

Bible Alliance Mission, Inc.
See: Aurora Ministries

Bible League, The
(708)331-2094 **Fax: (708)331-7172**
E-Mail: BibleLeague@xc.org
Web: www.bibleleague.org
16801 Van Dam Rd., South Holland, IL 60473
Rev. Dennis M. Mulder, President

An interdenominational specialized agency of evangelical tradition engaged in Bible distribution, church planting, evangelism, leadership development, support of national churches and support of national workers.

Purpose: "...provides Scriptures and training worldwide to bring people into fellowship with Christ and His Church."

Year Founded in USA 1938
Income for Overseas Mins $19,880,121
Gifts-in-Kind $1,153,292
Fully Supported USA Personnel Overseas:
Nonresidential mission personnel 11
Other Personnel:
Non-USA serving in own/other country 289
Home ministry & office staff in USA 101
Countries: Albania, Armenia, Belarus, Bulgaria, Cambodia, Cameroon, China, Colombia, Dominican Rep., Egypt, Ethiopia, Ghana, India, Indonesia, Kazakhstan, Kenya, Kyrgyzstan, Laos, Liberia, Mexico, Moldava, Mozambique, Myanmar, Nigeria, Philippines, Romania, Russia, S Africa, Sudan, Taiwan, Tajikistan, Thailand, Ukraine, Venezuela, Vietnam, Zimbabwe

Bible Literature International
(614)267-3116 **Fax: (614)267-7110**
E-Mail: BLI@bli.org
Web: www.bli.org
P.O. Box 477, Columbus, OH 43216-0477
Mr. James R. Falkenberg, Intl. President

An interdenominational specialized agency of evangelical tradition engaged in literature/ Bible distribution, TEE, evangelism and funds transmission.

Purpose: "...to help individuals around the world find new life in Christ through God's Word..."

Year Founded in USA 1923
Income for Overseas Mins $1,736,233
Personnel:
Home ministry & office staff in USA 21

Bible Missionary Church
(208)337-3873 **Fax: (208)337-3860**
P.O. Box 2030, Homedale, ID 83628
Rev. Don Bowman, Gen. Foreign Missions Secretary

A denominational sending agency of Wesleyan tradition engaged in church planting, theological education, furloughed missionary support and support of national churches and workers. Statistical information from 1996.

Year Founded in USA 1956
Income for Overseas Mins $500,000
Fully Supported USA Personnel Overseas:
Expecting to serve more than 4 years 32
Countries: Germany 2, Ghana 2, Guyana 4, Japan 2, Mexico 2, Nigeria 2, Papua New Guin 8, Peru 2, Philippines 2, Russia 4, Venezuela 2

Bibles For The World, Inc.
(719)630-7733 **Fax: (719)630-1449**
E-Mail: JLPudaite@yahoo.com
P.O. Box 470, Colorado Springs, CO 80901
Dr. Rochunga Pudaite, President

A nondenominational support agency of evangelical tradition engaged in Bible distribution, childcare/orphanage programs,

Christian education, theological education, support of national churches and support of national workers.

Year Founded in USA 1972
Income for Overseas Mins $567,495
Gifts-in-Kind $271,270
Personnel:
- Non-USA serving in own/other country 400
- Short-Term less than 1 year from USA 16
- Home ministry & office staff in USA 18

Countries: India

Biblical Literature Fellowship

(630)858-0348 **Fax: (630)858-1946**
E-Mail: blfus@aol.com
P.O. Box 629, Wheaton, IL 60189-0629
Mr. Harry R. Enns, Exec. Director

A nondenominational specialized agency of evangelical tradition engaged in literature/ Bible distribution, funds transmission, furloughed missionary support, services for other agencies and short-term programs. Not included in personnel are 120 people who participated in mission trips of 11 days each.

Purpose: "...publishing and distributing quality Christian literature for evangelism, church planting and Christian growth."

Year Founded in USA 1958
Income for Overseas Mins $800,056
Fully Supported USA Personnel Overseas:
- Expecting to serve more than 4 years 10
- Expecting to serve 1 to 4 years 1

Other Personnel:
- Non-USA serving in own/other country 1
- Short-Term less than 1 year from USA 2
- Home ministry & office staff in USA 5

Countries: Belgium 11

Biblical Ministries Worldwide

(770)339-3500 **Fax: (770)513-1254**
E-Mail: 75534.546@compuserve.com
Web: www.biblicalministries.org
1595 Herrington Rd., Lawrenceville, GA 30043-5616
Rev. Paul G. Seger, Gen. Director

A nondenominational sending agency of independent and Baptist tradition engaged in church planting, theological education and evangelism.

Purpose: "...to evangelize and develop leaders who will reproduce themselves and the churches we serve."

Year Founded in USA 1948
Income for Overseas Mins $5,000,000
Fully Supported USA Personnel Overseas:
- Expecting to serve more than 4 years 125
- Nonresidential mission personnel 4

Other Personnel:
- Non-USA serving in own/other country 26
- Bivocational/Tentmaker from USA 8
- Short-Term less than 1 year from USA 22
- Home ministry & office staff in USA 19

Countries: Argentina 3, Australia 2, Austria 2, Cyprus 4, Fiji 4, France 2, Germany 7, Guam 4, Honduras 4, Hong Kong 5, Ireland 5, Italy 8, Japan 2, Luxembourg 2, Mexico 11, Netherlands 2, New Zealand 11, Puerto Rico 2, S Africa 9, Spain 5, UK 19, Uruguay 12

Big World Ventures Inc.

(800)599-8778 **Fax: (918)481-5257**
E-Mail: venture@bigworld.org
Web: www.bigworld.org
P.O. Box 703203, Tulsa, OK 74170-3203
Mr. Steve Goley, President

An interdenominational support agency of charismatic tradition engaged in youth programs, evangelism, leadership development, short-term programs and technical assistance. Statistical information from 1996.

Year Founded in USA 1994
Income for Overseas Mins $358,000
Personnel:
- Short-Term less than 1 year from USA 224

BILD International

(515)292-7012 **Fax: (515)292-1933**
E-Mail: info@bild.org
Web: www.bild.org
P.O. Box 1507, Ames, IA 50014-1507
Mr. Jeff Reed, Director of Ministry & Training

A transdenominational support agency of evangelical tradition engaged in leadership development for establishing churches, literature production, support of national churches and missionary training.

Year Founded in USA 1986
Income for Overseas Mins $1,450,000

Personnel:
Non-USA serving in own/other country 5
Home ministry & office staff in USA 4
Countries: Guatemala, India, Nigeria

Billy Graham Center, The

(630)752-5157 Fax: (630)752-5916
E-Mail: BGCadm@wheaton.edu
Web: www.wheaton.edu/bgc/bgc.html
500 College Ave., Wheaton, IL 60187
Dr. Lon Allison, Director
A transdenominational service agency of evangelical tradition engaged in training, missions information service, leadership development, evangelism strategy and mission-related research.
Purpose: "...to develop strategies and skills for evangelism...through leadership training, research, networking, strategic planning and communicating the gospel."
Year Founded in USA 1975
Income for Overseas Mins .... NA
Personnel:
Home ministry & office staff in USA 29

Blessings International

(918)250-8101 Fax: (918)250-1281
E-Mail: BlessingsInt@compuserve.com
Web: www.blessing.org
5881 S. Garnett St., Tulsa, OK 74146
Dr. Harold C. Harder, President
A nondenominational support agency of charismatic tradition engaged in shipping pharmaceutical and medical supplies to 125 countries.
Year Founded in USA 1981
Income for Overseas Mins $12,375,826
Gifts-in-Kind $12,188,510
Personnel:
Home ministry & office staff in USA 4

Blossoming Rose

(616)696-3435 Fax: (616)696-8280
E-Mail: blossomrose@juno.com
Web: www.blossomingrose.org
360 W. Pine St., Cedar Springs, MI 49319
Dr. DeWayne Coxon, President
A nondenominational service agency of evangelical tradition engaged in short-term programs. Statistical information from 1996.
Purpose: "...sponsoring projects in Israel which encourage peace, are restorative in nature..."
Year Founded in USA 1984
Income for Overseas Mins $150,000
Personnel:
Short-Term less than 1 year from USA 60

Brazil Gospel Fellowship Mission

(217)523-7176 Fax: (217)523-7186
E-Mail: bgfm@fgi.net
121 N. Glenwood, Springfield, IL 62702-4821
Rev. Larry Lipka, Exec. Director
An independent sending agency of fundamental tradition engaged in church planting, camping programs, theological education, evangelism and video/film production and distribution.
Year Founded in USA 1939
Income for Overseas Mins $837,914
Fully Supported USA Personnel Overseas:
Expecting to serve more than 4 years 64
Other Personnel:
Short-Term less than 1 year from USA 6
Home ministry & office staff in USA 4
Countries: Brazil 64

Bread for the World

(202)639-9400 Fax: (202)639-9401
E-Mail: bread@bread.org
Web: www.bread.org
50 F St. NW, #500, Washington, DC 20001-1530
Rev. David Beckmann, President
An interdenominational Christian citizen's movement of many traditions helping citizens be active in public-policy issues important to the reduction of hunger.
Purpose: "...seeking justice for the world's hungry people by lobbying our nation's decision makers."
Year Founded in USA 1974
Income for Overseas Mins .... NA

Brethren Assemblies

(No central office)
The Brethren Assemblies are also known as "Christian Brethren" or "Plymouth Brethren". Missionaries are sent from each local

assembly (church) and not through a central agency. Personnel totals are from the Christian Missions in Many Lands service agency.

Income for Overseas Mins .... NA

Fully Supported USA Personnel Overseas:

Expecting to serve more than 4 years 346

Expecting to serve 1 to 4 years 24

Nonresidential mission personnel 7

Other Personnel:

Non-USA serving in own/other country 30

Bivocational/Tentmaker from USA 2

Countries: Albania 6, Argentina 8, Austria 6, Bolivia 17, Brazil 7, Burundi 4, Caribbean Isls 3, Chad 1, Chile 1, Colombia 19, Congo 8, Dominican Rep 2, Ecuador 14, El Salvador 6, France 15, French Guiana 2, Germany 3, Greece 3, Guatemala 4, Honduras 10, Hong Kong 2, Hungary 1, India 7, Indonesia 3, Ireland 11, Italy 5, Japan 8, Kenya 1, Korea-S 1, Mexico 36, Mozambique 2, Netherlands 2, Nigeria 6, Papua New Guin 5, Paraguay 12, Peru 17, Philippines 14, Poland 4, Portugal 4, Puerto Rico 1, Romania 6, Russia 11, Senegal 3, S Africa 10, Spain 9, Taiwan (ROC) 2, Tanzania 2, Uganda 2, Unspecified 21, Uruguay 1, Venezuela 1, Zambia 20, Zimbabwe 1

Brethren Church Missionary Bd.

(419)289-1708 **Fax: (419)281-0450**

E-Mail: BrethrenCh@aol.com

524 College Ave., Ashland, OH 44805

Rev. Reilly R. Smith, Exec. Director

A denominational sending agency of Brethren tradition engaged in evangelism, childcare programs, church planting, leadership development, medical work, and support of national churches. Statistical information from 1996.

Year Founded in USA 1892

Income for Overseas Mins $636,752

Fully Supported USA Personnel Overseas:

Expecting to serve more than 4 years 3

Other Personnel:

Non-USA serving in own/other country 4

Home ministry & office staff in USA 4

Countries: Argentina 1, India, Mexico 2, Malaysia

Brethren in Christ World Missions

(717)697-2634 **Fax: (717)691-6053**

E-Mail: BICWM@messiah.edu

Web: www.bic-church.org/wm

P.O. Box 390, Grantham, PA 17027-0390

Rev. John Brubaker, Exec. Director

A denominational sending agency of Wesleyan tradition engaged in church planting, church construction, TEE, evangelism, leadership development and support of national churches.

Year Founded in USA 1895

Income for Overseas Mins $2,005,646

Fully Supported USA Personnel Overseas:

Expecting to serve more than 4 years 19

Expecting to serve 1 to 4 years 25

Other Personnel:

Non-USA serving in own/other country 134

Short-Term less than 1 year from USA 16

Home ministry & office staff in USA 9

Countries: Colombia 4, Honduras 2, Malawi 2, Mexico 4, Nicaragua 2, Spain 2, UK 2, Venezuela 8, Zambia 5, Zimbabwe 13

Bridge Builders International

(541)929-5627 **Fax: (541)929-5628**

E-Mail: chuck@bridgebuildersint.com

Web: www.bridgebuildersint.com

P.O. Box 625, Philomath, OR 97370

Mr. Charles D. Kelley, President

A transdenominational mobilization agency of evangelical tradition specializing in facilitating international partnerships for ministry and mission training.

Purpose: "...builds partnerships for effective ministry, mission, development and assistance [and] cultivates relationships that lead to strategic partnerships..."

Year Founded in USA 1994

Income for Overseas Mins .... NR

Gifts-in-Kind $45,000

Fully Supported USA Personnel Overseas:

Nonresidential mission personnel 2

Other Personnel:

Non-USA serving in own/other country 2

Short-Term less than 1 year from USA 80

Home ministry & office staff in USA 6

Bright Hope International

(847)526-5566 Fax: (847)526-0073
E-Mail: BrightHope@compuserve.com
Web: www.brighthope.org
1000 Brown Street #207, Wauconda, IL 60084
Mr. Craig H. Dyer, President

A nondenominational service agency of evangelical tradition engaged in development, Bible distribution, relief and/or rehabilitation and support of national workers in 39 countries.

Year Founded in USA 1968
Income for Overseas Mins $497,480
Personnel:
Home ministry & office staff in USA 6

Cadence International

(303)762-1400 Fax: (303)788-0661
E-Mail: hdqtrs@cadence.org
Web: www.cadence.org
P.O. Box 1268, Englewood, CO 80150
Mr. David Schroeder, Gen. Director

An interdenominational service agency of evangelical tradition engaged in evangelism and youth programs to U.S. and foreign military communities.

Year Founded in USA 1954
Income for Overseas Mins $2,559,477
Gifts-in-Kind $17,460
Fully Supported USA Personnel Overseas:
Expecting to serve more than 4 years 22
Expecting to serve 1 to 4 years 41
Other Personnel:
Non-USA serving in own/other country 32
Short-Term less than 1 year from USA 12
Home ministry & office staff in USA 10
Countries: Germany 37, Italy 4, Japan 14, Korea-S 3, Panama 2, Philippines 2, Spain 1

Caleb Project

(303)730-4170 Fax: (303)730-4177
E-Mail: info@cproject.com
Web: www.calebproject.org
#10 W. Dry Creek Circle, Littleton, CO 80120-4413
Mr. Gregory E. Fritz, President

An interdenominational service agency of evangelical tradition engaged in mobilization for mission, services for other agencies, short-term programs, missionary training and video/film production and distribution.

Purpose: "...serves churches, mission agencies and campus ministries throughout the United States by educating, assisting and challenging them to complete their part in the goal of evangelizing the people groups of the world."

Year Founded in USA 1980
Income for Overseas Mins $150,631
Gifts-in-Kind $10,340
Fully Supported USA Personnel Overseas:
Expecting to serve more than 4 years 6
Nonresidential mission personnel 7
Other Personnel:
Home ministry & office staff in USA 28
Countries: Central Asia 6

Calvary Commission, Inc.

(903)882-5501 Fax: (903)882-7282
E-Mail: calcom@lakecountry.net
Web: www.calvarycommission.org
P.O. Box 100, Lindale, TX 75771
Rev. Joe L. Fauss, Intl. Director

An interdenominational sending agency of Pentecostal and charismatic tradition engaged in church planting, camping programs, childcare/orphanage programs, relief and/or rehabilitation, short-term programs and youth programs.

Year Founded in USA 1977
Income for Overseas Mins $300,000
Gifts-in-Kind $100,000
Fully Supported USA Personnel Overseas:
Expecting to serve more than 4 years 19
Expecting to serve 1 to 4 years 20
Nonresidential mission personnel 4
Other Personnel:
Non-USA serving in own/other country 64
Bivocational/Tentmaker from USA 5
Short-Term less than 1 year from USA 250
Home ministry & office staff in USA 49
Countries: Belize 2, Mexico 25, Romania 12

Calvary Evangelistic Mission (WIVV & WBMJ Radio)

(787)724-2727 Fax: (787)723-9633
P.O. Box 367000, San Juan, PR 00936-7000
Mrs. Ruth Luttrell, Co-Founder/President

An interdenominational specialized agency of evangelical tradition engaged in broadcasting, Bible distribution, correspondence courses, evangelism, literature distribution and services for other agencies.

Purpose: "...winning, challenging, training and motivating people to work for Jesus..."

Year Founded in USA 1953

Income for Overseas Mins $1,173,474

Gifts-in-Kind $76,379

Fully Supported USA Personnel Overseas:

Expecting to serve more than 4 years 4

Expecting to serve 1 to 4 years 6

Other Personnel:

Non-USA serving in own/other country 2

Bivocational/Tentmaker from USA 2

Short-Term less than 1 year from USA 85

Countries: Caribbean Isls 10

Calvary International

(904)398-6559 Fax: (904)398-6840

E-Mail: min.usoffice@calvary-international.org

Web: www.calvary-international.org

P.O. Box 10305, Jacksonville, FL 32247

Mr. Jerry L. Williamson, President

A transdenominational sending agency of charismatic tradition engaged in leadership training, evangelism, social ministry, church planting/development and missions mobilization.

Purpose: "...to strategically reach the unreached peoples of the world through an international missionary force to help bring closure to the Great Commission."

Year Founded in USA 1981

Income for Overseas Mins $2,264,000

Fully Supported USA Personnel Overseas:

Expecting to serve more than 4 years 104

Nonresidential mission personnel 45

Other Personnel:

Non-USA serving in own/other country 51

Short-Term less than 1 year from USA 100

Home ministry & office staff in USA 25

Countries: Africa 4, Costa Rica 7, Czech Rep 2, Guatemala 27, Jamaica 2, Japan 1, Jordan 2, Latvia 6, Mexico 14, Nepal 2, Philippines 17, Russia 15, Ukraine 2, UK 2, Venezuela 1

CAM International

(214)327-8206 Fax: (214)327-8201

E-Mail: CAM@caminternational.org

Web: www.caminternational.org

8625 La Prada Dr., Dallas, TX 75228

Mr. Daniel Wicher, President

A nondenominational sending agency of evangelical tradition engaged in church planting, broadcasting, Christian education, theological education, evangelism and support of national churches.

Purpose: "...to produce and empower committed followers of Jesus Christ in Spanish speaking areas to reach the world."

Year Founded in USA 1890

Income for Overseas Mins $5,313,538

Fully Supported USA Personnel Overseas:

Expecting to serve more than 4 years 169

Expecting to serve 1 to 4 years 22

Nonresidential mission personnel 2

Other Personnel:

Non-USA serving in own/other country 25

Short-Term less than 1 year from USA 150

Home ministry & office staff in USA 25

Countries: Albania 1, Costa Rica 17, El Salvador 7, Guatemala 53, Honduras 14, Mexico 60, Nicaragua 4, Panama 7, Spain 16, Unspecified 12

Campus Crusade for Christ, Intl.

(407)826-2000 Fax: (407)826-2851

E-Mail: postmaster@ccci.org

Web: www.ccci.org

100 Lake Hart Drive, Orlando, FL 32832-0100

Dr. William R. Bright, Founder/President

Stephen B. Douglass, Pres. & CEO Elect

An interdenominational sending agency of evangelical tradition engaged in evangelism, Christian education, support of national workers, training and small group discipleship. Includes the JESUS Film Project and other overseas ministries.

Year Founded in USA 1951

Income for Overseas Mins $65,739,000

Fully Supported USA Personnel Overseas:

Expecting to serve more than 4 years 553

Expecting to serve 1 to 4 years 420

Other Personnel:

Non-USA serving in own/other country .. 9265

Short-Term less than 1 year from USA 3499

Home ministry & office staff in USA 6205

Countries: Africa 15, Albania 9, Argentina 10, Asia 267, Australia 5, Austria 3, Belarus 11, Brazil 11, Bulgaria 12, Burkina Faso 2, Central Asia 15, Costa Rica 3, Croatia 17, Czech Rep 9, Djibouti 3, Egypt 5, Estonia 5, France 42, Germany 33, Greece 5, Guatemala 3, Hungary 75, India 2, Indonesia 2, Italy 6, Japan 22, Kenya 23, Latvia 19, Lesotho 2, Lithuania 9, Macedonia 2, Malawi 2, Malaysia 2, Mexico 24, Netherlands 4, New Zealand 8, Nigeria 6, Philippines 28, Poland 14, Romania 17, Russia 66, Senegal 1, Singapore 16, Slovakia 14, Slovenia 11, S Africa 6, Spain 36, Thailand 6, Ukraine 26, UK 18, Venezuela 7, Yugoslavia 2, Zimbabwe 12

Caring Partners International, Inc.

(513)727-1400 Fax: (513)727-1401
E-Mail: Roy@caringpartners.com
Web: www.caringpartners.com
P.O. Box 44707, Middletown, OH 45044-0707
Mr. Roy W. Cline, President & CEO

A transdenominational specialized agency of evangelical tradition engaged in providing medical supplies, medical work and short-term programs. Medical supplies and equipment with an estimated value of $600,000 sent overseas in 1998.

Purpose: "...to help change lives of people around the world while serving their medical needs with treatment, training and materials."

Year Founded in USA 1975
Income for Overseas Mins $138,000
Personnel:
Short-Term less than 1 year from USA 45
Home ministry & office staff in USA 4

Carpenter's Tools International

(320)235-0155 Fax: (320)235-0185
E-Mail: dlanning@carpenterstools.org
Web: www.carpenterstools.org
P.O. Box 100, Willmar, MN 56201-0100
Mr. David Lien, President

An interdenominational support agency of evangelical and ecumenical tradition engaged in youth concerts and evangelism in developing and other countries. An associate ministry of Youth for Christ International.

Year Founded in USA 1988
Income for Overseas Mins $300,000
Personnel:
Short-Term less than 1 year from USA 51
Home ministry & office staff in USA 9

Carver International Missions, Inc.

(770)484-0610 Fax: (770)484-0615
E-Mail: carverfm@aol.com
Morris Brown Sta., Box 92091, Atlanta, GA 30314
Rev. Glenn Mason, Director

A nondenominational missionary agency of Baptist and evangelical tradition specializing in training and deploying national disciples to biblically analyze, attack, and resolve issues in their homes, communities, churches, and workplaces.

Year Founded in USA 1955
Income for Overseas Mins $150,000
Fully Supported USA Personnel Overseas:
Nonresidential mission personnel 4
Other Personnel:
Short-Term less than 1 year from USA 10
Home ministry & office staff in USA 2

CBInternational

(720)283-2000 Fax: (720)283-9383
E-Mail: CBI@cbi.org
Web: www.cbi.org
1501 W. Mineral Ave., Littleton, CO 80120
Dr. Hans Finzel, Exec. Director

A denominational sending agency of Baptist tradition engaged in church planting, development, theological education, TEE, evangelism, leadership development, literature distribution and medical work.

Purpose: "In vital partnership with churches at home and abroad…[to] be a pioneering force in fulfilling Christ's commission."

Year Founded in USA 1943
Income for Overseas Mins $18,955,637
Fully Supported USA Personnel Overseas:
Expecting to serve more than 4 years 480
Expecting to serve 1 to 4 years 70
Other Personnel:
Bivocational/Tentmaker from USA 4
Short-Term less than 1 year from USA 70
Home ministry & office staff in USA 82

Countries: Africa 16, Albania 2, Argentina 13, Asia 17, Austria 13, Belgium 10, Brazil 31, Central Asia 7,

Congo/Zaire 4, Cote d'Ivoire 64, Czech Rep 4, France 20, Hong Kong 9, Hungary 11, India 12, Indonesia 11, Ireland 5, Italy 18, Japan 22, Jordan 10, Kenya 18, Korea-S 2, Lebanon 2, Lithuania 3, Macao 10, Madagascar 12, Mongolia 1, Netherlands 3, Pakistan 10, Philippines 49, Poland 15, Portugal 6, Romania 12, Russia 13, Rwanda 6, Senegal 10, Singapore 2, Slovenia 5, Spain 11, Taiwan (ROC) 14, Uganda 14, Ukraine 12, UK 4, Uruguay 2, Venezuela 13, Zambia 2

Cedar Lane Missionary Homes

(856)783-6525 Fax: (856)783-8538
E-Mail: Cedarlane@juno.com
Web: www.furloughhomes.org
103 Cedar Lane, Laurel Springs, NJ 08021
Rev. James Callahan, Director

A nondenominational support agency of Baptist and evangelical tradition engaged in furloughed missionary support.

Purpose: "...providing restful homes and otherwise assisting missionaries on furlough."

Year Founded in USA 1949
Income for Overseas Mins .... NA
Personnel:
Home ministry & office staff in USA 4

CEIFA Ministries International

(618)377-0579
E-Mail: CEIFA@aol.com
729 Albers Lane, Bethalto, IL 62010-1120
Rev. David W. Runyan, President

An interdenominational service agency of evangelical tradition engaged in literature distribution, childcare/orphanage programs, TEE, evangelism, leadership development and literature production.

Purpose: "To proclaim and demonstrate, through word and deed, the gospel of Jesus Christ in neglected world areas in cooperation with the Church."

Year Founded in USA 1991
Income for Overseas Mins $120,000
Gifts-in-Kind $50,000
Fully Supported USA Personnel Overseas:
Nonresidential mission personnel 3
Other Personnel:
Bivocational/Tentmaker from USA 3
Short-Term less than 1 year from USA 60
Home ministry & office staff in USA 3

Celebrant Singers

(559)740-4000 Fax: (559)740-4040
E-Mail: celebrants@celebrants.com
Web: www.celebrants.com
P.O. Box 1416, Visalia, CA 93279
Mr. Jon F. Stemkoski, President

An interdenominational service agency of ecumenical tradition engaged in evangelism, audio recording/distribution, short-term programs and video/film production and distribution. Statistical information from 1996.

Year Founded in USA 1977
Income for Overseas Mins $1,200,000
Fully Supported USA Personnel Overseas:
Nonresidential mission personnel 8
Other Personnel:
Short-Term less than 1 year from USA 175
Home ministry & office staff in USA 32

Central Missionary Fellowship

(703)698-5705 Fax: (703)698-0692
E-Mail: cmfusa@compuserve.com
Web: www.cmfusa.org
2601 Bowling Green Dr., Vienna, VA 22180
Mr. Simon Chung, Exec. Director

An interdenominational sending agency of Presbyterian tradition engaged in church planting, leadership development, providing medical supplies, support of national churches, mobilization for mission and missionary training.

Year Founded in USA 1990
Income for Overseas Mins $682,000
Gifts-in-Kind $440,000
Fully Supported USA Personnel Overseas:
Expecting to serve more than 4 years 9
Expecting to serve 1 to 4 years 5
Nonresidential mission personnel 12
Other Personnel:
Bivocational/Tentmaker from USA 2
Short-Term less than 1 year from USA 68
Home ministry & office staff in USA 4

Countries: Argentina 1, Brazil 2, Chad 1, China (PRC) 2, Kenya 1, Mexico 3, Thailand 1, Uzbekistan 3

Central Yearly Meeting of Friends Missions

(317)896-5082

P.O. Box 542, Westfield, IN 46074
Rev. Joseph A. Enyart, President

A denominational sending agency of Friends tradition engaged in church planting, Bible distribution and evangelism. Statistical information from 1996.

Year Founded in USA 1925
Income for Overseas Mins $28,899
Fully Supported USA Personnel Overseas:
Expecting to serve more than 4 years 5
Expecting to serve 1 to 4 years 2
Other Personnel:
Short-Term less than 1 year from USA 17
Countries: Bolivia 7

Child Evangelism Fellowship Inc.

(636)456-4321 Fax: (636)456-5000
E-Mail: overseas@cefinc.org
Web: www.cefinc.org
P.O. Box 348, Warrenton, MO 63383
Mr. Reese R. Kauffman, President

An interdenominational sending agency of evangelical tradition engaged in evangelism, camping programs, support of national workers and training.

Purpose: "...to evangelize boys and girls...and establish them in the Word of God and the local church..."

Year Founded in USA 1937
Income for Overseas Mins $4,371,412
Fully Supported USA Personnel Overseas:
Expecting to serve more than 4 years 72
Expecting to serve 1 to 4 years 1
Nonresidential mission personnel 14
Other Personnel:
Non-USA serving in own/other country 169
Bivocational/Tentmaker from USA 2
Short-Term less than 1 year from USA 55
Home ministry & office staff in USA 913
Countries: Albania 1, Argentina, Australia 2, Austria 1, Belgium 2, Belize 2, Botswana 1, Brazil 2, Burkina Faso, Burundi, Cameroon, Chad, Colombia, Congo, Cote d'Ivoire, Croatia 2, Cuba, Cyprus 8, Czech Rep 1, Denmark 3, Ecuador, El Salvador, Fiji 3, France 2, Gambia 2, Germany 3, Ghana, Greece 2, Guatemala, Haiti 2, Honduras 1, Hong Kong 1, Hungary 1, Ireland 1, Israel 2, Italy, Japan, Kenya 6, Liberia, Malawi, Mali, Mexico 1, Micronesia 2, Mozambique, Namibia 2, Neth Antilles 2, Niger, Nigeria, Pakistan, Papua New Guin, Philippines, Poland, Portugal, Russia 2, Senegal, Sierra Leone, Singapore, Slovenia, Solomon Islands, S Africa 2, Suriname, Switzerland 5, Taiwan (ROC) 2, Thailand, Togo, Tonga, Uganda, UK 2, Yugoslavia 2, Zambia, Zimbabwe

Childcare International

(360)647-2283 Fax: (360)647-2392
E-Mail: CCIbham@aol.com
P.O. Box W, Bellingham, WA 98227-1582
Dr. Max Lange, President

A nondenominational service agency of Baptist tradition engaged in childcare/orphanage programs, church planting, relief and/or rehabilitation, short-term programs and training. Statistical information from 1996.

Year Founded in USA 1981
Income for Overseas Mins $10,000,000
Personnel:
Non-USA serving in own/other country 144
Short-Term less than 1 year from USA 100
Home ministry & office staff in USA 12
Countries: Belarus, Haiti, India, Kenya, Mexico, Peru, Philippines, Sri Lanka, Uganda

Children of India Foundation

(401)596-0846 Fax: (860)599-3626
E-Mail: jlrunge@smet.net
P.O. Box 354, Westerly, RI 02891-0354
Dr. Janna L. Runge, Exec. Director

A nondenominational support agency of Pentecostal tradition engaged in childcare programs, funds transmission and providing medical supplies. Statistical information from 1992.

Year Founded in USA 1977
Income for Overseas Mins $19,540
Personnel:
Non-USA serving in own/other country 2

Children of Promise International

(660)674-2262 Fax: (660)674-2755
E-Mail: 74347.420@compuserve.com
Web: www.promise.org
P.O. Box 200, Alma, MO 64001
Rev. Norman L. Knudsen, Exec. Director

An interdenominational sending agency of evangelical tradition engaged in evangelism, church planting, literature distribution and support of national workers. Statistical information from 1992. Name changed from BALL World Missions.

Year Founded in USA 1973
Income for Overseas Mins $878,433
Fully Supported USA Personnel Overseas:
Expecting to serve more than 4 years 2
Expecting to serve 1 to 4 years 8
Nonresidential mission personnel 4
Other Personnel:
Short-Term less than 1 year from USA 41
Home ministry & office staff in USA 7
Countries: Guatemala 4, Hong Kong 2, Kenya 4

Children's Haven International

(956)787-7378 **Fax: (956)783-4637**
E-Mail: chii@prodigy.net
400 E. Minnesota Rd., Pharr, TX 78577
Rev. Tim Kliewer, Chairman

An interdenominational service agency of evangelical tradition engaged in childcare/orphanage programs and youth programs.

Year Founded in USA 1972
Income for Overseas Mins $200,000
Fully Supported USA Personnel Overseas:
Expecting to serve 1 to 4 years 2
Other Personnel:
Non-USA serving in own/other country 8
Short-Term less than 1 year from USA 2
Home ministry & office staff in USA 6
Countries: Mexico 2

Children's Hunger Relief Fund

(707)528-8000 **Fax: (707)525-1310**
E-Mail: ICRF@sonic.net
Web: www.chrf.org
182 Farmers Lane, #200, Santa Rosa, CA 95405-4718
Kathleen Macall, Vice President
Colonel V. Doner, Chairman

A nondenominational service agency of evangelical tradition engaged in relief and/or rehabilitation and development. Formerly International Church Relief Fund.

Year Founded in USA 1976
Income for Overseas Mins .... NR

Children's Medical Ministries

(301)261-3211 **Fax: (888)410-4647**
E-Mail: childmed@olg.com
P.O. Box 3382, Crofton, MD 21114
Bill K. Collins, Founder/CEO

A nondenominational support agency engaged in medical missions, child evangelism programs, literature distribution, relief aid and exchanging of medical technology and information with foreign national and missionary counterparts in 13 countries.

Year Founded in USA 1988
Income for Overseas Mins $5,000,000
Gifts-in-Kind $5,000,000

China Campus Outreach

(918)495-7045 **Fax: (918)495-6050**
E-Mail: LoveChina@gorilla.net
P.O. Box 702434, Tulsa, OK 74170

A transdenominational service agency of charismatic and evangelical tradition engaged in evangelism, church planting, short-term programs and missionary training.

Year Founded in USA 1984
Income for Overseas Mins $38,443
Personnel:
Bivocational/Tentmaker from USA 15
Short-Term less than 1 year from USA 6
Home ministry & office staff in USA 3

China Connection

(626)793-3737 **Fax: (626)793-3362**
E-Mail: chinaconnection@juno.com
Web: www.chinaconnection.org
458 S. Pasadena Ave., Pasadena, CA 91105
Ms. Kathy Call, Founder/Director

A nondenominational support agency of evangelical tradition engaged in missions information service, agricultural programs, Bible distribution, childcare/orphanage programs, church construction and medical work.

Year Founded in USA 1989
Income for Overseas Mins $338,522
Fully Supported USA Personnel Overseas:
Expecting to serve more than 4 years 1
Nonresidential mission personnel 1
Other Personnel:
Short-Term less than 1 year from USA 2
Home ministry & office staff in USA 1
Countries: China (PRC) 1

China Ministries International

(626)398-2343 **Fax: (626)398-2361**
E-Mail: cmius@compuserve.com
Web: www.ccea.org.tw/~cmi
P.O. Box 40489, Pasadena, CA 91104
Dr. Jonathan Chao, Founder/President

A nondenominational support agency of evangelical tradition engaged in theological education, Bible distribution, extension education, TEE, evangelism, mission-related research and missionary training.

Purpose: "...for the evangelization of China, the strengthening of the Chinese Church...by engaging in ministries of research, training of workers and sending them to the harvest field..."

Year Founded in USA 1987
Income for Overseas Mins $379,907
Personnel:
Home ministry & office staff in USA 1

China Outreach Ministries

(703)273-3500 **Fax: (703)273-3500**
E-Mail: chinaout@aol.com
Web: www.chinaoutreach.org
P.O. Box 310, Fairfax, VA 22030
Rev. Earnest W. Hummer, President

A nondenominational support agency of Presbyterian and Wesleyan tradition engaged in training, discipleship and literature distribution, primarily among Chinese intellectuals on U.S. university campuses.

Purpose: "...focuses on giving Christ to China's future leaders by...showing them the love of Christ...leading them to faith in Christ...discipling, training and mentoring them and equipping them to minister creatively to other Chinese people."

Year Founded in USA 1969
Income for Overseas Mins $222,300
Fully Supported USA Personnel Overseas:
Expecting to serve more than 4 years 1
Other Personnel:
Non-USA serving in own/other country 1
Short-Term less than 1 year from USA 4
Home ministry & office staff in USA 38
Countries: Asia 1

China Partner

(303)795-3190 **Fax: (303)795-3176**
E-Mail: mail@chinapartner.org
Web: www.chinapartner.org
14A W. Dry Creek Cir., Littleton, CO 80120
Dr. Werner Burklin, President/Founder

A nondenominational service agency of evangelical tradition engaged in evangelism training of nationals, Bible distribution, theological education, literature distribution and support of national churches. Formerly known as Werner Burklin Ministries.

Purpose: "...to help the Church in China fulfill the Great Commission through training emerging Christian leaders."

Year Founded in USA 1989
Income for Overseas Mins $98,474
Fully Supported USA Personnel Overseas:
Nonresidential mission personnel 2
Other Personnel:
Short-Term less than 1 year from USA 10
Home ministry & office staff in USA 2

China Service Coordinating Ofc.
See: ChinaSource

ChinaSource

(714)449-0611 **Fax: (714)449-0624**
E-Mail: China@xc.org
Web: www.chsource.org
P.O. 4343, Fullerton, CA 92834-4343
Dr. Brent Fulton, President

A specialized agency engaged in mission-related research, partnership development, and consulting/training. Founded as a cooperative effort of the EFMA, IFMA, WEF, Chinese Coordination Centre for World Evangelization, and the Billy Graham Center at Wheaton College. Including merger of the Institute of Chinese Studies (Colorado Springs) in 2000.

Purpose: "Strategically connecting knowledge and leaders to advance the Kingdom of God in China."

Year Founded in USA 1995
Income for Overseas Mins .... NA
Personnel:
Home ministry & office staff in USA 9

Chosen People Ministries

(704)357-9000 **Fax: (704)357-6359**
E-Mail: missiondirector@chosen-people.com
Web: www.chosenpeople.com
1300 Cross Beam Dr., Charlotte, NC 28217-2834
Mr. Mitch Glaser, President & CEO

A nondenominational service agency of independent and evangelical tradition engaged in evangelism, literature distribution and missionary training.

Year Founded in USA 1894
Income for Overseas Mins $297,112
Personnel:
Non-USA serving in own/other country 8
Short-Term less than 1 year from USA 21
Home ministry & office staff in USA 82
Countries: Germany, Israel, Ukraine

CHOSEN, Inc.

(814)833-3023 **Fax: (814)833-4091**
E-Mail: chosen4jay@aol.com
Web: http://chosen.gosee.net
3642 W. 26th St., Erie, PA 16506
Rev. Jay W. Sterling, Exec. Director

An interdenominational specialized agency of evangelical tradition engaged in supplying equipment, providing medical supplies, medical work, technical assistance and training.

Purpose: "...to promote health care programs in conjunction with missionaries and national Christian health care workers in a tangible effort to bring the love of Christ to those least able to help themselves."

Year Founded in USA 1969
Income for Overseas Mins $701,043
Gifts-in-Kind $485,378
Personnel:
Home ministry & office staff in USA 5

Christ Community Church

(847)746-1411 **Fax: (847)746-1452**
E-Mail: CCCZion@aol.com
2500 Dowie Memorial Dr., Zion, IL 60099
Ken Langley, Senior Pastor

A denominational sending agency of evangelical tradition engaged in support of national churches, church planting, evangelism and literature production.

Year Founded in USA 1896
Income for Overseas Mins $208,004
Fully Supported USA Personnel Overseas:
Expecting to serve more than 4 years 10
Countries: Angola 2, Egypt 2, Japan 2, S Africa 4

Christ for India, Inc.

(972)771-7221 **Fax: (972)771-4021**
P.O. Box 271086, Dallas, TX 75227
Dr. P. J. Titus, Founder/President
Arlene Phelps, Admin. Secretary

A nondenominational service agency engaged in church planting, training of nationals, correspondence courses, evangelism, literature distribution and medical work.

Purpose: "...to 'make ready a people, prepared for the coming of the Lord'."

Year Founded in USA 1981
Income for Overseas Mins $187,254
Personnel:
Non-USA serving in own/other country 500
Short-Term less than 1 year from USA 30
Home ministry & office staff in USA 1
Countries: India

Christ for the City International

(402)592-8332 **Fax: (402)592-8312**
E-Mail: InfoCFC@aol.com
Web: www.cfci.org
P.O. Box 241827, Omaha, NE 68124-5827
Mr. Duane Anderson, President

An interdenominational sending agency of evangelical tradition engaged in church planting, evangelism, leadership development, medical work, mobilization for mission and relief and/or rehabilitation.

Purpose: "To multiply churches...which in turn...send multinational teams into the least evangelized cities of the world."

Year Founded in USA 1995
Income for Overseas Mins $351,588
Gifts-in-Kind $3,000
Fully Supported USA Personnel Overseas:
Expecting to serve more than 4 years 4
Other Personnel:
Non-USA serving in own/other country 60
Bivocational/Tentmaker from USA 14
Short-Term less than 1 year from USA 34
Home ministry & office staff in USA 7

Countries: Colombia 2, Costa Rica 2, Mexico, Spain, Switzerland

Christ for the Island World
See: Christ for the Lost World

Christ for the Lost World

(336)855-0656 **Fax: (336)854-1555**
E-Mail: cftiw@worldnet.att.net
Web: www.christforindonesia.org
P.O. Box 18962, Greensboro, NC 27419
Rev. Ken Taylor, President

An interdenominational support agency of evangelical tradition engaged in evangelism, literature distribution, supplying equipment, support of national workers and youth programs. Name changed from Christ for the Island World.

Year Founded in USA 1983
Income for Overseas Mins $63,000
Personnel:
Non-USA serving in own/other country 113
Home ministry & office staff in USA 2
Countries: Indonesia, Russia

Christ for the Nations, Inc.

(214)376-1711 **Fax: (214)302-6228**
E-Mail: Info@cfni.org
Web: www.cfni.org
P.O. Box 769000, Dallas, TX 75376
Rev. Dennis Lindsay, President/CEO

An interdenominational support agency and Bible School of charismatic tradition engaged in literature distribution, church construction, missionary education and short-term programs.

Year Founded in USA 1948
Income for Overseas Mins .... NA
Personnel:
Short-Term less than 1 year from USA 350
Home ministry & office staff in USA 139

Christ to the Nations Missions

(407)504-0778 **Fax: (407)633-6653**
E-Mail: CTTNDLR@aol.com
Web: www.cttn.org
P.O. Box 1824, Cocoa, FL 32923-1824
Dr. David L. Ralston, Founder/Director

A sending agency of Baptist and independent tradition engaged in church planting, Bible distribution, childrens programs, support of national churches, support of national workers and missionary training.

Purpose: "...to help local churches and God's people reach the unreached millions with the Gospel of Jesus Christ..."

Year Founded in USA 1989
Income for Overseas Mins $160,000
Fully Supported USA Personnel Overseas:
Expecting to serve more than 4 years 47
Other Personnel:
Non-USA serving in own/other country 47
Short-Term less than 1 year from USA 1
Home ministry & office staff in USA 6
Countries: Australia 2, Cuba 10, Ghana 2, Hungary 2, Indonesia 2, Kenya 2, Lithuania 13, Philippines 10, Russia 4

Christar

(610)375-0300 **Fax: (610)375-6862**
E-Mail: Info@christar.org
Web: www.christar.org
P.O. Box 14866, Reading, PA 19612-4866
Dr. Patrick O. Cate, Gen. Director

A nondenominational sending agency of evangelical tradition engaged in church planting, correspondence courses, development, theological education, evangelism and medical work. Formerly known as International Missions, Inc.

Purpose: "To...proclaim the Gospel...and establish local indigenous churches, primarily among unreached Asian communities worldwide."

Year Founded in USA 1930
Income for Overseas Mins $7,400,000
Fully Supported USA Personnel Overseas:
Expecting to serve more than 4 years 84
Expecting to serve 1 to 4 years 3
Nonresidential mission personnel 2
Other Personnel:
Non-USA serving in own/other country 6
Bivocational/Tentmaker from USA 144
Short-Term less than 1 year from USA 22
Home ministry & office staff in USA 36
Countries: Albania 8, France 12, Germany 4, Japan 15, Kenya 6, Mongolia 6, Netherlands 3, Philippines 23, Suriname 3, UK 7

Christian Advance International

(713)981-9033 **Fax: (713)981-9055**
E-Mail: CAIHOU@aol.com
P.O. Box 741427, Houston, TX 77274-1427
Rev. Chris G. Jones, President

An interdenominational sending agency of Pentecostal tradition engaged in children's programs, evangelism, medical work, short-term programs and youth programs. Financial data from 1996.

Year Founded in USA 1984
Income for Overseas Mins $617,000
Gifts-in-Kind $120,000
Fully Supported USA Personnel Overseas:
Expecting to serve more than 4 years 3
Other Personnel:
Non-USA serving in own/other country 30
Bivocational/Tentmaker from USA 2
Short-Term less than 1 year from USA 10
Home ministry & office staff in USA 2
Countries: Mexico 3

Christian Aid Ministries

(330)893-2428 **Fax: (330)893-2305**
P.O. Box 360, Berlin, OH 44610
Mr. David N. Troyer, Gen. Director

An interdenominational service agency of Mennonite tradition engaged in relief and/or rehabilitation, Bible distribution, church construction and providing medical supplies.

Year Founded in USA 1981
Income for Overseas Mins $73,940,211
Gifts-in-Kind $63,892,975
Fully Supported USA Personnel Overseas:
Expecting to serve 1 to 4 years 54
Other Personnel:
Non-USA serving in own/other country 124
Short-Term less than 1 year from USA 12
Home ministry & office staff in USA 55
Countries: Ghana 2, Haiti 14, Nicaragua 2, Romania 36

Christian Aid Mission

(804)977-5650 **Fax: (804)295-6814**
E-Mail: ask@christianaid.org
Web: www.christianaid.org
3045 Ivy Road, Charlottesville, VA 22903
Dr. Robert V. Finley, Chairman & CEO

A nondenominational service agency of evangelical tradition raising financial support for indigenous mission boards and Bible institutes involved in Bible distribution, broadcasting, church planting and evangelism.

Year Founded in USA 1953
Income for Overseas Mins $6,619,182
Fully Supported USA Personnel Overseas:
Nonresidential mission personnel 18
Other Personnel:
Non-USA serving in own/other country 18809
Home ministry & office staff in USA 19
Countries: Albania, Angola, Argentina, Armenia, Bangladesh, Belarus, Belize, Benin, Bolivia, Bosnia, Botswana, Brazil, Bulgaria, Burundi, Cambodia, Chile, China, Colombia, Congo/ Zaire, Costa Rica, Croatia, Czech Republic, Dominican Republic, Ecuador, Egypt, France, Gambia, Ghana, Guatemala, Haiti, Honduras, Hong Kong, Hungary, India, Indonesia, Iran, Israel, Ivory Coast, Jordan, Kazakhstan, Kenya, Kosovo, Kyrgyzstan, Laos, Lebanon, Liberia, Macedonia, Malawi, Mexico, Mongolia, Morocco, Myanmar, Namibia, Nepal, New Guinea, Nicaragua, Niger, Nigeria, Pakistan, Paraguay, Peru, Philippines, Poland, Romania, Russia, Rwanda, Senegal, Sierra Leone, Slovakia, Slovenia, S Africa, Spain, Sri Lanka, Sudan, Syria, Tajikistan, Tanzania, Thailand, Togo, Tunisia, Turkey, Uganda, Ukraine, Uruguay, Uzbekistan, Vietnam, Yugoslavia, Zambia, Zimbabwe

Christian and Missionary Alliance

(719)599-5999 **Fax: (719)262-5393**
E-Mail: Info@cmalliance.org
Web: www.cmalliance.org
P.O. Box 35000, Colorado Springs, CO 80935-3500
Dr. Peter Nanfelt, President
Dr. Robert L. Fetherlin, VP Intl. Ministries

A denominational sending agency of evangelical tradition engaged in church planting, broadcasting, church construction, correspondence courses, development, theological education, TEE, evangelism and leadership development.

Purpose: "...committed to world missions, stressing the fullness of Christ in personal experiences, building the Church and preaching the Gospel to the ends of the earth."

Year Founded in USA 1887
Income for Overseas Mins $19,215,697

Fully Supported USA Personnel Overseas:
Expecting to serve more than 4 years 591
Expecting to serve 1 to 4 years 135
Nonresidential mission personnel 722
Other Personnel:
Bivocational/Tentmaker from USA 62
Short-Term less than 1 year from USA 980
Home ministry & office staff in USA 11
Countries: Africa 4, Argentina 14, Bolivia 4, Bosnia 9, Brazil 26, Burkina Faso 20, Cambodia 25, Chile 21, China (PRC) 19, Colombia 20, Congo 6, Congo/Zaire 2, Costa Rica 1, Cote d'Ivoire 57, Dominican Rep 14, Ecuador 60, France 18, Gabon 34, Germany 12, Guinea Bissau 35, Indonesia 46, Israel 10, Japan 11, Jordan 1, Korea-S 2, Laos 9, Lebanon 2, Malaysia 32, Mali 27, Mexico 10, Mongolia 2, Peru 23, Philippines 39, Poland 4, Russia 25, Spain 9, Taiwan (ROC) 15, Thailand 29, UK 9, Venezuela 17, Vietnam 3

Christian Associates International

(818)865-1816 **Fax: (818)865-0317**
E-Mail: usoffice@christianassociates.org
Web: www.christianassociates.org
1534 N. Moorpark Rd. #356, Thousand Oaks, CA 91360
Dr. Linus Morris, President

A transdenominational sending agency of evangelical tradition engaged in church planting and support of national churches.
Purpose: "...to reach the unchurched through the multiplication of high-impact leaders and high-impact churches."
Year Founded in USA 1968
Income for Overseas Mins $1,466,673
Fully Supported USA Personnel Overseas:
Expecting to serve more than 4 years 30
Expecting to serve 1 to 4 years 4
Other Personnel:
Non-USA serving in own/other country 6
Home ministry & office staff in USA 12
Countries: Germany 4, Netherlands 19, Portugal 4, Russia 1, Spain 6

Christian Blind Mission Intl.

(864)239-0065 **Fax: (864)239-0069**
E-Mail: info@cbmi-usa.org
Web: www.cbmi-usa.org
P.O. Box 19000, Greenville, SC 29602
Alan Harkey, U.S. President

An interdenominational service agency of ecumenical tradition engaged in disability assistance programs, agricultural programs, medical work, relief and/or rehabilitation, support of national workers and training.
Purpose: "Worldwide Christian service in eye care and projects for people with disabilitites."
Year Founded in USA 1976
Income for Overseas Mins $5,761,302
Gifts-in-Kind $4,175,363
Fully Supported USA Personnel Overseas:
Expecting to serve more than 4 years 1
Expecting to serve 1 to 4 years 18
Nonresidential mission personnel 2
Other Personnel:
Home ministry & office staff in USA 11
Countries: Cameroon 1, Congo 1, Dominican Rep 1, Ecuador 1, Jordan 1, Kenya 2, Madagascar 1, Nigeria 1, Pakistan 1, Papua New Guin 2, Philippines 1, Tanzania 2, Thailand 1, Togo 1, Uganda 2

Christian Brethren See: Brethren Assemblies

Christian Broadcasting Network

(757)579-7000 **Fax: (757)579-2017**
Web: www.cbnnow.org
977 Centerville Turnpk., Virginia Beach, VA 23463
Mr. Pat Robertson, Chairman & CEO
Mr. Michael D. Little, President & COO

An interdenominational support agency of evangelical tradition engaged in TV broadcasting, Bible distribution, literature distribution and video/film production/distribution for evangelism efforts in 70 countries. See also Operation Blessing International, an affiliate organization of CBN. Financial and personnel information from 1997.
Year Founded in USA 1960
Income for Overseas Mins $12,688,500
Fully Supported USA Personnel Overseas:
Nonresidential mission personnel 14

Christian Business Men's Committee of USA

(423)698-4444 **Fax: (423)629-4434**
E-Mail: info@cbmc.com
Web: www.cbmc.com

P.O. Box 3308, Chattanooga, TN 37404
Mr. Phil Downer, President
An interdenominational support agency of evangelical tradition engaged in evangelism.
Purpose: "...saturating the business and professional community with the Gospel...by establishing, equipping and mobilizing teams where we work and live that yield spiritual reproducers."
Year Founded in USA 1950
Income for Overseas Mins .... NA

Christian Church (Disciples of Christ), Division of Overseas Ministries

(317)635-3100 **Fax: (317)635-4323**
E-Mail: DOM@disciples.org
Web: www.globalministries.org
P. O. Box 1986, Indianapolis, IN 46206
Julia Brown Karimu, Mission Exec.
A denominational sending agency of Christian (Restoration Movement) tradition engaged in support of missionaries and national churches through a combined Global Ministries partnership with United Church Board for World Ministries.
Year Founded in USA 1849
Income for Overseas Mins .... NR

Christian Church of North America Missions

(724)962-3501 **Fax: (724)962-1766**
E-Mail: CCNA@nauticom.net
Web: www.ccna.org
1294 Rutledge Rd., Transfer, PA 16154-9005
Rev. David Verzilli, Director Frgn. Missions
A denominational sending agency of Pentecostal and charismatic tradition engaged in evangelism, broadcasting, church construction, church planting, Christian education and support of national churches.
Year Founded in USA 1907
Income for Overseas Mins $600,000
Fully Supported USA Personnel Overseas:
Expecting to serve more than 4 years 12
Expecting to serve 1 to 4 years 2
Nonresidential mission personnel...................... 6
Other Personnel:
Non-USA serving in own/other country .. 1720
Short-Term less than 1 year from USA 40
Home ministry & office staff in USA 3
Countries: Argentina, Colombia 1, Europe 2, India 4, Italy 1, Kenya 2, Philippines, S Africa 4

Christian Churches / Churches of Christ

(No central office)
A body of autonomous congregations and agencies of the Christian "Restoration Movement" (using instrumental music in worship) which sends and supports missionaries directly from local congregations. Personnel totals compiled in 1992 by Mission Services Association. Income figure is a 1988 estimation.
Year Founded in USA 0
Income for Overseas Mins $24,000,000
Fully Supported USA Personnel Overseas:
Expecting to serve more than 4 years 1110
Expecting to serve 1 to 4 years 44
Nonresidential mission personnel...................... 8
Countries: Argentina 6, Australia 14, Austria 2, Bahamas 2, Bangladesh 2, Barbados 2, Belgium 2, Benin 4, Bophuthatswana 4, Botswana 2, Brazil 49, Cayman Isls 5, Chile 32, China (PRC) 5, Colombia 14, Congo/Zaire 34, Costa Rica 6, Cote d'Ivoire 10, Denmark 2, Dominican Rep 6, Ecuador 6, France 6, Germany 10, Ghana 7, Grenada 4, Guatemala 6, Guinea Bissau 1, Guyana 2, Haiti 29, Honduras 7, Hong Kong 18, India 23, Indonesia 24, Ireland 4, Israel 2, Italy 7, Jamaica 9, Japan 45, Kenya 69, Korea-S 4, Liberia 1, Malawi 7, Mali 2, Mexico 53, Mozambique 6, New Zealand 4, Nigeria 2, Panama 4, Papua New Guin 28, Philippines 46, Portugal 5, Puerto Rico 30, Russia 2, Singapore 6, S Africa 24, Spain 1, St Vincent 6, Taiwan (ROC) 10, Thailand 47, Ukraine 4, UK 57, Unspecified 228, Uruguay 8, Venezuela 10, Virgin Isls USA 2, Zambia 16, Zimbabwe 59

Christian Dental Society

(800)237-7368 **Fax: (319)578-8843**
E-Mail: cdssent@sbt.net
Web: www.christiandental.org
Box 296, Sumner, IA 50674
Mr. Mike Roberts, DDS, Exec. Director
An interdenominational specialized agency of evangelical tradition engaged in medical

work, purchasing services, services for other agencies and supplying equipment. Statistical information from 1996.

Year Founded in USA 1962
Income for Overseas Mins $457,409
Gifts-in-Kind $300,480
Personnel:
Bivocational/Tentmaker from USA 5
Short-Term less than 1 year from USA 27

Christian Dynamics

(602)878-6892
10878 N. 57th Ave., Glendale, AZ 85304
Dr. Harvey M. Lifsey, President

A transdenominational service agency of evangelical tradition engaged in support of national workers, childcare/orphanage programs, correspondence courses, evangelism and literacy work.

Purpose: "...to proclaim the Gospel of Jesus Christ first where His name has not been known, and to make all ministry methods serve the primary objective of bringing people to a saving knowledge of Christ."

Year Founded in USA 1976
Income for Overseas Mins $100,000
Gifts-in-Kind $50,000
Personnel:
Non-USA serving in own/other country 25
Countries: India

Christian Fellowship Union

(956)686-5886 **Fax: (956)686-6427**
E-Mail: cfunion@juno.com
P.O. Box 909, McAllen, TX 78502
Rev. Steven P. Johnson, Gen. Director

An interdenominational support agency of charismatic and fundamental tradition engaged in church planting, theological education, leadership development and support of national churches.

Year Founded in USA 1945
Income for Overseas Mins $159,000
Fully Supported USA Personnel Overseas:
Nonresidential mission personnel 3
Other Personnel:
Short-Term less than 1 year from USA 13
Home ministry & office staff in USA 4

Christian Information Service, Inc. Missions Division

(804)977-5650 **Fax: (804)295-6814**
E-Mail: bill@christianaid.org
P.O. Box 6511, Charlottesville, VA 22906
Mr. Rick Brown, President

A transdenominational support agency of evangelical tradition engaged in providing growth services to indigenous missions, helping more than 30,000 workers serving with 500 native mission boards on every continent.

Year Founded in USA 1972
Income for Overseas Mins $160,000
Personnel:
Short-Term less than 1 year from USA 150
Home ministry & office staff in USA 8

Christian Laymen's Missionary Evangelism Association

(509)786-3178 **Fax: (509)786-1000**
E-Mail: ltaylor@iopener.net
826 Ford St., Prosser, WA 99350
Larry Taylor, President

A nondenominational support agency of charismatic tradition engaged in evangelism and literature distribution.

Purpose: "To raise up laymen for world evangelism."

Year Founded in USA 1977
Income for Overseas Mins .... NR

Christian Leadership Development, Inc.

(270)821-0699 **Fax: (270)821-0699**
E-Mail: ftsdcld@vci.net
P.O. Box 402, Madisonville, KY 42431
Mr. Randall Wittig, Gen. Director

An interdenominational service agency of evangelical tradition engaged in leadership development, theological education, literature distribution, literature production, support of national churches and training.

Purpose: "...to provide teaching, encouragement and counseling...to Christian leaders, particularly those of limited resources who do not have other means of spiritual development available..."

Year Founded in USA 1978

Income for Overseas Mins $229,704
Fully Supported USA Personnel Overseas:
Expecting to serve more than 4 years 2
Nonresidential mission personnel 2
Other Personnel:
Non-USA serving in own/other country 2
Countries: Costa Rica 2, Mexico, Peru

Christian Literacy Associates

(412)364-3777
E-Mail: drliteracy@aol.com
311 Cumberland Rd., Pittsburgh, PA 15237
Dr. William E. Kofmehl Jr., President

An interdenominational specialized agency of ecumenical tradition engaged in literacy work. Christian literacy materials have been developed for use in 19 languages.
Year Founded in USA 1976
Income for Overseas Mins $6,500
Personnel:
Short-Term less than 1 year from USA 1
Home ministry & office staff in USA 3

Christian Literature Crusade

(215)542-1244 **Fax: (215)542-7580**
E-Mail: CLCUSA@compuserve.com
701 Pennsylvania Ave., Ft. Washington, PA 19034
Mr. William M. Almack, President

An interdenominational sending agency of evangelical tradition engaged in literature distribution, Bible distribution, correspondence courses, literacy work, literature production and missionary training.
Year Founded in USA 1957
Income for Overseas Mins .... NA
Fully Supported USA Personnel Overseas:
Expecting to serve more than 4 years 10
Expecting to serve 1 to 4 years 4
Other Personnel:
Home ministry & office staff in USA 28
Countries: Central Asia 2, Colombia 2, Hong Kong 2, Italy 2, Portugal 2, UK 4

Christian Medical & Dental Society

(423)844-1000 **Fax: (423)844-1005**
E-Mail: main@cmdsmail.org
Web: www.gocin.com/CMDS
P.O. Box 7500, Bristol, TN 37621
Mr. David Stevens, MD, Exec. Director

A nondenominational service agency of evangelical tradition engaged in medical work, evangelism and short-term programs. Personnel information from 1996.
Purpose: "...living out our faith through our professions in...opportunities for ministry afforded by medicine and dentistry, from whole person health care to missions around the world..."
Year Founded in USA 1931
Income for Overseas Mins $430,768
Personnel:
Short-Term less than 1 year from USA 1000
Home ministry & office staff in USA 42

Christian Ministries International

(513)874-3959 **Fax: (513)874-9084**
E-Mail: cmi@hotmail.com
Web: www.angelfire/oh/cmi2000
5841 Gilmore Dr., Fairfield, OH 45014-5101
Dr. L. Lynn Hood, President

A transdenominational sending agency of charismatic and ecumenical tradition engaged in leadership development, church planting, evangelism, mobilization for mission, services for other agencies and training.
Purpose: "...preparing national indigenous leaders of the local church to be empowered by New Testament principles of leadership to assist them in world evangelization and church planting in their generation."
Year Founded in USA 1984
Income for Overseas Mins $200,000
Gifts-in-Kind $10,000
Fully Supported USA Personnel Overseas:
Expecting to serve more than 4 years 4
Expecting to serve 1 to 4 years 14
Nonresidential mission personnel 2
Other Personnel:
Non-USA serving in own/other country 28
Bivocational/Tentmaker from USA 10
Short-Term less than 1 year from USA 40
Home ministry & office staff in USA 5
Countries: Brazil 2, China (PRC) 12, Russia 2, Ukraine 2

Christian Mission for the Deaf

(313)933-1424 **Fax: (313)933-1424**
E-Mail: CMDeaf@match.org
CMD4Africa@aol.com
P.O. Box 28005, Detroit, MI 48228-0005

Mrs. Berta Foster, Administrator
A denominational support agency of Christian/Plymouth Brethren tradition engaged in Christian education, theological education, evangelism, funds transmission and literacy work.
Year Founded in USA 1956
Income for Overseas Mins $85,713
Personnel:
Non-USA serving in own/other country 6
Home ministry & office staff in USA 2
Countries: Chad, Ethiopia, Nigeria, Sierra Leone

Christian Missions in Many Lands

(732)449-8880 Fax: (732)974-0888
P.O. Box 13, Spring Lake, NJ 07762-0013
Mr. Samuel E. Robinson, President
Mr. John G. Jeffers, Treasurer
A nondenominational service agency of Christian/Plymouth Brethren tradition assisting missionaries through funds transmission and various other services. Overseas personnel included under Brethren Assemblies.
Purpose: "...to provide necessary services which are difficult or impossible for the individual missionary or assembly to provide."
Year Founded in USA 1921
Income for Overseas Mins $12,800,000
Personnel:
Home ministry & office staff in USA 7

Christian Outreach International

(561)778-0571 Fax: (561)778-6781
E-Mail: COutrchFL@aol.com
Web: www.christianoutreachintl.org
P.O. Box 2823, Vero Beach, FL 32961-2823
Mr. Jack Isleib, Exec. Director
An interdenominational service agency of evangelical tradition engaged in short-term programs, evangelism, mobilization for mission, and support of national workers. Statistical data from 1996.
Year Founded in USA 1984
Income for Overseas Mins $1,400,000
Fully Supported USA Personnel Overseas:
Expecting to serve more than 4 years 3
Expecting to serve 1 to 4 years 24
Other Personnel:
Non-USA serving in own/other country 11
Short-Term less than 1 year from USA 500
Home ministry & office staff in USA 12
Countries: Czech Rep 7, France 1, Ukraine 9, Venezuela 10

Christian Pilots Association

(626)962-0381 Fax: (909)606-0759
P.O. Box 603, West Covina, CA 91793
Mr.Howard Payne, President
An interdenominational specialized agency of evangelical tradition engaged in aviation services and providing medical supplies.
Year Founded in USA 1972
Income for Overseas Mins $17,000
Gifts-in-Kind $10,000

Christian Reformed World Missions

(616)224-0700 Fax: (616)224-0834
E-Mail: CRWM@crcna.org
Web: www.crwm.org
2850 Kalamazoo Ave. SE, Grand Rapids, MI 49560-0200
Mr. Dave Radius, Acting Intl. Exec. Director
A denominational sending agency of Reformed and evangelical tradition engaged in church planting, theological education, evangelism, leadership development, linguistics and literacy work.
Year Founded in USA 1888
Income for Overseas Mins $10,400,000
Fully Supported USA Personnel Overseas:
Expecting to serve more than 4 years 155
Expecting to serve 1 to 4 years 71
Nonresidential mission personnel 2
Other Personnel:
Non-USA serving in own/other country 4
Bivocational/Tentmaker from USA 2
Short-Term less than 1 year from USA 120
Home ministry & office staff in USA 19
Countries: Asia 23, Belize 1, Costa Rica 9, Dominican Rep 25, Ecuador 1, El Salvador 2, France 2, Guam 7, Guinea Bissau 7, Haiti 10, Honduras 13, Hungary 7, Japan 22, Liberia 1, Mali 5, Mexico 13, Nicaragua 6, Nigeria 36, Philippines 26, Romania 3, Russia 1, Sierra Leone 2, Taiwan (ROC) 4

Christian Reformed World Relief Committee

(616)224-0740 **Fax: (616)224-0806**
Web: www.crwrc.org
2850 Kalamazoo Ave. SE, Grand Rapids, MI 49548
Mr. Andy Ryskamp, U.S. Director

A denominational service agency of Reformed tradition engaged in community development, Christian education and relief aid.

Purpose: "...showing God's love to people in need by working with them and their communities to create positive permanent change..."

Year Founded in USA 1962
Income for Overseas Mins $4,631,653
Fully Supported USA Personnel Overseas:
Expecting to serve more than 4 years 13
Expecting to serve 1 to 4 years 16
Nonresidential mission personnel 22
Other Personnel:
Non-USA serving in own/other country 32
Home ministry & office staff in USA 23

Countries: Bangladesh 2, Cambodia 1, Dominican Rep 1, El Salvador 1, Haiti 1, Honduras 2, Indonesia 1, Kenya 3, Malawi 1, Mali 3, Mexico 3, Nicaragua 1, Romania 3, Rwanda 1, Senegal 1, Sierra Leone 1, S Africa 1, Uganda 1, Zambia 1

Christian Resources International

(517)223-3193 **Fax: (517)223-7668**
E-Mail: csmbooks@ismi.net
Web: www.csmbooks.org
P.O. Box 356, Fowlerville, MI 48836-0356
Mr. Mark J. Campo, Director

A nondenominational specialized agency of evangelical tradition engaged in literature distribution worldwide by sending overseas surplus and reusable Christian literature and Bibles. Donated materials sent overseas were estimated to be worth $4,500,000. Name changed from Christian Salvage Mission.

Year Founded in USA 1956
Income for Overseas Mins $324,000
Personnel:
Home ministry & office staff in USA 7

Christian Salvage Mission See: Christian Resources International

Christian Service International

(765)286-0711 **Fax: (765)286-5773**
E-Mail: csimail@juno.com
804 W. McGalliard Rd., Muncie, IN 47303-1764
Mr. Eddy Cline, President

An interdenominational service agency of Methodist tradition engaged in short-term programs, funds transmission, providing medical supplies and medical work.

Year Founded in USA 1963
Income for Overseas Mins $741,205
Fully Supported USA Personnel Overseas:
Expecting to serve more than 4 years 5
Expecting to serve 1 to 4 years 7
Other Personnel:
Short-Term less than 1 year from USA 1041

Countries: Haiti 4, Jamaica 8

Christian Services, Inc.

(320)485-7496 **Fax: (320)485-7496**
E-Mail: MOOREDBMN@popmail.tds.net
Box 720, Winsted, MN 55395
Barbara Moore, Gen. Director

A nondenominational service agency of evangelical tradition engaged in funds transmission, childrens programs, Christian education and support of national workers. Statistical information from 1992.

Year Founded in USA 1973
Income for Overseas Mins $66,000
Fully Supported USA Personnel Overseas:
Expecting to serve more than 4 years 2
Other Personnel:
Home ministry & office staff in USA 1

Countries: Kenya 1, Liberia 1

Christian Union Mission

(419)533-4166
E-Mail: gspiess@bright.net
P.O. Box 454, Liberty Center, OH 43532
Mr. Gareld Spiess, Director

A denominational sending agency of independent tradition engaged in evangelism, church construction, literature distribution/

production and youth programs. Personnel information from 1996.

Year Founded in USA 1864

Income for Overseas Mins $95,450

Fully Supported USA Personnel Overseas:

Expecting to serve more than 4 years 5

Other Personnel:

Short-Term less than 1 year from USA 10

Home ministry & office staff in USA 1

Countries: Liberia 3, Mexico 2

Christian World Publishers

(510)689-9944 Fax: (510)689-1538

101 Gregory Lane #42, Pleasant Hill, CA 94523

Mr. Peter Cunliffe, President

A nondenominational specialized service agency of evangelical tradition engaged in literature production and distribution. Personnel information from 1996.

Year Founded in USA 1974

Income for Overseas Mins $223,000

Fully Supported USA Personnel Overseas:

Expecting to serve more than 4 years 2

Other Personnel:

Home ministry & office staff in USA 1

Countries: France 2

Christians In Action, Inc.

(559)564-3762 Fax: (559)564-1231

E-Mail: cinamissions@christiansinaction.org

Web: www.christiansinaction.org

P.O. Box 728, Woodlake, CA 93286-0728

Mr. David W. Konold, Jr., Exec. Director

A transdenominational sending agency of evangelical tradition engaged in evangelism, childcare/orphanage programs, church planting, support of national churches, relief and/or rehabilitation and missionary training.

Year Founded in USA 1957

Income for Overseas Mins $875,000

Fully Supported USA Personnel Overseas:

Expecting to serve more than 4 years 49

Nonresidential mission personnel 1

Other Personnel:

Non-USA serving in own/other country 49

Short-Term less than 1 year from USA 76

Home ministry & office staff in USA 35

Countries: Brazil 5, Colombia 3, Ecuador 2, Germany 4, Ghana 3, Guatemala 5, India 2, Japan 2, Macao 2, Mexico 3, Peru 2, Philippines 8, Sierra Leone 2, UK 6

Church Ministries International

(972)772-3406 Fax: (972)722-0012

E-Mail: church_ministries@compuserve.com

Web: www.churchministries.org

500 Turtle Cove Blvd. #101, Rockwall, TX 75087-5300

Mr. Jim Murray, Exec. Director

An interdenominational support agency of evangelical tradition engaged in church construction, church planting, services for other agencies and training. Income report from 1996.

Purpose: "...to help urban churches evangelize their nation."

Year Founded in USA 1989

Income for Overseas Mins $350,000

Fully Supported USA Personnel Overseas:

Expecting to serve more than 4 years 5

Nonresidential mission personnel 2

Other Personnel:

Non-USA serving in own/other country 1

Home ministry & office staff in USA 2

Countries: Latin America 5

Church Missions Link

(509)891-5595 Fax: (509)891-5595

E-Mail: CMLink@juno.com

P.O. Box 14175, Spokane, WA 99206

Rev. Ken Parker, Director

A transdenominational support agency of evangelical and independent tradition engaged in missions information service, management consulting/training and missionary training.

Year Founded in USA 1997

Income for Overseas Mins $10,000

Personnel:

Short-Term less than 1 year from USA 25

Home ministry & office staff in USA 2

Church of God (Anderson, Indiana), Missionary Board

(765)648-2131 Fax: (765)642-4279

E-Mail: ptoombs@chog.org

P.O. Box 2498, Anderson, IN 46018

Dr. Doris J. Dale, Global Missions Coordinator

A nondenominational sending agency of Holiness tradition engaged in leadership development, church planting, TEE, short-term programs and support of national workers.

Year Founded in USA 1909

Income for Overseas Mins $5,000,000

Fully Supported USA Personnel Overseas:

Expecting to serve more than 4 years 61

Nonresidential mission personnel 2

Other Personnel:

Short-Term less than 1 year from USA 58

Home ministry & office staff in USA 14

Countries: Belize 2, Bermuda 2, Bolivia 2, Brazil 4, Costa Rica 2, Cote d'Ivoire 2, Ecuador 4, Germany 2, Guam 2, Hong Kong 1, Japan 6, Kenya 7, Lebanon 2, Tanzania 7, Uganda 5, Unspecified 7, Venezuela 2, Zambia 2

Church of God (Cleveland, TN) World Missions

(423)478-7190 **Fax: (423)478-7155**

E-Mail: Info.cogwm.org

Web: cogwm.org

P.O. Box 8016, 2490 Keith Street NW, Cleveland, TN 37320-8016

Dr. Gene D. Rice, Gen. Director

A denominational sending agency of Pentecostal tradition engaged in church planting, church construction, missionary education, evangelism, literature distribution, medical work, support of national churches and support of national workers.

Purpose: "...to help unchurched or nominal Christians become committed disciples of Christ and non-Christian people become Christians..."

Year Founded in USA 1910

Income for Overseas Mins $18,308,916

Fully Supported USA Personnel Overseas:

Expecting to serve more than 4 years 155

Expecting to serve 1 to 4 years 17

Other Personnel:

Non-USA serving in own/other country 53

Bivocational/Tentmaker from USA 2

Short-Term less than 1 year from USA 1150

Home ministry & office staff in USA 53

Countries: Aruba 2, Asia 4, Australia 2, Belgium 4, Botswana 2, Brazil 7, Bulgaria 2, Caribbean Isls 1, China (PRC) 6, Colombia 3, Cote d'Ivoire 2, Ecuador 7, Europe 8, France 1, Germany 5, Guatemala 2, Haiti 4, Honduras 7, Indonesia 2, Ireland 2, Israel 7, Italy 4, Kenya 13, Latin America 4, Malaysia 2, Mongolia 3, Morocco 2, Netherlands 1, Nicaragua 2, Nigeria 1, Paraguay 2, Philippines 17, Portugal 2, Russia 3, Spain 3, Turkey 2, Uganda 2, Ukraine 2, Unspecified 19, Uruguay 2, Venezuela 3, Zambia 3

Church of God (Holiness), World Mission Board

(913)432-0303 **Fax: (913)722-0351**

E-Mail: WLHayton@aol.com

P.O. Box 4711, Overland Park, KS 66204

Rev. William L. Hayton, Exec. Secretary

A nondenominational sending agency of independent tradition engaged in support of national churches, church planting, theological education, evangelism and support of national workers.

Year Founded in USA 1917

Income for Overseas Mins $342,258

Fully Supported USA Personnel Overseas:

Expecting to serve more than 4 years 7

Expecting to serve 1 to 4 years 2

Other Personnel:

Non-USA serving in own/other country 11

Home ministry & office staff in USA 2

Countries: Bolivia 3, Cayman Isls 2, Nigeria 2, Ukraine 2

Church of God (Seventh Day) Gen. Conference, Missions Abroad

(303)452-7973

P.O. Box 33677, Denver, CO 80233

Mr. Victor Burford, Director

A denominational support agency of evangelical tradition engaged in funds transmission, Bible and literature distribution, and support of national churches in 16 countries. Statistical information from 1996.

Year Founded in USA 1860

Income for Overseas Mins $70,000

Personnel:

Short-Term less than 1 year from USA 4

Home ministry & office staff in USA 1

Church of God in Christ, Mennonite General Mission Board

(316)345-2532 Fax: (316)345-2582
P.O. Box 230, Moundridge, KS 67107
Dale Koehn

A denominational sending agency of Mennonite tradition engaged in evangelism, Bible distribution, childrens programs, providing medical supplies, support of national churches and relief and/or rehabilitation in 21 countries. Includes U.S. and Canadian totals. Personnel data from 1992.

Year Founded in USA 1933
Income for Overseas Mins $3,665,779
Fully Supported USA Personnel Overseas:
Expecting to serve more than 4 years 66
Countries: Unspecified 66

Church of God of Apostolic Faith

(918)437-7652 Fax: (918)437-7652
P.O. Box 691745, Tulsa, OK 74169
Rev. Joe L. Edmonson, Gen. Superintendent

A denominational sending agency of Pentecostal tradition engaged in theological education, Bible and literature distribution, and church construction. Statistical information from 1992.

Year Founded in USA 1951
Income for Overseas Mins $39,500
Fully Supported USA Personnel Overseas:
Expecting to serve more than 4 years 2
Expecting to serve 1 to 4 years 2
Other Personnel:
Home ministry & office staff in USA 2
Countries: Mexico 4

Church of God of Prophecy

(423)559-5336 Fax: (423)472-5037
E-Mail: WMCOGOP@aol.com
Web: www.cogop.org
P.O. Box 2910, Cleveland, TN 37320-2910
Mr. Randy Howard, Global Outreach Director
Mr. Billy Murray, General Overseer

A denominational sending agency of Pentecostal tradition engaged in church planting, evangelism, support of national churches and support of national workers.

Year Founded in USA 1903
Income for Overseas Mins $2,000,000
Fully Supported USA Personnel Overseas:
Expecting to serve more than 4 years 20
Other Personnel:
Non-USA serving in own/other country 71
Short-Term less than 1 year from USA 52
Home ministry & office staff in USA 4
Countries: Am Samoa 2, Argentina, Australia 1, Belarus, Belgium, Benin, Bolivia, Botswana, Brazil, Bulgaria, Cameroon, Chile, Colombia, Congo/Zaire, Costa Rica, Cote d'Ivoire, Cuba, Cyprus, Dominican Republic, Ecuador, Egypt, El Salvador, Ethiopia, France, Germany 7, Ghana, Greece, Guatemala, Guyana, Haiti, Honduras, Hungary, India, Indonesia, Italy, Japan 4, Kenya, Korea-S, Liberia, Malawi, Malaysia, Malta, Mexico, Mozambique, Nicaragua, Nigeria, Pakistan, Panama, Paraguay 1, Philippines 1, Portugal, Puerto Rico, Romania, Russia, Rwanda, Sierra Leone, S Africa, Spain, Suriname, Swaziland, Tanzania, Thailand, Trinidad & Tob., Uganda, Ukraine 3, UK, Uruguay, Venezuela 1, Virgin Islands, Zambia, Zimbabwe

Church of God, The

(270)622-3900
E-Mail: churchofgodusa@myworld.com
P.O. Box 525, Scottsville, KY 42164
Bishop Danny R. Patrick, General Overseer

A denominational support agency of Pentecostal tradition engaged in support of national churches.

Year Founded in USA 1903
Income for Overseas Mins .... NA

Church of the Brethren

(847)742-5100 Fax: (847)742-6103
E-Mail: mission_gb@brethren.org
1451 Dundee Ave., Elgin, IL 60120-1694
Mr. Mervin Keeney, Dir. Global Msn. Partnership

A denominational sending agency of Brethren tradition engaged in support of national churches, development and relief and/or rehabilitation. Statistical information from 1992.

Year Founded in USA 1884
Income for Overseas Mins .... NR
Fully Supported USA Personnel Overseas:
Expecting to serve more than 4 years 2

Expecting to serve 1 to 4 years 37

Other Personnel:

Short-Term less than 1 year from USA 5

Countries: China (PRC) 2, Germany 5, Haiti 2, Israel 4, Japan 2, Netherlands 2, Nigeria 8, Poland 2, Sudan 4, Switzerland 2, UK 6

Church of the Nazarene, World Mission Division

(816)333-7000 Fax: (816)363-3100
Web: www.nazarene.org/wm
6401 The Paseo, Kansas City, MO 64131
Dr. Louie E. Bustle, Director

A denominational sending agency of Holiness tradition engaged in church planting, aviation services, missionary education, TEE, providing medical supplies, relief and/or rehabilitation and missionary training.

Purpose: "...to respond to the Great Commission of Christ to 'go and make disciples of all nations'...to advance God's Kingdom by the preservation and propagation of Christian Holiness..."

Year Founded in USA 1895

Income for Overseas Mins $38,602,240

Fully Supported USA Personnel Overseas:

Expecting to serve more than 4 years 487
Nonresidential mission personnel 12

Other Personnel:

Non-USA serving in own/other country 193
Bivocational/Tentmaker from USA 15
Short-Term less than 1 year from USA 7389
Home ministry & office staff in USA 39

Countries: Albania 5, Argentina 14, Australia 6, Bolivia 4, Botswana 1, Brazil 10, Bulgaria 4, Cambodia 2, Caribbean Isls 7, Chile 4, China (PRC) 8, Costa Rica 9, Cote d'Ivoire 10, Dominican Rep 6, Ecuador 6, Ethiopia 2, Fiji 4, France 4, Germany 2, Ghana 2, Guam 4, Guatemala 23, Haiti 8, Honduras 2, Hungary 2, India 4, Indonesia 4, Ireland 2, Israel 2, Italy 2, Japan 9, Jordan 4, Kazakhstan 3, Kenya 19, Korea-S 8, Lesotho 2, Madagascar 6, Malawi 8, Mexico 16, Mozambique 11, Namibia 2, Nicaragua 2, Nigeria 3, Papua New Guin 40, Paraguay 4, Peru 10, Philippines 31, Portugal 3, Romania 4, Russia 11, Rwanda 4, Sao Tome & Prin 2, S Africa 37, Spain 2, Swaziland 14, Switzerland 27, Taiwan (ROC) 2, Tanzania 4, Thailand 8, Trinidad & Tobg 4, Uganda 2, Ukraine 2, Venezuela 8, Vietnam 2, W Samoa 2, Zambia 6, Zimbabwe 2

Church of the United Brethren in Christ, Department of Missions

(888)622-3019 Fax: (219)356-4730
E-Mail: kyle@ub.org
Web: www.ub.org
302 Lake St., Huntington, IN 46750
Rev. Kyle W. McQuillen, Jr., Dir. of Missions

A denominational sending agency of Brethren and evangelical tradition engaged in support of national workers, church planting, evangelism, support of national churches and relief and/or rehabilitation.

Purpose: "...to grow and multiply churches through worship, evangelism, discipleship and social concern by actively seeking and winning the lost..."

Year Founded in USA 1853

Income for Overseas Mins $700,000

Gifts-in-Kind $20,000

Fully Supported USA Personnel Overseas:

Expecting to serve 1 to 4 years 4
Nonresidential mission personnel 5

Other Personnel:

Non-USA serving in own/other country 1
Bivocational/Tentmaker from USA 1
Short-Term less than 1 year from USA 275
Home ministry & office staff in USA 5

Countries: India 1, Macao 3

Church Planting International

(904)444-9889 Fax: (904)444-9979
E-Mail: dondunk@gulf.net
P.O. Box 12268, Pensacola, FL 32581
Mr. Craig Merfeld, Director

An interdenominational support agency of Reformed and Presbyterian tradition engaged in support of indigenous church planting movements in developing nations.

Year Founded in USA 1994

Income for Overseas Mins $86,380

Personnel:

Non-USA serving in own/other country 39
Bivocational/Tentmaker from USA 1
Short-Term less than 1 year from USA 2
Home ministry & office staff in USA 2

Countries: Korea-S, Myanmar, Portugal, Uganda

Church Resource Ministries

(714)779-0370 Fax: (714)779-0189

E-Mail: CRM@crmnet.org
Web: www.crmnet.org
1240 N. Lakeview Ave. #120, Anaheim, CA 92807-1831
Dr. Samuel F. Metcalf, President

A transdenominational sending agency of evangelical tradition engaged in leadership development, church planting, evangelism, support of national churches and mobilization for mission.

Purpose: "...to develop leaders to strengthen and start churches worldwide."

Year Founded in USA 1980
Income for Overseas Mins $2,265,541
Gifts-in-Kind $57,298
Fully Supported USA Personnel Overseas:
Expecting to serve more than 4 years 56
Other Personnel:
Short-Term less than 1 year from USA 3
Home ministry & office staff in USA 7
Countries: Australia 2, Cambodia 5, France 4, Hungary 12, Japan 4, Poland 2, Romania 8, Russia 11, Singapore 2, Venezuela 6

Church World Service & Witness, Unit of the National Council of the Churches of Christ in the U.S.A.

(212)870-3004 **Fax: (212)870-3523**
E-Mail: cws@ncccusa.org
Web: www.churchworldservice.org
475 Riverside Dr., Rm. 678, New York, NY 10115
The Rev. Dr. Rodney Page, Exec. Director

An interdenominational service agency of ecumenical tradition engaged in relief and/or rehabilitation, agricultural programs, development and assistance to refugees with partner agencies in the USA and more than 70 other countries.

Purpose: "...meets basic needs of people in peril, works for justice and dignity with the poor and vulnerable, promotes peace and understanding among people of different faiths, races, and nations and affirms and preserves the diversity and integrity of God's creation."

Year Founded in USA 1946
Income for Overseas Mins $48,000,000
Gifts-in-Kind $8,200,000
Fully Supported USA Personnel Overseas:
Expecting to serve more than 4 years 8
Expecting to serve 1 to 4 years 204
Nonresidential mission personnel 10
Other Personnel:
Non-USA serving in own/other country 92
Home ministry & office staff in USA 35
Countries: Africa 5, Asia 27, Cambodia 1, Europe 1, Indonesia 1, Laos 1, Latin America 175, Thailand 1

Churches of Christ

(No central missions office)

A body of autonomous congregations and agencies of the Christian "Restoration Movement" (not using instrumental music in worship) which sends and supports missionaries directly from local congregations. Overseas personnel totals from 1994 Abilene Christian University survey.

Year Founded in USA 0
Income for Overseas Mins .... NA
Fully Supported USA Personnel Overseas:
Expecting to serve more than 4 years 1014
Countries: Africa 229, Asia 148, Europe-E 303, Latin America 273, Oceania 61

Churches of Christ in Christian Union
See: World Gospel Mission

Churches of God General Conference, Commission on Cross-Cultural Ministries

(419)424-1961 **Fax: (419)424-3433**
E-Mail: missions@cggc.org
Web: www.cggc.org
P.O. Box 926, Findlay, OH 45839
Don Dennison, Associate

A denominational sending agency of evangelical tradition engaged in leadership development, church planting, Christian education, evangelism, medical work and support of national churches.

Purpose: "...to evangelize, disciple and equip a community of Christians for effective witness and meaningful service within their own culture."

Year Founded in USA 1825
Income for Overseas Mins $809,537

Fully Supported USA Personnel Overseas:
Expecting to serve more than 4 years 5
Expecting to serve 1 to 4 years 3
Nonresidential mission personnel 1
Other Personnel:
Non-USA serving in own/other country 93
Bivocational/Tentmaker from USA 2
Home ministry & office staff in USA 5
Countries: Brazil 2, Haiti 5, India 1

Cities for Christ Worldwide

(760)233-9905 Fax: (760)233-9905
E-Mail: TimD1@planetall.com
P.O. Box 301032, Escondido, CA 92030-1032
Timothy Monsma, Exec. Director
A transdenominational support agency of evangelical and Reformed tradition providing information and training focused on developing-world cities.
Year Founded in USA 1985
Income for Overseas Mins $85,000
Personnel:
Short-Term less than 1 year from USA 2
Home ministry & office staff in USA 1

CityTeam Ministries

(408)232-5600 Fax: (408)428-9505
E-Mail: CityTeam@cityteam.org
Web: www.cityteam.org
2304 Zanker Rd., San Jose, CA 95131
Patrick J. Robertson, President
A transdenominational support agency of evangelical tradition engaged in evangelism, camping programs, leadership development, missionary training and youth programs. Statistical information from 1996.
Purpose: "...serving people in need, proclaiming the gospel, and establishing disciples among disadvantaged people of cities."
Year Founded in USA 1957
Income for Overseas Mins .... NA
Personnel:
Short-Term less than 1 year from USA 4
Home ministry & office staff in USA 102

CMF International

(317)578-2700 Fax: (317)578-2827
E-Mail: 76534.244@compuserve.com
Web: www.CMFI.org
P.O. Box 501020, Indianapolis, IN 46250-6020
Dr. Doug Priest, Gen. Director
A nondenominational sending agency of Christian (Restoration Movement) and evangelical tradition engaged in church planting, development, evangelism, leadership development, medical work and missionary training.
Purpose: "...to serve Jesus Christ and His Church in world evangelization...in partnership with Christians around the world through teams that make disciples and establish church-planting movements among unreached people."
Year Founded in USA 1949
Income for Overseas Mins $4,650,000
Gifts-in-Kind $55,000
Fully Supported USA Personnel Overseas:
Expecting to serve more than 4 years 88
Expecting to serve 1 to 4 years 25
Other Personnel:
Non-USA serving in own/other country 113
Bivocational/Tentmaker from USA 8
Short-Term less than 1 year from USA 44
Home ministry & office staff in USA 23
Countries: Africa 2, Asia 5, Benin 2, Brazil 5, Chile 6, Cote d'Ivoire 2, Ethiopia 13, Indonesia 6, Kenya 36, Mexico 9, Singapore 2, Thailand 6, Ukraine 5, UK 14

ComCare International

(914)876-3020 Fax: (914)876-3020
E-Mail: comcareint@juno.com
P.O. Box 45, Rhinebeck, NY 12572
Mr. Kenneth L. Plog, Chairman
A nondenominational specialized agency of evangelical tradition engaged in disability assistance programs, evangelism and short-term programs.
Purpose: "...to enable the hearing impaired to improve their hearing and communication to the glory of God."
Year Founded in USA 1989
Income for Overseas Mins $55,000
Fully Supported USA Personnel Overseas:
Expecting to serve more than 4 years 2
Other Personnel:
Non-USA serving in own/other country 2
Countries: Mexico 2

Compassion International, Inc.

(719)594-9900 **Fax: (719)594-6271**
E-Mail: CIinfo@ci.us.org
Web: www.ci.org
P.O. Box 7000, Colorado Springs, CO 80933
Dr. Wesley K. Stafford, President/CEO

A nondenominational service agency of evangelical tradition engaged in childcare/orphanage programs, extension education, evangelism, leadership development, relief and/or rehabilitation and youth programs.

Purpose: "...an advocate for children to release them from their spiritual, economic, social and physical poverty and enable them to become responsible and fulfilled Christian adults."

Year Founded in USA 1952
Income for Overseas Mins $73,110,343
Gifts-in-Kind $353,474
Fully Supported USA Personnel Overseas:
Expecting to serve more than 4 years 2
Nonresidential mission personnel 3
Other Personnel:
Non-USA serving in own/other country 340
Home ministry & office staff in USA 255
Countries: Africa, Asia 2, Bolivia, Brazil, Colombia, Congo/Zaire, Dominican Rep., Ecuador, Ethiopia, Guatemala, Haiti, India, Indonesia, Kenya, Peru, Philippines, Rwanda, Thailand, Uganda

Concordia Gospel Outreach

(314)268-1363 **Fax: (314)268-1329**
E-Mail: outreach@cphnet.org
Web: www.cgo-online.org
P.O. Box 201, St. Louis, MO 63166-0201
Annette Frank, Manager

A specialized agency of Lutheran tradition engaged in Bible and literature distribution.

Purpose: "...distributes Gospel materials and supports the expansion of the Gospel worldwide."

Year Founded in USA 1958
Income for Overseas Mins $38,000
Gifts-in-Kind $10,000
Personnel:
Home ministry & office staff in USA 2

Congregational Christian Churches, National Assoc. of

(414)764-1620 **Fax: (414)764-0319**
E-Mail: naccc@naccc.org
Web: www.naccc.org
8473 S. Howell Ave., Milwaukee, WI 53154
Dr. Donald P. Olsen, Missions Secretary

An association of churches of Congregational tradition engaged in funds transmission, childcare/orphanage programs, Christian education, providing medical supplies, services for other agencies and support of national workers.

Purpose: "To encourage and assist local churches in their development of vibrant and effective witnesses to Christ in Congregational ways."

Year Founded in USA 1953
Income for Overseas Mins $475,000
Personnel:
Non-USA serving in own/other country 22
Home ministry & office staff in USA 2
Countries: Bulgaria, Greece, Honduras, India, Kenya, Mexico, Nigeria, Philippines

Congregational Holiness Church World Missions

(770)228-4833 **Fax: (770)228-1177**
3888 Fayetteville Hwy., Griffin, GA 30223
Rev. Billy Anderson, Supt. of World Missions

A denominational support agency of Holiness and Pentecostal tradition engaged in support of national workers, church construction, Christian education, providing medical supplies and support of national churches in 12 countries. Income figure from 1992.

Year Founded in USA 1921
Income for Overseas Mins $390,099
Personnel:
Home ministry & office staff in USA 4

Congregational Methodist Church, Division of Mission Ministries

(601)845-8787 **Fax: (601)845-8788**
E-Mail: CMChdq@aol.com
P.O. Box 9, Florence, MS 39073
Rev. Billy Harrell, Director

A denominational sending agency of Wesleyan tradition engaged in church planting, broadcasting, camping programs,

Christian education, evangelism and medical work.

Year Founded in USA 1945
Income for Overseas Mins $240,253
Fully Supported USA Personnel Overseas:
Expecting to serve more than 4 years 13
Other Personnel:
Home ministry & office staff in USA 8
Countries: Honduras 1, Mexico 10, Uganda 2

Conservative Baptist Foreign Mission Society (CBFMS) See: CBInternational

Conservative Baptist Home Mission Society (CBHMS) See: Mission to the Americas

Conservative Congregational Christian Conference

(651)739-1474 **Fax: (651)739-0750**
E-Mail: cccc4@juno.com
Web: www.ccccusa.org
7582 Currell Blvd. #108, St. Paul, MN 55125
Rev. Clifford R. Christensen, Conf. Minister

A denominational support agency of Congregational and evangelical tradition engaged in support of national churches and short-term programs. Statistics from 1996.

Year Founded in USA 1948
Income for Overseas Mins $107,805
Fully Supported USA Personnel Overseas:
Expecting to serve more than 4 years 2
Expecting to serve 1 to 4 years 2
Other Personnel:
Home ministry & office staff in USA 3
Countries: Micronesia 4

Cook Communications Ministries International

(719)536-0100 **Fax: (719)536-3266**
E-Mail: ccmintl@ccmi.org
Web: www.cookministries.com
4050 Lee Vance View, Colorado Springs, CO 80918
Mr. David Mehlis, President

An interdenominational ministry of evangelical tradition engaged in making Christian literature available from translations of their English language product and through training Christian publishers to provide Christian literature in their own language and country.

Purpose: "To encourage the acceptance of Jesus Christ as personal Savior and to aid, promote and contribute to the teaching and putting into practice of His two great commands…"

Year Founded in USA 1944
Income for Overseas Mins $440,436
Gifts-in-Kind $40,000
Personnel:
Non-USA serving in own/other country 1
Home ministry & office staff in USA 12

Cooperative Baptist Fellowship

(770)220-1600 **Fax: (770)220-1680**
Web: www.cbfonline.org
P.O. Box 450329, Atlanta, GA 31145-0329
Mr. Gary Baldridge, Global Missions Co-Coord.
Mrs. Barbara Baldridge, Global Missions Co-Coord.

A denominational sending agency of Baptist tradition engaged in church planting, evangelism and mission-related research. Statistical information from 1996.

Purpose: "...to network, empower, and mobilize Baptist Christians and churches for effective missions and ministry in the name of Christ."

Year Founded in USA 1992
Income for Overseas Mins .... NA
Personnel:
Home ministry & office staff in USA 5

Cornerstone International

(606)858-4578 **Fax: (606)858-4578**
E-Mail: cornerstone407@juno.com
P.O. Box 192, Wilmore, KY 40390
Mr. E. Duane Jones, Director

A nondenominational sending agency of Wesleyan and charismatic tradition engaged in mobilization for mission, childrens programs, church planting, TEE, evangelism and short-term programs.

Purpose: "...to evangelize and disciple...[in] partnership with local churches in the launching of short-term and career missionaries."

Year Founded in USA 1972
Income for Overseas Mins $190,000

Fully Supported USA Personnel Overseas:
Expecting to serve more than 4 years 7
Other Personnel:
Bivocational/Tentmaker from USA 2
Short-Term less than 1 year from USA 6
Home ministry & office staff in USA 2
Countries: Brazil 2, France 2, India 1, S Africa 2

Correll Missionary Ministries

(540)362-5196 Fax: (540)366-7630
E-Mail: correllmin@aol.com
Web: www.correll.org
P.O. Box 12182, Roanoke, VA 24023
Rev. Jorge Parrott, President

An interdenominational service agency of evangelical tradition engaged in support of national workers, broadcasting, church construction and providing medical supplies.

Year Founded in USA 1978
Income for Overseas Mins $62,100
Gifts-in-Kind $62,100
Fully Supported USA Personnel Overseas:
Expecting to serve more than 4 years 2
Other Personnel:
Home ministry & office staff in USA 2
Countries: Guatemala 2

Covenant Celebration Church Global Outreach

(253)475-6454 Fax: (253)473-7515
E-Mail: jkling@covenantcelebration.org
Web: www.covenantcelebration.org
1819 E. 72nd St., Tacoma, WA 98404
Jo Kling, Director

A nondenominational support agency of charismatic tradition engaged in church planting, leadership development and support of national churches and workers for evangelism.

Purpose: "...[to] pursue the Great Commission both mono-culturally and cross-culturally through aggressive action in...evangelism and missions."

Year Founded in USA 1981
Income for Overseas Mins $50,000
Personnel:
Non-USA serving in own/other country 4
Bivocational/Tentmaker from USA 2
Home ministry & office staff in USA 1
Countries: Burundi, Philippines, UK

Crisis Consulting International

(805)642-2549 Fax: (805)642-1748
E-Mail: CrisisConsulting@xc.org
Web: www.hostagerescue.org
PMB 223, 9452 Telephone Rd., Ventura, CA 93004
Mr. Robert Klamser, Exec. Director

A nondenominational service agency of evangelical tradition engaged in security/ crisis management consulting/training and services for other agencies.

Purpose: "...providing security-related training and consultation services to...mission organizations with specific needs such as event security, protection of personnel and investigation of hostile acts..."

Year Founded in USA 1985
Income for Overseas Mins $46,716

Crossover Communications Intl.

(803)691-0688 Fax: (803)691-9355
E-Mail: info@crossoverusa.org
Web: www.crossoverusa.org
P.O. Box 211755, Columbia, SC 29221
Dr. William H. Jones, President

A transdenominational service agency of evangelical tradition engaged in evangelism, church planting, leadership development, medical work, mobilization for mission and short-term programs.

Purpose: "In the power of the Spirit...to communicate the message of Christ...to the peoples of the world."

Year Founded in USA 1987
Income for Overseas Mins $395,000
Fully Supported USA Personnel Overseas:
Expecting to serve more than 4 years 4
Other Personnel:
Non-USA serving in own/other country 4
Short-Term less than 1 year from USA 17
Home ministry & office staff in USA 51
Countries: Brazil, Moldava 4

CSI Ministries
See: Christian Service Intl.

Cumberland Presbyterian Church Board of Missions

(901)276-9988 Fax: (901)276-4578
E-Mail: missions@cumberland.org
Web: www.cumberland.org/center
1978 Union Ave., Memphis, TN 38104
Rev. Michael Sharpe, Exec. Director

A denominational sending agency of evangelical tradition engaged in church planting, evangelism, leadership development, support of national churches and support of national workers. Statistical information from 1996.

Year Founded in USA 1908
Income for Overseas Mins $500,000
Gifts-in-Kind $100,000
Fully Supported USA Personnel Overseas:
Expecting to serve more than 4 years 5
Expecting to serve 1 to 4 years 2
Other Personnel:
Bivocational/Tentmaker from USA 2
Short-Term less than 1 year from USA 2
Home ministry & office staff in USA 1
Countries: Brazil 3, Colombia 3, Hong Kong 1

David Livingstone KURE Foundation

(918)742-9902 Fax: (918)742-9903
E-Mail: DLMFKURE@aol.com
Web: www.dlmfkure.org
P.O. Box 232, Tulsa, OK 74102
Mr. H. Dwain Griffin, Chairman/CEO

A nondenominational service agency of independent tradition engaged in support of national workers. Name changed from David Livingstone Missionary Foundation.

Year Founded in USA 1969
Income for Overseas Mins $1,500,000
Personnel:
Non-USA serving in own/other country 113
Home ministry & office staff in USA 9
Countries: Korea-S, Mexico, Philippines, Thailand, Ukraine

Dawn Ministries

(719)548-7460 Fax: (719)548-7475
E-Mail: DAWNinformation@dawnministries.org
Web: www.dawnministries.org
5775 N. Union Blvd., Colorado Springs, CO 80918
Dr. James H. Montgomery, Chairman
Dr. Stephen D. Steele, CEO

A transdenominational service agency of evangelical tradition engaged in mobilizing the whole body of Christ in 148 nations. Statistics from 1996.

Purpose: "...to see saturation church planting become the generally accepted and fervently practiced strategy for completing the task of making disciples of all peoples in our generation."

Year Founded in USA 1985
Income for Overseas Mins $711,315
Fully Supported USA Personnel Overseas:
Nonresidential mission personnel 9
Other Personnel:
Home ministry & office staff in USA 15

Dayspring Enterprises International

(757)428-1092 Fax: (757)428-0257
E-Mail: DaySprgInt@aol.com
Web: www.dayspringintl.org
1062 Laskin Rd., Suite 21A, Virginia Beach, VA 23451
Rev. John E. Gilman, President

A nondenominational support agency of evangelical tradition engaged in video/film production/distribution, church planting and evangelism.

Purpose: "...to be an enabling servant to the indigenous church by providing innovative, creative and culturally relevant multi-media tools to aid in evangelizing and discipling of unreached people groups."

Year Founded in USA 1979
Income for Overseas Mins $1,235,026
Gifts-in-Kind $12,000
Personnel:
Home ministry & office staff in USA 9

Daystar U.S.

(612)928-2550 Fax: (612)928-2551
E-Mail: DAYSTARUS@compuserve.com
Web: www.daystarus.org
5701 Normandale Rd. #343, Edina, MN 55424
Mr. Robert J. Oehrig, Exec. Director

A nondenominational sending agency of evangelical tradition engaged in providing

support for Daystar Univ. in Nairobi, in missionary training, extension education, theological education, management consulting/training and mission-related research.
Purpose: "To expand God's Kingdom in Africa by equipping Christian servant leaders through B.A./M.A. programs, short courses and research services."
Year Founded in USA 1963
Income for Overseas Mins $1,370,000
Gifts-in-Kind $63,244
Fully Supported USA Personnel Overseas:
Expecting to serve more than 4 years 7
Other Personnel:
Bivocational/Tentmaker from USA 2
Short-Term less than 1 year from USA 13
Home ministry & office staff in USA 7
Countries: Kenya 7

Deaf Missions International

(727)530-3020 **Fax: (727)530-3020**
E-Mail: deafmissions@email.msn.com
P.O. Box 8514, Clearwater, FL 33758
M. Eldeny Hale, Director

A transdenominational specialized agency of evangelical tradition engaged in ministry to those with hearing disabilities through mission projects including missionary orientation and training. Statistical information from 1996.
Year Founded in USA 1967
Income for Overseas Mins $160,000
Fully Supported USA Personnel Overseas:
Expecting to serve more than 4 years 1
Nonresidential mission personnel 1
Other Personnel:
Home ministry & office staff in USA 1
Countries: Colombia 1

Derek Prince Ministries, Intl.

(704)357-3556 **Fax: (704)357-1413**
E-Mail: ContactUs@us.derekprince.com
Web: www.derekprince.com
P.O. Box 19501, Charlotte, NC 28219
Mr. David Selby, Exec. Director

A nondenominational support agency engaged in translation work, audio recording/distribution, broadcasting, literature distribution, literature production and video/film production/distribution in 13 languages.
Purpose: "...seeking to reach the unreached and teach the untaught with the pure truths of God's Word in all nations…through the distribution of teaching material by Derek Prince…"
Year Founded in USA 1963
Income for Overseas Mins $842,089
Personnel:
Home ministry & office staff in USA 29

Development Associates International

(719)598-7970 **Fax: (719)598-1556**
E-Mail: 75211.2414@compuserve.com
Web: www.daintl.org
P.O. Box 49278, Colorado Springs, CO 80949
Dr. James F. Engel, CEO

A specialized agency of evangelical tradition engaged in leadership development, extension education and management consulting/training.
Purpose: "[to] develop capacities for integrity and effectiveness in Christian leaders by providing educational resources, consultants and mentors to leaders with a vision for equipping and developing others."
Year Founded in USA 1996
Income for Overseas Mins .... NA
Fully Supported USA Personnel Overseas:
Nonresidential mission personnel 2
Other Personnel:
Non-USA serving in own/other country 4
Home ministry & office staff in USA 2

Donetsk Christian University

(918)249-2011
E-Mail: rwcornish@juno.com
8534 E. 77th Place, Tulsa, OK 74133
Dr. Richard W. Cornish, U.S. Director

A nondenominational specialized agency of evangelical and Baptist tradition engaged in theological education, missionary education and leadership development.
Purpose: "...to train national pastors, missionaries and teachers for the former Soviet Union."
Year Founded in USA 1991
Income for Overseas Mins $161,565
Fully Supported USA Personnel Overseas:
Expecting to serve 1 to 4 years 6

Other Personnel:
Non-USA serving in own/other country 20
Short-Term less than 1 year from USA 22
Home ministry & office staff in USA 1
Countries: Ukraine 6

Door of Hope International

(626)304-9130 Fax: (626)304-9125
669 N. Los Robles, Pasadena, CA 91101
Mr. Mike Patterson, Exec. Director

An interdenominational service agency of evangelical tradition engaged in support of national workers, services for other agencies and youth programs. Statistical information from 1996.

Year Founded in USA 1972
Income for Overseas Mins $101,109
Fully Supported USA Personnel Overseas:
Expecting to serve more than 4 years 6
Other Personnel:
Non-USA serving in own/other country 10
Short-Term less than 1 year from USA 2
Home ministry & office staff in USA 4
Countries: Albania 4, Macedonia 2

East Gates Ministries Intl.

(253)770-2625 Fax: (253)770-2817
E-Mail: EGMI@eastgates.org
Web: www.eastgates.org
P.O. Box 2010, Sumner, WA 98390-0440
Rev. Nelson Graham, President

A specialized agency of evangelical and ecumenical tradition engaged in Bible distribution, audio recording/distribution, church construction, literature distribution, literature production and support of national churches.

Purpose: "...to have a positive impact on the Church history of China through diplomatic activity that helps Chinese leaders, at all levels, better understand and appreciate their Christian population."

Year Founded in USA 1990
Income for Overseas Mins $1,145,826
Personnel:
Non-USA serving in own/other country 4
Short-Term less than 1 year from USA 4
Home ministry & office staff in USA 8

East West Ministries

(651)765-2550 Fax: (651)765-2523
E-Mail: jonesewm@juno.com
P.O. Box 270333, St. Paul, MN 55127
Annette L. Jones, Director

A support agency of evangelical tradition engaged in funds transmission in support of national workers, Bible distribution and supplying equipment. Income amount from 1996.

Purpose: "...serving those who serve in the name of Jesus Christ and seeking to fulfill the two-fold mandate of evangelism; to share the gospel message and to care for people in obvious need."

Year Founded in USA 1993
Income for Overseas Mins $48,000
Personnel:
Non-USA serving in own/other country 11
Home ministry & office staff in USA 1

East-West Ministries Intl.

(214)265-8300 Fax: (214)373-8571
E-Mail: info@eastwestministries.org
Web: www.eastwestministries.org
10310 N. Central Expressway, Bldg. 3 - Suite 400, Dallas, TX 75231
Mr. John Maisel, President

A nondenominational sending agency of Baptist tradition engaged in support of national churches, childrens programs, theological education, evangelism, leadership development and short-term programs.

Purpose: "...to provide church planting training and coordination of evangelistic resources to help plant churches that are doctrinally sound, spiritually alive, grace oriented and multiplying..."

Year Founded in USA 1993
Income for Overseas Mins $1,288,822
Fully Supported USA Personnel Overseas:
Expecting to serve more than 4 years 4
Expecting to serve 1 to 4 years 3
Nonresidential mission personnel...................... 1
Other Personnel:
Home ministry & office staff in USA 33
Countries: Kazakhstan 3, Russia 1, Spain 3

Eastern European Bible Mission
See: New Hope International

Eastern European Outreach, Inc.

(909)696-5244 **Fax: (909)696-5247**
E-Mail: Info@eeo.org
Web: www.eeo.org
P.O. Box 685, Murrieta, CA 92564
Mr. Jeff L. Thompson, Exec. Director

An interdenominational service agency of evangelical tradition engaged in childcare/orphanage programs, church planting, evangelism, literature production, child sponsorship and support of national churches. Financial data from 1996.

Purpose: "...to promote the Gospel of Jesus Christ, free of denominational prejudices and in the cultural context of each individual country."

Year Founded in USA 1980
Income for Overseas Mins $615,000
Gifts-in-Kind $250,000
Fully Supported USA Personnel Overseas:
Expecting to serve more than 4 years 7
Nonresidential mission personnel 1
Other Personnel:
Non-USA serving in own/other country 25
Short-Term less than 1 year from USA 105
Home ministry & office staff in USA 8
Countries: Albania 1, Romania 1, Russia 1, Ukraine 4

Eastern Mennonite Missions

(717)898-2251 **Fax: (717)898-8092**
E-Mail: info@emm.org
Web: www.emm.org
P.O. Box 458, 53 Brandt Blvd., Salunga, PA 17538-0458
Mr. Richard Showalter, President

A denominational sending agency of Mennonite tradition engaged in church planting, development, theological education, leadership development, relief and/or rehabilitation and youth programs.

Year Founded in USA 1914
Income for Overseas Mins $3,129,433
Fully Supported USA Personnel Overseas:
Expecting to serve more than 4 years 127
Expecting to serve 1 to 4 years 24
Other Personnel:
Non-USA serving in own/other country 2
Bivocational/Tentmaker from USA 16
Short-Term less than 1 year from USA 138
Home ministry & office staff in USA 53
Countries: Africa 9, Albania 8, Asia 19, Australia 2, Belize 4, Bosnia 1, Brazil 2, Burkina Faso 2, Cambodia 5, Ethiopia 6, Germany 4, Guatemala 11, Honduras 4, Hong Kong 6, Hungary 3, India 1, Kenya 25, Lithuania 4, Mali 2, Mexico 4, Netherlands 4, Papua New Guin 2, Peru 5, Somalia 1, Swaziland 2, Tanzania 3, Thailand 10, UK 2

ECHO (Educational Concerns for Hunger Organization)

(941)543-3246 **Fax: (941)543-5317**
E-Mail: echo@echonet.org
Web: www.echonet.org
17430 Durance Rd., N. Ft Myers, FL 33917
Dr. Martin L. Price, Exec. Director

An interdenominational service agency of evangelical tradition engaged in agricultural programs, services for other agencies, technical assistance and training.

Purpose: "...to strengthen the ministries of missionaries and national churches as they assist small-scale farmers or urban gardeners in the Third World."

Year Founded in USA 1973
Income for Overseas Mins $880,930
Gifts-in-Kind $79,114
Fully Supported USA Personnel Overseas:
Expecting to serve 1 to 4 years 2
Nonresidential mission personnel 8
Other Personnel:
Short-Term less than 1 year from USA 6
Home ministry & office staff in USA 11
Countries: Haiti 2

Educational Services International

(800)895-7955 **Fax: (626)821-2022**
E-Mail: teach@esimail.org
Web: www.esiadventure.org
444 E. Huntington Dr., Ste 200, Arcadia, CA 91006
Mr. Ron Nicholas, President

An interdenominational specialized agency of evangelical tradition engaged in leadership development and teaching English, Business, and other subjects in educational institutions in Asia and Eastern Europe.

Purpose: "…to recruit, train and send educators to developing countries to provide and implement this service in the spirit of Christ to express His life through the lives of our teachers."

Year Founded in USA 1981

Income for Overseas Mins .... NA

Personnel:

Bivocational/Tentmaker from USA 160

Short-Term less than 1 year from USA 75

Home ministry & office staff in USA 14

EFMA (Evangelical Fellowship of Mission Agencies)

(770)457-6677 Fax: (770)457-0037

E-Mail: efma@xc.org

4201 N. Peachtree Rd. #300, Atlanta, GA 30341-1207

Dr. Paul E. McKaughan, Pres. & CEO

A confederation of mission agencies which serves for the exchange of ideas and building of supportive relationships.

Purpose: "...to aid agencies and boards to work more efficiently, tapping into the rich resource of all our members so that the gifts God gives can be used most effectively in the task of world evangelization."

Year Founded in USA 1945

Income for Overseas Mins .... NA

Personnel:

Home ministry & office staff in USA 5

Elim Fellowship, World Missions Department

(716)582-2790 Fax: (716)624-1229

E-Mail: efmissions@compuserve.com

Web: www.frontiernet.net/~elim/

1703 Dalton Rd., P.O. Box 57A, Lima, NY 14485-0857

Mr. Thomas Brazell, Director

A nondenominational sending agency of charismatic tradition engaged in church planting, missionary education, theological education, and leadership development. See Teen World Outreach for short-term program. Statistical information from 1996.

Year Founded in USA 1947

Income for Overseas Mins $1,322,000

Fully Supported USA Personnel Overseas:

Expecting to serve more than 4 years 106

Other Personnel:

Home ministry & office staff in USA 3

Countries: Andorra 2, Argentina 2, Australia 2, Austria 1, Belgium 1, Cambodia 1, Colombia 6, Denmark 2, Ethiopia 1, Europe-E 2, Haiti 2, Hong Kong 4, Israel 2, Kenya 25, Kiribati 2, Malaysia 2, Mexico 15, Mozambique 2, New Zealand 2, Niger 2, Nigeria 3, Peru 2, S Africa 1, Spain 4, Tanzania 12, Uganda 3, UK 2, Zimbabwe 1

Emmanuel Intl. Mission (U.S.)

(803)831-1356 Fax: (803)831-1356

E-Mail: davemccauley@mindspring.com

Web: www.e-i.org

3878 Concord Rd., York, SC 29745

Mr. Dave McCauley, Chairman

An interdenominational service agency of evangelical tradition engaged in support of national churches, agricultural programs, TEE, medical work and relief and/or rehabilitation.

Purpose: "...assists local churches worldwide to meet physical and spiritual needs of the poor."

Year Founded in USA 1976

Income for Overseas Mins $80,000

Fully Supported USA Personnel Overseas:

Expecting to serve more than 4 years 2

Countries: Malawi 1, Philippines 1

Emmaus Road, International

(858)292-7020 Fax: (858)292-7020

E-Mail: Emmaus_Road@eri.org

Web: www.eri.org

7150 Tanner Court, San Diego, CA 92111-4236

Mr. Neal Pirolo, Director

A transdenominational service agency engaged in mobilization and training through publications, audio and video recordings, prefield courses, short-term trips and seminars.

Purpose: "...to benefit churches, mission agencies, cross-cultural teams and national ministries as they take the 'next step' in cross-cultural outreach ministry."

Year Founded in USA 1983

Income for Overseas Mins $54,000

Personnel:

Short-Term less than 1 year from USA 14

Home ministry & office staff in USA 3

Engineering Ministries Intl.

(719)633-2078 **Fax: (719)633-2970**
E-Mail: info@emiusa.org
Web: www.emiusa.org
110 S. Weber St., Suite 104, Colorado Springs, CO 80903
Mr. Michael T. Orsillo, Exec. Director

An interdenominational specialized agency of evangelical tradition engaged in technical assistance, development and mobilization for mission.

Purpose: "...to mobilize Christian design professionals to serve the poor in developing countries...by empowering people to transform their world through the design and development of hospitals, schools, orphanages, bridges, water supplies, wastewater facilities and more."

Year Founded in USA 1981
Income for Overseas Mins $911,300
Gifts-in-Kind $478,600
Fully Supported USA Personnel Overseas:
Expecting to serve 1 to 4 years 3
Other Personnel:
Non-USA serving in own/other country 3
Bivocational/Tentmaker from USA 2
Short-Term less than 1 year from USA 8
Home ministry & office staff in USA 1
Countries: India 3

Enterprise Development Intl.

(703)277-3360 **Fax: (703)277-3348**
E-Mail: edi1@ix.netcom.com
Web: www.endpoverty.com
10395-B Democracy Lane, Fairfax, VA 22030
Mr. Juan A. Benitez, President & CEO

A transdenominational service agency engaged in management consulting, training, and technical assistance for partner implementing agencies.

Purpose: "...enabling the poor to become productive, self supporting citizens."

Year Founded in USA 1985
Income for Overseas Mins .... NR
Gifts-in-Kind $158,000
Fully Supported USA Personnel Overseas:
Expecting to serve more than 4 years 1
Expecting to serve 1 to 4 years 1
Other Personnel:
Non-USA serving in own/other country 1
Home ministry & office staff in USA 8
Countries: Mexico 1, Nicaragua 1

Episcopal Church Missionary Community

(724)266-2810 **Fax: (724)266-6773**
E-Mail: ecmc@usaor.net
Web: www.episcopalian.org/ecmc
Box 278, Ambridge, PA 15003
Sharon Stockdale, Director

A denominational support agency of Episcopal and evangelical tradition engaged in missionary training, missions information service and mobilization for mission.

Purpose: "...to enable Episcopalians to be more knowledgeable, active and effective in world missions."

Year Founded in USA 1974
Income for Overseas Mins $22,000
Personnel:
Home ministry & office staff in USA 2

Episcopal Church, Domestic & Foreign Missionary Society

(212)716-6223 **Fax: (212)983-6377**
E-Mail: pmauney@dfms.org
Web: www.ecusa.anglican.org/agr
815 Second Ave., New York, NY 10017
The Rev. Canon J. Patrick Mauney, Director

A denominational sending agency of Anglican tradition engaged in support of national churches, development, funds transmission, missions information service, leadership development and missionary training. Statistical information from 1996.

Purpose: "…to ensure, in the most comprehensive and coordinated manner possible, the full participation of Episcopalians in the worldwide mission of the church…"

Year Founded in USA 1841
Income for Overseas Mins $10,322,549
Fully Supported USA Personnel Overseas:
Expecting to serve more than 4 years 21
Expecting to serve 1 to 4 years 32
Countries: Unspecified 53

Episcopal World Mission

(704)248-1377 **Fax: (704)248-2482**
E-Mail: EWM@rfci.net

P.O. Box 490, Forest City, NC 28043
The Rev. Kevin Higgins, President
A denominational sending agency of Episcopal tradition engaged in evangelism, support of national churches and mobilization for mission. Statistical information from 1992.
Year Founded in USA 1982
Income for Overseas Mins $399,409
Fully Supported USA Personnel Overseas:
Expecting to serve more than 4 years 11
Other Personnel:
Non-USA serving in own/other country 5
Home ministry & office staff in USA 6
Countries: Congo/Zaire 3, Israel 2, Madagascar 2, Pakistan 2, Solomon Isls 2

Equip, Inc.

(828)738-3891 Fax: (828)738-3946
E-Mail: webmaster@equipministries.org
Web: www.equipministries.org
P.O. Box 1126, Marion, NC 28752-1126
Rev. Barrie G. Flitcroft, President
An interdenominational sending agency of evangelical tradition engaged in development, agricultural programs, evangelism, medical work, technical assistance and missionary training.
Purpose: "...to assist the church around the world to be responsive to the poor, sensitive to the Holy Spirit, focused on personal evangelism and practically engaged in strengthening the Body of Christ."
Year Founded in USA 1995
Income for Overseas Mins $598,127
Gifts-in-Kind $30,145
Fully Supported USA Personnel Overseas:
Expecting to serve more than 4 years 20
Expecting to serve 1 to 4 years 5
Other Personnel:
Non-USA serving in own/other country 12
Short-Term less than 1 year from USA 6
Home ministry & office staff in USA 11
Countries: Bolivia 2, Brazil 8, Ethiopia 4, Japan 1, Mexico 2, Nicaragua 4, Philippines 2, Russia 2

Equipping the Saints

(540)234-6222 Fax: (540)234-6262
E-Mail: ETS@rica.net
Web: www.warrenton-bible.org/ets.htm
1254 Keezletown Road, Weyers Cave, VA 24486-2318
Rev. Keith A. Jones, Exec. Director
A nondenominational service agency of evangelical tradition engaged in purchasing services and supplying equipment.
Purpose: "...to enhance the outreach of indigenous evangelical ministries...by providing appropriate human, material and financial resources."
Year Founded in USA 1991
Income for Overseas Mins $370,176
Gifts-in-Kind $88,363
Personnel:
Home ministry & office staff in USA 4

European Christian Mission NA, Inc.

(604)943-0211 Fax: (604)943-0212
E-Mail: 74663.3176@compuserve.com
P.O. Box 1006, Point Roberts, WA 98281
Rev. Vincent Price, Director for N. America
An interdenominational sending agency of evangelical tradition engaged in evangelism, broadcasting, literature distribution and support of national churches and workers in E. Europe and the former USSR.
Year Founded in USA 1960
Income for Overseas Mins $723,800
Fully Supported USA Personnel Overseas:
Expecting to serve more than 4 years 35
Other Personnel:
Short-Term less than 1 year from USA 18
Home ministry & office staff in USA 3
Countries: Europe-E 15, Greece 7, Ireland 1, Italy 2, Spain 8, UK 2

European Evangelistic Society

(404)344-7458
E-Mail: euroevansoc@juno.com
P.O. Drawer 90150, East Point, GA 30364
Mr. James L. Evans, Exec. Director
A nondenominational sending agency of Christian (Restoration Movement) tradition engaged in theological education, church planting, evangelism and mission-related research. Statistical information from 1996.
Year Founded in USA 1932

Income for Overseas Mins $146,540
Fully Supported USA Personnel Overseas:
Expecting to serve more than 4 years 4
Other Personnel:
Home ministry & office staff in USA 2
Countries: Germany 2, Lithuania 2

European Missions Outreach

(804)978-4466 Fax: (804)978-4466
P.O. Box 6937, Charlottesville, VA 22906
Robert M. Baxter, President

A nondenominational sending agency of charismatic tradition engaged in funds transmission, audio recording/distribution, church planting and translation work. Statistical information from 1996.

Purpose: "[to] train and equip European leadership, establish and support local churches, reach tomorrow's leaders by evangelizing today's youth."

Year Founded in USA 1990
Income for Overseas Mins $70,000
Fully Supported USA Personnel Overseas:
Expecting to serve more than 4 years 4
Other Personnel:
Short-Term less than 1 year from USA 4
Home ministry & office staff in USA 1
Countries: France 2, Netherlands 2

Evangel Bible Translators

(972)722-2140 Fax: (972)722-1721
E-Mail: info@evangelbible.org
Web: www.evangelbible.org
P.O. Box 669, Rockwall, TX 75087
Rev. H. Syvelle Phillips, President

A nondenominational sending agency of Pentecostal tradition engaged in Bible translation, Bible distribution, church construction, linguistics, literacy work and support of national workers.

Year Founded in USA 1976
Income for Overseas Mins $534,007
Fully Supported USA Personnel Overseas:
Expecting to serve more than 4 years 13
Other Personnel:
Non-USA serving in own/other country 15
Home ministry & office staff in USA 6
Countries: France 2, Ghana 2, Guatemala 2, India 6, Philippines 1

Evangelical Baptist Missions

(765)453-4488 Fax: (765)455-0889
E-Mail: ebm@ebm.org
Web: www.ebm.org
P.O. Box 2225, Kokomo, IN 46904-2225
Dr. W. Paul Jackson, Gen. Director

A sending agency of independent and Baptist tradition engaged in church planting, childrens programs, extension education, evangelism, Bible translation and video/film production/distribution. Income information from 1992. Personnel information from 1996.

Year Founded in USA 1928
Income for Overseas Mins $2,696,762
Fully Supported USA Personnel Overseas:
Expecting to serve more than 4 years 117
Expecting to serve 1 to 4 years 4
Other Personnel:
Non-USA serving in own/other country 2
Short-Term less than 1 year from USA 22
Home ministry & office staff in USA 12
Countries: Argentina 8, Benin 1, Cote d'Ivoire 12, France 26, Germany 6, Italy 4, Japan 4, Mali 18, Nigeria 10, Romania 4, Russia 4, S Africa 14, Sweden 4, UK 6

Evangelical Bible Mission

(352)245-2560 Fax: (352)245-9783
E-Mail: EBMission@aol.com
Web: www.ebminternational.com
P.O. Drawer 189, Summerfield, FL 34492
Rev. Gerald Bustin, President
Rev. V. O. Agan, Chairman of the Board

An interdenominational sending agency of Holiness tradition engaged in church planting, Bible distribution, evangelism, literature distribution and supplying equipment. Personnel information from 1992. Financial information from 1996.

Year Founded in USA 1939
Income for Overseas Mins $1,700,000
Fully Supported USA Personnel Overseas:
Expecting to serve 1 to 4 years 65
Nonresidential mission personnel...................... 2
Other Personnel:
Home ministry & office staff in USA 5
Countries: Brazil 4, Haiti 6, Papua New Guin 55

Evangelical Congregational Church, Division of Missions

(717)866-7584 **Fax: (717)866-7383**
E-Mail: ECdom@nbn.net
P.O. Box 186, Myerstown, PA 17067
Dr. John P. Ragsdale, Director
A denominational service agency of Wesleyan tradition engaged in church planting, support of national churches and support of national workers.
Year Founded in USA 1922
Income for Overseas Mins $797,340

Evangelical Covenant Church, Board of World Mission

(773)784-3000 **Fax: (773)784-4366**
E-Mail: wm@covoffice.org
Web: www.covchurch.org
5101 N. Francisco Ave., Chicago, IL 60625
Rev. James W. Gustafson, Exec. Director
A denominational sending agency of evangelical and Congregational tradition engaged in church planting, development, evangelism, medical work, support of national churches, and missionary training.
Year Founded in USA 1885
Income for Overseas Mins $5,200,000
Fully Supported USA Personnel Overseas:
Expecting to serve more than 4 years 92
Expecting to serve 1 to 4 years 15
Nonresidential mission personnel 3
Other Personnel:
Non-USA serving in own/other country 2
Short-Term less than 1 year from USA 1500
Home ministry & office staff in USA 19
Countries: Africa 2, Asia 2, Burkina Faso 2, Cameroon 4, Cen Africa Rep 12, Colombia 11, Congo 2, Czech Rep 2, Ecuador 10, Equat Guinea 2, Europe 2, France 3, Germany 5, Japan 13, Laos 2, Latin America 2, Mexico 14, Spain 4, Taiwan (ROC) 2, Thailand 11

Evangelical Fellowship of Mission Agencies See: EFMA

Evangelical Free Church Mission

(952)853-1300 **Fax: (952)853-8474**
E-Mail: EFCM@efcm.org
Web: www.efcm.org
901 E. 78th St., Bloomington, MN 55420
Dr. Ben Sawatsky, Exec. Director
A denominational sending agency of evangelical tradition engaged in church planting, church construction, theological education, TEE, evangelism and relief and/or rehabilitation.
Purpose: "...making disciples of Jesus Christ and incorporating them into congregations with the same purpose."
Year Founded in USA 1887
Income for Overseas Mins $13,676,320
Fully Supported USA Personnel Overseas:
Expecting to serve more than 4 years 320
Expecting to serve 1 to 4 years 32
Nonresidential mission personnel 11
Other Personnel:
Bivocational/Tentmaker from USA 10
Short-Term less than 1 year from USA 400
Home ministry & office staff in USA 28
Countries: Austria 4, Belgium 15, Brazil 4, Cen Africa Rep 13, China (PRC) 18, Congo 6, Cote d'Ivoire 4, Czech Rep 13, France 14, Germany 16, Hong Kong 7, Hungary 4, India 4, Japan 25, Kenya 7, Macao 3, Malaysia 4, Mexico 12, Mongolia 8, Netherlands 2, Peru 8, Philippines 30, Poland 8, Portugal 2, Romania 21, Russia 20, Singapore 6, Slovakia 3, Spain 6, Taiwan (ROC) 2, Tanzania 9, Thailand 4, Turkey 4, Ukraine 6, UK 3, Uzbekistan 3, Venezuela 34

Evangelical Friends Mission

(303)421-8100 **Fax: (303)431-6455**
E-Mail: Norvalh@christcom.net
Web: www.friendsmission.org
P.O. Box 525, Arvada, CO 80001
Dr. Norval Hadley, Exec. Director
A denominational sending agency of Friends and evangelical tradition engaged in church planting, Christian education, extension education, theological education, TEE, evangelism and support of national workers.
Year Founded in USA 1978
Income for Overseas Mins $900,000
Fully Supported USA Personnel Overseas:
Expecting to serve more than 4 years 12
Other Personnel:
Non-USA serving in own/other country 10
Bivocational/Tentmaker from USA 2

Short-Term less than 1 year from USA 5
Home ministry & office staff in USA 5

Countries: Bolivia 2, India 2, Jordan 2, Mexico 2, Rwanda 4

Evangelical Greenhouse Ministries International

(630)682-0308 **Fax: (630)682-0308**
E-Mail: EGMI@aol.com
P.O. Box 141, Wheaton, IL 60189
Mr. Stephen Darling, Director

An interdenominational sending agency of evangelical tradition engaged in evangelism, church planting and theological education.

Year Founded in USA 1996
Income for Overseas Mins $301,600
Fully Supported USA Personnel Overseas:
Expecting to serve more than 4 years 6
Expecting to serve 1 to 4 years 1
Nonresidential mission personnel 2
Other Personnel:
Non-USA serving in own/other country 5
Short-Term less than 1 year from USA 1

Countries: France 7

Evangelical Lutheran Church in America, Division for Global Mission

(773)380-2650 **Fax: (773)380-2410**
Web: www.elca.org/dgm
8765 W. Higgins Road, Chicago, IL 60631
Rev. Bonnie Jensen, Exec. Director

A denominational sending agency of Lutheran tradition engaged in support of national churches, development, leadership development, medical work, short-term programs and missionary training.

Year Founded in USA 1842
Income for Overseas Mins $20,709,455
Fully Supported USA Personnel Overseas:
Expecting to serve more than 4 years 163
Expecting to serve 1 to 4 years 51
Other Personnel:
Bivocational/Tentmaker from USA 47
Short-Term less than 1 year from USA 25
Home ministry & office staff in USA 47

Countries: Argentina 2, Bangladesh 2, Brazil 5, Cameroon 19, Cen Africa Rep 11, Chile 3, China (PRC) 8, Colombia 2, Costa Rica 2, Denmark 2, Egypt 4, Ethiopia 2, Finland 2, Germany 3, Guatemala 1, Hong Kong 11, Indonesia 4, Israel 5, Jamaica 2, Japan 28, Liberia 5, Madagascar 12, Mexico 3, Namibia 6, Nicaragua 4, Nigeria 2, Panama 2, Papua New Guin 9, Russia 2, Senegal 11, Singapore 4, Slovakia 10, S Africa 2, Taiwan (ROC) 2, Tanzania 22

Evangelical Lutheran Synod

(507)344-7356 **Fax: (507)344-7426**
E-Mail: ELSoffice@aol.com
6 Browns Court, Mankato, MN 56001
Rev. George M. Orvick, President

A denominational sending agency of Lutheran tradition engaged in evangelism, church planting, theological education and literature production. Statistical information from 1992.

Year Founded in USA 1918
Income for Overseas Mins $215,000
Fully Supported USA Personnel Overseas:
Expecting to serve 1 to 4 years 10

Countries: Chile 2, Czech Rep 3, Peru 3, Ukraine 2

Evangelical Mennonite Church - International Ministries

(219)423-3649 **Fax: (219)420-1905**
E-Mail: EMCINTLMIN@aol.com
1420 Kerrway Court, Fort Wayne, IN 46805-5402
Dr. Harry L. Hyde, Exec. Director

A denominational sending agency of evangelical and Mennonite tradition engaged in church planting, TEE, leadership development and linguistics.

Year Founded in USA 1947
Income for Overseas Mins $1,000,000
Fully Supported USA Personnel Overseas:
Expecting to serve more than 4 years 36
Other Personnel:
Bivocational/Tentmaker from USA 2
Short-Term less than 1 year from USA 5
Home ministry & office staff in USA 2

Countries: Africa 6, Asia 8, Europe 7, Latin America 15

Evangelical Methodist Church, Board of Missions

(317)780-8017 **Fax: (317)780-8078**
E-Mail: headquarters@emchurch.org
Web: www.emchurch.org/missions

P.O. Box 17070, Indianapolis, IN 46217
Rev. James Coulston, Gen. Conf. Sec./Treasurer
A denominational sending agency of evangelical tradition engaged in evangelism, church planting, theological education and medical work. Statistical information from 1996.
Year Founded in USA 1946
Income for Overseas Mins $239,000
Fully Supported USA Personnel Overseas:
Expecting to serve more than 4 years 6
Other Personnel:
Home ministry & office staff in USA 2
Countries: Bolivia 4, Mexico 2

Evangelical Missions Information Service
See: Evangelism and Missions Information Service

Evangelical Presbyterian Church World Outreach

(734)261-2001 Fax: (734)261-3282
E-Mail: EPCWOD@aol.com
Web: www.epc.org
29140 Buckingham Ave., Suite 5, Livonia, MI 48154
Rev. Jeffrey Chadwick, Director
A denominational sending agency of Presbyterian and Reformed tradition engaged in church planting, evangelism, leadership development, linguistics, support of national churches and support of national workers.
Purpose: "…to establish the church of Jesus Christ in those cultures and people groups where opportunity and our ability to respond intersect."
Year Founded in USA 1981
Income for Overseas Mins $1,229,608
Fully Supported USA Personnel Overseas:
Expecting to serve more than 4 years 45
Nonresidential mission personnel 4
Other Personnel:
Home ministry & office staff in USA 2
Countries: Argentina 5, Asia 16, Central Asia 8, France 2, India 2, Japan 2, Kazakhstan 4, Kenya 2, Russia 4

Evangelism and Missions Information Service

(630)752-7158 Fax: (630)752-7155
E-Mail: EMIS@wheaton.edu
Web: www.wheaton.edu/bgc/emis
P.O. Box 794, Wheaton, IL 60189
Dr. Kenneth D. Gill, Director
The publishing department of the Billy Graham Center, providing evangelism and missions information through publications such as "Evangelical Missions Quarterly," "World Pulse," *Mission Handbook,* and books about evangelism and missions.
Year Founded in USA 1964
Income for Overseas Mins .... NA
Personnel:
Home ministry & office staff in USA 8

Evangelism Explosion International

(954)491-6100 Fax: (954)771-2256
E-Mail: info@eeinternational.org
Web: www.eeinternational.org
5554 N. Federal Hwy., Ft. Lauderdale, FL 33308
Dr. D. James Kennedy, President
Dr. Thomas Stebbins, Exec. VP
A transdenominational support agency of evangelical tradition engaged in evangelism, literature distribution, literature production and translation work. Support mission with contacts in 211 nations.
Purpose: "...equipping local churches worldwide to multiply through friendship, evangelism, discipleship and healthy growth."
Year Founded in USA 1970
Income for Overseas Mins $1,000,000
Fully Supported USA Personnel Overseas:
Nonresidential mission personnel 3
Other Personnel:
Short-Term less than 1 year from USA 3
Home ministry & office staff in USA 18

Evangelism Resources

(606)858-0777 Fax: (606)858-3596
E-Mail: evangel1@gte.net
P.O. Box 5, Wilmore, KY 40390
Rev. W. Paul Braun, President
An interdenominational sending agency of evangelical tradition engaged in leadership

development, evangelism, funds transmission, services for other agencies and video/film production/distribution.

Year Founded in USA 1976
Income for Overseas Mins $617,314
Fully Supported USA Personnel Overseas:
Expecting to serve more than 4 years 5
Expecting to serve 1 to 4 years 2
Other Personnel:
Non-USA serving in own/other country 4
Home ministry & office staff in USA 5
Countries: Cameroon 2, Congo/Zaire 2, India 1, Nigeria 2

Evangelistic Faith Mission

(812)275-7531 Fax: (812)275-7532
E-Mail: efmjsm@juno.com
P.O. Box 609, Hwy. 50 - 3 miles east, Bedford, IN 47421
Rev. J. Steven Manley, President

An interdenominational sending agency of Wesleyan and Holiness tradition engaged in evangelism, broadcasting, childcare/orphanage programs, church construction, church planting and theological education.

Year Founded in USA 1905
Income for Overseas Mins $595,848
Fully Supported USA Personnel Overseas:
Expecting to serve 1 to 4 years 13
Other Personnel:
Non-USA serving in own/other country 110
Short-Term less than 1 year from USA 12
Home ministry & office staff in USA 5
Countries: Bolivia 2, Eritrea 2, Guatemala 2, Honduras 7

Evangelize China Fellowship, Inc.

(626)288-8828 Fax: (626)288-6727
P.O. Box 418, Pasadena, CA 91102
Dr. Paul C. C. Szeto, Gen. Director

A nondenominational support agency of Baptist tradition engaged in evangelism, childcare/orphanage programs, disability assistance programs, Christian education, literature distribution and relief. Financial information from 1992.

Year Founded in USA 1947
Income for Overseas Mins $161,337
Personnel:
Non-USA serving in own/other country 78
Bivocational/Tentmaker from USA 5
Short-Term less than 1 year from USA 5
Home ministry & office staff in USA 8
Countries: Asia, China

Every Child Ministries, Inc.

(219)996-4201 Fax: (219)996-4203
E-Mail: ecmafrica@juno.com
Web: www.ecmafrica.org
P.O. Box 810, Hebron, IN 46341-0810
John & Lorella Rouster, Intl. Directors

A transdenominational service and sending agency of evangelical tradition engaged in training, childrens programs and leadership development.

Purpose: "...encouraging and empowering African churches to reach the youth of their continent."

Year Founded in USA 1985
Income for Overseas Mins $89,673
Personnel:
Non-USA serving in own/other country 16
Short-Term less than 1 year from USA 6
Home ministry & office staff in USA 2
Countries: Congo/Zaire, Rep. of Congo, Ghana

Every Home for Christ

(719)260-8888 Fax: (719)260-7408
E-Mail: everyhome@ehc.org
Web: www.ehc.org
P.O. Box 35930, Colorado Springs, CO 80935-3593
Dr. Dick Eastman, President
Rev. Wesley R. Wilson, VP Intl. Administration

A transdenominational service agency of evangelical tradition engaged in evangelism, church planting, literature distribution and support of national churches. An "Every Home Campaign" has been carried out in more than 186 countries.

Purpose: "…equipping and mobilizing believers everywhere to pray for and actively participate in the personal presentation of a printed or repeatable message of the Gospel of Jesus Christ, systematically, to every home in the whole world..."

Year Founded in USA 1946

Income for Overseas Mins $4,232,126
Gifts-in-Kind $225,000
Fully Supported USA Personnel Overseas:
Nonresidential mission personnel 4
Other Personnel:
Non-USA serving in own/other country .. 1217
Home ministry & office staff in USA 48
Countries: Albania, Argentina, Austria, Bangladesh, Belarus, Belgium, Benin, Bolivia, Brazil, Bulgaria, Burkina Faso, China (PRC), Congo, Congo/Zaire, Cote d'Ivoire, Croatia, Czech Republic, Equatorial Guinea, Ethiopia, Fiji, France, Germany, Ghana, Greece, Guinea Bissau, Honduras, India, Italy, Japan, Jordan, Kazakhstan, Malawi, Malaysia, Mexico, Mongolia, Mozambique, Myanmar, Namibia, Nepal, Nicaragua, Nigeria, Papua New Guinea, Philippines, Poland, Russia, Sierra Leone, Slovakia, Slovenia, Solomon Isls., Spain, Sri Lanka, Switzerland, Taiwan, Thailand, Ukraine, UK, Yugoslavia, Zambia, Zimbabwe

Faith Christian Fellowship Intl.

(918)492-5800 Fax: (918)492-6140
E-Mail: homepage@fcf.org
Web: www.fcf.org
P.O. Box 35443, Tulsa, OK 74153
Mrs. Pat Harrison, President
A fellowship of Pentecostal tradition engaged in church planting, community development, funds transmission, leadership development, and training.
Year Founded in USA 1978
Income for Overseas Mins $600,000
Gifts-in-Kind $1,200,000
Fully Supported USA Personnel Overseas:
Expecting to serve more than 4 years 22
Expecting to serve 1 to 4 years 29
Nonresidential mission personnel 12
Other Personnel:
Non-USA serving in own/other country 7
Bivocational/Tentmaker from USA 14
Short-Term less than 1 year from USA 60
Home ministry & office staff in USA 17
Countries: Am Samoa 2, Andorra 2, Botswana 2, Czech Rep 2, Guatemala 6, Jamaica 4, Kenya 2, Mexico 6, Netherlands 2, Nigeria 2, Philippines 6, S Africa 3, Spain 2, Tonga 2, Uganda 2, UK 4, Zimbabwe 2

Far East Broadcasting Co., Inc.

(562)947-4651 Fax: (562)943-0160
E-Mail: FEBC@febc.org
Web: www.febc.org
P.O. Box 1, La Mirada, CA 90637-0001
Mr. Jim Bowman, President
A nondenominational sending agency of evangelical tradition engaged in broadcasting.
Purpose: "…to develop radio programming and deliver it to listeners in Asia in such a way that they move toward Jesus Christ and into His Kingdom..."
Year Founded in USA 1945
Income for Overseas Mins $8,440,110
Fully Supported USA Personnel Overseas:
Expecting to serve more than 4 years 25
Expecting to serve 1 to 4 years 6
Nonresidential mission personnel 1
Other Personnel:
Non-USA serving in own/other country 525
Home ministry & office staff in USA 72
Countries: Cambodia, Indonesia, Korea-S 4, N Mariana Isls 8, Philippines 17, Russia, UK 2

FARMS International, Inc.

(218)834-2676 Fax: (218)834-2676
E-Mail: farms@lakenet.com
Web: www.farmsinternational.com
P.O. Box 270, Knife River, MN 55609-0270
Mr. Joseph E. Richter, Exec. Director
An interdenominational specialized agency of evangelical tradition engaged in development, agricultural programs, evangelism and technical assistance.
Purpose: "...serving the church by equipping Christian families in poverty with the means for self-support...[to help]...families find a biblical path out of poverty."
Year Founded in USA 1961
Income for Overseas Mins $75,184
Fully Supported USA Personnel Overseas:
Nonresidential mission personnel 2
Other Personnel:
Home ministry & office staff in USA 4

Fellowship International Mission

(610)435-9099 Fax: (610)435-2641
E-Mail: fim@juno.com
555 S. 24th St., Allentown, PA 18104-6666
Rev. Ray Shive, General Dir.
A nondenominational sending agency of independent tradition engaged in church

planting, camping programs, evangelism, leadership development, and youth programs. Country data from 1996.

Year Founded in USA 1950
Income for Overseas Mins $2,000,000
Fully Supported USA Personnel Overseas:
Expecting to serve more than 4 years 96
Other Personnel:
Non-USA serving in own/other country 40
Home ministry & office staff in USA 11
Countries: Australia 8, Belgium 1, Brazil 30, Colombia 2, Ecuador 4, Fiji 1, France 1, Germany 2, Japan 3, Mexico 8, Morocco 8, New Zealand 2, Niger 3, Nigeria 4, Poland 1, Spain 3, Suriname 2, Sweden 3, Ukraine 2, UK 4, Venezuela 4

Fellowship of Associates of Medical Evangelism

(812)379-4351 **Fax: (812)379-1105**
E-Mail: medicalmissions@fameworld.org
Web: www.fameworld.org
P.O. Box 688, Columbus, IN 47202
Mr. Kevin B. Dooley, Exec. Director

A denominational support agency of Christian (Restoration Movement) tradition engaged in medical work, evangelism, funds transmission and short-term programs. Statistical information from 1996.

Year Founded in USA 1970
Income for Overseas Mins $1,055,000
Personnel:
Bivocational/Tentmaker from USA 2
Short-Term less than 1 year from USA 250
Home ministry & office staff in USA 3

Fellowship of Missions See: FOM (Fellowship of Missions)

Final Frontiers Foundation, Inc.

(800)522-4324 **Fax: (912)625-9996**
E-Mail: postmaster@finalfrontiers.org
Web: www.finalfrontiers.org
1200 Peachtree St., Louisville, GA 30434-1544
Rev. Jon Nelms, Chairman

A support agency of independent and fundamental tradition engaged in support of national workers, church planting, evangelism and support of national churches.

Year Founded in USA 1987
Income for Overseas Mins $400,915
Personnel:
Non-USA serving in own/other country 734
Home ministry & office staff in USA 7

Floresta USA, Inc.

(800)633-5319 **Fax: (619)274-3728**
E-Mail: floresta@xc.org
Web: www.floresta.org
4903 Morena Blvd. #1215, San Diego, CA 92117-7352
Mr. Scott C. Sabin, Exec. Director

A support agency of ecumenical and evangelical tradition engaged in development and agricultural programs.

Purpose: "...to address...out of love and compassion for others as a Christian witness, the basic economic problems resulting from serious deforestation..."

Year Founded in USA 1984
Income for Overseas Mins $410,437
Gifts-in-Kind $20,932
Personnel:
Non-USA serving in own/other country 50
Short-Term less than 1 year from USA 4
Home ministry & office staff in USA 5
Countries: Dominican Republic, Haiti, Mexico

Flying Doctors of America

(770)447-6319 **Fax: (770)446-9634**
E-Mail: fdoamerica@aol.com
4015 Holcomb Bridge Rd., Suite 350-922, Norcross, GA 30092
Mr. Allan M. Gathercoal, President/Founder

An interdenominational service agency of Presbyterian tradition engaged in medical and dental work, providing medical supplies and rehabilitation through short-term medical missions in 14 countries. A division of Medical Mercy Missions, Inc.

Purpose: "...helping people help people...[by]...creating a network of God's love that reaches into the farthest corners of the world and the human heart."

Year Founded in USA 1990
Income for Overseas Mins $134,000
Personnel:
Short-Term less than 1 year from USA 162
Home ministry & office staff in USA 6

FOCAS (Foundation of Compassionate American Samaritans)

(513)621-5300 Fax: (513)621-5307
E-Mail: FOCAS@aol.com
P.O. Box 428760, Cincinnati, OH 45242
Richard P. Taylor, President

A transdenominational service agency of evangelical tradition engaged in evangelism, Bible distribution, childrens programs, development, medical work and youth programs.

Purpose: "...to serve hurting poor people [and] seek transformed lives by proclaiming the gospel of Jesus Christ and assisting with crucial physical and spiritual needs."

Year Founded in USA 1986
Income for Overseas Mins $400,000
Gifts-in-Kind $60,000
Personnel:
Non-USA serving in own/other country 5
Bivocational/Tentmaker from USA 1
Short-Term less than 1 year from USA 40
Home ministry & office staff in USA 7

FOM (Fellowship of Missions)

(440)243-0156 Fax: (440)243-3501
E-Mail: ladamsfom@cs.com
140 Jacqueline Drive, Berea, OH 44017-2730
Mr. Leigh Adams, President

An inter-mission service agency of fundamental tradition engaged in research and information service, acting as an accrediting agency for its constituents and encouraging the formation of missionary and church fellowships.

Year Founded in USA 1969
Income for Overseas Mins .... NA

Food for the Hungry, Inc.

(480)998-3100 Fax: (480)443-1420
E-Mail: Hunger@fh.org
Web: www.fh.org
7729 E. Greenway Rd., Scottsdale, AZ 85260
Dr. Tetsunao Yamamori, CEO

A nondenominational service agency of evangelical tradition engaged in relief and/or rehabilitation, childcare/orphanage programs, development, extension education, leadership development and mobilization for mission.

Purpose: "...an international organization of Christian motivation, committed to working with poor people to overcome hunger and poverty through integrated self-development and relief programs."

Year Founded in USA 1971
Income for Overseas Mins $45,497,314
Gifts-in-Kind $29,011,773
Fully Supported USA Personnel Overseas:
Expecting to serve more than 4 years 38
Expecting to serve 1 to 4 years 43
Nonresidential mission personnel 2
Other Personnel:
Non-USA serving in own/other country .. 1088
Short-Term less than 1 year from USA 3
Home ministry & office staff in USA 61
Countries: Bangladesh 3, Bolivia 9, Brazil, Cambodia 7, China (PRC) 5, Congo/Zaire 2, Dominican Rep 5, Ethiopia 2, Guatemala 2, Honduras 1, India 1, Kenya 5, Laos 6, Mozambique 8, Myanmar, Nicaragua 6, Peru 7, Philippines, Romania 6, Rwanda 2, Switzerland, Thailand, Uganda 4

For Haiti with Love Inc.

(727)938-3245 Fax: (727)942-6945
E-Mail: info@forhaitiwithlove.org
Web: www.forhaitiwithlove.org
P.O. Box 1017, Palm Harbor, FL 34683
Eva DeHart, Secretary-Treasurer

A transdenominational service agency engaged in community development, emergency medical care, relief aid (at no charge) and one-on-one evangelism.

Year Founded in USA 1982
Income for Overseas Mins $263,000
Gifts-in-Kind $60,000

Forward Edge International

(360)574-3343 Fax: (360)574-2118
E-Mail: fwdedge@wa-net.com
Web: www.forwardedge.org
15121-A NE 72nd Ave., Vancouver, WA 98686-1928
Rev. Joseph Anfuso, Director

A transdenominational service agency of evangelical tradition engaged in short-term programs coordination in support of national churches in evangelism, emergency relief and self-help projects.

Purpose: "...mobilizing ordinary Christians to spread the gospel and serve the poor...on U.S. Indian reservations and overseas."

Year Founded in USA 1983
Income for Overseas Mins $360,000
Gifts-in-Kind $200,000
Fully Supported USA Personnel Overseas:
Nonresidential mission personnel 3
Other Personnel:
Short-Term less than 1 year from USA 320
Home ministry & office staff in USA 7

Foundation For His Ministry

(818)834-4734 **Fax: (818)834-4724**
E-Mail: info@ffhm.org
Web: www.ffhm.org
P.O. Box 9803, N. Hollywood, CA 91609
Chuck & Charla Pereau, Founders

A transdenominational service agency of charismatic and evangelical tradition engaged in childcare/orphanage programs, church planting, Christian education, evangelism, medical work and support of national workers.

Year Founded in USA 1967
Income for Overseas Mins $702,402
Gifts-in-Kind $354,748
Personnel:
Non-USA serving in own/other country 124
Countries: Mexico

Foursquare Missions International

(213)989-4320 **Fax: (213)483-5863**
E-Mail: fmi@foursquare.org
Web: www.foursquare.org
P.O. Box 26902, Los Angeles, CA 90026-0176
Rev. Mike Larkin, Director

A denominational sending agency of evangelical tradition engaged in church planting, Christian education, TEE, evangelism, leadership development and support of national churches.

Purpose: "...to glorify God and advance His kingdom in obedience to Jesus Christ's mandate to preach the gospel and make disciples of all nations/peoples."

Year Founded in USA 1923
Income for Overseas Mins $7,413,980
Fully Supported USA Personnel Overseas:
Expecting to serve more than 4 years 41
Expecting to serve 1 to 4 years 10
Nonresidential mission personnel 10
Other Personnel:
Non-USA serving in own/other country 2
Short-Term less than 1 year from USA 2095
Home ministry & office staff in USA 24
Countries: Africa 4, Albania 2, Belize 2, Brazil 2, Bulgaria 2, Chile 1, Dominican Rep 2, Ecuador 2, France 2, Germany 4, Haiti 2, Israel 2, Japan 2, Latvia 2, Malawi 2, Papua New Guin 2, Philippines 2, Singapore 2, Taiwan (ROC) 2, Thailand 4, Uganda 4, Ukraine 2

Franconia Mennonite Conference

(215)723-5513 **Fax: (215)723-1211**
E-Mail: info@mrn.org
P.O. Box 116, Souderton, PA 18964
Walter Sawatzky, Director of Missions

A denominational sending agency of Mennonite tradition engaged in church planting and evangelism. Statistical information from 1996.

Year Founded in USA 1917
Income for Overseas Mins $140,000
Personnel:
Home ministry & office staff in USA 1

Free Gospel Church, Missions Department

(724)327-5454 **Fax: (724)327-3419**
E-Mail: cbeam@usaor.net
P.O. Box 477, Export, PA 15632
Rev. Chester H. Heath, Gen. Superintendent

A denominational support agency of Pentecostal and Holiness tradition engaged in church planting, Bible distribution, evangelism, support of national churches, support of national workers and youth programs.

Year Founded in USA 1916
Income for Overseas Mins .... NA
Fully Supported USA Personnel Overseas:
Expecting to serve 1 to 4 years 6
Other Personnel:
Non-USA serving in own/other country 21
Countries: Philippines 6, India, Sierra Leone

Free Methodist World Missions

(317)244-3660 **Fax: (317)241-1248**
E-Mail: FMCWorld@aol.com
Web: www.fmcna.org/fmwm
P.O. Box 535002, 770 N. High School Rd., Indianapolis, IN 46253
Dr. Arthur Brown, Gen. Director

A denominational sending agency of Wesleyan and evangelical tradition engaged in leadership development, childcare/ orphanage programs, church planting, theological education and evangelism.

Purpose: "To help Free Methodists establish a mature church among the peoples of the world."

Year Founded in USA 1885
Income for Overseas Mins $7,024,664
Fully Supported USA Personnel Overseas:
Expecting to serve more than 4 years 75
Nonresidential mission personnel 2
Other Personnel:
Non-USA serving in own/other country 6
Bivocational/Tentmaker from USA 2
Short-Term less than 1 year from USA 950
Home ministry & office staff in USA 20
Countries: Brazil 4, Burundi 2, Chile 2, Dominican Rep 4, Ecuador 2, Greece 2, Haiti 9, Hong Kong 9, Hungary 3, Kenya 2, Korea-S 2, Malawi 2, Mexico 2, Nigeria 4, Philippines 8, Rwanda 5, S Africa 2, Taiwan (ROC) 6, Tanzania 2, Ukraine 1, Zimbabwe 2

Free Will Baptists, Inc., National Assn., Board of Foreign Mission

(615)731-6812 **Fax: (615)731-5345**
E-Mail: James@nafwb.org
Web: www.nafwb.org
P.O. Box 5002, 5233 Mt. View Rd., Antioch, TN 37011
Rev. James Forlines, Gen. Director

A denominational sending agency of Baptist tradition engaged in church planting, audio recording/distribution, church construction, evangelism and medical work.

Year Founded in USA 1935
Income for Overseas Mins $4,558,846
Fully Supported USA Personnel Overseas:
Expecting to serve more than 4 years 87
Expecting to serve 1 to 4 years 5
Other Personnel:
Short-Term less than 1 year from USA 41
Home ministry & office staff in USA 14
Countries: Brazil 20, Cote d'Ivoire 29, France 8, India 1, Japan 10, Panama 8, Spain 9, Uruguay 7

Friends Church Southwest Yearly Meeting

(562)947-2883 **Fax: (562)947-9385**
E-Mail: Donfcsw@aol.com
Web: www.friendschurchsw.org
P.O. Box 1607, Whittier, CA 90609-1607
Mr. Verl Lindley, Director of Missions

A denominational sending agency of evangelical Friends engaged in church planting, theological education, TEE, evangelism and support of national workers. Financial data from 1996.

Year Founded in USA 1895
Income for Overseas Mins $263,425
Fully Supported USA Personnel Overseas:
Expecting to serve more than 4 years 8
Other Personnel:
Home ministry & office staff in USA 2
Countries: Cambodia 4, Guatemala 2, Honduras 2

Friends in the West

(360)435-8983 **Fax: (360)435-6334**
E-Mail: Info@fitw.com
Web: www.fitw.com
P.O. Box 250, Arlington, WA 98223
Rev. Raymond R. Barnett, President

An interdenominational service agency of evangelical tradition engaged in child-care/ orphanage programs, camping programs and relief and/or rehabilitation. Statistical information from 1992.

Year Founded in USA 1972
Income for Overseas Mins $810,267
Gifts-in-Kind $46,332
Fully Supported USA Personnel Overseas:
Expecting to serve 1 to 4 years 5
Nonresidential mission personnel 2
Other Personnel:
Non-USA serving in own/other country 59
Short-Term less than 1 year from USA 28
Home ministry & office staff in USA 11
Countries: Romania 1, Uganda 4

Friends of Israel Gospel Ministry

(609)853-5590 **Fax: (609)853-9565**
E-Mail: Daniel_n_p@msn.com

Web: www.foigm.org
P.O. Box 908, Bellmawr, NJ 08099
Dr. Elwood McQuaid, Exec. Director
A nondenominational support agency of evangelical tradition engaged in evangelism, broadcasting, correspondence courses, literature distribution, literature production and video/film production/distribution. Income for overseas ministries from 1996.
Year Founded in USA 1938
Income for Overseas Mins $522,393

Friends United Meeting, World Ministries

(765)962-7573 Fax: (765)966-1293
E-Mail: missions@xc.org
101 Quaker Hill Dr., Richmond, IN 47374
Retha McCutchen, Assoc. Secretary
A denominational sending agency of Friends tradition engaged in support of national churches, development, Christian education, evangelism, leadership development and short-term programs.
Purpose: "...to energize and equip Friends through the power of the Holy Spirit to gather people into fellowships where Jesus Christ is known..."
Year Founded in USA 1894
Income for Overseas Mins $1,500,000
Fully Supported USA Personnel Overseas:
Expecting to serve more than 4 years 8
Expecting to serve 1 to 4 years 7
Other Personnel:
Non-USA serving in own/other country 2
Short-Term less than 1 year from USA 50
Home ministry & office staff in USA 6
Countries: Belize 2, Israel 7, Jamaica 2, Kenya 4

Friendship International

(719)386-8808 Fax: (719)633-9994
E-Mail: FRINT@aol.com
Web: www.friendshipintl.org
Box 50884, Colorado Springs, CO 80949-0884
Rev. Del Huff, Exec. Director
An interdenominational service agency of evangelical tradition engaged in evangelism, audio recording/distribution, mobilization for mission, short-term programs and training.
Year Founded in USA 1990
Income for Overseas Mins $220,000
Personnel:
Short-Term less than 1 year from USA 20
Home ministry & office staff in USA 3

Friendship Ministries

(425)823-1454
E-Mail: CLA-DCJ@nowytarg.top.pl
Totem Lake P.O. Box 8387, Kirkland, WA 98034
Denise C. Johnson, President & Founder
An interdenominational support agency of evangelical and ecumenical tradition engaged in support of national churches and Christian education.
Purpose: "...to assist and equip the Western church to effectively minister to the church in the East, to come alongside and co-labor for the Gospel."
Year Founded in USA 1988
Income for Overseas Mins $17,500
Fully Supported USA Personnel Overseas:
Expecting to serve more than 4 years 2
Countries: Poland 2

Frontier Mission Fellowship

(626)398-2328 Fax: (626)398-2240
E-Mail: greg.parsons@uscwm.org
Web: www.uscwm.org
1605 E. Elizabeth St., Pasadena, CA 91104
Rev. Greg Parsons, Exec. Director
An interdenominational support agency of Presbyterian and Baptist tradition engaged in missionary training, Christian education, leadership development, literature distribution and production, services for other agencies and video/film production. Previously listed under United States Center for World Mission.
Purpose: "To stimulate and encourage the growth of a movement for frontier missions throughout the United States and the world..."
Year Founded in USA 1976
Income for Overseas Mins $100,000
Fully Supported USA Personnel Overseas:
Expecting to serve more than 4 years 4
Other Personnel:
Short-Term less than 1 year from USA 8

Home ministry & office staff in USA 100
Countries: India 2, Philippines 2

Frontiers

(480)834-1500 Fax: (480)834-1974
E-Mail: Info@frontiers.org
Web: www.frontiers.org
P.O. Box 31177, Mesa, AZ 85275-1177
Rev. Robert A. Blincoe, US Director

A nondenominational sending agency of evangelical tradition engaged in church planting, evangelism and mobilization for mission.
Purpose: "...planting reproducing churches among unreached Muslim peoples."
Year Founded in USA 1982
Income for Overseas Mins $6,100,000
Fully Supported USA Personnel Overseas:
Expecting to serve more than 4 years 297
Expecting to serve 1 to 4 years 14
Other Personnel:
Non-USA serving in own/other country 231
Short-Term less than 1 year from USA 74
Home ministry & office staff in USA 42
Countries: Africa 37, Asia 211, Europe 63

Full Gospel Evangelistic Association

(281)693-3782 Fax: (281)693-4082
E-Mail: FGEAearl@aol.com
1202 Three Forks Dr., Katy, TX 77450
Rev. Earl Pruitt, President

An interdenominational support agency of Pentecostal tradition helping to support full-time missionaries and national churches engaged in caring for orphans, evangelism, Bible distribution, church planting and church growth.
Year Founded in USA 1951
Income for Overseas Mins $87,000
Personnel:
Home ministry & office staff in USA 5

Full Gospel Grace Fellowship

(918)224-7837
E-Mail: fggf@juno.com
P.O. Box 4564, Tulsa, OK 74159
Rev. F. W. Peck, President

A nondenominational sending agency of Pentecostal tradition engaged in church planting and evangelism. Personnel information from 1992.
Year Founded in USA 1970
Income for Overseas Mins $83,078
Fully Supported USA Personnel Overseas:
Expecting to serve more than 4 years 11
Countries: Argentina 3, Ghana 1, Indonesia 1, Mexico 2, Paraguay 2, Suriname 2

Fundamental Baptist Mission of Trinidad & Tobago

(304)345-9479
P.O. Box 582011, Charleston, WV 25358
Pastor Bobby M. Sizemore, Board Chairman

A sending agency of Baptist and fundamental tradition engaged in church planting, evangelism and support of national workers. Report covers both U.S. and Canadian Boards.
Year Founded in USA 1921
Income for Overseas Mins $139,000
Fully Supported USA Personnel Overseas:
Expecting to serve more than 4 years 5
Other Personnel:
Non-USA serving in own/other country 6
Countries: Trinidad & Tobg 5

Galcom International (U.S.)

(813)933-8111 Fax: (813)933-8886
E-Mail: GalcomUSA@aol.com
Web: www.galcom.org
Box 270956, Tampa, FL 33688-0956
Mr. Gary Nelson, U.S. Administrator

A nondenominational support agency of independent and Baptist tradition engaged in supplying communications equipment, purchasing services, services for other agencies and technical assistance in nearly 100 countries.
Purpose: "To provide durable technical equipment for communicating the Gospel worldwide."
Year Founded in USA 1991
Income for Overseas Mins $300,000
Personnel:
Home ministry & office staff in USA 1

General Association of Regular Baptist Churches

(847)843-1600 **Fax: (847)843-3757**
E-Mail: garbc@garbc.org
Web: www.garbc.org
1300 N. Meacham Rd., Schaumburg, IL 60173
Mr. John Greening, Natl. Representative

An association of Baptist tradition providing information for its associated local churches relative to cooperating mission agencies.

Year Founded in USA 1932
Income for Overseas Mins .... NA

General Baptists International

(573)785-7746 **Fax: (573)785-0564**
E-Mail: eback@pbmo.net
100 Stinson Dr., Poplar Bluff, MO 63901
Rev. Jack Eberhardt, Director

A denominational sending agency of Baptist tradition engaged in church planting, agricultural programs, childcare/orphanage programs, missions information service, literacy work and support of national churches.

Purpose: "...to assist [local associations and churches of General Baptists] in the task of winning people to Christ at home and abroad..."

Year Founded in USA 1903
Income for Overseas Mins $622,542
Fully Supported USA Personnel Overseas:
Expecting to serve more than 4 years 9
Nonresidential mission personnel 1
Other Personnel:
Short-Term less than 1 year from USA 2
Home ministry & office staff in USA 2
Countries: Honduras 5, N Mariana Isls 2, Philippines 2

General Conf. Mennonite Church, Commission on Overseas Mission

(316)283-5100 **Fax: (316)283-0454**
E-Mail: COM@gcmc.org
P.O. Box 347, Newton, KS 67114-0347
Mr. Ron Flaming, Exec. Secretary

A denominational sending agency of Mennonite tradition engaged in evangelism, church planting, development, theological education and support of national churches. Statistical information from 1996.

Year Founded in USA 1891
Income for Overseas Mins $2,630,742
Fully Supported USA Personnel Overseas:
Expecting to serve more than 4 years 42
Expecting to serve 1 to 4 years 2
Other Personnel:
Non-USA serving in own/other country 55
Bivocational/Tentmaker from USA 41
Short-Term less than 1 year from USA 18
Home ministry & office staff in USA 9
Countries: Botswana 3, Brazil 1, Burkina Faso 3, China (PRC) 2, Colombia 2, Congo/Zaire 1, France 2, Gambia 2, Hong Kong 2, Hungary 2, India 2, Israel 2, Japan 3, Kenya 4, Mozambique 2, Nepal 2, Paraguay 2, S Africa 2, Taiwan (ROC) 5

Gideons International, The

(615)883-8533
E-Mail: tgi@gideons.org
Web: www.gideons.org
2900 Lebanon Road, Nashville, TN 37214
Mr. Wendell McClinton, Exec. Director

An international Christian professional men's association of evangelical tradition engaged in Bible distribution and evangelism. Active in 172 countries with 58,500 overseas members.

Year Founded in USA 1899
Income for Overseas Mins .... NR
Fully Supported USA Personnel Overseas:
Nonresidential mission personnel 5

Global Advance

(972)771-9042 **Fax: (972)771-3315**
E-Mail: globaladv@earthlink.net
Web: www.globaladvance.org
P.O. Box 742077, Dallas, TX 75374-2077
Dr. David Shibley, President

An interdenominational service agency of evangelical tradition engaged in training, leadership development, literature distribution and support of national churches.

Purpose: "...to help fulfill the Great Commission...by empowering national leaders to evangelize and disciple their own and surrounding nations..."

Year Founded in USA 1990

Income for Overseas Mins $530,462
Gifts-in-Kind $9,800
Fully Supported USA Personnel Overseas:
Nonresidential mission personnel 2
Other Personnel:
Short-Term less than 1 year from USA 35

Global Evangelization Movement See: World Evangelization Research Center and Global Evangelization Movement

Global Fellowship

(530)888-9208
E-Mail: don@globalfellowship.org
Web: www.globalfellowship.org
P.O. Box 1, Meadow Vista, CA 95722
Mr. Don Oates, President

A nondenominational support agency of evangelical tradition engaged in support of national workers, childcare/orphanage programs, church planting, evangelism, support of national churches, mission-related research and missionary training.

Year Founded in USA 1989
Income for Overseas Mins $110,000
Personnel:
Non-USA serving in own/other country 603
Short-Term less than 1 year from USA 10

Global Harvest Ministries

(719)262-9922 **Fax: (818)262-9920**
E-Mail: info@wpccs.org
Web: www.wpccs.org
P.O. Box 63060, Colorado Springs, CO 80962-3060
Dr. C. Peter Wagner, President
Doris Wagner, Exec. Director

A transdenominational support agency of evangelical tradition engaged in literature production and training. Statistical information from 1996.

Purpose: "...to unite existing national and international prayer networks to focus prayer power on world evangelization, especially the '10/40 window'..."

Year Founded in USA 1991
Income for Overseas Mins .... NA
Personnel:
Home ministry & office staff in USA 6

Global Health Ministries

(763)586-9590 **Fax: (763)586-9591**
E-Mail: ghm@compuserve.com
Web: www.ghm.org
7831 Hickory St. NE, Fridley, MN 55432
Mr. Kenneth Grosch, Exec. Director

A denominational support agency of Lutheran tradition engaged in providing medical supplies, funds transmission, medical work and supplying equipment.

Purpose: "...providing financial support, shipping of urgently needed medical supplies, assisting in recruiting of medical personnel, funding for training of national health care givers."

Year Founded in USA 1987
Income for Overseas Mins $742,817
Gifts-in-Kind $220,447
Personnel:
Home ministry & office staff in USA 3

Global Mapping International

(719)531-3599 **Fax: (719)548-7459**
E-Mail: Info@gmi.org
Web: www.gmi.org
7899 Lexington Dr., Suite 200A, Colorado Springs, CO 80920-4279
Mr. Michael O'Rear, President

An interdenominational specialized agency of evangelical tradition engaged in missions information service, leadership development, mission-related research, services for other agencies, technical assistance and missionary training.

Purpose: "To enable ministry decision makers to acquire, manage, analyze, apply, communicate and share strategic information."

Year Founded in USA 1983
Income for Overseas Mins .... NA
Personnel:
Home ministry & office staff in USA 12

Global Opportunities

(626)398-2393 **Fax: (626)398-2396**
E-Mail: info@globalopps
Web: www.globalopps.org

1600 Elizabeth St., Pasadena, CA 91104-2720
Mr. David E. English, Exec. Director
A nondenominational support agency of evangelical tradition engaged in mobilization for mission and training.
Purpose: "...to mobilize and equip missions-committed lay Christians to serve abroad as effective tentmakers, especially in countries of greatest spiritual need."
Year Founded in USA 1984
Income for Overseas Mins .... NA
Personnel:
Home ministry & office staff in USA 3

Global Outreach Mission

(716)688-5048 **Fax: (716)688-5049**
E-Mail: glmiss1@aol.com
P.O. Box 2010, Buffalo, NY 14231-2010
Dr. James O. Blackwood, President
A transdenominational sending agency of independent and evangelical tradition engaged in evangelism, broadcasting, church planting, medical work and supplying equipment. Now includes Mexican Mission Ministries and Missionary Dentists.
Purpose: "...sharing the Gospel of Jesus Christ around the world, planting and encouraging His church, helping the hurting physically and serving in every area of Christian development."
Year Founded in USA 1943
Income for Overseas Mins $2,539,772
Fully Supported USA Personnel Overseas:
Expecting to serve more than 4 years 100
Other Personnel:
Non-USA serving in own/other country 98
Short-Term less than 1 year from USA 120
Home ministry & office staff in USA 6
Countries: Australia 2, Austria 1, Belgium 2, Belize 2, Brazil 2, Congo 5, Denmark 2, France 30, Germany 7, Greece 2, Honduras 2, Ireland 8, Mexico 11, Micronesia 2, Neth Antilles 2, Paraguay 2, Russia 4, UK 14

Global Outreach, Ltd.

(662)842-4615 **Fax: (662)842-4620**
E-Mail: world@netbci.com
Web: www.globaloutreach.org
P.O. Box 1, Tupelo, MS 38802
Dr. Sammy Simpson, Exec. Director
A nondenominational sending agency of evangelical tradition engaged in development, evangelism and medical work.
Year Founded in USA 1970
Income for Overseas Mins $2,933,610
Fully Supported USA Personnel Overseas:
Expecting to serve more than 4 years 51
Expecting to serve 1 to 4 years 16
Nonresidential mission personnel 1
Other Personnel:
Short-Term less than 1 year from USA 402
Home ministry & office staff in USA 5
Countries: Belize 6, Brazil 1, Chile 2, China (PRC) 12, Ecuador 4, Haiti 8, Honduras 3, India 2, Poland 2, Romania 2, Slovakia 1, Uganda 18, Unspecified 6

Global Strategy Mission Assoc.

(504)536-3000 **Fax: (504)536-6550**
E-Mail: usdept@gsma.org
Web: www.gsma.org
P.O. Box 2800, Reserve, LA 70084
Mr. Jerry Claunch, Director
A nondenominational sending agency of charismatic tradition engaged in church planting, evangelism, funds transmission, mobilization for mission and missionary training. Personnel information from 1996.
Year Founded in USA 1986
Income for Overseas Mins $1,359,743
Fully Supported USA Personnel Overseas:
Expecting to serve more than 4 years 10
Expecting to serve 1 to 4 years 40
Nonresidential mission personnel 1
Other Personnel:
Non-USA serving in own/other country 2
Bivocational/Tentmaker from USA 4
Short-Term less than 1 year from USA 75
Home ministry & office staff in USA 9
Countries: China (PRC) 4, Haiti 2, Japan 2, Mexico 5, Russia 35, Singapore 2

Global Youth Ministry Network

(419)756-4433 **Fax: (419)756-3041**
E-Mail: office@global-youth.com
Web: www.global-youth.com
283 Cline Ave. Ste. A, Mansfield, OH 44907
Mr. Chris Davis, Exec. Director
An interdenominational agency of evangelical tradition engaged in leadership development,

Christian education, youth programs and training.

Year Founded in USA 1997

Income for Overseas Mins $26,729

Fully Supported USA Personnel Overseas:

Nonresidential mission personnel 1

Other Personnel:

Home ministry & office staff in USA 1

Globe Missionary Evangelism

(904)453-3453 **Fax: (904)456-6001**

E-Mail: info@gme.org

Web: www.gme.org

P.O. Box 3040, Pensacola, FL 32516-3040

Mr. J. Robert Bishop, President

An independent sending agency of charismatic and evangelical tradition engaged in church planting, childrens programs, evangelism, leadership development, support of national churches and relief aid.

Year Founded in USA 1973

Income for Overseas Mins $2,209,831

Fully Supported USA Personnel Overseas:

Expecting to serve more than 4 years 94

Expecting to serve 1 to 4 years 13

Nonresidential mission personnel 6

Other Personnel:

Bivocational/Tentmaker from USA 2

Short-Term less than 1 year from USA 475

Home ministry & office staff in USA 10

Countries: Albania 3, Bolivia 2, Cyprus 2, France 2, Germany 2, Ghana 2, Guatemala 15, Haiti 6, Honduras 2, India 9, Japan 2, Kenya 5, Malaysia 4, Mexico 17, Nicaragua 2, Philippines 4, Romania 2, Russia 1, Sierra Leone 2, Taiwan (ROC) 2, Tanzania 2, Thailand 8, UK 8, Vietnam 3

GO InterNational

(606)858-3171 **Fax: (606)858-4324**

E-Mail: gointernational@gointernational.org

Web: www.gointernational.org

P.O. Box 123, Wilmore, KY 40390

Rev. Larry G. Cochran, President

An interdenominational agency of Wesleyan tradition providing assistance through ministry teams of believers from other countries, engaging in development, childrens programs, church planting, evangelism, leadership development and short-term programs.

Purpose: "...[to] collaborate with indigenous ministries [and] give Christians in the USA the opportunity to become directly involved in the life and ministry of the church in the Two-Thirds World..."

Year Founded in USA 1968

Income for Overseas Mins $615,194

Fully Supported USA Personnel Overseas:

Nonresidential mission personnel 3

Other Personnel:

Short-Term less than 1 year from USA 250

Home ministry & office staff in USA 13

Go Ye Fellowship

(626)398-2305 **Fax: (626)797-5576**

E-Mail: GYFint@cs.com

P.O. Box 40039, Pasadena, CA 91114

Mr. William H. Gustafson, President

An interdenominational support agency of evangelical tradition providing administrative and spiritual support for missionaries.

Purpose: "...enabling missionaries to pursue their God-given call and vision by serving as the link between missionaries and those who send them."

Year Founded in USA 1944

Income for Overseas Mins .... NR

Good News for India

(909)593-7753 **Fax: (909)593-1155**

E-Mail: GNFI@aol.com

Web: www.indiagospel.net/gnfi/

P.O. Box 7576, LaVerne, CA 91750

Mr. George Kuruvila Chavanikamannil, President

An interdenominational support agency of evangelical and charismatic tradition engaged in theological education, church planting, Christian education, missionary education, leadership development and support of national workers.

Purpose: "To train, send out and support 'national missionaries' to plant churches in the unreached areas of India and neighboring countries."

Year Founded in USA 1986

Income for Overseas Mins $427,434

Personnel:

Non-USA serving in own/other country 57

Short-Term less than 1 year from USA 10
Home ministry & office staff in USA 2

Good News Productions Intl.

(417)782-0060 **Fax: (417)782-3999**
E-Mail: GNPI@xc.org
Web: www.gnpi.com
P.O. Box 222, Joplin, MO 64802
Mr. Ziden L. Nutt, Exec. Director

A nondenominational specialized agency of Christian (Restoration Movement) tradition engaged in video/film production and distribution and broadcasting. Statistical information from 1992.

Year Founded in USA 1976
Income for Overseas Mins $700,000
Personnel:
Short-Term less than 1 year from USA 6
Home ministry & office staff in USA 21

Good Shepherd Ministries

(407)631-1499 **Fax: (407)631-1499**
E-Mail: goodshepmin@juno.com
P.O. Box 360963, Melbourne, FL 32936-1499
Mr. William S. Younger, Exec. Director

A support agency of fundamental tradition engaged in Christian education.

Year Founded in USA 1974
Income for Overseas Mins $61,000
Personnel:
Non-USA serving in own/other country 49
Home ministry & office staff in USA 1

Gospel Fellowship Association

(864)609-5500 **Fax: (864)609-5501**
E-Mail: GFA@gfamissions.org
1809 Wade Hampton Blvd. #130, Greenville, SC 29609
Dr. Mark Batory, Director of Missions

A nondenominational sending agency of fundamental tradition engaged in church planting, camping programs, theological education and evangelism.

Year Founded in USA 1961
Income for Overseas Mins .... NR
Fully Supported USA Personnel Overseas:
Expecting to serve more than 4 years 156
Expecting to serve 1 to 4 years 9
Nonresidential mission personnel 4
Other Personnel:
Non-USA serving in own/other country 165
Short-Term less than 1 year from USA 11
Home ministry & office staff in USA 35
Countries: Albania 2, Australia 4, Austria 4, Azores 4, Brazil 8, Cambodia 2, Cameroon 17, Chile 6, Costa Rica 2, Dominica 2, Equat Guinea 2, Germany 19, Italy 2, Japan 3, Kenya 2, Korea-S 6, Marshall Isls 6, Mexico 15, New Zealand 2, Papua New Guin 4, Philippines 16, Puerto Rico 4, S Africa 6, Spain 6, UK 21

Gospel for Asia

(972)416-0340 **Fax: (972)416-6131**
E-Mail: info@gfa.org
Web: www.gfa.org
1800 Golden Trail Ct., Carrollton, TX 75010-4649
Rev. K. P. Yohannan, President

A nondenominational service agency of evangelical tradition engaged in church planting, broadcasting, evangelism, leadership development, support of national workers and missionary training.

Year Founded in USA 1979
Income for Overseas Mins $10,220,539
Gifts-in-Kind $158,047
Personnel:
Non-USA serving in own/other country 11286
Short-Term less than 1 year from USA 3
Home ministry & office staff in USA 31
Countries: Bangladesh, Bhutan, China, India, Myanmar, Nepal, Pakistan, Sri Lanka

Gospel Furthering Fellowship

(717)866-1964 **Fax: (717)866-1325**
E-Mail: GFF@paonline.com
Web: www.gffministries.com
221 Hamilton Ave., Myerstown, PA 17067
Rev. Bruce Busch, Gen. Director

A nondenominational sending agency of Baptist tradition engaged in church planting, theological education, evangelism and support of national churches. Statistical information from 1996.

Year Founded in USA 1935
Income for Overseas Mins $230,000
Fully Supported USA Personnel Overseas:
Expecting to serve more than 4 years 7

Other Personnel:
Non-USA serving in own/other country 3
Home ministry & office staff in USA 17
Countries: Kenya 3, Spain 2, Tanzania 2

Gospel Literature Intl., Inc.

(909)481-5222 Fax: (909)481-5216
E-Mail: GLINT@glint.org
Web: www.glint.org
2910 Inland Empire Blvd., #104, Ontario, CA 91764
Georgalyn B. Wilkinson, President

A nondenominational service agency of evangelical tradition providing copyrighted English Christian education curriculum and literature for adaptation, translation, and publication in over 70 non-English languages.

Purpose: "To provide resources for literature projects worldwide for effective Bible teaching and learning materials in national languages, with the goal of making disciples, developing godly Christian leaders and building the Church."

Year Founded in USA 1961
Income for Overseas Mins $177,342
Personnel:
Home ministry & office staff in USA 8

Gospel Mission of South America

(954)587-2975
E-Mail: gmsamerica@email.msn.com
Web: www.gmsa.org
1401 SW 21st Ave., Fort Lauderdale, FL 33312-3109
Rev. Terry Thompson, Gen. Director

A nondenominational sending agency of Baptist and fundamental tradition engaged in church planting, broadcasting, theological education, literature distribution and literature production.

Purpose: "...to evangelize the people of Latin America by means of itinerant and localized work, with the object of establishing and developing indigenous churches."

Year Founded in USA 1923
Income for Overseas Mins $1,130,180
Fully Supported USA Personnel Overseas:
Expecting to serve more than 4 years 34
Nonresidential mission personnel 2
Other Personnel:
Non-USA serving in own/other country 34
Short-Term less than 1 year from USA 4
Home ministry & office staff in USA 7
Countries: Argentina 8, Chile 20, Uruguay 6

Gospel Missionary Union

(816)734-8500 Fax: (816)734-4601
E-Mail: info@gmu.org
Web: www.gmu.org
10000 N. Oak Trafficway, Kansas City, MO 64155
Dr. Carl McMindes, President

An interdenominational sending agency of evangelical and Baptist tradition engaged in church planting, broadcasting, camping programs, correspondence courses, theological education, TEE and evangelism. Fifty-three missionaries serving in North America with non-English-speaking groups included in home ministry total.

Year Founded in USA 1892
Income for Overseas Mins $8,400,000
Fully Supported USA Personnel Overseas:
Expecting to serve more than 4 years 163
Expecting to serve 1 to 4 years 34
Other Personnel:
Non-USA serving in own/other country 113
Short-Term less than 1 year from USA 142
Home ministry & office staff in USA 79
Countries: Argentina 9, Austria 6, Bahamas 4, Belgium 4, Belize 2, Bolivia 20, Brazil 24, Colombia 4, Czech Rep 1, Ecuador 42, France 14, Germany 7, Greece 1, Italy 2, Kyrgyzstan 2, Mali 21, Morocco 4, Panama 4, Romania 1, Russia 3, Spain 17, UK 5

Gospel Outreach

(707)445-2135 Fax: (707)445-1562
E-Mail: goe@radc.com
P.O. Box 1022, Eureka, CA 95502-1022
Pastor Dave Sczepanski, Director

A nondenominational support agency of charismatic tradition engaged in church planting and Christian education. Statistical information from 1992.

Year Founded in USA 1971
Income for Overseas Mins $180,000

Gospel Outreach Ministries Intl.

(636)789-2160 **Fax: (636)797-2789**
E-Mail: gomint@aol.com
P.O. Box 380, Hillsboro, MO 63050-0380
Dr. Sam Paul Gokanakonda, Founder/CEO

A nondenominational support agency of evangelical tradition engaged in evangelism, church planting, mission-related research and support of national workers. Personnel information from 1996.

Year Founded in USA 1988
Income for Overseas Mins $99,229
Fully Supported USA Personnel Overseas:
Nonresidential mission personnel 1
Other Personnel:
Non-USA serving in own/other country 250
Short-Term less than 1 year from USA 6
Home ministry & office staff in USA 3

Gospel Recordings (Global Recordings Network)

(213)250-0207 **Fax: (213)250-0136**
E-Mail: MINFO@gospelrecordings.com
Web: www.gospelrecordings.com
122 Glendale Blvd., Los Angeles, CA 90026-5889
Mr. Colin Stott, Exec. Director

An interdenominational specialized agency of evangelical tradition engaged in audio recording/distribution, evangelism, mission-related research, services for other agencies, support of national workers and technical assistance in more than 4900 languages.

Purpose: "...helps spread the Gospel by recording and distributing evangelistic messages in thousands of languages and dialects."

Year Founded in USA 1939
Income for Overseas Mins $430,805
Fully Supported USA Personnel Overseas:
Expecting to serve more than 4 years 8
Nonresidential mission personnel 2
Other Personnel:
Non-USA serving in own/other country 218
Short-Term less than 1 year from USA 53
Home ministry & office staff in USA 48
Countries: Australia, Bangladesh, Belgium, Brazil, Burkina Faso, Cameroon, Chad, Germany, Ghana, Guinea, India, Indonesia, Kenya, Korea-S, Liberia, Malawi 1, Mexico 4, Nepal, Netherlands, Nigeria, Papua New Guinea, Phillipines, Sierra Leone, Singapore, Solomon Isls., S Africa, Senegal, Switzerland, Thailand 1, Togo, UK, Unspecified 2

Gospel Revival Ministries

(616)798-7373 **Fax: (616)798-4274**
E-Mail: ggnstaff@gogoodnews.com
Web: www.gogoodnews.com
P.O. Box 340, Grandville, MI 49468-0340
Mr. John Musser, President/Evangelist

A nondenominational support agency of Pentecostal tradition engaged in support of national workers, Bible distribution, evangelism, funds transmission, literature distribution and supplying equipment.

Year Founded in USA 1980
Income for Overseas Mins $106,594
Personnel:
Non-USA serving in own/other country 235
Short-Term less than 1 year from USA 3
Home ministry & office staff in USA 4
Countries: Cameroon, Chad, Ghana, India, Malaysia, Niger, Nigeria, Sudan, Ukraine

Grace and Truth, Inc.

(217)442-1120 **Fax: (217)443-1163**
E-Mail: gtpress@gtpress.org
Web: www.gtpress.org
210 Chestnut St., Danville, IL 61832
Mr. Sam O. Hadley, Exec. Officer

A nondenominational support agency of Christian/Plymouth Brethren tradition engaged in literature production/distribution in 12 languages, broadcasting and correspondence courses.

Year Founded in USA 1931
Income for Overseas Mins $465,000

Grace Baptist Missions Intl.

(570)833-4192 **Fax: (570)833-4192**
E-Mail: ddenny9@aol.com
Web:www.netministries.org/see/charmin/CM00013
P.O. Box 9, Mehoopany, PA 18629-9731
Dr. David A. Denny, Exec. Director

A denominational specialized agency of Baptist tradition engaged in services for other agencies, church planting, extension education, missions information service, support of national churches and missionary training.

Purpose: "...to provide education and research services to local Baptist churches sending missionaries directly to the field."
Year Founded in USA 1989
Income for Overseas Mins .... NA
Fully Supported USA Personnel Overseas:
Expecting to serve more than 4 years 3
Other Personnel:
Non-USA serving in own/other country 3
Short-Term less than 1 year from USA 3
Countries: Australia 2, Germany 1

Grace Brethren International Missions

(219)268-1888 Fax: (219)267-5210
E-Mail: gbim@gbim.org
Web: www.gbim.org
P.O. Box 588, 999 College Ave., Winona Lake, IN 46590
Mr. Dave Guiles, Exec. Director

A denominational sending agency of Brethren tradition engaged in church planting, Christian education, evangelism, leadership development and mobilization for mission.
Purpose: "To partner with Grace Brethren Churches worldwide in order to call out a people for His name."
Year Founded in USA 1900
Income for Overseas Mins $4,178,922
Fully Supported USA Personnel Overseas:
Expecting to serve more than 4 years 92
Expecting to serve 1 to 4 years 14
Nonresidential mission personnel 2
Other Personnel:
Bivocational/Tentmaker from USA 2
Short-Term less than 1 year from USA 124
Home ministry & office staff in USA 17
Countries: Argentina 10, Brazil 5, Cambodia 1, Cen Africa Rep 17, Czech Rep 4, France 21, Germany 13, Japan 4, Kyrgyzstan 2, Mexico 4, Philippines 9, Portugal 7, Spain 2, UK 7

Grace Ministries International

(616)241-5666 Fax: (616)241-2542
E-Mail: SAM@gracem.org
P.O. Box 9405, 2125 Martindale SW, Grand Rapids, MI 49509
Dr. Samuel R. Vinton, Jr., Exec. Director

A nondenominational sending agency of evangelical tradition engaged in church planting, Christian education, extension education, TEE, leadership development and medical work.
Year Founded in USA 1939
Income for Overseas Mins $1,647,627
Fully Supported USA Personnel Overseas:
Expecting to serve more than 4 years 55
Expecting to serve 1 to 4 years 3
Other Personnel:
Non-USA serving in own/other country 19
Short-Term less than 1 year from USA 63
Home ministry & office staff in USA 6
Countries: Australia 7, Bolivia 7, Brazil 2, Congo/ Zaire 13, Costa Rica 5, Puerto Rico 8, Tanzania 14, Zambia 2

Grand Old Gospel Fellowship

(215)361-8111 Fax: (215)643-2288
E-Mail: bsamhart@gogf.org
Web: www.gogf.org
160 E. Main St., Lansdale, PA 19446-2519
Dr. B. Sam Hart, President

A nondenominational support agency of independent and evangelical tradition engaged in broadcasting, audio recording/ distribution, camping programs, church planting and evangelism.
Year Founded in USA 1962
Income for Overseas Mins $40,000
Personnel:
Home ministry & office staff in USA 2

Great Commission Center International

(940)455-2205 Fax: (940)455-2198
E-Mail: gccusa@unicomp.net
Web: www.gccusa.org/gccusa
769 Orchid Hill Lane, Argyle, TX 76226
Dr. Thomas Wang, President

An interdenominational support agency of evangelical tradition engaged in missionary training, church planting, TEE and evangelism.
Year Founded in USA 1989
Income for Overseas Mins $345,922
Fully Supported USA Personnel Overseas:
Expecting to serve 1 to 4 years 4

Nonresidential mission personnel 2
Other Personnel:
Non-USA serving in own/other country 3
Countries: Spain 2, Unspecified 2

Great Commission Ministries, Inc.

(614)885-4500 Fax: (614)885-6867
P.O. Box 6034, 870 High St., Ste 010,
Worthington, OH 43085
Mr. Jeff Kern, Exec. Director

A transdenominational sending agency of evangelical tradition engaged in church planting, evangelism, leadership development, management consulting/training and youth programs.

Year Founded in USA 1990
Income for Overseas Mins $1,547,145
Fully Supported USA Personnel Overseas:
Expecting to serve more than 4 years 7
Expecting to serve 1 to 4 years 3
Nonresidential mission personnel 1
Other Personnel:
Non-USA serving in own/other country 2
Short-Term less than 1 year from USA 112
Home ministry & office staff in USA 148
Countries: Germany 2, Ukraine 8

Greater Europe Mission

(719)488-8008 Fax: (719)488-8018
E-Mail: info@gemission.com
Web: www.gemission.org
18950 Base Camp Rd., Monument, CO 80132-8009
Rev. Ted Noble, President/CEO
Mr. D. Michael Clabaugh, Exec. Vice-President

A nondenominational sending agency of evangelical tradition engaged in theological education, camping programs, church planting, evangelism and services for other agencies.

Year Founded in USA 1949
Income for Overseas Mins $9,666,000
Fully Supported USA Personnel Overseas:
Expecting to serve more than 4 years 300
Expecting to serve 1 to 4 years 20
Other Personnel:
Non-USA serving in own/other country 30
Short-Term less than 1 year from USA 200
Home ministry & office staff in USA 40
Countries: Europe 320

Greater Grace World Outreach

(410)483-3700 Fax: (410)483-3708
E-Mail: missions@ggwo.org
Web: www.ggwo.org
P.O. Box 18715, Baltimore, MD 21206
Mr. Guy V. Duff, Missions Director
Mr. Carl H. Stevens, Senior Pastor

A nondenominational support agency of evangelical tradition engaged in church planting, missionary education, theological education, evangelism, short-term programs and missionary training.

Year Founded in USA 1986
Income for Overseas Mins .... NR
Fully Supported USA Personnel Overseas:
Nonresidential mission personnel 2
Other Personnel:
Non-USA serving in own/other country 108
Bivocational/Tentmaker from USA 150
Short-Term less than 1 year from USA 80
Home ministry & office staff in USA 45
Countries: Argentina, Azerbaijan, Belarus, Brazil, Czech Republic, El Salvador, Finland, France, Germany, Ghana, Greece, Hungary, India, Ireland, Kazakhstan, Kenya, Kyrgyzstan, Liberia, Lithuania, Nepal, Netherlands, Pakistan, Poland, Romania, Russia, Slovakia, Swaziland, Sweden, Thailand, Togo, Turkmenistan, Ukraine, UK

Habitat for Humanity International

(912)924-6935 Fax: (912)924-6541
E-Mail: Info@habitat.org
Web: www.habitat.org
121 Habitat St., Americus, GA 31709-3498
Dr. Millard D. Fuller, President

A specialized service agency of ecumenical tradition engaged in building low-income housing in partnership with/for people in need. Overseas personnel totals from 1996.

Purpose: "...works in partnership with God and people everywhere to develop communities with God's people in need by building and renovating houses...in which people can live and grow into all that God intended."

Year Founded in USA 1976

Income for Overseas Mins $17,081,351
Fully Supported USA Personnel Overseas:
Expecting to serve more than 4 years 11
Expecting to serve 1 to 4 years 108
Other Personnel:
Non-USA serving in own/other country 538
Short-Term less than 1 year from USA 1200
Home ministry & office staff in USA 463
Countries: Antigua 1, Bolivia 2, Botswana 6, Brazil 2, Cen Africa Rep 3, Colombia 3, Congo/Zaire 1, Costa Rica 3, Dominican Rep 4, Egypt 1, Ethiopia 5, Fiji 4, Ghana 3, Guatemala 2, Guyana 4, Haiti 3, Honduras 3, Hungary 3, India 3, Jamaica 1, Kenya 4, Korea-S 1, Kyrgyzstan 1, Malawi 6, Mexico 5, Netherlands 1, Nicaragua 2, Papua New Guin 9, Paraguay 2, Peru 2, Philippines 2, Poland 1, Romania 2, Slovenia 1, S Africa 2, Sri Lanka 2, Tanzania 4, Trinidad & Tobg 2, Uganda 3, UK 4, Zambia 2, Zimbabwe 4

Handclasp International, Inc.

(909)337-1894 **Fax: (909)336-1674**
E-Mail: DanHenrich@xc.org
Web: home.sprynet.com/sprynet/danhenri/hpage.htm
P.O. Box 159, Crest Park, CA 92326
Mr. Daniel J. Henrich, President

A transdenominational service agency of Baptist tradition engaged in video/film production/distribution, extension education, mission-related research and services for other agencies.
Year Founded in USA 1970
Income for Overseas Mins $175,000
Gifts-in-Kind $160,000
Personnel:
Short-Term less than 1 year from USA 7

Hands for Christ

(540)362-1214 **Fax: (540)563-8285**
E-Mail: HFCRB@aol.com
5720 Williamson Road NW, Suite III, Roanoke, VA 24012
Mr. R. W. Bowers, President

An interdenominational specialized agency of evangelical tradition engaged in literature distribution and production, audio recording/distribution, and Bible distribution.
Purpose: "...providing Christian materials in the form of books, audio and video cassettes, tracts, bumper stickers and magazines which are educational, inspirational and biblically based."
Year Founded in USA 1929
Income for Overseas Mins $388,000
Gifts-in-Kind $300,000
Personnel:
Home ministry & office staff in USA 10

Harvest

(480)968-2600 **Fax: (480)894-6599**
E-Mail: 70153.1444@compuserve.com
P.O. Box 15577, Scottsdale, AZ 85267
Mr. Robert C. Moffitt, Exec. Director

A nondenominational service agency of evangelical tradition engaged in leadership development, funds transmission, literature distribution and production, development and support of national workers.
Year Founded in USA 1981
Income for Overseas Mins $152,000
Fully Supported USA Personnel Overseas:
Nonresidential mission personnel 3
Other Personnel:
Non-USA serving in own/other country 16
Short-Term less than 1 year from USA 3
Home ministry & office staff in USA 2
Countries: Brazil, Dominican Rep., Haiti, Honduras, India, Rwanda, Venezuela

Harvest Evangelism, Inc.

(408)927-9052 **Fax: (408)927-9830**
E-Mail: mail@harvestevan.org
Web: www.harvestevan.org
P.O. Box 20310, San Jose, CA 95160
Rev. Ed Silvoso, President

An interdenominational specialized agency of evangelical tradition engaged in training, evangelism, support of national churches, mobilization for mission and short-term programs.
Purpose: "...to help the Church of the city, comprised of its various congregations, implement a comprehensive strategy to effectively saturate the city with the Good News of the gospel..."
Year Founded in USA 1980
Income for Overseas Mins $200,000
Fully Supported USA Personnel Overseas:
Expecting to serve more than 4 years 2

Expecting to serve 1 to 4 years 2
Nonresidential mission personnel 4

Other Personnel:

Non-USA serving in own/other country 2
Bivocational/Tentmaker from USA 5
Short-Term less than 1 year from USA 20
Home ministry & office staff in USA 20

Countries: Argentina 3, Philippines 1

Harvest International Christian Outreach / Target Teams

(800)840-4426 **Fax: (402)895-4237**
E-Mail: TargetTeam@aol.com
P.O. Box 45656, Omaha, NE 68145
Michael Darr, Director

An interdenominational specialized agency of Wesleyan tradition engaged in evangelism, literature distribution, mobilization for mission and short-term programs.

Purpose: "Mobilizing churches into missions through short-term mission experiences."

Year Founded in USA 1992
Income for Overseas Mins $80,000
Personnel:

Short-Term less than 1 year from USA 90
Home ministry & office staff in USA 2

Harvesting In Spanish

(503)260-2754 **Fax: (503)261-0938**
E-Mail: harvest@es.com.sv
Web: www.harvest.org.sv
Amilat Vip Sal 723, P.O. Box 02-5364, Miami, FL 33102
Rev. Donald W. Benner, President

A nondenominational sending agency of charismatic and evangelical tradition engaged in childcare/orphanage programs, Bible distribution, church planting, Christian education, literature distribution and short-term programs.

Purpose: "...to be the Lord's hand extended to spiritually and physically needy Spanish-speaking people, in obedience to God's admonition to care for the poor, the widows and the fatherless, while fulfilling the Great Commission."

Year Founded in USA 1980
Income for Overseas Mins $300,000
Fully Supported USA Personnel Overseas:

Expecting to serve more than 4 years 3
Expecting to serve 1 to 4 years 5

Other Personnel:

Short-Term less than 1 year from USA 125

Countries: El Salvador 8

Have Christ Will Travel Ministries

(215)438-6308 **Fax: (215)438-6308**
528 E. Church Lane, Philadelphia, PA 19144
Rev. Joseph C. Jeter, Director/President

An interdenominational support agency of independent and Baptist tradition engaged in evangelism, Christian education, support of national churches and supplying equipment.

Year Founded in USA 1965
Income for Overseas Mins $180,000
Gifts-in-Kind $67,000
Fully Supported USA Personnel Overseas:

Nonresidential mission personnel 5

Other Personnel:

Non-USA serving in own/other country 38
Short-Term less than 1 year from USA 23
Home ministry & office staff in USA 8

Countries: Haiti, India, Liberia

HBI Global Partners

(828)286-8317 **Fax: (828)286-8317**
E-Mail: hbi@blueridge.net
Web: www.globalpartners.org
P.O. Box 245, Union Mills, NC 28167
Mr. John Gupta, U.S. Chair

A nondenominational sending agency of evangelical tradition engaged in church planting, broadcasting, childcare/orphanage programs, theological education, evangelism and support of national workers.

Purpose: "...enabling the North American Church to develop partnerships with national movements to reach the unreached in India and beyond."

Year Founded in USA 1950
Income for Overseas Mins $377,000
Fully Supported USA Personnel Overseas:

Expecting to serve more than 4 years 2

Other Personnel:

Short-Term less than 1 year from USA 30
Home ministry & office staff in USA 2

Countries: India 2

HCJB World Radio

(719)590-9800 Fax: (719)590-9801
E-Mail: info@hcjb.org
Web: www.hcjb.org
P.O. Box 39800, Colorado Springs, CO 80949
Dr. Ronald A. Cline, President

An interdenominational service agency of evangelical tradition engaged in broadcasting, audio recording and distribution, theological education, medical work and video/film production and distribution.

Purpose: "To communicate the gospel of Jesus Christ to all nations so that people are transformed and become an active, vital part of the Body of Christ."

Year Founded in USA 1931
Income for Overseas Mins $8,260,270
Gifts-in-Kind $700,291
Fully Supported USA Personnel Overseas:
- Expecting to serve more than 4 years 179
- Expecting to serve 1 to 4 years 4
- Nonresidential mission personnel 4

Other Personnel:
- Non-USA serving in own/other country 50
- Short-Term less than 1 year from USA 57
- Home ministry & office staff in USA 93

Countries: Argentina, Brazil, Czech Republic, Ecuador 183, UK

Health Teams International

(918)481-1115 Fax: (918)523-2677
E-Mail: HTIteams@cs.com
7518 S. Evanston Ave., Tulsa, OK 74136
Dr. Robert W. Miller, President

An interdenominational specialized agency of ecumenical tradition engaged in medical work, evangelism and services for other agencies.

Year Founded in USA 1986
Income for Overseas Mins $50,000

Heart of God Ministries

(405)737-9446 Fax: (405)737-9448
Web: www.heartofgod.com
3720 S. Hiwassee Rd., Choctaw, OK 73020
Rev./Dr. James Lee West, Exec. Director

An interdenominational specialized agency of evangelical and Holiness tradition engaged in missionary training, mobilization for mission and youth programs.

Year Founded in USA 1993
Income for Overseas Mins $30,000
Personnel:
- Short-Term less than 1 year from USA 20
- Home ministry & office staff in USA 20

Heart to Heart Intl. Ministries

(760)789-8798 Fax: (760)789-8798
E-Mail: Sorrels@adnc.com
P.O. Box 1832, Ramona, CA 92065
Mr. Thomas Sorrels, Gen. Director

A nondenominational support agency of evangelical tradition engaged in childrens programs, camping programs, childcare/orphanage programs, development, evangelism and short-term programs.

Purpose: "...to evangelize and build up believers where the church has been greatly hampered by oppression and where there are few or no indigenous churches..."

Year Founded in USA 1994
Income for Overseas Mins $178,115
Fully Supported USA Personnel Overseas:
- Expecting to serve 1 to 4 years 5
- Nonresidential mission personnel 3

Other Personnel:
- Non-USA serving in own/other country 2
- Short-Term less than 1 year from USA 50
- Home ministry & office staff in USA 2

Countries: Hungary 2, Romania 3

Heifer Project International

(501)907-2600 Fax: (501)907-2602
E-Mail: info@heifer.org
Web: www.heifer.org
1015 Louisiana Street, Little Rock, AR 72202
Jo Luck, Exec. Director

An interdenominational support agency of ecumenical tradition engaged in agricultural programs, development, extension education, technical assistance and training. Statistical information from 1996. Eleven denominations have "covenant agency representatives" on the board.

Year Founded in USA 1944
Income for Overseas Mins $5,500,000
Gifts-in-Kind $715,000

Fully Supported USA Personnel Overseas:
Expecting to serve more than 4 years 2
Expecting to serve 1 to 4 years 1
Other Personnel:
Short-Term less than 1 year from USA 6
Home ministry & office staff in USA 100
Countries: Mozambique 1, Tanzania 2

Hellenic Ministries

(630)462-7088 Fax: (630)462-3740
E-Mail: Info@hmnet.org.gr
Web: www.hmnet.org.gr
P.O. Box 726, Wheaton, IL 60189
Mr. Trevor Eby, Acting N. American Director
A nondenominational sending agency of evangelical tradition engaged in church planting, evangelism and youth programs.
Year Founded in USA 1986
Income for Overseas Mins $180,539
Fully Supported USA Personnel Overseas:
Expecting to serve more than 4 years 5
Expecting to serve 1 to 4 years 1
Other Personnel:
Non-USA serving in own/other country 4
Short-Term less than 1 year from USA 22
Home ministry & office staff in USA 2
Countries: Greece 6

Help for Christian Nationals, Inc.

(972)780-5909
P.O. Box 381006, Duncanville, TX 75138
Dr. John Jauchen, Director
A transdenominational sending agency of evangelical tradition engaged in leadership development, extension education, literature distribution, support of national churches, support of national workers and training.
Purpose: "...serving Christian national workers through economic and educational assistance, equipping them to be more effective in reaching their own people for Jesus Christ."
Year Founded in USA 1982
Income for Overseas Mins $450,000
Fully Supported USA Personnel Overseas:
Expecting to serve more than 4 years 4
Nonresidential mission personnel 2
Other Personnel:
Non-USA serving in own/other country 10
Home ministry & office staff in USA 1
Countries: Guatemala, India, Philippines 2, Russia, Spain 2

Helps International Ministries

(828)277-3812 Fax: (828)274-7770
E-Mail: HIM@juno.com
Web: www.helpsintl.com
P.O. Box 1640, Asheville, NC 28802
Rev. David A. Summey, Exec. Director
A nondenominational specialized agency of evangelical and fundamental tradition engaged in services for other agencies and technical assistance.
Purpose: "...strengthening and equipping ministries serving God's kingdom by providing various 'helps'..."
Year Founded in USA 1976
Income for Overseas Mins $121,661
Fully Supported USA Personnel Overseas:
Expecting to serve more than 4 years 4
Nonresidential mission personnel 4
Other Personnel:
Non-USA serving in own/other country 3
Short-Term less than 1 year from USA 12
Home ministry & office staff in USA 43
Countries: UK 2, West Bank 2

Hermano Pablo Ministries

(949)645-0676 Fax: (949)645-0374
E-Mail: hpm@box100.org
Web: www.box100.org
P.O. Box 100, Costa Mesa, CA 92628
Rev. Paul Finkenbinder, Chairman of the Board
Rev. Charles Stewart, President
An interdenominational agency of evangelical tradition whose four-minute "Message to the Conscience" is broadcast more than 14,000 times per week throughout the Spanish-speaking world. Income and home staff amounts from 1996.
Year Founded in USA 1964
Income for Overseas Mins $396,000
Personnel:
Home ministry & office staff in USA 5

High Adventure Ministries / Voice of Hope Broadcasting Network

(805)520-9460 Fax: (805)520-7823
Web: www.highadventure.org

P.O. Box 100, Simi Valley, CA 93062
Mr. George Otis, President Emeritus
Jackie Yockey, Chief Operations Officer

An interdenominational service agency of evangelical tradition engaged in broadcasting, correspondence courses and evangelism. Personnel and financial information from 1996.

Year Founded in USA 1972
Income for Overseas Mins $388,511
Fully Supported USA Personnel Overseas:
Expecting to serve more than 4 years 2
Other Personnel:
Non-USA serving in own/other country 26
Short-Term less than 1 year from USA 3
Home ministry & office staff in USA 33
Countries: Belau(Palau) 1, Israel 1

High School Evangelism Fellowship, Inc.
See: Touch the World Ministries

Holt International Children's Services, Inc.

(541)687-2202 Fax: (541)683-6175
E-Mail: info@holtintl.org
Web: www.holtintl.org
P.O. Box 2880, Eugene, OR 97402
Mr. John L. Williams, President/CEO

A nondenominational service agency of evangelical tradition serving the needs of homeless children and families at risk through childcare, medical and camping programs. Statistical information from 1996.

Purpose: "...to carry out God's plan for every child to have a permanent loving home through family preservation, in-country adoption or international adoption."

Year Founded in USA 1956
Income for Overseas Mins $6,094,101
Fully Supported USA Personnel Overseas:
Expecting to serve 1 to 4 years 6
Other Personnel:
Non-USA serving in own/other country 552
Short-Term less than 1 year from USA 5
Home ministry & office staff in USA 120
Countries: China (PRC), Ecuador, Guatemala, Hong Kong 1, India, Korea-S, Philippines, Romania 2, Thailand, Vietnam 3

HOPE Bible Mission, Inc.

(973)543-4492 Fax: (973)543-4492
E-Mail: H.O.P.E.BibleMission@juno.com
P.O. Box 161, Morristown, NJ 07963
Mr. Rick Carey, Director

A nondenominational support agency of evangelical tradition engaged in Bible distribution, evangelism and support of national workers. Statistical information from 1996.

Year Founded in USA 1950
Income for Overseas Mins .... NR
Personnel:
Short-Term less than 1 year from USA 6
Countries: Haiti, Spain

Hope for the Hungry

(254)939-0124 Fax: (254)939-0882
E-Mail: hhungry@sage.net
Web: www.hopeforthehungry.org
P.O. Box 786, Belton, TX 76513
Rev. Dan Kirkley, President

An interdenominational sending agency of charismatic and evangelical tradition engaged in childcare/orphanage programs, evangelism, funds transmission, support of national churches, short-term programs and missionary training.

Purpose: "To share Jesus Christ with those in the world who do not know Him and will suffer eternal death without Him."

Year Founded in USA 1982
Income for Overseas Mins $505,000
Fully Supported USA Personnel Overseas:
Expecting to serve more than 4 years 18
Expecting to serve 1 to 4 years 8
Nonresidential mission personnel 4
Other Personnel:
Non-USA serving in own/other country 19
Bivocational/Tentmaker from USA 3
Short-Term less than 1 year from USA 78
Home ministry & office staff in USA 6
Countries: Australia 1, Belize 2, China (PRC) 3, Colombia 2, Costa Rica 2, France 3, Haiti 4, Japan 2, Mexico 3, Philippines 1, S Africa 2, Taiwan (ROC) 1

Hope Missions Outreach International

(816)425-2277 Fax: (816)425-2279

P.O. Box 73, Bethany, MO 64424
Bob & Sharon Johnson, Directors
An interdenominational service agency of evangelical tradition engaged in short-term programs, church construction and mobilization for mission. Name changed from Missions Outreach International.
Purpose: "...to serve the local evangelical church for the purpose of discipleship training through cross-cultural team ministries..."
Year Founded in USA 1976
Income for Overseas Mins $450,000
Fully Supported USA Personnel Overseas:
Expecting to serve more than 4 years 3
Other Personnel:
Short-Term less than 1 year from USA 190
Home ministry & office staff in USA 5
Countries: Haiti 3

Hosanna / Faith Comes By Hearing

(505)881-3321 **Fax: (505)881-1681**
E-Mail: FCBH@hosanna.org
Web: www.faithcomesbyhearing.org
2421 Aztec Rd. NE, Albuquerque, NM 87107-4224
Mr. Jerry Jackson, President
An interdenominational service agency of ecumenical tradition serving as a repository of Bible recordings in all available languages in addition to providing training, equipment, funding for recordings, and support of national workers. Personnel and income information from 1996.
Year Founded in USA 1972
Income for Overseas Mins $86,992
Personnel:
Short-Term less than 1 year from USA 6
Home ministry & office staff in USA 92

ICI University

(972)751-1111 **Fax: (972)714-8185**
E-Mail: info@ici.edu
Web: www.ici.edu
6300 N. Belt Line Rd., Irving, TX 75063
Dr. Ronald A. Iwasko, President
A service agency of Pentecostal and evangelical tradition engaged in TEE, correspondence courses, theological education, evangelism and literature distribution.
Year Founded in USA 1967
Income for Overseas Mins $819,731
Personnel:
Home ministry & office staff in USA 42

IFMA (Interdenominational Foreign Mission Association)

(630)682-9270 **Fax: (630)682-9278**
E-Mail: ifma@aol.com
Web: www.ifmamissions.org
P.O. Box 398, Wheaton, IL 60189-0398
Dr. John H. Orme, Exec. Director
An association of mission agencies without denominational affiliation organized for the purpose of strengthening the effectiveness and outreach of interdenominational missions.
Year Founded in USA 1917
Income for Overseas Mins .... NA
Personnel:
Home ministry & office staff in USA 3

Impact International

(561)338-7515 **Fax: (561)338-7516**
E-Mail: ImpactInternational@juno.com
P.O. Box 160, Boca Raton, FL 33429-0160
Rev. Bruce Woodman, Exec. Director
An interdenominational sending agency of evangelical tradition engaged in evangelism, broadcasting, church planting and short-term programs.
Year Founded in USA 1959
Income for Overseas Mins $320,000
Fully Supported USA Personnel Overseas:
Expecting to serve more than 4 years 7
Nonresidential mission personnel 4
Other Personnel:
Non-USA serving in own/other country 18
Short-Term less than 1 year from USA 15
Home ministry & office staff in USA 4
Countries: Argentina, Colombia 2, Costa Rica 1, Guatemala 2, Honduras 2, Mexico, Peru, Venezuela

In Touch Mission International

(602)968-4100 **Fax: (602)968-5462**
E-Mail: itmi@itmi.org
Web: www.itmi.org

P.O. Box 28240, Tempe, AZ 85285-8240
Mr. Bill Bathman, Director
A nondenominational service agency of Baptist and evangelical tradition engaged in support of national churches, Bible distribution, evangelism, missions information service, literature distribution and providing medical supplies.
Year Founded in USA 1981
Income for Overseas Mins $376,156
Fully Supported USA Personnel Overseas:
Expecting to serve more than 4 years 2
Nonresidential mission personnel 2
Other Personnel:
Home ministry & office staff in USA 4
Countries: Unspecified 2

Independent Faith Mission

(336)292-1255
P.O. Box 7791, Greensboro, NC 27417
Rev. Robert F. Kurtz, Exec. Director
A nondenominational service agency of Baptist tradition providing various services to local churches sending missionaries engaged in church planting and evangelism.
Year Founded in USA 1950
Income for Overseas Mins $2,500,000
Fully Supported USA Personnel Overseas:
Expecting to serve more than 4 years 101
Other Personnel:
Short-Term less than 1 year from USA 6
Countries: Antigua 2, Congo/Zaire 8, Italy 5, Kenya 8, Korea-S 2, Mexico 2, Micronesia 2, Philippines 2, S Africa 9, Suriname 17, UK 2, Unspecified 26, Zambia 12, Zimbabwe 4

Independent Gospel Missions

(724)342-1090 Fax: (724)342-1371
E-Mail: IGM7@juno.com
Web: www.crosswinds.net/pittsburgh/~igm
Box 1533, Hermitage, PA 16148
Rev. Gary Newhart/Director
A nondenominational service agency of Baptist and independent tradition engaged in funds transmission, childcare/orphanage programs, church planting, support of national churches, short-term programs and support of national workers.
Year Founded in USA 1968
Income for Overseas Mins $900,000
Fully Supported USA Personnel Overseas:
Nonresidential mission personnel 4

India Evangelical Mission, Inc.

(714)739-8068 Fax: (714)739-8068
E-Mail: iemusa@jps.net
P.O. Box 1633, Lakewood, CA 90716-0633
Dr. G. V. Mathai, President
A nondenominational service agency of Brethren tradition engaged in missionary education, childcare/orphanage programs, church planting, evangelism and support of national workers.
Purpose: "...winning the lost, building and equipping the saints and then sending them forth to fulfill the Great Commission of our Lord."
Year Founded in USA 1966
Income for Overseas Mins $241,117
Fully Supported USA Personnel Overseas:
Nonresidential mission personnel 3
Other Personnel:
Non-USA serving in own/other country 525
Short-Term less than 1 year from USA 10
Home ministry & office staff in USA 4
Countries: India

India Gospel Outreach

(909)948-2404 Fax: (909)948-2406
E-Mail: indiago@compuserve.com
Web: www.indiago.org
P.O. Box 550, Rancho Cucamonga, CA 91729-0550
Rev. T. Valson Abraham, Founder/Director
A transdenominational service agency of evangelical tradition engaged in church planting, broadcasting, theological education, evangelism, leadership development, support of national churches and support of national workers. Personnel information from 1996.
Purpose: "...planting dynamic churches in all 3,000 castes and tribes...and establishing Bible training centers in all states of India...by the year 2000."
Year Founded in USA 1984
Income for Overseas Mins $447,000
Personnel:
Short-Term less than 1 year from USA 8
Home ministry & office staff in USA 7

India National Inland Mission

(818)241-4010
E-Mail: 110532.3373@compuserve.com
P.O. Box 652, Verdugo City, CA 91046
Mr. Paul Pillai, Director

An interdenominational support agency of fundamental tradition engaged in funds transmission, childcare/orphanage programs, church planting and Christian education through partners in India.

Year Founded in USA 1964
Income for Overseas Mins $800,000
Fully Supported USA Personnel Overseas:
Expecting to serve more than 4 years 3
Other Personnel:
Non-USA serving in own/other country 330
Bivocational/Tentmaker from USA 13
Short-Term less than 1 year from USA 45
Home ministry & office staff in USA 1
Countries: India 3

India Rural Evangelical Fellowship

(847)680-6767 **Fax: (847)680-4270**
E-Mail: Info@irefusa.org
Web: www.irefusa.org
P.O. Box 1332, Park Ridge, IL 60068-7332
Mr. Emmanuel Rebba, President

An interdenominational service agency of evangelical tradition engaged in evangelism, Bible distribution, childcare/orphanage programs, church planting, Christian education and theological education.

Purpose: "...to promote the gospel within the state of Andhra Pradesh; to print and publish Christian literature...to establish and maintain individual churches...Christian schools...homes for orphans and destitute children; to provide financial assistance in supporting medical services for the rural poor; and to encourage human development..."

Year Founded in USA 1985
Income for Overseas Mins $476,258
Personnel:
Non-USA serving in own/other country 127
Short-Term less than 1 year from USA 48
Home ministry & office staff in USA 1

Institute for International Christian Communication

(503)234-1639 **Fax: (503)234-1639**
E-Mail: worldviewcenter@juno.com
6012 SE Yamhill St., Portland, OR 97215
Dr. Donald K. & Mrs. Faye Smith, Directors

A transdenominational service agency of evangelical tradition supporting the leadership of Third World churches by forging meaningful collaborations that result in sharing resources of research, education, personnel, and materials. Sponsors of WorldView Center, a residential and training center for missionary candidates.

Year Founded in USA 1967
Income for Overseas Mins $52,000
Fully Supported USA Personnel Overseas:
Nonresidential mission personnel 1
Other Personnel:
Home ministry & office staff in USA 6

Institute of Chinese Studies

(714)449-0611 **Fax: (714)449-0624**
E-Mail: china@xc.org
Web: www.chsource.org
P.O. Box 4343, Fullerton, CA 92834-4343
Dr. Brent Fulton, President
Rev. Jim Nickel, Intl. Vice President

An interdenominational service agency of evangelical tradition engaged in services for other agencies, literature production, mission-related research and video/film production/distribution. Merging with ChinaSource in 2000.

Purpose: "Strategically connecting knowledge and leaders to advance the Kingdom of God in China."

Year Founded in USA 1977
Income for Overseas Mins .... NA

Institute of Hindu Studies

(626)398-2314 **Fax: (626)398-2263**
E-Mail: ihs@uscwm.org
Web: www.uscwm.org
1605 Elizabeth St., Pasadena, CA 91104-2721
Mr. Jamie Bean, Coordinator

An interdenominational service agency of evangelical tradition engaged in missions mobilization, training, research and strategy with a focus on the Hindu world.

Year Founded in USA 1976
Income for Overseas Mins .... NA
Personnel:
Short-Term less than 1 year from USA 1
Home ministry & office staff in USA 1

INTENT

(773)921-0457 **Fax: (773)921-9738**
E-Mail: info@intent.org
Web: www.intent.org
5840 W. Midway Park, Chicago, IL 60644-1803
Mr. Gary D. Ginter, Board Chairman

A nondenominational service agency of evangelical tradition providing tentmaking-related services, literature production and distribution, and missions-related research.

Year Founded in USA 1987
Income for Overseas Mins .... NA
Personnel:
Home ministry & office staff in USA 3

InterAct Ministries

(503)668-5571 **Fax: (503)668-6814**
E-Mail: InterAct@interactministries.org
Web: www.interactministries.org
31000 SE Kelso Rd., Boring, OR 97009
Rev. Gary Brumbelow, Gen. Director

A nondenominational sending agency of evangelical tradition engaged in church planting, aviation services, camping programs, disability assistance programs, evangelism and leadership development.

Purpose: "...to see culturally relevant churches established and making disciples among unreached peoples of the world."

Year Founded in USA 1951
Income for Overseas Mins $208,028
Fully Supported USA Personnel Overseas:
Expecting to serve more than 4 years 8
Expecting to serve 1 to 4 years 2
Other Personnel:
Home ministry & office staff in USA 86
Countries: Asia 2, Russia 8

Interchurch Medical Assistance

(410)635-8720 **Fax: (410)635-8726**
E-Mail: ima@ecunet.org
Web: www.interchurch.org
P.O. Box 429, New Windsor, MD 21776
Mr. Paul Derstine, President

An interdenominational support agency of ecumenical tradition distributing medical supplies to healthcare facilities in 53 countries affiliated with member and associate organizations.

Purpose: "...to provide essential products and services for emergency, health and development programs of interest to members, which serve people in need with preference given to the poorest of the poor..."

Year Founded in USA 1960
Income for Overseas Mins $14,717,252
Gifts-in-Kind $13,863,509
Fully Supported USA Personnel Overseas:
Expecting to serve 1 to 4 years 1
Other Personnel:
Short-Term less than 1 year from USA 3
Home ministry & office staff in USA 9
Countries: Tanzania 1

INTERCOMM

(219)267-5834 **Fax: (219)267-5876**
E-Mail: MARG@kconline.com
1520 E. Winona Ave., Warsaw, IN 46580
Mr. Raymond Monteith, Exec. Director

A nondenominational support agency of evangelical tradition engaged in video/film production/distribution, audio recording/distribution and evangelism, equipping national workers in more than 100 countries in evangelism outreach. A ministry of Ken Anderson Films.

Purpose: "...to equip national Christian leaders with appropriate Christian media to help them evangelize their country."

Year Founded in USA 1990
Income for Overseas Mins $200,000
Fully Supported USA Personnel Overseas:
Nonresidential mission personnel 2
Other Personnel:
Short-Term less than 1 year from USA 2
Home ministry & office staff in USA 5

Intercristo

(800)251-7740 **Fax: (206)546-7375**
E-Mail: lmh@crista.org

Web: www.jobsinaflash.org
19303 Fremont Ave., N., Seattle, WA 98133
Ann Brooks, Exec. Director
An interdenominational service agency of evangelical tradition providing assistance and information to mission agencies in locating qualified personnel for positions at home and abroad. An affiliate of CRISTA Ministries.
Year Founded in USA 1967
Income for Overseas Mins .... NA
Personnel:
Home ministry & office staff in USA 12

Interdenominational Foreign Mission Association See: IFMA

INTERDEV

(425)775-8330 Fax: (425)775-8326
E-Mail: interdev-us@xc.org
P.O. Box 3883, Seattle, WA 98124
Mr. Phillip W. Butler, President
A nondenominational service agency of evangelical tradition engaged in partnership development and services for other agencies.
Purpose: "...to serve the Church in accelerating fulfillment of the Great Commission through the development, formation and long-term effective operation of international partnerships for evangelism among the world's unreached people."
Year Founded in USA 1974
Income for Overseas Mins $1,472,204
Fully Supported USA Personnel Overseas:
Expecting to serve more than 4 years 1
Nonresidential mission personnel 1
Other Personnel:
Non-USA serving in own/other country 6
Home ministry & office staff in USA 17
Countries: Asia 1

International Aid

(616)846-7490 Fax: (616)846-3842
E-Mail: iai@internationalaid.org
Web: www.internationalaid.org
17011 W. Hickory St., Spring Lake, MI 49456
Mr. Ralph E. Plumb, President/CEO
A nondenominational specialized agency of evangelical tradition engaged in providing relief and development assistance in 166 countries. Personnel information from 1996. The income total does not include an estimated $71 million of donated medicines, medical equipment/supplies, food, vitamins, etc.
Purpose: "...linking caring people and organizations with Christian partners worldwide, changing lives through the power of compassion."
Year Founded in USA 1980
Income for Overseas Mins $5,075,731
Personnel:
Home ministry & office staff in USA 60

International Bible Institute

(562)907-5555 Fax: (562)907-5552
E-Mail: ibibible@aol.com
Web: www.ibibible.org
P.O. Box 2473, Santa Fe Sprgs., CA 90670
Dr. Earle E. Williams, President
A nondenominational service agency of evangelical tradition establishing extension Bible institutes in local churches using audio tapes, printed materials and other means.
Year Founded in USA 1971
Income for Overseas Mins $44,000
Fully Supported USA Personnel Overseas:
Expecting to serve more than 4 years 1
Expecting to serve 1 to 4 years 1
Nonresidential mission personnel 1
Other Personnel:
Non-USA serving in own/other country 2
Short-Term less than 1 year from USA 1
Home ministry & office staff in USA 3
Countries: India 1, Philippines 1

International Bible Society

(719)488-9200 Fax: (719)488-0912
E-Mail: IBS@gospelcom.org
Web: www.ibs.org
1820 Jet Stream Drive, Colorado Springs, CO 80921
Mr. Peter J. Bradley, President
A nondenominational service agency of evangelical tradition engaged in Bible distribution, evangelism, literature distribution and Bible translation.
Purpose: "To serve the church in evangelism and discipleship by providing God's Word so that people around the world may come to faith and life in Jesus Christ."

Year Founded in USA 1809
Income for Overseas Mins $3,904,000
Personnel:
Non-USA serving in own/other country 314
Home ministry & office staff in USA 130

International Board of Jewish Missions, Inc.

(423)876-8150 **Fax: (423)876-8156**
E-Mail: amolam@voy.net
Web: www.voyageronline.net/ibjm
1928 Hamill Road, Hixson, TN 37343
Dr. Orman L. Norwood, President

A sending board of Baptist and independent tradition engaged in evangelism, Bible distribution, broadcasting, church planting, literature distribution and video/film production/distribution.

Year Founded in USA 1949
Income for Overseas Mins $50,000
Personnel:
Short-Term less than 1 year from USA 30
Home ministry & office staff in USA 15

International Child Care

(614)447-9952 **Fax: (614)447-1123**
E-Mail: iccusa1@aol.com
Web: www.intlchildcare.org
P.O. Box 14485, Columbus, OH 43214
Dr. John Yates, Exec. Director

An interdenominational service agency of evangelical tradition engaged in medical work, development, disability assistance programs, providing medical supplies and technical assistance. Statistical information from 1996.

Year Founded in USA 1965
Income for Overseas Mins $354,456
Fully Supported USA Personnel Overseas:
Expecting to serve more than 4 years 2
Other Personnel:
Home ministry & office staff in USA 4
Countries: Haiti 2

International Children's Care

(360)573-0429 **Fax: (360)573-0491**
Web: www.forhiskids.org
P.O. Box 4406, Vancouver, WA 98662
Mr. Rick Fleck, President

A nondenominational service agency of Adventist tradition engaged in childcare/orphanage programs. Statistical information from 1992.

Year Founded in USA 1978
Income for Overseas Mins $901,104
Fully Supported USA Personnel Overseas:
Expecting to serve 1 to 4 years 10
Nonresidential mission personnel 1
Other Personnel:
Short-Term less than 1 year from USA 3
Home ministry & office staff in USA 10
Countries: Costa Rica 1, Dominican Rep 2, Guatemala 6, Romania 1

International Christian Leprosy Mission, Inc. (USA)

(503)244-5935 **Fax: (503)244-5935**
E-Mail: HealingHands8414@aol.com
P.O. Box 23353, Portland, OR 97281
Dr. Daniel G. Pulliam, President

A support agency engaged in providing medical supplies and support of national medical ministries. Income figure from 1996.

Year Founded in USA 1943
Income for Overseas Mins $24,000
Personnel:
Non-USA serving in own/other country 7
Home ministry & office staff in USA 4
Countries: India, Philippines

International Christian Literature Distributors, Inc.

(612)822-7065
P.O. Box 8295, Minneapolis, MN 55408
Mr. E. Michael Ondov, President

A nondenominational support agency of evangelical tradition recycling Christian literature to overseas countries. Personnel information from 1996.

Purpose: "...to provide Bibles, Christian books, devotional and other Gospel literature, primarily to Third World countries."

Year Founded in USA 1961
Income for Overseas Mins $90,000
Personnel:
Short-Term less than 1 year from USA 7

International Church Relief Fund See: Children's Hunger Relief

International Cooperating Ministries

(757)827-6704 **Fax: (757)838-6486**
E-Mail: icm@icmmbc.org
Web: www.icmmbc.org
606 Aberdeen Rd., Hampton, VA 23661
Mr. Dois I. Rosser, Jr., Chairman

An interdenominational support agency of evangelical tradition engaged in church construction, audio recording/distribution, broadcasting, theological education and translation work in support of national ministries in 8 countries.

Purpose: "...to nurture believers and to assist the growth of the Church worldwide in accordance with Christ's Great Commission..."

Year Founded in USA 1987
Income for Overseas Mins $1,602,850
Personnel:
Home ministry & office staff in USA 15

International Crusades, Inc.

(214)747-1444 **Fax: (214)747-1417**
E-Mail: crusades@crusades.com
Web: www.crusades.com
500 S. Ervay St., #409, Dallas, TX 75201
Rev. Gary Baird, President

A denominational service agency of Baptist tradition engaged in short-term programs, evangelism and training in Africa, Latin America, Philippines, and Russia. Income figure from 1992.

Purpose: "...working with Southern Baptist Churches in the U.S. to facilitate partnership mission crusades with Baptist churches overseas..."

Year Founded in USA 1971
Income for Overseas Mins $500,000
Personnel:
Short-Term less than 1 year from USA 661
Home ministry & office staff in USA 18

International Discipleship Mission

(714)990-2738
P.O. Box 655, Brea, CA 92822
Mr. Emil Aanderud, Director

A nondenominational sending agency of fundamental tradition engaged in evangelism and literature distribution. Statistical information from 1992.

Year Founded in USA 1951
Income for Overseas Mins $73,000
Fully Supported USA Personnel Overseas:
Expecting to serve more than 4 years 4
Countries: Germany 2, Mexico 2

International Family Missions

(303)665-7927 **Fax: (303)661-0732**
E-Mail: ifmcolorado@juno.com
P.O. Box 309, Lafayette, CO 80026-0309
Rev. Joseph Hart, Minister/Director

A transdenominational support agency of evangelical tradition engaged in short-term programs, childrens programs, missionary education, evangelism, leadership development and missionary training.

Year Founded in USA 1987
Income for Overseas Mins $150,000
Gifts-in-Kind $30,000
Fully Supported USA Personnel Overseas:
Nonresidential mission personnel 1
Other Personnel:
Bivocational/Tentmaker from USA 1
Short-Term less than 1 year from USA 480
Home ministry & office staff in USA 9

International Fellowship of Evangelical Students - USA See: InterVarsity Mission

International Foundation for EWHA Woman's University

(212)864-5759 **Fax: (212)864-2552**
475 Riverside Dr. Rm. 915, New York, NY 10115
Ms. Miran Kim, Exec. Director

An interdenominational support agency of ecumenical tradition providing financial and other support to EWHA University in South Korea.

Year Founded in USA 1969
Income for Overseas Mins $400,000

International Gospel League

(626)304-9233 Fax: (626)304-9233
P.O. Box 519, Pasadena, CA 91102
Mr. Bruce Lewis, Administrator
A nondenominational sending agency of evangelical tradition engaged in evangelism, literature distribution and support of national workers. Statistical information from 1992.
Year Founded in USA 1906
Income for Overseas Mins $1,000,000
Fully Supported USA Personnel Overseas:
Expecting to serve more than 4 years 10
Countries: Kenya 5, Uganda 5

International Gospel Outreach

(334)645-2117 Fax: (334)645-2118
E-Mail: intgospl@aol.com
P.O. Drawer 1008, Semmes, AL 36575
Mr. Bertist Rouse, President
Mr. James Graham, Director
An interdenominational sending agency of charismatic and Wesleyan tradition engaged in missionary training, church planting, TEE, evangelism, mobilization for mission and short-term programs.
Year Founded in USA 1973
Income for Overseas Mins $213,737
Gifts-in-Kind $17,285
Fully Supported USA Personnel Overseas:
Expecting to serve more than 4 years 10
Expecting to serve 1 to 4 years 4
Other Personnel:
Non-USA serving in own/other country 3
Short-Term less than 1 year from USA 15
Home ministry & office staff in USA 19
Countries: Australia 1, Belize 2, Chile 1, Cuba 1, Honduras 1, India 1, Indonesia 1, Kenya 1, Korea-S 1, Mexico 2, Russia 2

International Health Services

(610)293-0966 Fax: (610)293-0611
E-Mail: IHSUSA@compuserve.com
P.O. Box 265, Southeastern, PA 19399-0265
Mr. Peter Baur, U.S. Director Operations
An interdenominational service agency of evangelical tradition engaged in leadership development, evangelism and medical work.
Year Founded in USA 1995
Income for Overseas Mins $200,000
Fully Supported USA Personnel Overseas:
Expecting to serve more than 4 years 2
Expecting to serve 1 to 4 years 1
Other Personnel:
Non-USA serving in own/other country 4
Home ministry & office staff in USA 2
Countries: Hungary 3

International Institute for Christian Studies

(913)962-4422 Fax: (913)962-1912
E-Mail: iics@iics.com
Web: www.iics.com
P.O. Box 12147, Overland Park, KS 66282-2147
Dr. Daryl McCarthy, CEO
A nondenominational service agency of evangelical tradition engaged in leadership development and in teaching Christian truth in public universities
Purpose: "To develop leaders who think and live Christianly, by establishing Departments of Christian Studies in secular universities and by providing evangelical academicians, business leaders and professional teaching with a Christian worldview overseas."
Year Founded in USA 1986
Income for Overseas Mins $780,243
Gifts-in-Kind $83,425
Fully Supported USA Personnel Overseas:
Expecting to serve more than 4 years 26
Expecting to serve 1 to 4 years 3
Other Personnel:
Non-USA serving in own/other country 16
Bivocational/Tentmaker from USA 1
Short-Term less than 1 year from USA 13
Home ministry & office staff in USA 7
Countries: Bangladesh 2, Czech Rep 8, Nigeria 8, Russia 2, Ukraine 3, Unspecified 6

International Leadership Seminars

(716)624-9660 Fax: (716)624-9129
E-Mail: ils_inc@compuserve.com
P.O. Box 56A, Lima, NY 14485
Mr. Salim C. Deir, Exec. Director
A nondenominational specialized agency of charismatic and Pentecostal tradition engaged in leadership development through seminars and publications.

Purpose: "...to reach, edify, mature and train the leadership in the Christian church worldwide to effectively reach the world with the gospel message of Jesus Christ."
Year Founded in USA 1973
Income for Overseas Mins $8,000
Personnel:
Short-Term less than 1 year from USA 1
Home ministry & office staff in USA 4

International Lutheran Laymen's League / Lutheran Hour Ministries

(314)951-4100 **Fax: (314)951-4295**
E-Mail: cheerful@lhmint.org
Web: www.lhmint.org
2185 Hampton Ave., St. Louis, MO 63139
Mr. Rodger Hebermehl, Exec. Director

A denominational specialized agency of Lutheran tradition engaged in evangelism through broadcasting in 47 countries through 297 national staff.
Year Founded in USA 1917
Income for Overseas Mins .... NR
Fully Supported USA Personnel Overseas:
Nonresidential mission personnel 5
Other Personnel:
Short-Term less than 1 year from USA 50
Home ministry & office staff in USA 130

International Messengers

(515)357-6700 **Fax: (515)357-6791**
E-Mail: imusa@netins.net
Web: www.internationalmessengers.org
P.O. Box R, Clearlake, IA 50428-0618
Mr. Robert P. Rasmusson, President

A transdenominational sending agency of evangelical tradition engaged in evangelism, camping programs, church planting, mobilization for mission, short-term programs and missionary training.
Purpose: "...partnering with local churches to renew, train and mobilize believers for active involvement in reaching the world for Christ."
Year Founded in USA 1984
Income for Overseas Mins $675,000
Gifts-in-Kind $10,000
Fully Supported USA Personnel Overseas:
Expecting to serve more than 4 years 13
Expecting to serve 1 to 4 years 7
Nonresidential mission personnel 24
Other Personnel:
Non-USA serving in own/other country 16
Bivocational/Tentmaker from USA 2
Short-Term less than 1 year from USA 150
Home ministry & office staff in USA 9
Countries: Czech Rep 1, Germany 2, Hungary 4, Poland 7, Romania 2, Slovakia 4

International Missions, Inc. See: Christar

International Needs - USA

(360)354-1991 **Fax: (360)354-1991**
E-Mail: inusa@international-needs.org
Web: www.international-needs.org
P.O. Box 977, Lynden, WA 98264
Mr. David Culross, Exec. Director

A transdenominational service agency of evangelical tradition engaged in support of national workers.
Year Founded in USA 1974
Income for Overseas Mins $967,955
Personnel:
Non-USA serving in own/other country 420
Short-Term less than 1 year from USA 10
Home ministry & office staff in USA 8

International Outreach Ministries

(334)633-7171 **Fax: (334)639-0489**
E-Mail: IOM@erestamail.com
P.O. Box 850998, Mobile, AL 36685
Rev. Gary Henley, Coordinator

A nondenominational sending agency of Reformed and charismatic tradition engaged in church planting, development, Christian education and evangelism.
Year Founded in USA 1986
Income for Overseas Mins $900,000
Fully Supported USA Personnel Overseas:
Expecting to serve more than 4 years 26
Expecting to serve 1 to 4 years 7
Nonresidential mission personnel 1
Other Personnel:
Non-USA serving in own/other country 5
Short-Term less than 1 year from USA 150
Home ministry & office staff in USA 3

Countries: Africa 2, Asia 2, Congo 13, Costa Rica 3, Europe 5, Jamaica 2, Jordan 2, Kenya 2, Papua New Guin 2

International Partnership Ministries, Inc.

(717)637-7388 **Fax: (717)637-1618**
E-Mail: ipm@ipmworld.org
Web: www.ipmworld.org
P.O. Box 41, Hanover, PA 17331-0041
Dr. Timothy B. Shorb, President

A nondenominational agency of Baptist and fundamental tradition supporting, in partnership with Two-Thirds World mission agencies, national workers involved in church planting, evangelism and leadership development.

Year Founded in USA 1982
Income for Overseas Mins $780,500
Fully Supported USA Personnel Overseas:
Expecting to serve more than 4 years 6
Other Personnel:
Non-USA serving in own/other country 122
Home ministry & office staff in USA 6
Countries: Chile, Cote d'Ivoire, Cuba, Ghana 2, Haiti, India, Lebanon, Liberia, Mexico, Myanmar, Nepal, Paraguay, Peru, Spain 2, Togo 2

International Pentecostal Church of Christ, Global Missions Dept.

(404)627-2681 **Fax: (404)627-0702**
E-Mail: hqipcc@aol.com
P.O. Box 18145, Atlanta, GA 30316
Dr. James B. Keiller, Director

A denominational sending agency of Pentecostal and charismatic tradition engaged in support of national churches, childcare/orphanage programs, Christian education, theological education, leadership development and literature distribution. Statistical data from 1996.

Year Founded in USA 1917
Income for Overseas Mins $186,504
Fully Supported USA Personnel Overseas:
Expecting to serve more than 4 years 5
Other Personnel:
Home ministry & office staff in USA 1
Countries: India 1, Kenya 3, Mexico 1

International Pentecostal Holiness Church World Missions Ministries

(405)787-7110 **Fax: (405)787-7729**
E-Mail: Ray@iphc.org
Web: www.iphc.org
P.O. Box 12609, Oklahoma City, OK 73157
Rev. M. Donald Duncan, Exec. Director

A denominational sending agency of Pentecostal and Holiness tradition engaged in church planting, theological education, furloughed missionary support, leadership development, support of national churches and mobilization for mission.

Year Founded in USA 1904
Income for Overseas Mins $5,447,555
Fully Supported USA Personnel Overseas:
Expecting to serve more than 4 years 95
Expecting to serve 1 to 4 years 14
Nonresidential mission personnel.................... 19
Other Personnel:
Non-USA serving in own/other country 7
Bivocational/Tentmaker from USA 9
Home ministry & office staff in USA 15
Countries: Africa 4, Asia 2, Australia 2, Costa Rica 2, Cote d'Ivoire 2, Germany 3, Ghana 2, Guatemala 2, Haiti 6, Hong Kong 2, Hungary 2, India 2, Japan 2, Kenya 9, Malawi 2, Mexico 2, Mozambique 2, Nicaragua 1, Norway 3, Panama 3, Philippines 3, Romania 1, Singapore 2, S Africa 22, Spain 4, Tanzania 3, Trinidad & Tobg 2, UK 8, Venezuela 2, Zambia 2, Zimbabwe 5

International Street Kids Outreach Ministries

(800)265-1970
E-Mail: iskom@juno.com
P.O. Box 8551, Clearwater, FL 33758-8551
Rev. John M. Schmidt, President

A nondenominational support agency of Baptist tradition engaged in childcare/ orphanage programs, camping programs and training.

Year Founded in USA 1995
Income for Overseas Mins $59,000
Fully Supported USA Personnel Overseas:
Expecting to serve more than 4 years 1
Other Personnel:
Non-USA serving in own/other country 1

Short-Term less than 1 year from USA 20
Home ministry & office staff in USA 1
Countries: Brazil 1

International Students, Inc

(719)576-2700 **Fax: (719)576-5363**
E-Mail: isiteam@isionline.org
Web: www.isionline.org
P.O. Box C, Colorado Springs, CO 80901
Mr. Tom K. Phillips, President

A transdenominational agency of evangelical and ecumenical tradition engaged in international student friendship, evangelism and discipleship in the USA with students from other countries

Year Founded in USA 1953
Income for Overseas Mins .... NA
Personnel:
Non-USA serving in own/other country 4
Bivocational/Tentmaker from USA 1
Home ministry & office staff in USA 180

International Teams, U.S.A.

(847)429-0900 **Fax: (847)429-0800**
E-Mail: info@itusa.org
Web: www.iteams.org
411 W. River Rd., Elgin, IL 60123
Mr. Stephen Freed, President

A nondenominational sending agency of evangelical tradition engaged in evangelism, childcare/orphanage programs, church planting, relief and/or rehabilitation, missionary training and youth programs.

Year Founded in USA 1960
Income for Overseas Mins $6,647,736
Fully Supported USA Personnel Overseas:
Expecting to serve more than 4 years 99
Expecting to serve 1 to 4 years 90
Other Personnel:
Non-USA serving in own/other country 125
Bivocational/Tentmaker from USA 6
Short-Term less than 1 year from USA 125
Home ministry & office staff in USA 60
Countries: Albania 2, Australia 1, Austria 38, Bolivia 2, Bulgaria 3, Colombia 2, Costa Rica 6, Czech Rep 13, Ecuador 6, France 20, Germany 5, Greece 14, Hungary 5, Italy 4, Jordan 2, Kazakhstan 2, Mexico 9, Poland 5, Romania 7, Russia 2, Slovakia 4, Spain 5, Thailand 2, Ukraine 5, UK 13, Uzbekistan 4, Vietnam 8

International Urban Associates

(773)275-9260 **Fax: (773)275-9969**
E-Mail: SeattleIUA@earthlink.net
5151 N. Clark St., 2nd Floor, Chicago, IL 60640
Dr. Ray Bakke, Exec. Director

A transdenominational information and service agency of evangelical tradition engaged in urban leadership development through church consultations and theological education and training.

Purpose: "...to empower God's people in the largest cities of the world by means of leadership consultations that generate vision, partnerships, motivations and resources, so that the 'whole church can take the whole gospel to the whole city'."

Year Founded in USA 1989
Income for Overseas Mins $275,000
Personnel:
Home ministry & office staff in USA 3

InterServe/USA

(610)352-0581 **Fax: (610)352-4394**
E-Mail: InterServeUSA@xc.org
Web: www.interserve.org
P.O. Box 418, Upper Darby, PA 19082-0418
Dr. Ralph W. Eckardt, Jr., Exec. Director

An interdenominational agency of evangelical tradition whose personnel/partners are engaged in medical work, church planting, development, Christian education, and support of national churches.

Year Founded in USA 1964
Income for Overseas Mins $3,486,021
Fully Supported USA Personnel Overseas:
Expecting to serve more than 4 years 70
Expecting to serve 1 to 4 years 3
Nonresidential mission personnel 4
Other Personnel:
Bivocational/Tentmaker from USA 39
Short-Term less than 1 year from USA 15
Home ministry & office staff in USA 15
Countries: Afghanistan 10, Bangladesh 6, China (PRC) 1, Cyprus 2, India 4, Jordan 3, Kyrgyzstan 11, Nepal 8, Pakistan 10, Turkey 16, Yemen 2

InterVarsity Mission

(608)274-9001 **Fax: (608)274-9680**
E-Mail: jcriswell@ivcf.org

Web: www.ivcf.org
P.O. Box 7895, Madison, WI 53707
Mr. John M. Criswell, Dir. InterVarsity LINK
An interdenominational sending agency of evangelical tradition engaged in evangelism, leadership development, literature production, mobilization for mission, missionary training and video/film production and distribution. As a member movement of the International Fellowship of Evangelical Students, IVCF/USA is supporting work with student ministries in 141 countries.
Purpose: "...to establish and advance at colleges and universities witnessing communities of students and faculty who follow Jesus as Savior and Lord: growing in love for God, God's word, God's people of every ethnicity and culture and God's purposes in the world."
Year Founded in USA 1941
Income for Overseas Mins $4,006,000
Fully Supported USA Personnel Overseas:
Expecting to serve more than 4 years 34
Expecting to serve 1 to 4 years 26
Nonresidential mission personnel 1
Other Personnel:
Short-Term less than 1 year from USA 520
Home ministry & office staff in USA 9
Countries: Africa 1, Armenia 1, Asia 2, Belarus 1, Belgium 1, Central Asia 10, Croatia 2, Ecuador 2, France 2, Gabon 2, Italy 5, Kenya 2, Romania 3, Russia 10, Slovakia 2, Switzerland 2, Ukraine 4, UK 6, Unspecified 2

Iranian Christians International

(719)596-0010 Fax: (719)574-1141
E-Mail: IranianChristiansInternational@compuserve.com
P.O. Box 25607, Colorado Springs, CO 80936
Mr. Ebrahim (Abe) Ghaffari, Exec. Director
An interdenominational support agency of evangelical tradition engaged in support of national churches, evangelism, literature distribution/production and training focused on Persian speaking peoples.
Year Founded in USA 1981
Income for Overseas Mins $50,000
Gifts-in-Kind $10,000
Fully Supported USA Personnel Overseas:
Expecting to serve more than 4 years 2
Expecting to serve 1 to 4 years 1
Other Personnel:
Home ministry & office staff in USA 3
Countries: Unspecified 3

Ireland Outreach International Inc.

(319)277-8883
E-Mail: charleville@tinet.ie
P.O. Box 1772, Waterloo, IA 50704
Mr. James W. Gillett, President
A nondenominational sending agency of Christian/Plymouth Brethren tradition engaged in evangelism, Bible distribution, church planting, correspondence courses, and literature distribution and production by missions teams in Ireland as well as training nationals in Nigeria and Ghana.
Year Founded in USA 1981
Income for Overseas Mins .... NR
Fully Supported USA Personnel Overseas:
Expecting to serve more than 4 years 6
Expecting to serve 1 to 4 years 2
Other Personnel:
Non-USA serving in own/other country 7
Short-Term less than 1 year from USA 40
Countries: Ghana, Ireland 8, Nigeria

Island Missionary Society

(717)566-2708 Fax: (717)892-7078
P.O. Box 725, Ephrata, PA 17522
Rev. Earl Gray, Chairman
A nondenominational sending agency of evangelical tradition engaged in church planting, evangelism and support of national churches.
Year Founded in USA 1973
Income for Overseas Mins $225,000
Fully Supported USA Personnel Overseas:
Expecting to serve more than 4 years 8
Other Personnel:
Non-USA serving in own/other country 2
Short-Term less than 1 year from USA 50
Countries: Jamaica 8, Bahamas

ISOH/Impact

(419)878-8546 Fax: (419)878-2869
905 Farnsworth Rd., Waterville, OH 43566
Dr. Linda A. Green, Administrator

An interdenominational service agency of ecumenical tradition engaged in providing medical supplies, childrens programs and medical work. Statistical information from 1992.

Year Founded in USA 1982
Income for Overseas Mins $968,091
Gifts-in-Kind $896,710
Fully Supported USA Personnel Overseas:
Expecting to serve 1 to 4 years 2
Other Personnel:
Short-Term less than 1 year from USA 10
Countries: Bolivia 1, Haiti 1

Issachar Frontier Missions Strategies

(425)814-9777 **Fax: (425)814-9155**
E-Mail: IssacharHQ@aol.com
3906A S. 74th St., Suite 103, Tacoma, WA 98409
Andrew Y. Low, President & CEO

A transdenominational service agency of evangelical tradition engaged in missions information service, mobilization for mission, mission-related research and services for other agencies.

Purpose: "...seeks to empower, train, and coach North American local churches to effectively activate their business and professional people for strategic impact among unreached people groups, especially in the 10/40 window."

Year Founded in USA 1981
Income for Overseas Mins $150,000
Gifts-in-Kind $20,000
Fully Supported USA Personnel Overseas:
Expecting to serve more than 4 years 2
Expecting to serve 1 to 4 years 4
Nonresidential mission personnel 3
Other Personnel:
Bivocational/Tentmaker from USA 2
Short-Term less than 1 year from USA 8
Home ministry & office staff in USA 6
Countries: Central Asia 6

JAARS, Inc.

(704)843-6000 **Fax: (704)843-6385**
E-Mail: info@jaars.org
Web: www.jaars.org
P.O. Box 248, Waxhaw, NC 28173
Mr. Jim Akovenko, Exec. Director

An interdenominational agency of evangelical tradition serving Wycliffe Bible translators with various technical support services including aviation and radio.

Purpose: "...providing construction, technology and transportation services for Wycliffe Bible Translators."

Year Founded in USA 1947
Income for Overseas Mins $539,000

JAF Ministries
See: Joni and Friends

Japan - North American Commission on Cooperative Mission

(212)870-2021 **Fax: (212)870-2055**
475 Riverside Dr., Rm. 618, New York, NY 10115
Ms. Patricia J. Patterson, Coordinator

An interdenominational ecumenical forum for cooperative Christian mission in and between two denominations in Japan, two in Canada, and five in the USA. Income amount from 1992.

Year Founded in USA 1973
Income for Overseas Mins $500,000

Japanese Evangelical Missionary Society

(213)613-0022 **Fax: (213)613-0211**
E-Mail: info@jems.org
Web: www.jems.org
948 E. Second St., Los Angeles, CA 90012
Rev. Sam Tonomura, Exec. Director

An interdenominational service agency of evangelical tradition engaged in support of national churches, evangelism, short-term programs and missionary training. Statistical information from 1996.

Year Founded in USA 1950
Income for Overseas Mins $300,000
Fully Supported USA Personnel Overseas:
Expecting to serve more than 4 years 1
Expecting to serve 1 to 4 years 2
Nonresidential mission personnel 7
Other Personnel:
Non-USA serving in own/other country 6

Short-Term less than 1 year from USA 24
Home ministry & office staff in USA 8
Countries: Brazil 1, Japan 2

Japanese Evangelization Center

(626)794-4400
1605 Elizabeth St., Pasadena, CA 91104
Dr. John Mizuki, Exec. Director

A nondenominational specialized agency of evangelical tradition engaged in missions information service, mission-related research and missionary training.

Purpose: "...to provide information to churches, mission agencies, pastors, missionaries, missionary candidates, students and to serve as consultants to those interested in Japanese culture and evangelization."

Year Founded in USA 1981
Income for Overseas Mins .... NA
Personnel:
Short-Term less than 1 year from USA 1

JESUS Film Project, The
See: Campus Crusade for Christ, Intl.

Jews for Jesus

(415)864-2600 Fax: (415)552-8325
E-Mail: jfj@jewsforjesus.org
Web: www.jewsforjesus.org
60 Haight St., San Francisco, CA 94102
Mr. David Brickner, Exec. Director

A nondenominational sending agency of evangelical tradition engaged in evangelism, literature distribution, literature production and missionary training.

Year Founded in USA 1973
Income for Overseas Mins $403,400
Fully Supported USA Personnel Overseas:
Expecting to serve more than 4 years 4
Other Personnel:
Non-USA serving in own/other country 41
Short-Term less than 1 year from USA 21
Home ministry & office staff in USA 127
Countries: Australia 1, Israel 1, S Africa 1, Russia, Ukraine, UK 1

Joni and Friends

(818)707-5664 Fax: (818)707-2391
E-Mail: jafmin@joniandfriends.org
Web: www.joniandfriends.org
P.O. Box 3333, Agoura Hills, CA 91301
Mrs. Joni Eareckson Tada, President
Mr. Doug Mazza, Vice-President

A nondenominational service agency of evangelical tradition engaged in disability assistance programs, broadcasting, technical assistance and training. Personnel information from 1996.

Purpose: "...accelerating Christian ministry in the disability community...by advocating a biblical response toward disabilities...providing opportunities for disability awareness...educating the church community in practical ways of serving disabled persons...assisting persons with disabilities..."

Year Founded in USA 1979
Income for Overseas Mins $766,138
Gifts-in-Kind $1,754,400
Personnel:
Short-Term less than 1 year from USA 35
Home ministry & office staff in USA 25

Key Communications

(503)233-7680 Fax: (503)236-0733
P.O. Box 13620, Portland, OR 97213
Mr. Bryan L. Turner, Director

A nondenominational specialized agency of Christian (Restoration Movement) tradition engaged in broadcasting, Bible distribution and literature distribution.

Year Founded in USA 1978
Income for Overseas Mins $26,000

Kids Alive International

(219)464-9035 Fax: (219)462-5611
E-Mail: kidsalive@juno.com
Web: www.kidsalive.org
2507 Cumberland Dr., Valparaiso, IN 46383
Mr. Alfred Lackey, President

An interdenominational sending agency of evangelical tradition engaged in childcare/orphanage programs, Christian education, medical work, mobilization for mission, relief and/or rehabilitation and short-term programs.

Purpose: "...meeting the spiritual, physical, educational and emotional needs of children and youth who have no other reasonable means of support..."

Year Founded in USA 1916

Income for Overseas Mins $1,416,930

Gifts-in-Kind $100,000

Fully Supported USA Personnel Overseas:

Expecting to serve more than 4 years 6

Expecting to serve 1 to 4 years 19

Nonresidential mission personnel 1

Other Personnel:

Non-USA serving in own/other country 93

Short-Term less than 1 year from USA 360

Home ministry & office staff in USA 9

Countries: Dominican Rep 10, Guatemala 2, Papua New Guin 2, Peru 8, Romania 1, Taiwan (ROC) 2

Kingdom Building Ministries

(303)745-8191 **Fax: (303)745-4196**

E-Mail: laborers@kbm.org

Web: www.kbm.org

14140 E. Evans Ave., Denver, CO 80014

Mr. Dwight Robertson, President

An interdenominational support agency of evangelical tradition engaged in mobilization for mission, evangelism, support of national churches, short-term programs and training.

Purpose: "...to raise up a new generation of laborers for Kingdom service worldwide."

Year Founded in USA 1986

Income for Overseas Mins .... NA

Personnel:

Short-Term less than 1 year from USA 100

Larry Jones International Ministries (Feed the Children)

(405)942-0228 **Fax: (405)945-4177**

E-Mail: ftc@feedthechildren.org

Web: www.feedthechildren.org

P.O. Box 36, Oklahoma City, OK 73101-0228

Dr. Larry W. Jones, President

An interdenominational service agency of evangelical tradition engaged in food aid, evangelism, and other assistance in more than 20 countries.

Purpose: "...providing food, clothing, educational supplies, medical equipment and other necessities to people who lack these essentials because of famine, drought, flood, war or other calamities."

Year Founded in USA 1964

Income for Overseas Mins $45,178,413

Gifts-in-Kind $41,870,450

Fully Supported USA Personnel Overseas:

Nonresidential mission personnel 4

Other Personnel:

Non-USA serving in own/other country 131

Home ministry & office staff in USA 5

Latin America Assistance, Inc.

(800)925-6359 **Fax: (800)693-9222**

E-Mail: lamapent@sol.racsa.co.cr

Web: www.lama4youth.org

P.O. Box 123, Solvang, CA 93464-0123

Mr. Joseph B. Pent, Director

An interconfessional service agency of evangelical and ecumenical tradition engaged in evangelism, camping programs, leadership development, discipleship, and relief aid.

Purpose: "...to equip youth leaders for aggressive evangelism and radical discipleship."

Year Founded in USA 1976

Income for Overseas Mins $9,384

Personnel:

Non-USA serving in own/other country 4

Bivocational/Tentmaker from USA 2

Home ministry & office staff in USA 1

Latin America Lutheran Mission

(956)722-4047 **Fax: (956)722-4047**

E-Mail: vgolalm@aol.com

3519 Salinas Ave., Laredo, TX 78041

Mr. V. Gary Olson, Director

A denominational support agency of Lutheran tradition engaged in support of national churches, evangelism, leadership development, literature distribution, short-term programs and support of national workers. Income from 1997.

Purpose: "...to encourage Bible study and discipleship, and to train and equip the Mexican people to fulfill Christ's 'Great Commission'."

Year Founded in USA 1936

Income for Overseas Mins $258,405

Fully Supported USA Personnel Overseas:

Expecting to serve more than 4 years 1

Other Personnel:
- Non-USA serving in own/other country 18
- Short-Term less than 1 year from USA 4
- Home ministry & office staff in USA 6

Countries: Mexico 1

Latin America Mission

(305)884-8400 **Fax: (305)885-8649**
E-Mail: info@lam.org
Web: www.lam.org
P.O. Box 52-7900, 5465 NW 36th Street, Miami, FL 33152-7900
Dr. David R. Befus, President

An interdenominational sending agency of evangelical tradition engaged in evangelism, camping programs, childcare/orphanage programs, church planting, theological education, leadership development and support of national churches.

Purpose: "...to encourage, assist and participate with the Latin church in the task of building the church of Jesus Christ in the Latin world and beyond."

Year Founded in USA 1921
Income for Overseas Mins $5,141,810
Fully Supported USA Personnel Overseas:
- Expecting to serve more than 4 years 112
- Expecting to serve 1 to 4 years 2
- Nonresidential mission personnel 26

Other Personnel:
- Non-USA serving in own/other country 56
- Short-Term less than 1 year from USA 52
- Home ministry & office staff in USA 25

Countries: Argentina 3, Bolivia 1, Brazil 2, Colombia 13, Costa Rica 55, Ecuador 1, Honduras 1, Mexico 27, Peru 2, Spain 4, Switzerland 2, Venezuela 3

Latin American Indian Ministries

(626)398-2105 **Fax: (626)398-2491**
E-Mail: dale@kietz.sheperd.com
P.O. Box 2050, Orange, CA 92859
Mr. Dale W. Kietzman, President

A nondenominational service agency of evangelical tradition engaged in support of national churches, agricultural programs, Bible distribution, childrens programs, church planting and training.

Purpose: "...to encourage, strengthen and support the indigenous communities of Latin America in their efforts to evangelize and disciple their own people, as well as to help them improve living standards for their families..."

Year Founded in USA 1972
Income for Overseas Mins $256,243
Gifts-in-Kind $198,000
Personnel:
- Non-USA serving in own/other country 3
- Short-Term less than 1 year from USA 1
- Home ministry & office staff in USA 1

Liberia Christian Mission

(217)498-7014
E-Mail: 71242.2321@compuserve.com
9622 Ginder Rd., Rochester, IL 62563-6157
Mr. Ken Vogel, President

A nondenominational sending agency of Christian (Restoration Movement) tradition engaged in support of national churches, broadcasting, Christian education and TEE.

Year Founded in USA 1982
Income for Overseas Mins $81,000
Fully Supported USA Personnel Overseas:
- Expecting to serve more than 4 years 2

Other Personnel:
- Home ministry & office staff in USA 1

Countries: Cote d'Ivoire 2

Liberty Corner Mission

(908)647-1777 **Fax: (908)647-4117**
P.O. Box 204, Liberty Corner, NJ 07938
Rev. E. E. Achenbach, President

An interdenominational sending agency of evangelical tradition engaged in evangelism and support of national churches. Statistical information from 1996.

Year Founded in USA 1933
Income for Overseas Mins $170,736
Fully Supported USA Personnel Overseas:
- Expecting to serve more than 4 years 4

Other Personnel:
- Non-USA serving in own/other country 16
- Short-Term less than 1 year from USA 1
- Home ministry & office staff in USA 1

Countries: Japan 2, Taiwan (ROC) 2

Liebenzell Mission USA

(908)852-3044 **Fax: (908)852-4531**
E-Mail: Liebenzell_usa@compuserve.com

Web: ourworld.compuserve.com/ homepages/ liebenzell_usa
P.O. Box 66, Schooley's Mtn., NJ 07870
Rev. Larry C. Mills, Exec. Director
An interdenominational sending agency of evangelical tradition engaged in church planting, theological education, evangelism and missionary training.
Year Founded in USA 1941
Income for Overseas Mins $510,606
Fully Supported USA Personnel Overseas:
Expecting to serve more than 4 years 23
Expecting to serve 1 to 4 years 2
Other Personnel:
Non-USA serving in own/other country 4
Home ministry & office staff in USA 10
Countries: Asia 3, Belau(Palau) 3, Ecuador 1, Germany 3, Guam 10, Philippines 2, Spain 2, Thailand 1

LIFE Ministries

(626)914-8990 **Fax: (626)914-9572**
E-Mail: info@lifejapan.org
Web: www.lifejapan.org
P.O. Box 200, San Dimas, CA 91773
Rev. S. Douglas Birdsall, CEO
An interdenominational sending agency of evangelical tradition engaged in evangelism, church planting, leadership development and support of national churches.
Purpose: "...to strengthen and start Japanese churches in partnership with visionary pastors and congregations through innovation in evangelism and leadership training."
Year Founded in USA 1967
Income for Overseas Mins $1,731,492
Fully Supported USA Personnel Overseas:
Expecting to serve more than 4 years 29
Expecting to serve 1 to 4 years 3
Other Personnel:
Non-USA serving in own/other country 44
Short-Term less than 1 year from USA 43
Home ministry & office staff in USA 11
Countries: Japan 32

Lifewater International

(626)962-4187 **Fax: (626)962-6786**
E-Mail: lifewater@xc.org
Web: www.lifewater.org
15854 Business Center Dr., Irwindale, CA 91706-2052
Mr. William A. Ashe, Director
A nondenominational specialized agency of evangelical tradition engaged in development, agricultural programs, missions information service, management consulting/training, relief and/or rehabilitation and technical assistance in more than 20 countries.
Purpose: "To provide water resource development information, training, equipment and technical support to the rural poor...[and]...teach the development and maintenance of safe drinking water supplies, sanitation facilities, irrigation systems and cottage industries...[and train]...teams to become themselves a resource to others."
Year Founded in USA 1979
Income for Overseas Mins $354,973
Gifts-in-Kind $222,250
Personnel:
Non-USA serving in own/other country 5
Bivocational/Tentmaker from USA 3
Short-Term less than 1 year from USA 30
Home ministry & office staff in USA 7

LIGHT International, Inc.

(916)467-5373 **Fax: (916)467-3686**
E-Mail: BWaymire@sisqtel.net
P.O. Box 368, Etna, CA 96027
Mr. Robert H. Waymire, President
A transdenominational specialized agency of evangelical tradition engaged in church mobilization and mission-related research and training.
Year Founded in USA 1991
Income for Overseas Mins $12,000
Fully Supported USA Personnel Overseas:
Nonresidential mission personnel 2
Other Personnel:
Home ministry & office staff in USA 1

Link Care Center

(559)439-5920 **Fax: (559)439-2214**
E-Mail: 75027.2265@compuserve.com
Web: www.linkcare.org
1734 W. Shaw Ave., Fresno, CA 93711-3486
Dr. Brent Lindquist, President
A nondenominational specialized agency of evangelical tradition engaged in psychological counseling, linguistics, mission-related research and missionary training.

Year Founded in USA 1965
Income for Overseas Mins .... NA
Personnel:
Home ministry & office staff in USA 25

Lion and Lamb Outreach

(970)223-4350 Fax: (970)377-9697
E-Mail: 74267.1676@compuserve.com
P.O. Box 271037, Fort Collins, CO 80527-1037
Rev. Richard C. Borgman, President

A nondenominational sending agency of charismatic tradition engaged in leadership development, support of national workers and missionary training. Statistical information from 1996.

Year Founded in USA 1972
Income for Overseas Mins $52,480
Fully Supported USA Personnel Overseas:
Expecting to serve more than 4 years 3
Other Personnel:
Non-USA serving in own/other country 9
Short-Term less than 1 year from USA 15
Countries: Cote d'Ivoire 1, France 2

Literacy & Evangelism Intl.

(918)585-3826 Fax: (918)585-3224
E-Mail: general@literacyevangintl.org
Web: www.literacyevangintl.org
1800 S. Jackson Ave., Tulsa, OK 74107-1897
Rev. John C. Taylor, Director

An interdenominational sending agency of evangelical and Presbyterian tradition engaged in literacy work, evangelism, literature production and services for other agencies.

Year Founded in USA 1967
Income for Overseas Mins .... NR
Fully Supported USA Personnel Overseas:
Expecting to serve more than 4 years 4
Other Personnel:
Non-USA serving in own/other country 1
Short-Term less than 1 year from USA 6
Home ministry & office staff in USA 11
Countries: Pakistan 2, Peru 2

Living Water Teaching Intl.

(903)527-4160 Fax: (903)527-2134
E-Mail: LWTcaddo@aol.com
P.O. Box 1190, Caddo Mills, TX 75135
Marion Zirkle, Co-Founder & President

An interdenominational sending agency of evangelical tradition engaged in theological education, evangelism, funds transmission and missionary training. Statistical information from 1996.

Year Founded in USA 1979
Income for Overseas Mins $1,444,697
Fully Supported USA Personnel Overseas:
Expecting to serve more than 4 years 18
Expecting to serve 1 to 4 years 19
Other Personnel:
Non-USA serving in own/other country 15
Short-Term less than 1 year from USA 15
Home ministry & office staff in USA 11
Countries: Costa Rica, El Salvador 4, Guatemala 26, Honduras 5, Mexico, Nicaragua, Paraguay 2

LOGOI/FLET

(305)232-5880 Fax: (305)232-3592
E-Mail: LOGOI@logoi.org
Web: www.logoi.org
14540 SW 136th St., Suite 200, Miami, FL 33186
Rev. Leslie J. Thompson, President

A transdenominational service agency of Reformed tradition engaged in non-formal theological education and publishing print and video materials used in 11 Spanish speaking countries.

Year Founded in USA 1968
Income for Overseas Mins $800,290
Personnel:
Home ministry & office staff in USA 11

Lott Carey Baptist Mission Conv.

(202)667-8493 Fax: (202)483-8626
E-Mail: LottCarey@aol.com
Web: www.lottcarey.org
1501 11th St. NW, Washington, DC 20001
Dr. David E. Goatley, Exec. Director

An independent service agency of Baptist tradition engaged in evangelism, education, health care, and hunger relief supporting national workers.

Year Founded in USA 1897
Income for Overseas Mins $1,100,000
Personnel:
Non-USA serving in own/other country 595

Short-Term less than 1 year from USA 16
Home ministry & office staff in USA 8

Ludhiana Christian Medical College Board, USA, Inc.

(717)651-0990 Fax: (717)651-0992
E-Mail: Ludhianamc@aol.com
900 S Arlington Ave. Rm. 221, Harrisburg, PA 17109
Rev. Roberta K. Jones, Exec. Director
An interdenominational service agency of ecumenical tradition engaged in medical work and providing medical supplies. Statistical information from 1996.
Year Founded in USA 1894
Income for Overseas Mins $505,133
Gifts-in-Kind $405,133
Personnel:
Short-Term less than 1 year from USA 2
Home ministry & office staff in USA 5

Luis Palau Evangelistic Assoc.

(503)614-1500 Fax: (503)614-1599
E-Mail: LPEA@palau.org
Web: www.lpea.org
P.O. Box 1173, Portland, OR 97207
Dr. Luis Palau, President
A nondenominational service agency of evangelical tradition engaged in evangelism, broadcasting, leadership development and literature production.
Purpose: "...to win people...to Jesus Christ throughout the world, proclaiming His Good News by all available means...to stimulate, revive, train and mobilize the Church to continuous, effective evangelism, follow-up and church growth...raising up a new generation of godly leaders..."
Year Founded in USA 1978
Income for Overseas Mins $2,500,000
Personnel:
Non-USA serving in own/other country 12
Home ministry & office staff in USA 55
Countries: Argentina, Guatemala, Latin America

Luke Society, The

(605)373-9686 Fax: (605)373-9711
E-Mail: wrede@lukesociety.org
Web: www.lukesociety.org
2204 S. Minnesota Ave., Sioux Falls, SD 57105
Dr. Wrede Vogel, Exec. Director
An interdenominational service agency of evangelical tradition engaged in medical work, development, funds transmission and leadership development.
Year Founded in USA 1964
Income for Overseas Mins $1,511,473
Personnel:
Home ministry & office staff in USA 7

Lutheran Bible Translators

(630)897-0660 Fax: (630)897-3567
E-Mail: LBT@xc.org
Web: www.lbt.org
P.O. Box 2050, Aurora, IL 60507
Dr. Marshall R. Gillam, Exec. Director
A denominational sending agency of Lutheran tradition engaged in Bible translation, linguistics and literacy work.
Purpose: "...to help people come to faith in Jesus Christ specifically through Bible translation and literacy work."
Year Founded in USA 1964
Income for Overseas Mins $2,559,969
Fully Supported USA Personnel Overseas:
Expecting to serve more than 4 years 33
Expecting to serve 1 to 4 years 7
Nonresidential mission personnel 42
Other Personnel:
Non-USA serving in own/other country 78
Short-Term less than 1 year from USA 3
Home ministry & office staff in USA 28
Countries: Africa 1, Botswana 7, Cameroon 6, Cote d'Ivoire 7, Guatemala 9, Liberia 3, Namibia 6, Papua New Guin 1

Lutheran Brethren World Missions

(218)739-3336 Fax: (218)739-2346
E-Mail: LBWM@clba.org
Web: www.lbwm.org
P.O. Box 655, Fergus Falls, MN 56538-0655
Rev. Matthew Rogness, Exec. Director
A denominational sending agency of Lutheran and evangelical tradition engaged in church planting, development, leadership development, literature production, support of national churches and Bible translation.

Purpose: "...serving the congregations of the Church of the Lutheran Brethren to facilitate their task of fulfilling the Great Commission..."
Year Founded in USA 1900
Income for Overseas Mins $900,000
Fully Supported USA Personnel Overseas:
Expecting to serve more than 4 years 20
Expecting to serve 1 to 4 years 3
Other Personnel:
Bivocational/Tentmaker from USA 2
Short-Term less than 1 year from USA 14
Home ministry & office staff in USA 7
Countries: Asia 2, Chad 6, Japan 9, Taiwan (ROC) 6

Lutheran Church—Missouri Synod, Board for Mission Services

(314)965-9000 **Fax: (314)965-0959**
Web: www.lcms.org
1333 S. Kirkwood Rd., St. Louis, MO 63122
Dr. Glenn O'Shoney, Exec. Director
A denominational sending agency of Lutheran tradition engaged in church planting, theological education, TEE, evangelism and leadership development. Statistical information from 1996.
Year Founded in USA 1893
Income for Overseas Mins $17,432,620
Gifts-in-Kind $3,480,000
Fully Supported USA Personnel Overseas:
Expecting to serve more than 4 years 222
Expecting to serve 1 to 4 years 127
Other Personnel:
Non-USA serving in own/other country 2
Short-Term less than 1 year from USA 50
Home ministry & office staff in USA 57
Countries: Botswana 4, Brazil 1, China (PRC) 10, Cote d'Ivoire 8, Eritrea 2, Europe-E 3, Ghana 16, Guatemala 13, Guinea Bissau 2, Honduras 2, Hong Kong 40, Hungary 5, India 1, Jamaica 4, Japan 31, Kazakhstan 7, Korea-S 6, Liberia 2, Macao 4, Mexico 6, Nigeria 24, Panama 12, Papua New Guin 17, Paraguay 2, Peru 2, Philippines 7, Puerto Rico 4, Russia 33, Slovakia 7, S Africa 2, Sri Lanka 2, Taiwan (ROC) 20, Thailand 12, Togo 9, Venezuela 27, Vietnam 2

Lutheran Literature Society for the Chinese

(218)724-1068
E-Mail: Revelness@aol.com
1827 Woodland Ave., Duluth, MN 55803
Rev. Jerome Elness, President
An interdenominational support agency of Lutheran tradition engaged in literature production/distribution, audio recording/ distribution, and Bible distribution.
Purpose: "...to promote evangelism among the Chinese...by supporting the production and distribution of Christian literature...and by using mass media..."
Year Founded in USA 1942
Income for Overseas Mins $23,538

Lutheran World Relief

(410)230-2700 **Fax: (410)230-2882**
E-Mail: LWR@lwr.org
Web: www.lwr.org
700 Light St., Baltimore, MD 21230
Dr. Kathryn F. Wolford, President
A denominational service agency of Lutheran tradition engaged in relief and/or rehabilitation, development, agricultural programs, and leadership development.
Purpose: "...to alleviate suffering caused by natural disaster, conflict or poverty; through development efforts to enable marginalized people to realize more fully their God-given potential; and through education and advocacy efforts to promote a peaceful, just and sustainable global community."
Year Founded in USA 1945
Income for Overseas Mins $22,598,621
Gifts-in-Kind $11,763,386
Fully Supported USA Personnel Overseas:
Expecting to serve more than 4 years 2
Other Personnel:
Non-USA serving in own/other country 4
Home ministry & office staff in USA 38
Countries: Kenya, Niger 2, Peru

Lutheran Youth Encounter

(612)789-3556 **Fax: (612)789-6027**
E-Mail: encounter@youthencounter.org
Web: www.youthencounter.org

2500-39th Ave. NE, #222, Minneapolis, MN 55421
Rev. Larry Dean Johnson, President
A denominational specialized agency of Lutheran tradition engaged in youth programs, audio recording/distribution and missionary training. Statistical information from 1993.
Year Founded in USA 1965
Income for Overseas Mins $167,600
Personnel:
Short-Term less than 1 year from USA 15
Home ministry & office staff in USA 43

M/E International

(714)630-2000 Fax: (714)630-5279
E-Mail: OUTREACH@me-intl.org
Web: www.me-intl.org
1061-D N. Shepard St., Anaheim, CA 92806
Mr. James R. Ford, President
An interdenominational support agency of evangelical tradition engaged in support of national workers, audio recording/distribution, church planting and evangelism.
Purpose: "To enable nationals in developing countries to reach their own with the Gospel of the Lord Jesus Christ."
Year Founded in USA 1948
Income for Overseas Mins $35,000
Personnel:
Non-USA serving in own/other country 60
Countries: India

Macedonia World Baptist Missions

(770)963-9079 Fax: (770)963-3090
E-Mail: mwbm@compuserve.com
Web: www.mwbm.org
P.O. Box 551, Lawrenceville, GA 30046
Dr. Thurman Wade, Exec. Director
A sending agency of Baptist tradition engaged in church planting, aviation services, theological education, evangelism, and literature production/distribution. Statistical information from 1996.
Year Founded in USA 1967
Income for Overseas Mins $3,000,562
Fully Supported USA Personnel Overseas:
Expecting to serve more than 4 years 106
Other Personnel:
Bivocational/Tentmaker from USA 3
Home ministry & office staff in USA 6
Countries: Belize 2, Brazil 14, Caribbean Isls 2, Chile 2, China (PRC) 6, Colombia 2, Costa Rica 2, Cote d'Ivoire 2, Cyprus 2, Germany 4, Grenada 2, Haiti 2, Indonesia 2, Jamaica 6, Japan 2, Mexico 10, Moldava 6, N Mariana Isls 2, Peru 12, Puerto Rico 14, Romania 2, St Lucia 2, Taiwan (ROC) 2, United Arab Emr 2, Uzbekistan 2

Macedonian Missionary Service

(941)984-4060 Fax: (941)984-4505
E-Mail: secretary@macedonianms.org
Web: www.macedonianms.org
P.O. Box 68, Polk City, FL 33868-0068
Dr. Harold R. Williams, Chairman
A denominational support agency of Baptist tradition engaged in short-term programs, broadcasting, church construction, correspondence courses and medical work.
Year Founded in USA 1973
Income for Overseas Mins $300,000
Personnel:
Short-Term less than 1 year from USA 12
Home ministry & office staff in USA 10

Mahesh Chavda Ministries Intl.

(704)543-7272 Fax: (704)541-5300
E-Mail: Info@watchofthelord.com
Web: www.watchofthelord.com
P.O. Box 472009, Charlotte, NC 28247
Rev. Mahesh Chavda, Founder/President
A nondenominational support agency of charismatic tradition engaged in evangelism, leadership development, literature production and support of national churches.
Year Founded in USA 1985
Income for Overseas Mins $20,000
Personnel:
Non-USA serving in own/other country 6
Home ministry & office staff in USA 1

Mailbox Club International

(912)244-6812 Fax: (912)245-8977
E-Mail: e-mail@mailboxclub.org
Web: www.mailboxclub.org
404 Eager Rd., Valdosta, GA 31602
Mr. John Mark Eager, Director

A nondenominational support agency of independent tradition producing correspondence courses for children in 20 languages.
Year Founded in USA 1965
Income for Overseas Mins $210,000
Personnel:
Home ministry & office staff in USA 12

MAP International

(912)265-6010 Fax: (912)265-6170
E-Mail: MAPUS@map.org
Web: www.map.org
P.O. Box 215000, Brunswick, GA 31521-5000
Mr. Michael Nyenhuis, President/CEO

A nondenominational specialized agency of ecumenical tradition engaged in medical work, development, literature production, and relief and/or rehabilitation.
Purpose: "...promotes the total health of people living in the world's poorest communities by partnering in the provision of essential medicines, prevention and eradication of disease and the promotion of community health development."
Year Founded in USA 1954
Income for Overseas Mins $148,197,924
Gifts-in-Kind $141,758,104
Personnel:
Non-USA serving in own/other country 47
Home ministry & office staff in USA 52
Countries: Bolivia, Cote d'Ivoire, Ecuador, Kenya

Maranatha Baptist Mission

(601)442-0141 Fax: (601)446-5105
E-Mail: maranatha.mission@juno.com
P.O. Drawer 1425, Natchez, MS 39121
Dr. William McCorkle, Vice-President

A nondenominational sending agency of Baptist tradition engaged in funds transmission for missionaries involved in church planting. Statistical information from 1992.
Year Founded in USA 1961
Income for Overseas Mins $1,956,000
Fully Supported USA Personnel Overseas:
Expecting to serve more than 4 years 102
Countries: Argentina 4, Australia 8, Bolivia 8, Brazil 8, Chile 4, Colombia 4, France 8, Germany 4, Grenada 2, Guatemala 2, Israel 2, Japan 2, Mexico 12, Norway 2, Papua New Guin 4, Peru 2, Puerto Rico 2, Solomon Isls 2, S Africa 2, Spain 2, UK 11, Venezuela 7

MARC (Mission Advanced Research & Communications Center) See: World Vision International

Marriage Ministries International

(303)933-7495 Fax: (303)933-2153
E-Mail: MMI@marriage.org
Web: www.marriage.org
P.O. Box 1040, Littleton, CO 80160-1040
Co-Presidents, Mike & Marilyn Phillipps
Mr. Chad Arnold, Intl. Administrator

A specialized agency providing training materials in 70 countries for strengthening married couples for evangelism and other ministries.
Purpose: "To minister life and fulfillment to marriages and to train couples to work together as powerful teams, sharing the truth of God's Word with other couples."
Year Founded in USA 1983
Income for Overseas Mins $70,000
Personnel:
Non-USA serving in own/other country 10
Bivocational/Tentmaker from USA 10
Short-Term less than 1 year from USA 6
Home ministry & office staff in USA 20

MATS International, Inc.

(765)965-7777 Fax: (765)962-9966
E-Mail: car@mats.org
Web: www.mats.org
4444 National Road E., Richmond, IN 47374
Mr. Tom Daugherty, Director

A nondenominational support agency of evangelical tradition providing a purchasing service for vehicles used abroad and in the USA by mission agencies, churches, and other ministries. Formerly known as Missionary Auto-Truck Service.
Year Founded in USA 1977
Income for Overseas Mins .... NA

Mazahua Mission

(419)352-7919
E-Mail: mazahua@netspace.com.mx

Web: www.hplink.com/mazahua.html
16011 W. Poe Rd., Bowling Green, OH 43402
Mr. Barry Milliron, Co-Chairperson
A nondenominational support agency of evangelical and Congregational tradition engaged in leadership development, agricultural programs, camping programs, theological education and funds transmission.
Year Founded in USA 1986
Income for Overseas Mins $86,604
Gifts-in-Kind $2,000
Personnel:
Non-USA serving in own/other country 35
Short-Term less than 1 year from USA 10
Countries: Mexico

MBMS International

(559)456-4600 Fax: (559)251-1432
E-Mail: mbmsi@mbmsinternational.org
Web: www.mbmsinternational.org
4867 E. Townsend Ave., Fresno, CA 93727
Rev. Harold Ens, Gen. Director
A denominational sending agency of Mennonite and evangelical tradition engaged in church planting, theological education, furloughed missionary support, leadership development, support of national churches and support of national workers.
Purpose: "...to participate in making disciples of all people groups, sharing the gospel of Jesus Christ cross-culturally and globally, in Spirit-empowered obedience to Christ's Commission and in partnership with local Mennonite Brethren churches."
Year Founded in USA 1878
Income for Overseas Mins $937,665
Fully Supported USA Personnel Overseas:
Expecting to serve 1 to 4 years 19
Other Personnel:
Non-USA serving in own/other country 56
Bivocational/Tentmaker from USA 11
Short-Term less than 1 year from USA 167
Home ministry & office staff in USA 11
Countries: Brazil 2, Burkina Faso 2, Central Asia 2, Colombia 1, Germany 2, Guatemala 2, Mexico 2, Peru 2, Portugal 2, Thailand 2

Media Associates International

(630)893-1977 Fax: (630)893-1141
E-Mail: MAI_Littworld@compuserve.com
Web: www.littworld.org
P.O. Box 218, Bloomingdale, IL 60108-0218
Mr. John Maust, President
Mr. Robert Reekie, Dir. Training Resources
A nondenominational specialized agency of evangelical tradition engaged in print media training, leadership development, and technical assistance. Publishing and consulting for missions and national agencies in the Two-Thirds world.
Year Founded in USA 1985
Income for Overseas Mins $170,326
Gifts-in-Kind $12,610
Personnel:
Home ministry & office staff in USA 5

Medical Ambassadors Intl.

(209)524-0600 Fax: (209)571-3538
E-Mail: MedAmb@ix.netcom.com
P.O. Box 576645, 4048 Tully Rd., Modesto, CA 95357-6645
Dr. Paul Calhoun, Exec. Director
An interdenominational specialized agency of evangelical tradition engaged in medical work, agricultural programs, development, Christian education and support of national workers.
Purpose: "...recruits, trains and supports national leaders among developing peoples...to reach their own people physically and spiritually..."
Year Founded in USA 1974
Income for Overseas Mins $2,223,937
Gifts-in-Kind $4,923
Fully Supported USA Personnel Overseas:
Expecting to serve more than 4 years 5
Nonresidential mission personnel 6
Other Personnel:
Non-USA serving in own/other country 251
Home ministry & office staff in USA 27
Countries: Argentina, Bangladesh, Congo, Dominican Rep., El Salvador, Ethiopia, Gabon, Guatemala, Haiti 1, India, Kenya 1, Mexico 1, Nepal, Philippines 2, Romania, Tanzania, Uganda, Ukraine, Venezuela

Medical Missions Philippines

(209)527-7466
E-Mail: elisarmi@epic.net
P.O. Box 3656, Modesto, CA 95352

Mr. Richard G. Hagerty, President

A nondenominational support agency of Baptist tradition engaged in training, development, evangelism, providing medical supplies, medical work and support of national workers.

Year Founded in USA 1987
Income for Overseas Mins $34,500
Personnel:
Non-USA serving in own/other country 60

Men for Missions International

(317)881-6752 Fax: (317)865-1076
E-Mail: mfmi@omsinternational.org
Web: www.omsinternational.org
P.O. Box A, Greenwood, IN 46142-6599
Mr. Warren Hardig, Exec. Director

A nondenominational support agency of evangelical tradition engaged in overseas missionary housing construction, literature production, and providing other technical assistance as a short-term arm of OMS International. Statistical information from 1996.

Year Founded in USA 1954
Income for Overseas Mins .... NA
Personnel:
Short-Term less than 1 year from USA 200
Home ministry & office staff in USA 9

Mennonite Board of Missions

(219)294-7523 Fax: (219)294-8669
E-Mail: info@mbm.org
Web: www.mbm.org
P.O. Box 370, Elkhart, IN 46515
Mr. Stanley W. Green, President

A denominational sending agency of Mennonite tradition engaged in leadership development, theological education, literature production, medical work and missionary training. Statistical information from 1992.

Purpose: "…to shape a vision for global mission, and partner to implement programs of evangelism and service, mobilizing church members to share God's healing and hope through Jesus Christ."

Year Founded in USA 1906
Income for Overseas Mins $2,104,000
Fully Supported USA Personnel Overseas:
Expecting to serve more than 4 years 80
Expecting to serve 1 to 4 years 1
Nonresidential mission personnel 2
Other Personnel:
Non-USA serving in own/other country 5
Bivocational/Tentmaker from USA 32
Short-Term less than 1 year from USA 28
Home ministry & office staff in USA 5
Countries: Argentina 8, Asia 2, Belgium 2, Benin 4, Brazil 7, Chile 2, China (PRC) 2, France 4, Ghana 6, India 4, Ireland 2, Israel 4, Japan 8, Liberia 3, Nepal 12, Puerto Rico 2, Spain 2, Suriname 2, UK 5

Mennonite Brethren Missions/ Services
See: MBMS International

Mennonite Central Committee International

(717)859-1151 Fax: (717)859-2171
E-Mail: MailBox@mcc.org
Web: www.mcc.org
P.O. Box 500, Akron, PA 17501-0500
Dr. Ronald J. R. Mathies, Exec. Director

A binational denominational service agency of Mennonite tradition engaged in community development, agricultural programs, extension education, medical work, relief and/or rehabilitation, technical assistance, training and youth programs. Overseas personnel totals are for the U.S. and Canada.

Purpose: "...to demonstrate God's love by working among people suffering from poverty, conflict, oppression and natural disaster."

Year Founded in USA 1920
Income for Overseas Mins $48,444,000
Gifts-in-Kind $9,290,437
Fully Supported USA Personnel Overseas:
Expecting to serve more than 4 years 200
Other Personnel:
Non-USA serving in own/other country 520
Home ministry & office staff in USA 310
Countries: Unspecified 200

Mercy Ships

(903)882-0887 Fax: (903)882-0336
E-Mail: Info@mercyships.org
Web: www.mercyships.org

P.O. Box 2020, Garden Valley, TX 75771-2020
Mr. Don K. Stephens, President/CEO
A service agency of evangelical tradition engaged in medical work, development, evangelism, leadership development and missionary training. More than 40 nations currently involved as staff. Part of the family of ministries of YWAM.
Purpose: "...dedicated to presenting Jesus Christ personally to this generation, to mobilizing as many as possible to help in this task and to the training and equipping of believers for their part in fulfilling the Great Commission."
Year Founded in USA 1978
Income for Overseas Mins $19,682,881
Gifts-in-Kind $13,501,582
Fully Supported USA Personnel Overseas:
Expecting to serve more than 4 years 200
Expecting to serve 1 to 4 years 125
Other Personnel:
Short-Term less than 1 year from USA 200
Home ministry & office staff in USA 75
Countries: Unspecified 325

Message of Life, Inc.
(559)683-7028 Fax: (559)683-7028
E-Mail: mdevida@aol.com
58607 Rd. 601, Ahwahnee, CA 93601
Mr. Ezequiel Mantilla, Gen. Manager
An interdenominational service agency of evangelical tradition engaged in literature production/distribution. Statistical information from 1996.
Year Founded in USA 1961
Income for Overseas Mins $60,000

Messenger Films, Inc.
(757)226-5897 Fax: (757)226-5851
E-Mail: mfinfo@messengerfilms.com
Web: www.messengerfilms.com
P.O. Box 65003, Virginia Beach, VA 23467
Mr. Cristobal Krusen, President/Founder
A transdenominational support agency of evangelical and charismatic tradition engaged in film/video production and distribution in support of mass evangelism especially in Latin America and Africa.
Year Founded in USA 1988
Income for Overseas Mins .... NA

Mexican Border Missions
(956)838-2895
P.O. Box 2138, Brownsville, TX 78522-2138
Mrs. Dorothy Blodget, Exec. Director
A nondenominational sending agency of independent tradition engaged in church planting, church construction, evangelism and support of national workers. Statistical information from 1996.
Year Founded in USA 1961
Income for Overseas Mins $47,485
Fully Supported USA Personnel Overseas:
Expecting to serve more than 4 years 2
Other Personnel:
Non-USA serving in own/other country 5
Countries: Mexico 2

Mexican Christian Mission
(800)658-1600
P.O. Box 7273, Lincoln Acres, CA 91947-7273
Mr. Pablo Flores, Exec. Director
A sending agency of independent Baptist tradition engaged in evangelism, church construction and planting, TEE, leadership development, literature distribution and support of national workers.
Year Founded in USA 1956
Income for Overseas Mins $45,000
Gifts-in-Kind $15,000
Fully Supported USA Personnel Overseas:
Expecting to serve more than 4 years 3
Expecting to serve 1 to 4 years 2
Other Personnel:
Non-USA serving in own/other country 5
Bivocational/Tentmaker from USA 1
Home ministry & office staff in USA 2
Countries: Mexico 5

Mexican Medical, Inc.
(619)420-9750 Fax: (619)420-9570
E-Mail: info@mexicanmedical.com
Web: www.mexicanmedical.com
251 Landis Ave., Chula Vista, CA 91910-2628
Rev. Melvin Peabody
A nondenominational service agency of evangelical tradition engaged in medical work, using nationals and teams of medical and non-medical volunteers from the USA and Canada, including approximately 2,000 people serving 7-10 days.

Purpose: "...to bring the Gospel of Jesus Christ to the various age groups of Mexican people through a variety of ministries."
Year Founded in USA 1967
Income for Overseas Mins $1,160,000
Gifts-in-Kind $686,000
Fully Supported USA Personnel Overseas:
Expecting to serve more than 4 years 12
Other Personnel:
Bivocational/Tentmaker from USA 2
Short-Term less than 1 year from USA 100
Home ministry & office staff in USA 6
Countries: Mexico 12

Mexican Mission Ministries See: Global Outreach Mission

Middle East Christian Outreach

(317)271-4026 Fax: (317)271-4026
E-Mail: 75227.633@compuserve.com
Web: www.gospelcom.net/meco
P.O. Box 531151, Indianapolis, IN 46253-1151
Rev. James R. Smith, U.S. Director

An interdenominational sending agency of evangelical tradition engaged in support of national churches, development, Christian education, evangelism, literature distribution and video/film production/distribution.
Year Founded in USA 1978
Income for Overseas Mins $60,922
Fully Supported USA Personnel Overseas:
Expecting to serve more than 4 years 4
Expecting to serve 1 to 4 years 2
Other Personnel:
Non-USA serving in own/other country 68
Short-Term less than 1 year from USA 1
Home ministry & office staff in USA 2
Countries: Africa 1, Asia 5

Middle East Media - USA

(908)301-9730 Fax: (908)301-9733
E-Mail: ED@mem-usa.org
P.O. Box 2033, Westfield, NJ 07091
Mrs. Rosemary Boehm, Exec. Director

A transdenominational support agency of ecumenical and evangelical tradition engaged in video/film production and distribution, audio recording/distribution, evangelism, literature production and technical assistance.
Year Founded in USA 1976
Income for Overseas Mins $1,777,026
Fully Supported USA Personnel Overseas:
Expecting to serve more than 4 years 5
Expecting to serve 1 to 4 years 4
Other Personnel:
Non-USA serving in own/other country 66
Short-Term less than 1 year from USA 4
Home ministry & office staff in USA 3
Countries: Asia 7, Turkey 2

Middle Eastern Outreach

(626)359-5242 Fax: (626)358-3331
E-Mail: meo.e@usa.net
P.O. Box 405, Duarte, CA 91009-0405
Rev. Elie Elbayadi, Founder/President

A nondenominational support agency of Baptist and Presbyterian tradition engaged in evangelism, missions information service, literature distribution, mobilization for mission and missionary training.
Year Founded in USA 1995
Income for Overseas Mins $14,000
Gifts-in-Kind $9,000
Personnel:
Home ministry & office staff in USA 3

Ministries In Action

(305)234-7855 Fax: (305)234-7825
E-Mail: info@mia.org
Web: www.mia.org
P.O. Box 571357, Miami, FL 33257-1357
Rev. E. Walford Thompson, President

An interdenominational sending agency of evangelical tradition engaged in support of national churches, development, extension education and relief aid.
Year Founded in USA 1961
Income for Overseas Mins $539,595
Fully Supported USA Personnel Overseas:
Expecting to serve more than 4 years 2
Expecting to serve 1 to 4 years 1
Nonresidential mission personnel 2
Other Personnel:
Non-USA serving in own/other country 8
Home ministry & office staff in USA 4
Countries: Grenada 1, Haiti 1, St Vincent 1

Ministry of Jesus, Inc.

(410)875-9111 **Fax: (410)635-2929**
E-Mail: moj1@juno.com
2017 W. Old Liberty Rd., Westminster, MD 21157
Rev. Thomas W. Beak, President

A service agency of charismatic tradition engaged in church planting, agricultural programs, development, evangelism, leadership development and support of national churches.

Year Founded in USA 1984
Income for Overseas Mins $263,400
Fully Supported USA Personnel Overseas:
Expecting to serve more than 4 years 4
Nonresidential mission personnel 2
Other Personnel:
Short-Term less than 1 year from USA 16
Home ministry & office staff in USA 1
Countries: Benin 2, Togo 2

Ministry to Eastern Europe

(804)320-6456 **Fax: (804)320-6456**
E-Mail: mtee@erols.com
Web: www.gospelcom.net/mtee
2520 Professional Rd., Suite C, Richmond, VA 23235
Dr. John F. McGeorge, Jr., President

An interdenominational sending agency of charismatic and evangelical tradition engaged in theological education, childrens programs, leadership development, literature production and translation work.

Year Founded in USA 1983
Income for Overseas Mins $283,000
Fully Supported USA Personnel Overseas:
Expecting to serve more than 4 years 6
Expecting to serve 1 to 4 years 6
Nonresidential mission personnel 1
Other Personnel:
Non-USA serving in own/other country 29
Bivocational/Tentmaker from USA 2
Short-Term less than 1 year from USA 25
Home ministry & office staff in USA 3
Countries: Bulgaria 1, Hungary 5, Poland 2, Ukraine 4

Mission 21 India

(616)453-8855 **Fax: (616)791-9926**
E-Mail: m21india@missionindia.org
Web: www.missionindia.org
P.O. Box 141312, Grand Rapids, MI 49514
Rev. John F. DeVries, President

An interdenominational support agency of evangelical tradition engaged in church planting, Bible distribution, childrens programs, development, literacy work and literature distribution.

Purpose: "...assists national Indian Christians in the planting of 'Reproducing Churches' in a systematic and measurable pattern throughout India."

Year Founded in USA 1990
Income for Overseas Mins $3,200,000
Gifts-in-Kind $500,000
Fully Supported USA Personnel Overseas:
Nonresidential mission personnel 3
Other Personnel:
Short-Term less than 1 year from USA 2
Home ministry & office staff in USA 15

Mission Aides, Inc.

(626)355-3346 **Fax: (626)355-8689**
E-Mail: miscom@juno.com
P.O. Box 1, Sierra Madre, CA 91025
Mr. Hugh S. Bell, Jr., President

A nondenominational service agency of evangelical tradition engaged in technical assistance and broadcasting.

Year Founded in USA 1954
Income for Overseas Mins $6,000
Personnel:
Non-USA serving in own/other country 1
Home ministry & office staff in USA 3

Mission Aviation Fellowship

(909)794-1151 **Fax: (909)794-3016**
E-Mail: MAF-US@maf.org
Web: www.maf.org
P.O. Box 3202, 1849 Wabash, Redlands, CA 92373-0998
Mr. Gary L. Bishop, CEO/President

An interdenominational specialized agency of evangelical tradition engaged in aviation services and missions information service.

Purpose: "...to multiply the effectiveness of the Church using aviation and other strategic technologies to reach the world for Christ."

Year Founded in USA 1945

Income for Overseas Mins $18,127,895
Gifts-in-Kind $523,282
Fully Supported USA Personnel Overseas:
Expecting to serve more than 4 years 215
Expecting to serve 1 to 4 years 35
Other Personnel:
Non-USA serving in own/other country 7
Home ministry & office staff in USA 123
Countries: Africa 3, Albania 5, Asia 8, Botswana 4, Brazil 6, Congo/Zaire 26, Ecuador 34, Guatemala 8, Haiti 13, Indonesia 72, Kenya 6, Lesotho 8, Mali 16, Mexico 10, Russia 5, Suriname 8, Uganda 4, Venezuela 10, Zimbabwe 4

Mission Ministries, Inc.

(714)722-1304
E-Mail: missin19@idt.net
P.O. Box 10044, Costa Mesa, CA 92627
Dr. John A. Lindvall, President

A nondenominational sending agency of evangelical and Congregational tradition engaged in childrens programs, development, evangelism, funds transmission and relief and/or rehabilitation.

Year Founded in USA 1980
Income for Overseas Mins $197,500
Fully Supported USA Personnel Overseas:
Expecting to serve more than 4 years 4
Other Personnel:
Non-USA serving in own/other country 3
Bivocational/Tentmaker from USA 4
Short-Term less than 1 year from USA 2
Home ministry & office staff in USA 4
Countries: Uganda 2, Venezuela 2

Mission O.N.E., Inc.

(615)672-9504 **Fax: (615)672-9513**
E-Mail: missionwun@aol.com
Web: www.mission1.org
P.O. Box 70, White House, TN 37188
Mr. Bob Schindler, Founder/Chairman
Mr. Werner Mischke, President

An interdenominational support agency of Baptist and evangelical tradition engaged in missionary training, church planting, evangelism and support of national workers.

Purpose: "...to mobilize the Church for the training and support of national missionaries, focusing primarily on unreached people groups in developing nations."

Year Founded in USA 1991
Income for Overseas Mins $121,963

Mission of Mercy

(719)481-0400 **Fax: (719)481-4649**
E-Mail: dvagle@mofm.org
Web: www.missionofmercy.org
P.O. Box 62600, Colorado Springs, CO 80962
Mr. Bob Houlihan, President

An interdenominational support agency of charismatic and evangelical tradition engaged in relief and/or rehabilitation, childcare/orphanage programs, church construction, development, Christian education and providing medical supplies in 13 countries. A division of Bethesda Ministries.

Purpose: "...helping to meet the physical and spiritual needs of hurting people in poverty stricken areas of the world through emergency and support roles..."

Year Founded in USA 1977
Income for Overseas Mins $7,047,876
Fully Supported USA Personnel Overseas:
Expecting to serve more than 4 years 1
Other Personnel:
Home ministry & office staff in USA 29
Countries: Asia 1

Mission Possible Foundation, Inc.

(940)382-1508 **Fax: (940)566-1875**
E-Mail: mp@xc.org
Web: www.mp.org
P.O. Box 2014, Denton, TX 76202-2014
Mr. Mark Krantz, President/CEO

A nondenominational support agency of charismatic tradition engaged in TEE, childcare/orphanage programs, church planting, literature distribution, literature production and youth programs.

Purpose: "...to serve local national churches and enable them to evangelize unbelievers and disciple new believers..."

Year Founded in USA 1974
Income for Overseas Mins $360,051
Personnel:
Non-USA serving in own/other country 44

Short-Term less than 1 year from USA 4
Home ministry & office staff in USA 5
Countries: Albania, Bulgaria, China (PRC), Finland, Russia, Ukraine

Mission Possible, Inc.

(561)465-0373 **Fax: (561)465-0639**
E-Mail: mpi@gate.net
Web: www.odyssey.on.ca/~missionpossible
P.O. Box 520, Fort Pierce, FL 34954
Mr. George E. Wadsworth, President

A nondenominational agency of evangelical tradition engaged in evangelism, Christian education, relief and/or rehabilitation and support of national workers.

Year Founded in USA 1974
Income for Overseas Mins $552,807
Gifts-in-Kind $103,067
Fully Supported USA Personnel Overseas:
Expecting to serve more than 4 years 1
Nonresidential mission personnel...................... 1
Other Personnel:
Non-USA serving in own/other country 138
Short-Term less than 1 year from USA 4
Home ministry & office staff in USA 14
Countries: Haiti 1, Dominican Republic

Mission Safety International

(423)542-8892 **Fax: (423)542-8892**
E-Mail: info@msisafety.org
Web: www.msisafety.org
328 E. Elk Ave. #1, Elizabethton, TN 37643-3210
Mr. Charles Henson, President

A nondenominational specialized agency of evangelical tradition engaged in aviation safety services for other agencies in 10 countries.

Purpose: "...to provide educational and consulting services to assist missions and related agencies in realizing their [aircraft operations] objectives effectively and efficiently."

Year Founded in USA 1983
Income for Overseas Mins $200,000
Gifts-in-Kind $120,000
Personnel:
Short-Term less than 1 year from USA 6
Home ministry & office staff in USA 2

Mission Services Association

(423)577-9740 **Fax: (423)577-9743**
E-Mail: msa@missionservices.org
Web: www.missionservices.org
P.O. Box 13111, Knoxville, TN 37920-0111
Mr. W. Reggie Hundley, Exec. Director

A nondenominational support agency of Christian (Restoration Movement) tradition engaged in services for missionaries and local churches including mission research, video distribution, and newsletter printing/mailing.

Year Founded in USA 1946
Income for Overseas Mins $300,000
Personnel:
Short-Term less than 1 year from USA 2
Home ministry & office staff in USA 10

Mission Society for United Methodists, The

(770)446-1381 **Fax: (770)446-3044**
Web: msum.org
P.O. Box 922637, Norcross, GA 30010-2637
Dr. Alvern L. Vom Steeg, President

A denominational sending agency of Methodist tradition engaged in evangelism, church planting, medical work, support of national churches, mobilization for mission and missionary training.

Purpose: "…reaching the unreached with the Gospel, and helping national churches finish the task of winning their own people for Christ."

Year Founded in USA 1984
Income for Overseas Mins $6,031,151
Gifts-in-Kind $1,208,820
Fully Supported USA Personnel Overseas:
Expecting to serve more than 4 years 55
Expecting to serve 1 to 4 years 30
Nonresidential mission personnel................. 133
Other Personnel:
Non-USA serving in own/other country 2
Bivocational/Tentmaker from USA 1
Short-Term less than 1 year from USA 249
Home ministry & office staff in USA 29
Countries: China (PRC) 3, Costa Rica 5, France 9, Ghana 6, India 2, Japan 2, Kazakhstan 18, Mexico 2, Paraguay 8, Peru 10, Philippines 2, Russia 18

Mission to the Americas

(630)260-3800 **Fax: (630)653-4936**

E-Mail: mtta@mtta.org
Web: www.mtta.org
P.O. Box 828, Wheaton, IL 60189-0828
Rev. Rick Miller, Exec. Director

A sending agency engaged in church planting, broadcasting, theological education, evangelism, leadership development and support of national churches in North and Central America (including Canada, USA, Mexico, and the Caribbean).

Purpose: "...to evangelize, disciple and congregationalize the unreached of the Americas, including disenfranchised and ethnically diverse people."

Year Founded in USA 1950
Income for Overseas Mins $1,000,000
Fully Supported USA Personnel Overseas:
Expecting to serve more than 4 years 12
Nonresidential mission personnel 5
Other Personnel:
Non-USA serving in own/other country 12
Bivocational/Tentmaker from USA 3
Home ministry & office staff in USA 3
Countries: Belize 1, Costa Rica 1, Guatemala 1, Honduras 5, Mexico 4

Mission to the World (PCA), Inc.

(404)320-3373 Fax: (404)325-5974
E-Mail: info@mtw.org
Web: www.pcanet.org/mtw
P.O. Box 29765, Atlanta, GA 30359-0765
Dr. Paul D. Kooistra, Coordinator

A denominational sending agency of Presbyterian tradition engaged in church planting, theological education and support of national churches.

Purpose: "To reach the world's unreached responsive peoples with God's Good News through the testimony of church-planting teams and strategic technical and support personnel..."

Year Founded in USA 1973
Income for Overseas Mins $26,591,547
Fully Supported USA Personnel Overseas:
Expecting to serve more than 4 years 461
Expecting to serve 1 to 4 years 118
Nonresidential mission personnel 31
Other Personnel:
Short-Term less than 1 year from USA 3946
Home ministry & office staff in USA 73
Countries: Argentina 2, Asia 52, Australia 23, Austria 12, Belize 5, Brazil 5, Bulgaria 7, Chile 16, Colombia 13, Cote d'Ivoire 12, Czech Rep 12, Ecuador 26, Ethiopia 4, France 34, Germany 10, Guam 2, Hong Kong 2, Hungary 4, India 8, Indonesia 11, Ireland 2, Italy 2, Jamaica 3, Japan 52, Kenya 11, Korea-S 2, Mexico 52, Micronesia 2, Niger 2, Nigeria 4, Papua New Guin 6, Peru 24, Philippines 17, Portugal 9, Russia 3, Senegal 7, Slovakia 2, S Africa 30, Spain 7, Sweden 5, Taiwan (ROC) 8, Tanzania 4, Uganda 6, Ukraine 44, UK 13, Virgin Isls USA 2

Mission To Unreached Peoples

(206)781-3151 Fax: (206)781-3182
E-Mail: mupinfo@mup.org
Web: www.mup.org
P.O. Box 30947, Seattle, WA 98103-0947
Mr. David M. Hupp, U.S. Director

An interdenominational sending agency of evangelical tradition engaged in church planting, agricultural programs, mobilization for mission, relief and/or rehabilitation, services for other agencies and youth programs.

Year Founded in USA 1982
Income for Overseas Mins $1,594,507
Gifts-in-Kind $20,572
Fully Supported USA Personnel Overseas:
Expecting to serve more than 4 years 37
Expecting to serve 1 to 4 years 12
Other Personnel:
Non-USA serving in own/other country 5
Bivocational/Tentmaker from USA 41
Short-Term less than 1 year from USA 13
Home ministry & office staff in USA 12
Countries: Cambodia 5, China (PRC) 6, Hungary 4, India 6, Indonesia 2, Japan 2, Malaysia 4, Nepal 6, Philippines 2, Poland 1, Russia 4, Taiwan (ROC) 1, Thailand 4, Vietnam 2

Mission Training and Resource Center

(626)797-7903 Fax: (626)797-7906
E-Mail: phil@aol.com
3800 Canon Blvd., Altadena, CA 91001
Mr. Phillip Elkins, President

A transdenominational service agency of evangelical tradition engaged in missionary training, missions information service and mission-related research.

Year Founded in USA 1979
Income for Overseas Mins .... NA
Personnel:
Home ministry & office staff in USA 15

Mission Training International

(719)594-0687 **Fax: (719)594-4682**
E-Mail: Info@mti.org
Web: www.mti.org
P.O. Box 50110, Colorado Springs, CO 80949-0110
Mr. Paul E. Nelson, President/CEO

A nondenominational specialized agency of evangelical tradition engaged in missionary training, development, missionary education, furloughed missionary support and leadership development.

Purpose: "Working together with churches and mission agencies to train and nurture Christians for effective intercultural service."

Year Founded in USA 1954
Income for Overseas Mins .... NA
Personnel:
Home ministry & office staff in USA 10

Mission: Moving Mountains

(612)440-9100 **Fax: (612)440-9104**
E-Mail: MMM@movingmountains.org
Web: www.movingmountains.org
P.O. Box 1168, Burnsville, MN 55044
Dr. Gary T. Hipp, President

A transdenominational sending agency of evangelical tradition engaged in development, agricultural programs, church planting, evangelism, medical work and discipleship.

Purpose: "...to facilitate the physical and spiritual well-being of impoverished people in developing countries."

Year Founded in USA 1978
Income for Overseas Mins $950,321
Fully Supported USA Personnel Overseas:
Expecting to serve more than 4 years 31
Other Personnel:
Non-USA serving in own/other country 7
Short-Term less than 1 year from USA 4
Home ministry & office staff in USA 10

Countries: Ethiopia 4, Kenya 5, Senegal 6, Tanzania 16

Missionaire International

(308)235-4147 **Fax: (308)235-4147**
P.O. Box 474, Kimball, NE 69145-0474
Jon Foote, Director of Operations

An interdenominational service agency of evangelical tradition engaged in aviation services, services for other agencies and support of national workers.

Year Founded in USA 1988
Income for Overseas Mins .... NA
Personnel:
Home ministry & office staff in USA 7

Missionary Athletes International

(719)528-1636 **Fax: (719)528-1638**
E-Mail: 103016.1115@compuserve.com
P.O. Box 25010, Colorado Springs, CO 80936-5010
Mr. Bruce Johnson, Interim CEO

An interdenominational specialized agency of evangelical and fundamental tradition engaged in soccer evangelism, Bible distribution and short-term programs.

Year Founded in USA 1983
Income for Overseas Mins $620,000
Gifts-in-Kind $61,000
Fully Supported USA Personnel Overseas:
Expecting to serve more than 4 years 9
Other Personnel:
Short-Term less than 1 year from USA 60
Countries: Czech Rep 2, UK 7

Missionary Auto-Truck Service Inc.
See: MATS International, Inc.

Missionary Dentists
See: Global Outreach Mission

Missionary Flights International

(561)686-2488 **Fax: (561)697-4882**
E-Mail: MFIPBI@aol.com
P.O. Box 15665, West Palm Beach, FL 33406
Mr. Richard Snook, President

A nondenominational support agency of Baptist and evangelical tradition engaged in aviation and mail services for 125 mission organizations.

Year Founded in USA 1964
Income for Overseas Mins $2,000,000
Gifts-in-Kind $20,000
Personnel:
Home ministry & office staff in USA 17

Missionary Gospel Fellowship

(209)634-8575 Fax: (209)634-8472
E-Mail: mgf@ainet.com
Web: www.mgfhq.org
P.O. Box 1535, Turlock, CA 95380-1535
Mr. John L. Harvey, Director

An interdenominational sending agency of evangelical tradition engaged in multi-ethnic ministries of church planting, broadcasting, camping programs, correspondence courses and TEE in the USA, Canada and Mexico.

Purpose: "...to share the Gospel and to disciple various ethnic or unreached groups of people in or near the USA."

Year Founded in USA 1939
Income for Overseas Mins $151,067
Fully Supported USA Personnel Overseas:
Expecting to serve more than 4 years 13
Nonresidential mission personnel 3
Other Personnel:
Non-USA serving in own/other country 2
Home ministry & office staff in USA 54
Countries: Mexico 13

Missionary Maintenance Services See: MMS Aviation

Missionary Retreat Fellowship Inc.

(717)689-2984 Fax: (717)689-2984
E-Mail: MRF65@juno.com
R.R. #4, Box 303, Lake Ariel, PA 18436
Rev. Gene McBride, Exec. Director

An interdenominational support agency of evangelical tradition engaged in furloughed missionary support and services for other agencies.

Purpose: "...to provide the furloughing missionary with fully furnished housing...at subsidized rates."

Year Founded in USA 1965
Income for Overseas Mins .... NA

Missionary Revival Crusade

(972)293-8181 Fax: (972)293-8182
E-Mail: 110320.544@compuserve.com
101 Kenya St., Ste. 106, Cedar Hill, TX 75104
Rev. Roger J. West, President

An interdenominational support agency of charismatic and evangelical tradition engaged in church planting, audio recording/distribution, broadcasting, correspondence courses, evangelism and leadership development.

Year Founded in USA 1959
Income for Overseas Mins $160,000
Fully Supported USA Personnel Overseas:
Expecting to serve more than 4 years 38
Nonresidential mission personnel 10
Other Personnel:
Non-USA serving in own/other country 52
Home ministry & office staff in USA 2
Countries: Argentina 3, Colombia 4, France 4, Germany 3, Mexico 24

Missionary TECH Team

(903)757-4530 Fax: (903)758-2799
E-Mail: Administration@techteam.org
Web: www.techteam.org
25 FRJ Dr., Longview, TX 75602-4703
Mr. Birne D. Wiley, President

A nondenominational service agency of fundamental tradition engaged in technical assistance, furloughed missionary support and services for other agencies.

Purpose: "...providing technical assistance, 'know-how' and support services to mission organizations around the world."

Year Founded in USA 1969
Income for Overseas Mins $400,000
Gifts-in-Kind $51,000
Personnel:
Short-Term less than 1 year from USA 6

Missionary Ventures International

(407)859-7322 Fax: (407)856-7934
E-Mail: mviusa@aol.com
Web: www.missionaryventures.org
P.O. Box 593550, Orlando, FL 32859-3550

Mr. Steven Beam, President

An interdenominational specialized agency engaged in short-term programs, childrens programs, church planting, leadership development, and support of national churches and national workers.

Year Founded in USA 1983

Income for Overseas Mins $2,140,098

Fully Supported USA Personnel Overseas:

Expecting to serve more than 4 years 10

Nonresidential mission personnel 7

Other Personnel:

Non-USA serving in own/other country 15

Home ministry & office staff in USA 9

Countries: Haiti 2, Honduras 4, Peru 4

Missions Outreach International See: Hope Missions Outreach

Missions Resource Center

(513)522-2847 **Fax: (513)522-2846**

E-Mail: MarvinGrooms@xc.org

Web: www.ccmrc.org

9452 Winton Road, Cincinnati, OH 45231

Mr. Marvin D. Grooms, Director

A nondenominational specialized agency of Christian (Restoration Movement) tradition engaged in missions information service and mission-related research.

Purpose: "...to collect, store and disseminate to the local church and its support agencies, data related to the worldwide fulfillment of the mission of God..."

Year Founded in USA 1991

Income for Overseas Mins .... NA

Personnel:

Home ministry & office staff in USA 2

Missions To Japan, Inc.

(408)998-1768

P.O. Box 1203, Campbell, CA 95009-9984

Rev. Joe Weigand, President

A nondenominational support agency of evangelical tradition engaged in support of national churches, Christian education and evangelism.

Purpose: "...to promote fellowship, cooperation, protection, recognition and the propagation of, the Christian Gospel at home and abroad..."

Year Founded in USA 1959

Income for Overseas Mins $26,313

Fully Supported USA Personnel Overseas:

Expecting to serve more than 4 years 2

Other Personnel:

Home ministry & office staff in USA 3

Countries: China (PRC) 1, Philippines 1

Missions to Military, Inc.

(757)479-2288 **Fax: (757)479-3705**

E-Mail: HQ@mtmi.org

Web: www.mtmi.org

2221 Centerville Turnpike, Virginia Beach, VA 23464

Mr. Keith Davey, Founder/Director

A sending agency of Independent Baptist tradition engaged in church planting, correspondence courses, and military Christian centers.

Year Founded in USA 1958

Income for Overseas Mins $151,000

Fully Supported USA Personnel Overseas:

Expecting to serve more than 4 years 5

Expecting to serve 1 to 4 years 2

Other Personnel:

Home ministry & office staff in USA 5

Countries: France 5, Ukraine 2

MMS Aviation

(740)622-6848 **Fax: (740)622-8277**

E-Mail: admin@MMSaviation.org

Web: www.mmsaviation.org

P.O. Box 1118, Coshocton, OH 43812

Mr. Dwight Jarboe, President & CEO

A nondenominational support agency of evangelical tradition engaged in technical assistance, aviation services and training.

Purpose: "...to train individuals in aviation maintenance and prepare them for service in the Christian mission aviation community."

Year Founded in USA 1975

Income for Overseas Mins .... NA

Personnel:

Home ministry & office staff in USA 24

Moody Institute of Science Division of Moody Bible Institute

(800)647-6909 **Fax: (800)647-6910**

Web: www.moodyvideo.org

820 N. LaSalle Dr., Chicago, IL 60610-4406
Ms. Barbara Goodwin, Vice President
A nondenominational support agency of evangelical tradition engaged in video/film production/distribution.
Year Founded in USA 1945
Income for Overseas Mins .... NA

Moravian Church in North America, Board of World Mission

(610)868-1732 **Fax: (610)866-9223**
E-Mail: hampton@mcnp.org
Web: www.moravianmission.org
P.O Box 1245, Bethlehem, PA 18016-1245
Rev. E. Hampton Morgan, Exec. Director
A denominational sending agency of Moravian tradition engaged in medical work, theological education, evangelism, funds transmission, leadership development and relief and/or rehabilitation.
Year Founded in USA 1949
Income for Overseas Mins $500,000
Gifts-in-Kind $50,000
Fully Supported USA Personnel Overseas:
Expecting to serve more than 4 years 3
Other Personnel:
Non-USA serving in own/other country 1
Bivocational/Tentmaker from USA 2
Short-Term less than 1 year from USA 50
Home ministry & office staff in USA 4
Countries: Asia 2, Honduras 1

Morelli Ministries International

(918)664-2552 **Fax: (918)743-3265**
E-Mail: michael.mmi@juno.com
Web: www.morelliministries.org
Box 700026, Tulsa, OK 74170
Mr. Michael Morelli, Founder-President
An interdenominational support agency of evangelical tradition engaged in support of national churches, church planting, evangelism, leadership development, literature distribution and supplying equipment in 7 countries.
Year Founded in USA 1995
Income for Overseas Mins $32,000
Fully Supported USA Personnel Overseas:
Nonresidential mission personnel 1

Other Personnel:
Short-Term less than 1 year from USA 2
Home ministry & office staff in USA 3

Muslim Hope

(513)932-8121 **Fax: (513)932-8121**
1000 Franklin Road, Lebanon, OH 45036
Mr. Donald S. Tingle, Director of Ministries
Marty Egelston, Co-ordinator
A nondenominational service agency of Christian (Restoration Movement) tradition engaged in evangelism, Bible and literature distribution, and relief aid. Statistical information from 1996.
Year Founded in USA 1996
Income for Overseas Mins $45,000
Fully Supported USA Personnel Overseas:
Expecting to serve more than 4 years 3
Other Personnel:
Non-USA serving in own/other country 2
Bivocational/Tentmaker from USA 4
Short-Term less than 1 year from USA 6
Home ministry & office staff in USA 3
Countries: Asia 1, Ukraine 2

Mustard Seed, Inc., The

(626)791-5123 **Fax: (626)398-2392**
E-Mail:
themustardseed@themustardseed.org
Web: www.themustardseed.org
P.O. Box 400, Pasadena, CA 91114-7000
Rev. Garry O. Parker, President
An interdenominational sending agency of evangelical tradition partnering with churches engaged in Christian education, childcare/orphanage programs, church planting, theological education, medical work and relief aid.
Purpose: "...to bear witness to the Lord Jesus Christ through a ministry of holistic evangelism…and compassionate services and verbal witness among tribal peoples..."
Year Founded in USA 1948
Income for Overseas Mins $737,951
Fully Supported USA Personnel Overseas:
Expecting to serve more than 4 years 7
Expecting to serve 1 to 4 years 1
Nonresidential mission personnel 2

Other Personnel:

Non-USA serving in own/other country 298
Short-Term less than 1 year from USA 10
Home ministry & office staff in USA 8

Countries: India 3, Indonesia 2, Mongolia 1, Papua New Guin 2

Mutual Faith Ministries Intl.

(818)837-3400 **Fax: (818)837-4686**
E-Mail: info@mutualfaith.org
Web: www.mutualfaith.org
P.O. Box 951060, Granada Hills, CA 91395-1060
Keith Hershey, President/Founder

A nondenominational support agency of independent tradition engaged in short-term programs for evangelism teams in Central America and other nations.

Year Founded in USA 1984
Income for Overseas Mins $250,000
Gifts-in-Kind $100,000
Fully Supported USA Personnel Overseas:

Expecting to serve more than 4 years 2
Nonresidential mission personnel 1

Other Personnel:

Non-USA serving in own/other country 16
Short-Term less than 1 year from USA 24
Home ministry & office staff in USA 7

Countries: Costa Rica 1, Guatemala 1

Narramore Christian Foundation

(626)821-8400 **Fax: (626)821-8409**
E-Mail: ncf@pacbell.net
Web: www.ncfliving.org
P.O. Box 661900, Arcadia, CA 91066-1900
Dr. Clyde M. Narramore, Founder
Dr. Bruce Narramore, President

A nondenominational specialized agency of evangelical tradition providing crisis counseling and seminars for missionaries on location throughout the world and post high school children in the USA.

Year Founded in USA 1955
Income for Overseas Mins .... NA
Personnel:

Home ministry & office staff in USA 27

National Baptist Convention of America, Foreign Mission Bd.

(214)942-3311 **Fax: (214)943-4924**
P.O. Box 223665, Dallas, TX 75222
Rev. David A. Rooks, Interim Director

A denominational support agency of Baptist tradition engaged in evangelism, church construction, Christian education, funds transmission and support of national workers.

Purpose: "...operates as 'partner in ministry' with indigenous Christians and church bodies."

Year Founded in USA 1915
Income for Overseas Mins $222,071
Personnel:

Non-USA serving in own/other country 87
Short-Term less than 1 year from USA 26
Home ministry & office staff in USA 4

Countries: Ghana, Haiti, Jamaica, Panama, Virgin Islands

National Baptist Convention USA, Inc., Foreign Mission Board

(215)735-7868 **Fax: (215)735-1721**
P.O. Box 15783, Philadelphia, PA 19103
Dr. William J. Harvey III, Exec. Secretary

A denominational sending agency of Baptist tradition engaged in church planting, church construction, Christian education and providing medical supplies. Statistical information from 1996.

Year Founded in USA 1880
Income for Overseas Mins $1,746,418
Fully Supported USA Personnel Overseas:

Expecting to serve more than 4 years 12
Expecting to serve 1 to 4 years 10
Nonresidential mission personnel 5

Other Personnel:

Non-USA serving in own/other country 381
Short-Term less than 1 year from USA 14

Countries: Bahamas 2, Barbados 2, Guinea Bissau 2, Lesotho 2, Liberia 2, Malawi 2, Nicaragua 2, Sierra Leone 2, S Africa 2, Swaziland 2, Zambia 2

National Religious Broadcasters

(703)330-7000 **Fax: (703)330-7100**
E-Mail: bgustavson@nrb.org
Web: www.nrb.com
7839 Ashton Ave., Manassas, VA 20109
Dr. E. Brandt Gustavson, President

An interdenominational association of Christian communicators of evangelical tradition engaged in broadcasting, leadership development and training, including a Caribbean chapter and International Committee involving overseas associate members.

Year Founded in USA 1944
Income for Overseas Mins .... NA
Personnel:
Home ministry & office staff in USA 17

Navigators, U.S. International Ministries Group

(719)598-1212 Fax: (719)260-0479
E-Mail: info@navigators.org
Web: www.navigators.org
P.O. Box 6000, Colorado Springs, CO 80934
Mr. Alan Andrews, U.S. Director
Mr. Rod Beidler, VP/Intl. Ministries Group

A nondenominational sending agency of evangelical tradition engaged in missionary training, camping programs, evangelism, literature production and support of national workers.

Purpose: "To reach, disciple and equip people to know Christ and to make Him known through successive generations."

Year Founded in USA 1949
Income for Overseas Mins $17,343,709
Fully Supported USA Personnel Overseas:
Expecting to serve more than 4 years 173
Expecting to serve 1 to 4 years 250
Other Personnel:
Bivocational/Tentmaker from USA 1445
Short-Term less than 1 year from USA 135
Home ministry & office staff in USA 524

Countries: Argentina 8, Asia 73, Australia 5, Austria 1, Bahrain 1, Brazil 5, Bulgaria 5, Cameroon 2, Central Asia 31, Chad 1, Chile 3, Colombia 2, Congo/Zaire 2, Cote d'Ivoire 7, Croatia 2, Estonia 2, France 6, Ghana 2, Guatemala 2, Hungary 2, Iceland 2, Indonesia 7, Italy 2, Japan 25, Kenya 3, Lithuania 2, Malawi 2, Mexico 5, Mongolia 1, Morocco 4, Nepal 3, New Zealand 2, Philippines 9, Romania 2, Russia 54, Slovakia 2, Slovenia 2, S Africa 2, Spain 8, Taiwan (ROC) 6, Thailand 4, Uganda 4, Ukraine 8, Unspecified 96, Venezuela 4, Zambia 2

Nazarene Church World Mission See: Church of the Nazarene, World Mission Division

NEED, Inc.

(623)879-9676 Fax: (623)879-9674
P.O. Box 54541, Phoenix, AZ 85078
Mr. Dulal C. Borpujari, Intl. President

A nondenominational support agency of evangelical tradition engaged in funds transmission, Christian education, medical work and relief aid in India and Vietnam. Statistical information from 1996.

Year Founded in USA 1985
Income for Overseas Mins $203,782
Gifts-in-Kind $80,060
Fully Supported USA Personnel Overseas:
Nonresidential mission personnel 1
Other Personnel:
Short-Term less than 1 year from USA 8
Home ministry & office staff in USA 1

Network of International Christian Schools

(901)452-1830 Fax: (901)276-8389
E-Mail: dennislugar@nics.org
Web: www.nics.org
P.O. Box 18151, Memphis, TN 38181
Dr. Joe Hale, Exec. Directorr
Rev. Dennis Lugar, Chief Operations Officer

A nondenominational service agency of evangelical tradition engaged in Christian education and evangelism.

Purpose: "...to establish a worldwide network of international Christian schools staffed by qualified Christian educators, instilling in each student a Biblical worldview in an environment of academic excellence and respect for people of all cultures and religions."

Year Founded in USA 1991
Income for Overseas Mins $700,000
Fully Supported USA Personnel Overseas:
Expecting to serve more than 4 years 38
Expecting to serve 1 to 4 years 161
Other Personnel:
Non-USA serving in own/other country 12
Home ministry & office staff in USA 8

Countries: Argentina 11, Austria 16, Brazil 8, Indonesia 18, Korea-S 80, Singapore 10, Suriname 2, Thailand 54

New Hope International

(719)577-4450 Fax: (719)577-4453
E-Mail: newhopeinternational@compuserve.com
Web: www.newhopeinternational.org
P.O. Box 110, Colorado Springs, CO 80901-0110
Mr. Hank Paulson, Founder & President

A nondenominational support agency of evangelical tradition engaged in support of national churches, leadership development, literature production, support of national workers and youth programs. Name changed from Eastern European Bible Mission in 1998.

Year Founded in USA 1972
Income for Overseas Mins $600,000
Fully Supported USA Personnel Overseas:
Nonresidential mission personnel 2
Other Personnel:
Non-USA serving in own/other country 97
Short-Term less than 1 year from USA 40
Home ministry & office staff in USA 8
Countries: Czech Republic, Hungary, Moldava, Romania, Slovakia, Ukraine

New Life League International

(602)650-2203 Fax: (602)650-2215
E-Mail: nlli@ix.netcom.com
740 E. Highland Ave. Suite 104, Phoenix, AZ 85014-3649
Rev. Stanley Runnels, President

A nondenominational sending agency of evangelical tradition engaged in literature distribution, Bible distribution, childcare/orphanage programs, evangelism, literature production and support of national workers.

Year Founded in USA 1954
Income for Overseas Mins $675,000
Fully Supported USA Personnel Overseas:
Expecting to serve more than 4 years 10
Other Personnel:
Non-USA serving in own/other country 6
Bivocational/Tentmaker from USA 2
Short-Term less than 1 year from USA 5
Home ministry & office staff in USA 4
Countries: Bhutan, Brazil 1, Guatemala 5, Haiti 2, India, Nepal, Turkey 2

New Tribes Mission

(407)323-3430 Fax: (407)330-0376
E-Mail: Research-Planning-HQ@ntm.org
Web: www.ntm.org
1000 E. First St., Sanford, FL 32771-1487
Mr. Dave Calderwood, Chairman

A nondenominational sending agency of independent tradition engaged in church planting, theological education, linguistics, literacy work, short-term programs, missionary training and Bible translation. Statistical information from 1996.

Purpose: "...to assist the ministry of the local church through mobilizing, equipping, and coordinating of missionaries to evangelize unreached people groups, translate the Scriptures, and see indigenous New Testament churches established..."

Year Founded in USA 1942
Income for Overseas Mins $24,822,164
Fully Supported USA Personnel Overseas:
Expecting to serve more than 4 years 1434
Expecting to serve 1 to 4 years 80
Other Personnel:
Non-USA serving in own/other country 158
Short-Term less than 1 year from USA 293
Home ministry & office staff in USA 480
Countries: Bolivia 105, Brazil 165, Colombia 57, Cote d'Ivoire 68, Germany 2, Greenland 1, Guinea Bissau 41, India 1, Indonesia 70, Japan 2, Korea-S 2, Mexico 84, Mongolia 7, Panama 81, Papua New Guin 374, Paraguay 69, Philippines 108, Russia 18, Senegal 71, Singapore 4, Thailand 67, Venezuela 117

No Greater Love Ministries, Inc.

(618)542-4503 Fax: (618)542-4503
E-Mail: NGL1FRED@midwest.net
Web: www.nogreaterlove.org
P.O. Box 263, DuQuoin, IL 62832
Rev. Fred L. Bishop

An interdenominational support agency of evangelical tradition engaged in evangelism, leadership development and short-term programs for the purpose of training Christians.

Year Founded in USA 1975
Income for Overseas Mins $10,000
Personnel:
Bivocational/Tentmaker from USA 10

Short-Term less than 1 year from USA 2
Home ministry & office staff in USA 3

North American Baptist Conf. Intl. Missions Dept.

(630)495-2000 Fax: (630)495-3301
E-Mail: NABmissions@nabconf.org
Web: www.nabconference.org
1 S. 210 Summit Ave., Oakbrook Terr., IL 60181
Mr. Ronald D. Salzman, Intl. Missions Dir.

A denominational sending agency of Baptist tradition engaged in church planting, church construction, theological education and medical work.

Year Founded in USA 1891
Income for Overseas Mins $3,506,448
Fully Supported USA Personnel Overseas:
Expecting to serve more than 4 years 51
Expecting to serve 1 to 4 years 5
Other Personnel:
Short-Term less than 1 year from USA 44
Home ministry & office staff in USA 9
Countries: Brazil 6, Cameroon 22, Japan 8, Mexico 8, Nigeria 6, Philippines 6

OC International, Inc.

(719)592-9292 Fax: (719)592-0693
E-Mail: 72064.2174@compuserve.com
Web: www.oci.org
P.O. Box 36900, Colorado Springs, CO 80936-6900
Dr. Lawrence E. Keyes, President

An interdenominational sending agency of evangelical tradition engaged in evangelism, missions information service, management consulting/training, support of national churches, mobilization for mission and missionary training.

Purpose: "...to assist the Body of Christ to make disciples of all peoples..."

Year Founded in USA 1950
Income for Overseas Mins $8,799,442
Fully Supported USA Personnel Overseas:
Expecting to serve more than 4 years 122
Expecting to serve 1 to 4 years 5
Other Personnel:
Non-USA serving in own/other country 4
Short-Term less than 1 year from USA 121
Home ministry & office staff in USA 56
Countries: Argentina 2, Brazil 13, France 4, Germany 13, Greece 2, Guatemala 12, Indonesia 20, Japan 6, Kenya 8, Mexico 4, Philippines 17, Romania 5, Singapore 4, S Africa 9, Spain 4, Taiwan (ROC) 4

Omega World Missions

(760)241-2287 Fax: (760)245-4229
E-Mail: fbrasel@aol.com
P.O. Box 1423, Victorville, CA 92393
Rev. Frank Brasel, President

A transdenominational sending agency of charismatic tradition engaged in support of national workers, church planting, leadership development and literacy work. Statistical information from 1996.

Year Founded in USA 1980
Income for Overseas Mins $166,000
Fully Supported USA Personnel Overseas:
Expecting to serve more than 4 years 7
Other Personnel:
Non-USA serving in own/other country 15
Countries: Indonesia 2, Philippines 5

OMF International

(303)730-4160 Fax: (303)730-4165
E-Mail: OMFUS@omf.org
Web: www.omf.org
10 W. Dry Creek Circle, Littleton, CO 80120-4413
Mr. Jim Morris, Interim U.S. National Director

An interdenominational sending agency of evangelical tradition engaged in church planting, theological education, evangelism, leadership development and literature production.

Purpose: "...to see an indigenous biblical church movement in each people group of East Asia, evangelizing their own people and reaching out in mission to other peoples."

Year Founded in USA 1888
Income for Overseas Mins $6,923,636
Gifts-in-Kind $194,749
Fully Supported USA Personnel Overseas:
Expecting to serve more than 4 years 136
Expecting to serve 1 to 4 years 20
Other Personnel:
Non-USA serving in own/other country 736
Short-Term less than 1 year from USA 92
Home ministry & office staff in USA 49
Countries: Asia 47, Hong Kong 4, Indonesia 10,

Japan 32, Korea-S 8, Philippines 15, Singapore 11, Taiwan (ROC) 13, Thailand 16

OMS International, Inc.

(317)881-6751 **Fax: (317)888-5275**
E-Mail: Info@omsinternational.org
Web: www.omsinternational.org
P.O. Box A, Greenwood, IN 46142
Dr. J. B. Crouse, Jr., President

A nondenominational sending agency of Holiness and evangelical tradition engaged in church planting, theological education and evangelism.

Purpose: "...to reach around the world with the good news of Jesus Christ...in cooperation with national churches..."

Year Founded in USA 1901
Income for Overseas Mins $10,813,795
Gifts-in-Kind $278,843
Fully Supported USA Personnel Overseas:
Expecting to serve more than 4 years 139
Expecting to serve 1 to 4 years 23
Nonresidential mission personnel 5
Other Personnel:
Non-USA serving in own/other country 40
Bivocational/Tentmaker from USA 2
Short-Term less than 1 year from USA 700
Home ministry & office staff in USA 105
Countries: Brazil 5, Colombia 12, Ecuador 18, Haiti 6, Hong Kong 10, Hungary 3, Indonesia 13, Ireland 2, Japan 12, Korea-S 6, Mexico 15, Mozambique 10, Philippines 8, Russia 23, Spain 8, Taiwan (ROC) 11

On The Go Ministries / Keith Cook Evangelistic Association

(615)382-7929 **Fax: (615)382-1344**
E-Mail: onthegokc@aol.com
Web: www.onthego.org
P.O. Box 963, Springfield, TN 37172
Rev. Keith Cook, President

A transdenominational support agency of evangelical tradition engaged in evangelism, leadership development, short-term programs, training and youth programs in 9 countries.

Year Founded in USA 1980
Income for Overseas Mins $200,000
Gifts-in-Kind $50,000
Fully Supported USA Personnel Overseas:
Nonresidential mission personnel 12
Other Personnel:
Bivocational/Tentmaker from USA 4
Short-Term less than 1 year from USA 1000
Home ministry & office staff in USA 12

Open Air Campaigners - Overseas Ministries

(561)692-4283 **Fax: (561)692-4712**
E-Mail: info@oaci.org
Web: www.oaci.org
P.O. Box 2542, Stuart, FL 34995
Rev. David Wilson, International President

An interdenominational support agency of evangelical tradition engaged in evangelism and assisting in church planting. Each national branch is autonomous.

Year Founded in USA 1956
Income for Overseas Mins $527,304
Fully Supported USA Personnel Overseas:
Nonresidential mission personnel 1
Other Personnel:
Non-USA serving in own/other country 16
Short-Term less than 1 year from USA 12
Home ministry & office staff in USA 2

Open Bible Ministries

(570)253-1544
E-Mail: obm316@juno.com
R.R. 4, Box 1705, Honesdale, PA 18431
Mr. Bruce R. Burke, Director

A nondenominational sending agency of fundamental tradition engaged in church planting, Bible distribution, evangelism and literature distribution. Statistical information from 1996.

Year Founded in USA 1971
Income for Overseas Mins $40,000
Fully Supported USA Personnel Overseas:
Expecting to serve more than 4 years 2
Other Personnel:
Short-Term less than 1 year from USA 3
Countries: S Africa 2

Open Bible Standard Churches, International Ministries

(515)288-6761 **Fax: (515)288-2510**
E-Mail: Missions@openbible.org

Web: www.openbible.org
2020 Bell Ave., Des Moines, IA 50315-1096
Rev. Paul V. Canfield, Exec. Director

A denominational sending agency of Pentecostal and charismatic tradition engaged in church planting, church construction, TEE, furloughed missionary support, leadership development and support of national workers.

Purpose: "…exists to serve Open Bible churches by assisting them to fulfill the Great Commission."

Year Founded in USA 1935
Income for Overseas Mins $1,237,882
Fully Supported USA Personnel Overseas:
- Expecting to serve more than 4 years 14
- Expecting to serve 1 to 4 years 2
- Nonresidential mission personnel...................... 2

Other Personnel:
- Short-Term less than 1 year from USA 2
- Home ministry & office staff in USA 4

Countries: El Salvador 2, Guinea Bissau 2, Mexico 3, Papua New Guin 4, Philippines 4, Romania 1

Open Door Baptist Missions

(864)297-7890 **Fax: (864)297-5222**
E-Mail: info@odbm.org
Web: www.odbm.org
1115 Pelham Rd., Greenville, SC 29615
Rev. John Burnette, Director

A sending agency of Independent Baptist and fundamental tradition engaged in church planting, Bible distribution, evangelism, leadership development, literature distribution and support of national churches.

Purpose: "…to promote the work of Christ in regions that have been closed to the gospel or that presently have little or no fundamental gospel witness."

Year Founded in USA 1990
Income for Overseas Mins $265,500
Fully Supported USA Personnel Overseas:
- Expecting to serve more than 4 years 17

Other Personnel:
- Non-USA serving in own/other country 2
- Short-Term less than 1 year from USA 1
- Home ministry & office staff in USA 15

Countries: Haiti 4, Israel 2, Lithuania 4, Puerto Rico 2, Senegal 2, Spain 2, Taiwan (ROC) 1

Open Doors with Brother Andrew USA

(949)752-6600 **Fax: (949)752-6442**
E-Mail: USA@opendoors.org
Web: www.opendoorsusa.org
P.O. Box 27001, Santa Ana, CA 92799
Mr. Terry Madison, President/CEO

A nondenominational support agency of evangelical tradition engaged in Bible distribution, audio recording/distribution, broadcasting and literature distribution. Statistical information from 1992.

Year Founded in USA 1973
Income for Overseas Mins $2,024,000
Gifts-in-Kind $97,231
Personnel:
- Short-Term less than 1 year from USA 160
- Home ministry & office staff in USA 34

Operation Blessing International

(757)579-3400 **Fax: (757)226-3657**
E-Mail: operationblessing@ob.org
Web: www.ob.org
977 Centerville Turnpike, Virginia Beach, VA 23463
Mr. Michael D. Little, President

A nondenominational specialized agency of evangelical tradition engaged in relief and/or rehabilitation, childrens programs, development, short-term programs, mobilizing medical teams, and providing medical supplies in 12 countries. An affiliate of the Christian Broadcasting Network.

Purpose: "...to demonstrate God's love by alleviating human need and suffering in the United States and around the world."

Year Founded in USA 1978
Income for Overseas Mins $11,461,175
Gifts-in-Kind $2,147,122
Personnel:
- Short-Term less than 1 year from USA 540
- Home ministry & office staff in USA 29

Operation Mobilization, Inc.

(770)631-0432 **Fax: (770)631-0439**
E-Mail: info@usa.om.org
Web: www.usa.om.org
P.O. Box 444, Tyrone, GA 30290
Dr. Rick Hicks, President

An interdenominational sending agency of evangelical tradition engaged in missionary training, church planting, evangelism, literature distribution and mobilization for mission.

Purpose: "...to motivate, develop and equip people for world evangelization, and to strengthen and help plant churches, especially among the unreached in the Middle East, South and Central Asia and Europe."

Year Founded in USA 1957
Income for Overseas Mins $7,842,778
Fully Supported USA Personnel Overseas:
Expecting to serve more than 4 years 161
Expecting to serve 1 to 4 years 132
Other Personnel:
Bivocational/Tentmaker from USA 10
Home ministry & office staff in USA 94

Countries: Africa 9, Albania 6, Asia 48, Bangladesh 2, Belgium 10, Central Asia 14, Czech Rep 5, Estonia 2, Europe 31, France 3, Germany 1, Hungary 3, India 8, Israel 10, Italy 2, Latin America 6, Papua New Guin 2, Russia 7, S Africa 3, Sweden 2, Turkey 12, UK 43, Unspecified 64

Opportunity International USA

(800)793-9455 **Fax: (630)645-1458**
E-Mail: Getinfo@opportunity.org
Web: www.opportunity.org
P.O. Box 3695, Oak Brook, IL 60522
Mr. Charles Dokmo, President

A service agency engaged in microenterprise development in 27 countries. Statistical information from 1996.

Purpose: "...to provide opportunities for people in chronic poverty to transform their lives."

Year Founded in USA 1971
Income for Overseas Mins $13,000,000
Fully Supported USA Personnel Overseas:
Expecting to serve 1 to 4 years 18
Other Personnel:
Short-Term less than 1 year from USA 4
Home ministry & office staff in USA 27

Countries: Africa 2, Asia 5, Europe-E 7, Latin America 4

ORA International

(513)771-4555 **Fax: (513)771-4534**
E-Mail: info@orainternational.org
Web: www.orainternational.org
P.O. Box 46306, Cincinnati, OH 45246-0306
Dr. James Lee, Director

An interdenominational sending agency of Pentecostal and charismatic tradition engaged in missionary training, childcare/orphanage programs, church planting, evangelism, support of national churches, relief and/or rehabilitation and support of national workers.

Year Founded in USA 1981
Income for Overseas Mins $2,345,496
Gifts-in-Kind $2,083,407
Fully Supported USA Personnel Overseas:
Expecting to serve more than 4 years 3
Expecting to serve 1 to 4 years 1
Nonresidential mission personnel 1
Other Personnel:
Non-USA serving in own/other country 37
Short-Term less than 1 year from USA 2
Home ministry & office staff in USA 3

Countries: Bulgaria 2, Ethiopia 2

Oriental Missionary Crusade

(714)582-5041
P.O. Box 6336, Laguna Niguel, CA 92607
Rev. Ernest A. Reb, President

An interdenominational sending agency of charismatic tradition engaged in church construction, literature distribution and training. Personnel information from 1996.

Year Founded in USA 1958
Income for Overseas Mins $93,361
Fully Supported USA Personnel Overseas:
Expecting to serve more than 4 years 2
Other Personnel:
Home ministry & office staff in USA 3

Countries: Philippines 2

Orthodox Presbyterian Church, Committee on Foreign Missions

(215)830-0900 **Fax: (215)830-0350**
E-Mail: info@opc.org
Web: www.opc.org
P.O. Box P, Willow Grove, PA 19090-0920
Mr. Mark T. Bube, Gen. Secretary

A denominational sending agency committed to the establishment of indigenous churches in the Presbyterian and Reformed tradition, primarily through the ministry of the Word. Actively engaged in church planting, theological education, evangelism, and literature production/distribution. Medical ministries of mercy supplement the gospel proclamation.

Year Founded in USA 1937
Income for Overseas Mins $1,400,000
Fully Supported USA Personnel Overseas:
- Expecting to serve more than 4 years 26
- Expecting to serve 1 to 4 years 3
- Nonresidential mission personnel 2

Other Personnel:
- Bivocational/Tentmaker from USA 10
- Short-Term less than 1 year from USA 5
- Home ministry & office staff in USA 3

Countries: Cyprus 2, Ethiopia 2, Japan 8, Kenya 2, Korea-S 2, S Africa 2, Suriname 2, Uganda 9

Outreach To Asia Nationals

(540)665-6418 **Fax: (540)665-0793**
E-Mail: 102045.2310@compuserve.com
P.O. Box 1909, Winchester, VA 22604
Mr. Otis S. Goodwin, Director

A support agency engaged in support of national workers, Bible distribution, church planting, theological education, leadership development and literature distribution. Financial and personnel totals from 1996.

Year Founded in USA 1986
Income for Overseas Mins $250,000
Personnel:
- Non-USA serving in own/other country 169
- Short-Term less than 1 year from USA 10
- Home ministry & office staff in USA 3

Outreach, Inc.

(616)363-7817 **Fax: (616)363-7880**
E-Mail: its@gospelcom.net
Web: www.gospelcom.net/its/
3140 3 Mile Rd. NE, Grand Rapids, MI 49525-3165
Rev. Richard A. Cotton, Exec. Director

A nondenominational support agency of Reformed tradition engaged in theological education and funds transmission.

Purpose: "...to assist in the theological education of individuals preparing for church leadership and cross-cultural ministry."

Year Founded in USA 1966
Income for Overseas Mins $347,732
Personnel:
- Home ministry & office staff in USA 8

Overcomer Press, Inc.

(517)723-8277 **Fax: (517)725-3103**
P.O. Box 248, Owosso, MI 48867
Mr. Gordon H. Bennett, President

A nondenominational specialized agency of Christian/Plymouth Brethren tradition engaged in print and audio publications in Spanish and English.

Year Founded in USA 1963
Income for Overseas Mins .... NA

Overseas Council International

(317)788-7250 **Fax: (317)788-7257**
E-Mail: octeam@octeam.org
Web: www.octeam.org
P.O. Box 17368, 6239 S. East St., Ste. B, Indianapolis, IN 46217-0368
Dr. L. David Lewis, Interim CEO
Dr. Charles W. Spicer, Jr., Founding President

A nondenominational support agency of evangelical tradition engaged in establishing partnerships between Western Christians and non-Western students and evangelical theological schools. Affiliated organizations in Australia, Canada, Europe, New Zealand, and UK. 93 overseas partner schools. Name changed from Overseas Council for Theological Education & Missions.

Purpose: "...help develop biblical Christian leaders equipped as pastors, teachers, evangelists, missionaries and lay leaders in their own cultural context."

Year Founded in USA 1974
Income for Overseas Mins $7,250,000
Gifts-in-Kind $469,055
Personnel:
- Home ministry & office staff in USA 24

Overseas Ministries Study Center

(203)624-6672 **Fax: (203)865-2857**
E-Mail: mailbox@omsc.org
Web: www.omsc.org

490 Prospect St., New Haven, CT 06511-2196
Dr. Jonathan J. Bonk, Director
Dr. Gerald H. Anderson, Emeritus Director
A nondenominational study center of evangelical and ecumenical tradition providing education and related activities. Publishes the *International Bulletin of Missionary Research, Dictionary of African Christian Biography* (web only at www.dacb.org) and *Biographical Dictionary of Christian Missions.*
Purpose: "...to strengthen the Christian world mission by providing residential programs for the renewal of missionaries and international church leaders, continuing education in cross-cultural Christian ministries and advancement of mission scholarship through research and publication."
Year Founded in USA 1922
Income for Overseas Mins .... NA
Personnel:
Home ministry & office staff in USA 17

Overseas Missionary Fellowship
See: OMF International

Overseas Radio & Television, Inc.

(206)634-1919 **Fax: (206)547-0400**
E-Mail: ORTV_seattle@msn.com
Web: www.ortv.com.tw
P.O. Box 118, Seattle, WA 98118
Sherry Soepardjo, Administrative Director
An interdenominational support agency of evangelical tradition engaged in broadcasting, audio recording/distribution, evangelism, linguistics and video/film production and distribution.
Year Founded in USA 1960
Income for Overseas Mins $145,000
Fully Supported USA Personnel Overseas:
Expecting to serve more than 4 years 6
Expecting to serve 1 to 4 years 14
Other Personnel:
Non-USA serving in own/other country 168
Short-Term less than 1 year from USA 15
Home ministry & office staff in USA 3
Countries: Taiwan (ROC) 20

Pacific Northwest Mennonite Conf Evang. & Missions Comte.
See: PNMC Missions

Pan American Missions

(619)449-9612
E-Mail: fjappe@juno.com
P.O. Box 710097, Santee, CA 92072-0097
Mr. Fred Jappe, President
A nondenominational support agency of Baptist and evangelical tradition engaged in church planting, broadcasting, childrens programs, evangelism, support of national churches/workers and video/film production and distribution.
Year Founded in USA 1960
Income for Overseas Mins $24,000
Fully Supported USA Personnel Overseas:
Expecting to serve more than 4 years 1
Expecting to serve 1 to 4 years 1
Other Personnel:
Non-USA serving in own/other country 2
Bivocational/Tentmaker from USA 2
Short-Term less than 1 year from USA 1
Home ministry & office staff in USA 3
Countries: Mexico 2

Paraclete Mission Group, Inc.

(480)854-4444 **Fax: (480)854-4741**
E-Mail: kwbutler@earthlink
P.O. Box 6507, Mesa, AZ 85216-6507
Mr. Keith Butler, Acting CEO
Mr. Phillip W. Elkins, Vice-President
A nondenominational support agency of evangelical tradition engaged in missionary training, management consulting/training and mission-related research.
Purpose: "...to serve mission agencies and churches in their efforts to effectively plant churches among unreached people groups."
Year Founded in USA 1988
Income for Overseas Mins .... NA
Fully Supported USA Personnel Overseas:
Expecting to serve more than 4 years 2
Nonresidential mission personnel 4
Other Personnel:
Home ministry & office staff in USA 14
Countries: Asia 2

Partners in Asian Missions

(205)854-8418
E-Mail: jfsharpe@mindspring.com
Web: www.pam-ee.org
P.O. Box 531011, Birmingham, AL 35253-1011

Rev. Jerry F. Sharpe, Intl. Director

A nondenominational support agency of independent tradition engaged in leadership development, church planting, evangelism, support of national churches and support of national workers.

Purpose: "...establishes strategic-level alliances with key regional leaders in order to develop cooperative projects and share evangelism training materials."

Year Founded in USA 1972

Income for Overseas Mins $84,000

Fully Supported USA Personnel Overseas:

Expecting to serve more than 4 years 1

Nonresidential mission personnel 1

Other Personnel:

Non-USA serving in own/other country 50

Home ministry & office staff in USA 1

Countries: Asia

Partners International

(509)343-4000 Fax: (509)343-4015

E-Mail: info@partnersintl.org

Web: www.partnersintl.org

1313 N. Atlantic St., Ste 4000, Spokane, WA 99201

Rev. Paul-Gordon Chandler, President

A nondenominational support agency of evangelical tradition engaged in support of national workers, church planting, development, leadership development, management consulting/training and relief and/or rehabilitation.

Purpose: "...to multiply the effectiveness of indigenous Christian ministries who are taking Christ to neglected peoples around the world."

Year Founded in USA 1943

Income for Overseas Mins $7,901,493

Gifts-in-Kind $3,231,900

Fully Supported USA Personnel Overseas:

Expecting to serve more than 4 years 5

Other Personnel:

Non-USA serving in own/other country .. 4053

Short-Term less than 1 year from USA 55

Home ministry & office staff in USA 53

Countries: Africa 1, Asia 3, Bangladesh, Bolivia, Brazil, Bulgaria, Cambodia, China (PRC), Cote d'Ivoire, Egypt, El Salvador, France, Ghana, Guatemala, Hong Kong, India, Indonesia, Iraq, Jordan, Kenya, Korea-S, Latin America 1, Liberia, Macedonia, Malaysia, Malta, Myanmar, Nigeria, Philippines, Singapore, Sudan, Taiwan, Tanzania, Thailand, Vietnam, Zimbabwe

Pass the Torch Ministries

(701)223-6117 Fax: (701)223-6117

E-Mail: ptm@btigate.com

P.O. Box 7392, Bismarck, ND 58507

Mr. Greg Runyon, President

An interdenominational support agency of charismatic tradition engaged in training, church planting, evangelism and short-term programs. Financial information from 1997.

Year Founded in USA 1987

Income for Overseas Mins $12,000

Fully Supported USA Personnel Overseas:

Expecting to serve 1 to 4 years 3

Nonresidential mission personnel 1

Other Personnel:

Non-USA serving in own/other country 8

Short-Term less than 1 year from USA 12

Home ministry & office staff in USA 2

Countries: Myanmar/Burma 1, Philippines 1, Thailand 1

PAZ International
See: Project AmaZon

Pentecostal Church of God, World Missions Department

(417)624-7050 Fax: (417)624-7102

E-Mail: wm@pcg.org

Web: www.pcg.org

P.O. Box 2248, Joplin, MO 64803

Dr. James D. Gee, Gen. Superintendent

A denominational sending agency of Pentecostal tradition engaged in church planting, Bible distribution, church construction, evangelism, literature distribution, and support of national churches and workers.

Year Founded in USA 1919

Income for Overseas Mins $1,367,284

Fully Supported USA Personnel Overseas:

Expecting to serve more than 4 years 32

Other Personnel:

Home ministry & office staff in USA 4

Countries: Africa 4, Belize 2, Bolivia 2, Haiti 2, Honduras 2, India 2, Mexico 6, Nicaragua 2, Philippines 6, Russia 2, Trinidad & Tobg 2

Pentecostal Free Will Baptist Church, World Witness Dept.

(910)892-4161 **Fax: (910)892-6876**
Web: www.pfwb.org
P.O. Box 1568, Dunn, NC 28335
Rev. Dock Hobbs, Director

A denominational sending agency of Holiness tradition engaged in church planting, church construction, evangelism and support of national churches. Statistical information from 1996.

Year Founded in USA 1959
Income for Overseas Mins $160,000
Fully Supported USA Personnel Overseas:
- Expecting to serve more than 4 years 4
- Nonresidential mission personnel 1

Other Personnel:
- Non-USA serving in own/other country 16
- Bivocational/Tentmaker from USA 1
- Home ministry & office staff in USA 2

Countries: Costa Rica, El Salvador, Guatemala 2, Mexico, Nicaragua, Nigeria, Philippines, Venezuela 2

Pentecostal Holiness Church See: International Pentecostal Holiness Church World Missions

People International

(253)884-1933 **Fax: (253)884-1934**
E-Mail: homebaseusa@compuserve.com
P.O. Box 158, Vaughn, WA 98394
Mr. Tom Longley, Acting U.S. Director

An interdenominational sending agency of evangelical tradition engaged in church planting, development, evangelism and mission-related research.

Purpose: "...to see churches established that proclaim the Good News among the Muslim peoples of Central Asia and model true Christian living on the example of Jesus Christ."

Year Founded in USA 1992
Income for Overseas Mins $504,649
Fully Supported USA Personnel Overseas:
- Expecting to serve more than 4 years 31
- Expecting to serve 1 to 4 years 3

Other Personnel:
- Bivocational/Tentmaker from USA 1
- Home ministry & office staff in USA 1

Countries: Central Asia 34

Peoples Mission International

(719)531-9208 **Fax: (719)531-9208**
E-Mail: larrypate@csi.com
445C E. Cheyenne Mtn. Blvd., #279, Colorado Springs, CO 80906
Dr. Larry D. Pate, President

A transdenominational mission agency of evangelical tradition engaged in missionary orientation, training and strategy development focusing on Christian missionaries sent from the non-Western world.

Year Founded in USA 1992
Income for Overseas Mins .... NR
Fully Supported USA Personnel Overseas:
- Nonresidential mission personnel 4

Other Personnel:
- Short-Term less than 1 year from USA 1
- Home ministry & office staff in USA 1

Perimeter Church, Global Outreach

(770)582-6700 **Fax: (770)582-6709**
9500 Medlock Bridge Pkwy., Duluth, GA 30097
Rev. Carl L. Wilhelm, Director

A denominational support agency of Presbyterian tradition engaged in funds transmission, church planting, evangelism, leadership development, medical work and support of national workers.

Purpose: "To faciliate movements of discipleship-based, saturation church planting in the United States and abroad by providing strategic, human and financial resources to Perimeter Ministries International and to nationals of other countries who share our vision for planting churches…"

Year Founded in USA 1996
Income for Overseas Mins $1,062,901
Fully Supported USA Personnel Overseas:
- Expecting to serve 1 to 4 years 4
- Nonresidential mission personnel 3

Other Personnel:
- Non-USA serving in own/other country 30
- Short-Term less than 1 year from USA 149
- Home ministry & office staff in USA 7

Countries: Albania 2, Bosnia, Guatemala 2, Poland, Russia

Peter Deyneka Russian Ministries

(630)462-1739 **Fax: (630)690-2976**
E-Mail: RMUSA@mcimail.com
Web: www.russian-ministries.org
P.O. Box 496, 1415 Hill Avenue, Wheaton, IL 60189
Rev. Peter Deyneka, President

An interdenominational support agency of evangelical tradition engaged in literature distribution, camping programs, church construction, church planting, extension education and support of national workers.

Purpose: "To promote indigenous evangelism and church growth in the former Soviet Union by developing creative and strategic partnerships between national and Western Christians."

Year Founded in USA 1991
Income for Overseas Mins $3,007,960
Fully Supported USA Personnel Overseas:
Expecting to serve 1 to 4 years 3
Nonresidential mission personnel 5
Other Personnel:
Non-USA serving in own/other country 295
Home ministry & office staff in USA 19
Countries: Russia 3

Pilgrim Fellowship, Inc.

(717)867-1767 **Fax: (717)867-1767**
P.O. Box 557, Lebanon, PA 17042-0557
Mr. William Martindale, Board President

A nondenominational support agency of fundamental tradition engaged in funds transmission for mission workers involved in audio recording/distribution and church planting.

Year Founded in USA 1943
Income for Overseas Mins .... NR
Fully Supported USA Personnel Overseas:
Expecting to serve more than 4 years 11
Other Personnel:
Non-USA serving in own/other country 3
Home ministry & office staff in USA 11
Countries: Asia 1, Belgium 1, Brazil 5, Philippines 2, Spain 2

Pillar of Fire Missions Intl.

(303)430-8260
3455 W. 83rd Ave., Westminster, CO 80030
Rev. Bernard Dawson

A sending agency of Holiness tradition engaged in Christian education, church construction, theological education and support of national workers. Personnel information from 1996.

Year Founded in USA 1960
Income for Overseas Mins $157,873
Fully Supported USA Personnel Overseas:
Expecting to serve 1 to 4 years 5
Other Personnel:
Home ministry & office staff in USA 1
Countries: UK 5

Pioneer Bible Translators

(972)709-2460 **Fax: (972)709-2463**
E-Mail: pbt@xc.org
Web: www.pioneerbible.org
7500 W. Camp Wisdom Rd., Dallas, TX 75236
Dr. Rondal B. Smith, President

A nondenominational sending agency of Christian (Restoration Movement) tradition engaged in Bible translation/distribution, linguistics, literacy work, mobilization for mission and training.

Purpose: "...discipling of the nations by: Providing Scripture in the language of the people. Developing mother-tongue literacy programs. Establishing and strengthening congregations. Training leadership among nationals for partnership in reaching our goals."

Year Founded in USA 1975
Income for Overseas Mins $2,150,000
Fully Supported USA Personnel Overseas:
Expecting to serve more than 4 years 57
Other Personnel:
Non-USA serving in own/other country 64
Short-Term less than 1 year from USA 12
Home ministry & office staff in USA 23
Countries: Asia 1, Guinea Bissau 18, Papua New Guin 30, Tanzania 7, Ukraine 1

Pioneer Clubs

(630)293-1600 **Fax: (630)293-3053**
E-Mail: pcjudy@enteract.com
Web: www.pioneerclubs.org

P.O. Box 788, Wheaton, IL 60189
Judy Bryson, President
A nondenominational service agency of evangelical tradition engaged in youth and camping programs that others have adapted to their culture.
Purpose: "...to serve God by assisting churches and other ministries in helping children and youth make Christ Lord in every aspect of life."
Year Founded in USA 1937
Income for Overseas Mins $10,197
Personnel:
Home ministry & office staff in USA 36

Pioneers

(407)382-6000 **Fax: (407)382-1008**
E-Mail: info@pioneers.org
Web: www.pioneers.org
12343 Narcoossee Rd., Orlando, FL 32827
Mr. Stephen L. Richardson, U.S. Director
An interdenominational sending agency of evangelical tradition engaged in church planting, evangelism, leadership development and short-term programs.
Purpose: "...mobilizes teams to glorify God among unreached peoples by initiating church planting movements in partnership with local churches."
Year Founded in USA 1979
Income for Overseas Mins $8,506,522
Fully Supported USA Personnel Overseas:
Expecting to serve more than 4 years 317
Expecting to serve 1 to 4 years 8
Other Personnel:
Non-USA serving in own/other country 90
Bivocational/Tentmaker from USA 10
Short-Term less than 1 year from USA 155
Home ministry & office staff in USA 38
Countries: Albania 3, Asia 172, Belize 4, Benin 2, Bolivia 8, Bosnia 15, Central Asia 35, CIS 19, Croatia 2, Europe-E 9, Hungary 5, Japan 6, Lebanon 6, N Mariana Isls 1, Papua New Guin 14, Peru 8, Senegal 4, Thailand 12

PNMC Missions

(503)492-4216
E-Mail: pnmcmissions@juno.com
19532 NE Glisan, Portland, OR 97230
Mr. Duncan Smith, Missions Minister
A denominational agency of Mennonite tradition engaged in support of national churches for church planting and training. Formerly known as Pacific Northwest Mennonite Conf. Evangelism & Missions Committee.
Year Founded in USA 1906
Income for Overseas Mins $27,100
Fully Supported USA Personnel Overseas:
Expecting to serve more than 4 years 1
Other Personnel:
Short-Term less than 1 year from USA 2
Home ministry & office staff in USA 1
Countries: Mexico 1

Pocket Testament League

(717)626-1919 **Fax: (717)626-5553**
E-Mail: info@tptl.org
Web: www.tptl.org
P.O. Box 800, Lititz, PA 17543-7026
Rev. John Kubinec, Assoc. Director
An interdenominational service agency of evangelical tradition engaged in Bible distribution, correspondence courses, evangelism and literature distribution.
Purpose: "To assist and equip Christians worldwide in the effective proclamation of the Gospel of Jesus Christ through a coordinated program of Scripture distribution and evangelism."
Year Founded in USA 1908
Income for Overseas Mins $366,138
Fully Supported USA Personnel Overseas:
Expecting to serve more than 4 years 3
Other Personnel:
Non-USA serving in own/other country 40
Short-Term less than 1 year from USA 60
Home ministry & office staff in USA 21
Countries: Austria 1, Brazil, France, Germany 2, Indonesia, Mexico, Philippines, Poland, Portugal, Spain, Thailand, Yugoslavia

Prakash Association USA

(831)763-0189 **Fax: (831)763-0193**
43 Via Arroyo, Corralitos, CA 95076
Mr. Vern Hart, CEO
An interdenominational support agency of Baptist tradition engaged in support of

national workers, agricultural programs, Bible distribution, church planting and Christian education. Statistical information from 1996.

Purpose: "...to support the training of nationals to become Christian businessmen and spiritual leaders...and carry out personal evangelism..."

Year Founded in USA 1969
Income for Overseas Mins $149,919
Fully Supported USA Personnel Overseas:
Nonresidential mission personnel 1
Other Personnel:
Non-USA serving in own/other country 35
Home ministry & office staff in USA 1
Countries: India

Precious Seed Ministries

(956)585-9966 Fax: (956)585-9966
Rte. 27, Box 5510, Mission, TX 78572
Wyman Pylant, President

A nondenominational support agency of charismatic tradition engaged in support of national workers, childcare/orphanage programs, church planting, evangelism and short-term programs coordination.

Year Founded in USA 1985
Income for Overseas Mins $35,000
Personnel:
Non-USA serving in own/other country 8
Home ministry & office staff in USA 3

Presbyterian Center for Mission Studies

(626)398-2468 Fax: (626)398-2391
E-Mail: PCMS.parti@ecunet.org
Web: prescms.org
1605 Elizabeth St., Pasadena, CA 91104
Mr. Michael Boyland, Exec. Director

A denominational support agency of Presbyterian tradition engaged in Christian education and mobilization for mission.

Purpose: "...to greatly multiply the mission efforts of individuals, congregations, and the Presbyterian Church (USA) toward completing the task of world evangelization."

Year Founded in USA 1972
Income for Overseas Mins .... NA
Personnel:
Home ministry & office staff in USA 3

Presbyterian Church (USA), Worldwide Ministries

(502)569-5000 Fax: (502)569-8039
Web: www.pcusa.org/pcusa/wmd
100 Witherspoon St., Louisville, KY 40202
Dr. Marian McClure, Director

A denominational sending agency of Presbyterian tradition engaged in support of national churches, church planting, development, theological education, evangelism, leadership development and medical work. Statistical totals from 1996.

Purpose: "...to share the transforming power of the Gospel of Jesus Christ and to carry out this mission by being committed to the whole church, the whole Gospel and the whole inhabited earth…assist the church in the quest for Christian unity and ecumenical commitment…nourish and strengthen the global perspective and mission effort of the General Assembly Council, the Divisions and the church-at-large."

Year Founded in USA 1837
Income for Overseas Mins $40,107,046
Fully Supported USA Personnel Overseas:
Expecting to serve more than 4 years 368
Expecting to serve 1 to 4 years 404
Other Personnel:
Bivocational/Tentmaker from USA 60
Short-Term less than 1 year from USA 150
Home ministry & office staff in USA 81
Countries: Albania 7, Argentina 13, Australia 2, Bangladesh 6, Belgium 3, Brazil 44, Cameroon 4, Chile 7, China (PRC) 24, Colombia 7, Congo/Zaire 22, Costa Rica 14, Croatia 2, Dominican Rep 3, Egypt 23, Ethiopia 24, Fiji 2, France 2, Germany 10, Ghana 4, Guatemala 34, Haiti 6, Honduras 9, Hong Kong 9, India 21, Indonesia 14, Israel 4, Italy 2, Jamaica 5, Japan 38, Kazakhstan 4, Kenya 21, Korea-S 25, Kyrgyzstan 6, Lebanon 3, Lesotho 2, Lithuania 2, Madagascar 3, Malawi 29, Mauritius 2, Mexico 34, Mozambique 2, Nepal 23, New Zealand 4, Nicaragua 15, Pakistan 20, Papua New Guin 3, Philippines 18, Poland 2, Portugal 2, Romania 5, Russia 7, Slovakia 4, S Africa 6, Spain 4, Sri Lanka 2, Sudan 15, Taiwan (ROC) 9, Thailand 30, Turkey 2, UK 79, Uzbekistan 3, Venezuela 10, Vietnam 4, Zambia 5, Zimbabwe 2

Presbyterian Church in America See: Mission to the World (PCA)

Presbyterian Evangelistic Fellowship

(404)244-0740 Fax: (404)244-0914
E-Mail: admin@pefministry.org
Web: www.pefministry.org
P.O. Box 1890, Decatur, GA 30031
Dr. Al Herrington, Exec. Director

An interdenominational sending agency of Presbyterian and Reformed tradition engaged in evangelism, camping programs, literature distribution, support of national workers and youth programs.

Purpose: "...to practice, train and equip God's people to do Biblical evangelism, anywhere, anytime, with anyone."

Year Founded in USA 1958
Income for Overseas Mins $871,545
Fully Supported USA Personnel Overseas:
Expecting to serve more than 4 years 47
Nonresidential mission personnel 10
Other Personnel:
Non-USA serving in own/other country 24
Bivocational/Tentmaker from USA 49
Short-Term less than 1 year from USA 3
Home ministry & office staff in USA 50
Countries: Bulgaria 2, Chile 1, Costa Rica 1, Europe-E 9, France 5, Greece 1, Japan 2, Kazakhstan 1, Kenya 2, Latin America 2, Mexico 8, Nigeria 1, Peru 4, Russia 2, Uganda 2, UK 4

Presbyterian Missionary Union

(615)228-4465 Fax: (707)371-7342
E-Mail: macpmu@aol.com
Web: www.bpc.org
P.O. Box 160070, Nashville, TN 37216
Dr. Morris McDonald, Field Representative

A denominational sending agency of Presbyterian tradition engaged in support of national churches, Bible distribution, funds transmission and literature distribution. Statistical information from 1996.

Purpose: "...to establish and strengthen indigenous Bible believing churches, related institutions and works agreeable to the (Westminster) doctrinal standards and principles of (Presbyterian) church government."

Year Founded in USA 1985
Income for Overseas Mins $50,400
Fully Supported USA Personnel Overseas:
Expecting to serve more than 4 years 2
Nonresidential mission personnel 2
Other Personnel:
Home ministry & office staff in USA 2
Countries: Kenya 2

Presbyterian Order for World Evangelization

(626)794-5544 Fax: (626)794-6655
1469 Bresee Ave., Pasadena, CA 91104
Dr. Ralph D. Winter, Assoc. Gen. Director

A denominational support agency of evangelical tradition engaged in evangelism, agricultural programs, church planting, and providing medical supplies.

Year Founded in USA 1974
Income for Overseas Mins $95,000
Fully Supported USA Personnel Overseas:
Expecting to serve more than 4 years 2
Nonresidential mission personnel 2
Countries: Asia 2

Primitive Methodist Church in the USA, International Mission Board

(607)797-1120
E-Mail: DSKidd@aol.com
219 Hudson St., Johnson City, NY 13790
Rev. Donald Kidd, Gen. Director

A denominational sending agency of Wesleyan and Methodist tradition engaged in support of national churches, church planting, correspondence courses, theological education, TEE and medical work.

Year Founded in USA 1922
Income for Overseas Mins $455,000
Fully Supported USA Personnel Overseas:
Expecting to serve more than 4 years 6
Other Personnel:
Short-Term less than 1 year from USA 25
Countries: Dominican Rep 2, Guatemala 4

Priority One International

(972)423-3800 Fax: (972)422-7535
E-Mail: info@total-tv.com
Web: www.total-tv.com

555 Republic Dr. #510, Plano, TX 75074
Marty Mosley, President
A nondenominational service agency of evangelical and Baptist tradition producing mission-related videos for mobilization and offering video production services to mission agencies.
Purpose: "...bringing awareness, focus and vision to the cause of world missions within the local church in order to mobilize Christian young people and adults for missionary service."
Year Founded in USA 1979
Income for Overseas Mins $340,000
Personnel:
Home ministry & office staff in USA 75

Prison Mission Association

(360)876-0918 Fax: (360)876-0972
E-Mail: pma-bcf@ix.netcom.com
P.O. Box 2300, Port Orchard, WA 98366
A nondenominational support agency of Reformed tradition engaged in correspondence courses, evangelism and literature distribution to prison inmates and others.
Year Founded in USA 1955
Income for Overseas Mins $13,025
Personnel:
Non-USA serving in own/other country 1
Bivocational/Tentmaker from USA 1
Home ministry & office staff in USA 4

PRM International
See: Audio Scripture Ministries

Progressive National Baptist Convention USA, Global Mission Bureau

(215)474-3939 Fax: (215)472-1648
163 N. 60th St., Philadelphia, PA 19139
Dr. Ronald K. Hill, Exec. Director
A denominational support agency of Baptist tradition engaged in supplying equipment, Bible distribution, childrens programs and church construction in 16 countries.
Year Founded in USA 1962
Income for Overseas Mins .... NR

Progressive Vision

(949)582-8600 Fax: (949)582-8608
E-Mail: info@progressivevision.org
Web: www.progressivevision.org
P.O. Box 2008, Laguna Hills, CA 92654-2008
Mr. Marcus Vegh, President
An international Christian digital publisher and distributor, committed to developing resources for discipling nations in the major languages of the world.
Purpose: "...to develop and distribute effective, digitally based, Christian leadership training resources in the major languages of the world."
Year Founded in USA 1995
Income for Overseas Mins .... NA
Personnel:
Home ministry & office staff in USA 3

Project AmaZon

(309)263-2299 Fax: (309)263-2299
E-Mail: dove@dpc.net
P.O. Box 913, Morton, IL 61550
Mr. Brian Donais, Chairman of the Board
A sending agency of evangelical tradition engaged in church planting, evangelism, medical work, support of national churches/workers and missionary training. Name changed from PAZ International.
Purpose: "...to plant 100,000 churches focusing on the Amazon Basin and extending around the world."
Year Founded in USA 1986
Income for Overseas Mins $975,000
Fully Supported USA Personnel Overseas:
Expecting to serve more than 4 years 35
Expecting to serve 1 to 4 years 3
Other Personnel:
Short-Term less than 1 year from USA 10
Countries: Brazil 35, Japan 3

Project Care

(253)529-2644 Fax: (253)529-2642
E-Mail: projectcare@xc.org
2034 S. 308th St., Federal Way, WA 98003
Mr. Chuck Schukar, Director
A nondenominational agency of evangelical tradition engaged in support of national workers, TEE, leadership development,

literature production, short-term programs and supplying equipment.

Year Founded in USA 1991
Income for Overseas Mins $15,000
Personnel:
Non-USA serving in own/other country 4
Short-Term less than 1 year from USA 10
Countries: Poland, Romania

Project Christ International

(718)845-6992 Fax: (718)845-6992
E-Mail: ssamraj@juno.com
124-08 Linden Blvd., So. Ozone Park, NY 11420
Dr. S. Samraj, President

An independent support agency of fundamental tradition engaged in missionary training, Bible distribution, childcare/orphanage programs, church planting, missionary education, medical work, short-term programs and support of national workers.

Year Founded in USA 1984
Income for Overseas Mins $52,000
Fully Supported USA Personnel Overseas:
Nonresidential mission personnel 1
Other Personnel:
Non-USA serving in own/other country 127
Short-Term less than 1 year from USA 10

Project Mercy, Inc.

(219)747-2559 Fax: (219)478-1361
E-Mail: pminfo@projectmercy.org
7011 Ardmore Ave., Fort Wayne, IN 46809
Marta Gabre-Tsadick, Exec. Director

An interdenominational agency engaged in the project of community development in Yetebon, Ethiopia and assistance to 8 evangelical Ethiopian refugee outreaches in Sudan and Djibouti.

Purpose: "...providing aid, comfort and support to those in need anywhere in Africa…also participates to alleviate human suffering anywhere in the work in the name of Jesus Christ."

Year Founded in USA 1977
Income for Overseas Mins $380,414
Gifts-in-Kind $65,365
Fully Supported USA Personnel Overseas:
Expecting to serve more than 4 years 2
Nonresidential mission personnel 2
Other Personnel:
Non-USA serving in own/other country 51
Short-Term less than 1 year from USA 26
Home ministry & office staff in USA 6
Countries: Djibouti, Ethiopia 2, Sudan

Project Partner with Christ

(513)425-0938 Fax: (513)425-6628
E-Mail: partner@projectpartner.com
Web: www.projectpartner.com
P.O. Box 610, Springboro, OH 45066-0610
Mr. Robert L. Gregory, President

An evangelical training ministry dedicated to the development of national-led ministries around the world.

Purpose: "...provides opportunities for national leaders and effective Christian leaders and laity in the United States to develop interdependent partnerships."

Year Founded in USA 1984
Income for Overseas Mins $770,268
Fully Supported USA Personnel Overseas:
Nonresidential mission personnel 2
Other Personnel:
Non-USA serving in own/other country 4
Short-Term less than 1 year from USA 27
Home ministry & office staff in USA 4
Countries: Costa Rica, India, Mexico, China (PRC)

Providence Mission Homes, Inc.

(626)293-1752
E-Mail: PMHomesl@juno.com
P.O. Box 40727, Pasadena, CA 91114
Dr. Richard Keilhacker, Co-Director
Mr. Paul Winter, President

A nondenominational support agency of evangelical tradition engaged in furloughed missionary support.

Year Founded in USA 1973
Income for Overseas Mins .... NA
Personnel:
Home ministry & office staff in USA 2

Radio Bible Class
See: RBC Ministries

Ramabai Mukti Mission

(908)735-8770
E-Mail: ramabai_mukti@compuserve.com

Web: www.pingnet.com/mukti
P.O. Box 4912, Clinton, NJ 08809-0912
Rev. David L. Scott, Exec. Director
An interdenominational support agency of evangelical tradition engaged in childcare/ orphanage programs, evangelism, medical work and support of national workers.
Year Founded in USA 1929
Income for Overseas Mins $309,550
Personnel:
Non-USA serving in own/other country 125
Short-Term less than 1 year from USA 4
Home ministry & office staff in USA 3
Countries: India

Ramesh Richard Evangelism and Church Helps International

(972)733-3402 Fax: (972)733-3495
E-Mail: info@rreach.org
Web: www.rreach.org
5500 W. Plano Parkway #100, Plano, TX 75093
Dr. Ramesh P. Richard, President
A nondenominational proclamation ministry of evangelical tradition engaged in pastoral training, TV/radio broadcasting and Internet, evangelism, theological education, funds transmission and follow-up. Previously listed as RREACH International.
Purpose: "…A global proclamation calling with a strategic burden to evangelize the opinion leaders and strengthen pastoral leaders of weaker economies."
Year Founded in USA 1987
Income for Overseas Mins $665,000
Personnel:
Short-Term less than 1 year from USA 1
Home ministry & office staff in USA 4
Countries: Asia, Africa, the Pacific, the Caribbean, the Middle East, Latin America

Ravi Zacharias International Ministries

(770)449-6766 Fax: (770)729-1729
E-Mail: rzim@rzim.com
Web: www.rzim.org
4725 Peachtree Corners Circle, #250, Norcross, GA 30092
Mr. Ravi Zacharias, President
An interdenominational specialized agency of evangelical tradition involved in apologetics training with professionals, theological education, evangelism and leadership development.
Purpose: "...to support, expand and enhance the preaching and teaching ministry of Ravi Zacharias, distinctive in its strong evangelistic and apologetic foundation, intended to touch both the heart and the intellect of the thinkers and opinion-makers of society..."
Year Founded in USA 1984
Income for Overseas Mins $1,000,000
Gifts-in-Kind $500,000
Fully Supported USA Personnel Overseas:
Expecting to serve more than 4 years 4
Nonresidential mission personnel 2
Other Personnel:
Non-USA serving in own/other country 4
Short-Term less than 1 year from USA 4
Home ministry & office staff in USA 26
Countries: India 2, UK 2

RBC Ministries

(616)942-6770 Fax: (616)957-5741
E-Mail: rbc@rbc.net
Web: www.rbc.net
3000 Kraft Ave. SE, Grand Rapids, MI 49512
Mr. Howard Liverance, Manager Intl. Ministries
A nondenominational service agency of evangelical tradition engaged in radio and TV broadcasting in Spanish and English, literature production/distribution in more than 20 languages, and audio webcasting available worldwide wherever the Internet can be accessed. Name changed from Radio Bible Class.
Year Founded in USA 1938
Income for Overseas Mins $267,000
Personnel:
Home ministry & office staff in USA 300

Reach Ministries International

(562)690-4252 Fax: (562)690-5612
E-Mail: reachmin@cosmoslink.net
P.O. Box 842, La Habra, CA 90631
Mr. Gene Tabor, Board Chairman
A nondenominational sending agency of evangelical tradition engaged in missionary training, evangelism, leadership development and Bible translation.

Year Founded in USA 1976
Income for Overseas Mins $134,468
Fully Supported USA Personnel Overseas:
Expecting to serve more than 4 years 9
Other Personnel:
Non-USA serving in own/other country 3
Home ministry & office staff in USA 3
Countries: Hong Kong 1, India 2, Philippines 6

Reciprocal Ministries International

(305)233-9903 **Fax: (305)233-9907**
E-Mail: RMIMIA@aol.com
14540 SW 136th St., Suite #208, Miami, FL 33186
Rev. Herbert L. Shoemaker, President
An interdenominational sending agency of evangelical tradition engaged in support of national churches, church construction, Christian education, funds transmission and training.
Year Founded in USA 1988
Income for Overseas Mins $500,000
Fully Supported USA Personnel Overseas:
Expecting to serve more than 4 years 3
Other Personnel:
Non-USA serving in own/other country 3
Home ministry & office staff in USA 4
Countries: Haiti 3

Red Sea Team International

(408)257-2948 **Fax: (408)257-5231**
E-Mail: drcondie@aol.com
P.O. Box 3331, Saratoga, CA 95070-1331
Dr. John Condie, Acting U.S. Home Director
An interdenominational support agency of evangelical tradition engaged in evangelism, agricultural programs, Bible distribution and funds transmission. Formerly Red Sea Missions Team.
Year Founded in USA 1953
Income for Overseas Mins $157,346
Fully Supported USA Personnel Overseas:
Expecting to serve more than 4 years 6
Countries: Unspecified 6

Reformation Translation Flwshp.

(812)339-1922
E-Mail: Bill4RTF@aol.com
Web: www.members.aol.com/Bill4RTF/rtf
302 E. 1st St., Bloomington, IN 47401
Rev. William Roberts, American Representative
A nondenominational service agency of Reformed tradition engaged in translation work and literature distribution/production.
Year Founded in USA 1950
Income for Overseas Mins $72,500

Reformed Baptist Mission Svcs.

(717)249-7473 **Fax: (717)258-0614**
E-Mail: arbca@reformedbaptist.com
P.O. Box 289, Carlisle, PA 17013
Rev. Robert B. Selph, Mission Coord.
A denominational mission service of Baptist tradition coordinating member churches to assist one another to send missionaries and plant churches worldwide. Financial information from 1996.
Purpose: "...to provide to churches that hold to the London Confession of 1689, those services that will assist them in promoting gospel missions."
Year Founded in USA 1985
Income for Overseas Mins $301,517
Fully Supported USA Personnel Overseas:
Expecting to serve more than 4 years 16
Other Personnel:
Non-USA serving in own/other country 8
Home ministry & office staff in USA 2
Countries: Bahrain 2, Colombia 2, France 2, Israel 2, Jamaica 2, Kenya 2, Namibia 2, UK 2

Reformed Church in America Gen. Synod Council, Mission Services

(616)698-7071 **Fax: (616)698-6606**
E-Mail: bmenning@rca.org
Web: www.rca.org
4500 - 60th St, S.E., Grand Rapids, MI 49512
Rev. Bruce Menning, Director Mission Services
A denominational sending agency of Reformed and Presbyterian tradition engaged in evangelism, theological education, leadership development, medical work, support of national churches, relief and/or rehabilitation and Bible translation.
Year Founded in USA 1857
Income for Overseas Mins $5,484,700

Fully Supported USA Personnel Overseas:
Expecting to serve more than 4 years 51
Nonresidential mission personnel 6
Other Personnel:
Non-USA serving in own/other country 11
Bivocational/Tentmaker from USA 21
Short-Term less than 1 year from USA 34
Home ministry & office staff in USA 53
Countries: Estonia 2, Ethiopia 4, Hungary 2, India 5, Indonesia 2, Japan 10, Kenya 8, Laos 1, Mexico 8, Sudan 3, Taiwan (ROC) 5, Ukraine 1

Reformed Episcopal Board of Foreign Missions

(713)862-5657 Fax: (713)862-4923
E-Mail: BFM@webtv.net
211 Byrne Ave., Houston, TX 77009
Very Rev. Jorge Garcia, President
A denominational sending agency of Anglican tradition engaged in church planting, medical work and Bible translation.
Year Founded in USA 1892
Income for Overseas Mins $176,338
Fully Supported USA Personnel Overseas:
Expecting to serve more than 4 years 9
Other Personnel:
Non-USA serving in own/other country 7
Short-Term less than 1 year from USA 50
Home ministry & office staff in USA 3
Countries: Brazil 1, France 2, Germany 2, Uganda 2, Unspecified 2

Reformed Presbyterian Church, Board of Foreign Missions

(724)846-5486 Fax: (724)843-6305
510 32nd St., Beaver Falls, PA 15010
Dr. Jonathan M. Watt, Exec. Secretary
A denominational sending agency of Reformed tradition engaged in church planting, evangelism and literature distribution.
Year Founded in USA 1856
Income for Overseas Mins .... NR
Fully Supported USA Personnel Overseas:
Expecting to serve more than 4 years 3
Expecting to serve 1 to 4 years 1
Other Personnel:
Bivocational/Tentmaker from USA 5
Countries: Cyprus 1, Japan 3

Rehoboth Ministries, Inc

(910)630-3730
333 Hilliard Dr., Fayetteville, NC 28311-8751
Lucia A. Adams, Secretary-Treasurer
Rev. Pritchard Adams, III, President
A transdenominational sending agency of Pentecostal tradition engaged in evangelism, Christian education, theological education and leadership development. Statistical information from 1996.
Year Founded in USA 1985
Income for Overseas Mins $63,270
Fully Supported USA Personnel Overseas:
Expecting to serve more than 4 years 2
Countries: Haiti 2

Rio Grande Bible Institute

(956)380-8100 Fax: (956)380-8256
E-Mail: RGBIMail@juno.com
4300 S. Business Hwy. #281, Edinburg, TX 78539
Dr. Roy S. LeTourneau, President
An interdenominational service agency of evangelical tradition engaged in theological education, correspondence courses, missionary education and video/film production/distribution. Personnel totals from 1996.
Purpose: "...serving the Hispanic church through equipping leaders, edifying believers and evangelizing the lost."
Year Founded in USA 1946
Income for Overseas Mins .... NA
Fully Supported USA Personnel Overseas:
Expecting to serve more than 4 years 51
Expecting to serve 1 to 4 years 8
Other Personnel:
Bivocational/Tentmaker from USA 5
Short-Term less than 1 year from USA 2
Home ministry & office staff in USA 59
Countries: Mexico 59

Ripe for Harvest, Inc.

(619)435-0432
E-Mail: rfhsandiego@aol.com
Web: www.ripeforharvest.org
P.O. Box 182184, San Diego, CA 92178
Dr. Tim Smith, President
A nondenominational sending agency of evangelical and independent tradition engaged in funds transmission, Bible

distribution, evangelism and support of national churches. Personnel totals from 1996.

Year Founded in USA 1979
Income for Overseas Mins $450,000
Fully Supported USA Personnel Overseas:
Expecting to serve more than 4 years 4
Expecting to serve 1 to 4 years 12
Other Personnel:
Bivocational/Tentmaker from USA 15
Home ministry & office staff in USA 8
Countries: El Salvador 1, Honduras 5, Hungary 1, India 2, Japan 2, Mexico 1, Russia 4

Romanian Mission of Chicago

(773)205-2732 **Fax: (773)205-3196**
E-Mail: isfan@geocities.com
5530 W. Montrose Ave., Chicago, IL 60641
Rev. Iosif J. Isfan, Director/Founder

An interdenominational service agency of Pentecostal tradition engaged in relief and/or rehabilitation, Bible distribution, childrens programs, church construction, literature distribution and support of national workers. Statistical information from 1996.

Year Founded in USA 1990
Income for Overseas Mins $85,199
Countries: Albania, Romania

Romanian Missionary Society

(630)665-6503 **Fax: (630)665-6538**
E-Mail: RMSda@aol.com
Web: www.rms-world.org
P.O. Box 527, Wheaton, IL 60189-0527
Dr. Darrel Anderson, Exec. Director

A nondenominational sending agency of Baptist tradition engaged in theological education, orphan ministry, sponsor-a-pastor program, broadcasting, leadership development, literature distribution/production and Bible translation. Statistical totals from 1996.

Year Founded in USA 1968
Income for Overseas Mins $757,179
Fully Supported USA Personnel Overseas:
Expecting to serve more than 4 years 4
Other Personnel:
Non-USA serving in own/other country 4
Home ministry & office staff in USA 9
Countries: Romania 4

Rosedale Mennonite Missions

(740)857-1366 **Fax: (740)857-1605**
E-Mail: rmmoffice@compuserve.com
9920 Rosedale Milford Ctr. Rd., Irwin, OH 43029
Mr. Nathan Miller, President

A denominational sending agency of Mennonite tradition engaged in church planting, leadership development, support of national churches, relief and/or rehabilitation, short-term programs and youth programs.

Purpose: "...to stimulate and facilitate Biblical, Spirit-led missions vision and action with local congregations to launch believers into Christ-centered evangelism, service and discipleship both at home and abroad."

Year Founded in USA 1919
Income for Overseas Mins $775,000
Gifts-in-Kind $700
Fully Supported USA Personnel Overseas:
Expecting to serve more than 4 years 27
Expecting to serve 1 to 4 years 2
Other Personnel:
Non-USA serving in own/other country 2
Bivocational/Tentmaker from USA 12
Short-Term less than 1 year from USA 27
Home ministry & office staff in USA 35
Countries: Bangladesh 1, Belarus 2, Costa Rica 4, Ecuador 7, Germany 4, Mexico 2, Turkey 9

RREACH International

See: Ramesh Richard Evangelism and Church Helps International

Russian Bible Society, Inc.

(828)681-0370 **Fax: (828)681-0371**
E-Mail: russianbibles@juno.com
P.O. Box 6068, Asheville, NC 28816
Dr. Robert Doom, Director

An interdenominational specialized agency of Baptist and fundamental tradition engaged in Bible translation/distribution. Statistical information from 1996.

Purpose: "...to continue providing the 'Synodal Translation' of the Russian Bible...and its translation into many of the minority languages [of Russia]."

Year Founded in USA 1944
Income for Overseas Mins $200,000
Personnel:
Short-Term less than 1 year from USA 10
Home ministry & office staff in USA 1

Salvation Army, U.S.A.

(703)684-5500 Fax: (703)684-3478
E-Mail:
Don_McDougald@usn.salvationarmy
Web: www.salvationarmyusa.org
P.O. Box 269, Alexandria, VA 22313
Commissioner John A. Busby, Natl. Commander

A denominational sending agency of Holiness tradition engaged in social services including camping/children's programs, community development, evangelism and youth programs in 107 countries.

Purpose: "...to preach the Gospel of Jesus Christ and to meet human needs in His name without discrimination."

Year Founded in USA 1880
Income for Overseas Mins $20,000,000
Gifts-in-Kind $500,000
Fully Supported USA Personnel Overseas:
Expecting to serve more than 4 years 96
Nonresidential mission personnel 14
Other Personnel:
Short-Term less than 1 year from USA 250
Home ministry & office staff in USA 650
Countries: Antigua 1, Brazil 4, Chile 6, Costa Rica 7, Czech Rep 2, Finland 5, Georgia 6, Germany 2, India 2, Italy 1, Jamaica 7, Kenya 2, Malawi 2, Mexico 5, Moldava 3, Philippines 2, Portugal 1, Russia 8, S Africa 2, Spain 2, UK 17, Zambia 7, Zimbabwe 2

Samaritan's Purse

(828)262-1980 Fax: (828)262-1796
E-Mail: usa@samaritan.org
Web: www.samaritan.org
P.O. Box 3000, Boone, NC 28607
Mr. Franklin Graham, President

A nondenominational specialized agency of evangelical tradition engaged in relief and/or rehabilitation, childrens programs, evangelism, medical work, and support of national churches.

Purpose: "...specializing in meeting the needs of victims of war, poverty, natural disasters and disease while sharing the Good News of Jesus Christ."

Year Founded in USA 1970
Income for Overseas Mins $58,715,127
Gifts-in-Kind $40,072,827

SAND Institutes International

(918)331-9319 Fax: (918)331-9319
E-Mail: sand32@juno.com
P.O. Box 3937, Bartlesville, OK 74006
Don & Lois Sobkoviak

An interdenominational support agency of evangelical and charismatic tradition engaged in training, agricultural programs and technical assistance.

Purpose: "...helping train mission and development workers in the 'two-handed' Gospel approach to evangelism."

Year Founded in USA 1982
Income for Overseas Mins $6,700
Gifts-in-Kind $500
Fully Supported USA Personnel Overseas:
Expecting to serve 1 to 4 years 1
Other Personnel:
Short-Term less than 1 year from USA 2
Countries: Poland 1

SAT-7 North America

(610)995-9151 Fax: (610)995-9155
E-Mail: USA@sat7.org
Web: www.sat7.org
P.O. Box 113, Wayne, PA 19087-0113
Mr. Ronald J. Ensminger, President & CEO

An interdenominational specialized agency of evangelical tradition engaged in broadcasting, evangelism, support of national churches and video/film production/distribution.

Purpose: "...a satellite television service...to serve the churches...present relevant television programs...mobilize related spiritual, financial and human resources for the [Middle East and North Africa]."

Year Founded in USA 1997
Income for Overseas Mins $784,853
Personnel:
Non-USA serving in own/other country 27
Home ministry & office staff in USA 3
Countries: Cyprus, Egypt, Lebanon, UK

Scripture Union, USA

(610)341-0830 Fax: (610)341-0836
E-Mail: SUUSA@aol.com
Web: www.scriptureunion.org
P.O. Box 6720, Wayne, PA 19087-8720
Whitney Kuniholm, President

An interdenominational service agency of evangelical tradition engaged in literature production/distribution, training and youth programs. Personnel information from 1992.

Year Founded in USA 1959
Income for Overseas Mins $400,000
Fully Supported USA Personnel Overseas:
Expecting to serve more than 4 years 3
Other Personnel:
Non-USA serving in own/other country 2
Home ministry & office staff in USA 9
Countries: Kenya 1, Peru 2

Seed Company, The
See: Wycliffe Bible Translators USA

Self-Help International

(319)352-4040 Fax: (319)352-4820
E-Mail: selfhelp@netins.net
Web: www.netins.net/showcase/selfhelp
805 W. Bremer Ave., Waverly, IA 50677-2027
Mr. Llewellyn Hille, Exec. Director

An interdenominational service agency of Methodist tradition engaged in rural development through agricultural programs, technical assistance and training.

Purpose: "To train small-scale farmers… improve and maintain their farming and transport methods; train people in developing countries… increase crop yields and improve nutrition…; cooperate with others in the introduction of appropriate farming practices…and help the people of the United States understand the problems of life in developing countries."

Year Founded in USA 1959
Income for Overseas Mins $275,000
Gifts-in-Kind $25,000
Fully Supported USA Personnel Overseas:
Expecting to serve 1 to 4 years 1
Other Personnel:
Non-USA serving in own/other country 13
Short-Term less than 1 year from USA 4
Home ministry & office staff in USA 3
Countries: Ghana 1

SEND International

(248)477-4210 Fax: (248)477-4232
E-Mail: sendus@send.org
Web: www.send.org
P.O. Box 513, Farmington, MI 48332
Dr. Frank M. Severn, Gen. Director

An interdenominational sending agency of evangelical tradition engaged in church planting, theological education, TEE, evangelism, leadership development and support of national churches.

Purpose: "...to make disciples through evangelism, nurturing new believers and developing leaders while planting the church where it does not exist and serving it where it does."

Year Founded in USA 1947
Income for Overseas Mins $9,464,770
Gifts-in-Kind $136,641
Fully Supported USA Personnel Overseas:
Expecting to serve more than 4 years 171
Expecting to serve 1 to 4 years 17
Nonresidential mission personnel 14
Other Personnel:
Non-USA serving in own/other country 16
Short-Term less than 1 year from USA 350
Home ministry & office staff in USA 68
Countries: Asia 7, Bulgaria 4, Croatia 3, Czech Rep 6, Hong Kong 4, Hungary 6, Japan 47, Macedonia 12, Philippines 31, Poland 11, Romania 2, Russia 16, Spain 7, Taiwan (ROC) 20, Ukraine 8, Unspecified 4

Sentinel Group, The

(425)672-2989 Fax: (425)672-3028
E-Mail: info@sentinelgroup.org
Web: www.sentinelgroup.org
P.O. Box 6334, Lynnwood, WA 98036
George K. Otis, Jr., President & CEO

A nondenominational support agency of evangelical and charismatic tradition engaged in services for other agencies, mission-related research and training.

Purpose: "...helping the Church mobilize prayer and ministry resources intelligently during the latter stages of world evangelization."

Year Founded in USA 1990
Income for Overseas Mins $11,214

Personnel:

Home ministry & office staff in USA 17

Servants in Faith & Technology

(205)396-2017 **Fax: (205)396-2501**
E-Mail: Info@sifat.org
Web: www.sifat.org
2944 County Rd. 113, Lineville, AL 36266
Mr. Tom Corson, Exec. Director

An interdenominational service agency of Methodist tradition engaged in training, development and technical assistance.

Purpose: "...teaching appropriate technology as a means of promoting self-help...to people in need."

Year Founded in USA 1979

Income for Overseas Mins $203,361

Personnel:

Bivocational/Tentmaker from USA 15
Short-Term less than 1 year from USA 7
Home ministry & office staff in USA 11

Seventh Day Baptist Missionary Society

(401)596-4326 **Fax: (401)596-4326**
E-Mail: sdbmissoc@edgenet.net
119 Main St., Westerly, RI 02891
Mr. G. Kirk Looper, Exec. Director

A denominational support agency of Baptist tradition engaged in funds transmission for support of national churches, evangelism, and literature distribution. Financial information from 1996.

Purpose: "...to coordinate and carry out...the message of salvation through faith in Christ to all who will hear, so they may accept Him as Savior."

Year Founded in USA 1842

Income for Overseas Mins $29,000

Fully Supported USA Personnel Overseas:

Expecting to serve 1 to 4 years 1

Other Personnel:

Home ministry & office staff in USA 4

Countries: Guyana 1

Seventh-day Adventists General Conference

(301)680-6000 **Fax: (301)680-6090**
E-Mail: 74431.1570@compuserve.com
12501 Old Columbia Pike, Silver Spring, MD 20904
Dr. Jan Paulsen, President

A denominational sending agency of Adventist tradition engaged in evangelism, broadcasting, church planting, theological education, literature production/distribution, medical work and relief aid.

Year Founded in USA 1874

Income for Overseas Mins $92,828,000

Fully Supported USA Personnel Overseas:

Expecting to serve more than 4 years 473
Expecting to serve 1 to 4 years 41

Other Personnel:

Non-USA serving in own/other country 410

Countries: Albania 2, Antigua 2, Argentina 4, Armenia 2, Australia 4, Bangladesh 4, Cambodia 9, Cameroon 4, Chile 4, China (PRC) 6, Colombia 2, Costa Rica 5, Cote d'Ivoire 4, Dominican Rep 2, Egypt 6, Ethiopia 6, Ghana 1, Guam 95, Haiti 8, Honduras 4, Hong Kong 17, India 8, Indonesia 6, Ireland 2, Israel 2, Italy 2, Jamaica 6, Japan 10, Kenya 26, Korea-S 14, Kyrgyzstan 2, Lebanon 8, Liberia 2, Madagascar 2, Malawi 4, Mexico 30, Mongolia 4, Mozambique 4, Nepal 5, Nicaragua 4, Nigeria 8, Norway 2, Pakistan 2, Papua New Guin 10, Peru 4, Philippines 46, Puerto Rico 12, Russia 18, Rwanda 2, S Africa 8, Sri Lanka 6, St Chris-Nevis 4, St Vincent 2, Sudan 7, Taiwan (ROC) 9, Thailand 16, Trinidad & Tobg 6, Uganda 3, UK 3, Vietnam 4, Zimbabwe 10

SGM International

See: American Scripture Gift Mission

Share International

(318)513-2997 **Fax: (318)513-2997**
E-Mail: shareusa@bayou.com
2101 Greenbriar Drive, Ruston, LA 71270-2778
Sammy Murimi, President

A support agency of evangelical tradition engaged in support of national workers, mobilization for mission, and training.

Purpose: "...challenging, training, sending, and supporting missionaries in partnership with the Church, with an initial emphasis on African nationals."

Year Founded in USA 1989

Income for Overseas Mins $90,000

Gifts-in-Kind $90,000

Personnel:
Non-USA serving in own/other country 4
Short-Term less than 1 year from USA 7
Home ministry & office staff in USA 1
Countries: Kenya

Shelter Now International, Inc.
(920)426-1207 Fax: (920)426-4321
E-Mail: Thor@shelter.org
Web: www.shelter.org
P.O. Box 1306, Oshkosh, WI 54902
Mr. Thor Armstrong, Exec. Director
A Christian relief and development agency committed to serving refugees and the poor all over the world, regardless of race, religion or country of origin.
Purpose: "...to respond quickly and with compassion to those who are homeless by equipping and deploying volunteers and indigenous workers to complete the task of building homes and providing immediate relief..."
Year Founded in USA 1979
Income for Overseas Mins $1,064,810
Gifts-in-Kind $28,000
Fully Supported USA Personnel Overseas:
Expecting to serve 1 to 4 years 13
Other Personnel:
Non-USA serving in own/other country 2
Home ministry & office staff in USA 8
Countries: Afghanistan 1, Honduras 1, Tajikistan 11

Shield of Faith Ministries
(254)939-0124
E-Mail: sofbol@tucan.cnb.net
P. O. Box 3172, Galveston, TX 77552
Mr. Rocky J. Malloy, Director
A nondenominational support agency of charismatic and evangelical tradition engaged in evangelism, church planting, Christian education, leadership development and youth programs.
Year Founded in USA 1990
Income for Overseas Mins $110,000
Fully Supported USA Personnel Overseas:
Nonresidential mission personnel 2
Other Personnel:
Non-USA serving in own/other country 66
Short-Term less than 1 year from USA 24
Home ministry & office staff in USA 2

Shield of Faith Mission Intl.
(541)382-7081 Fax: (541)382-4471
E-Mail: sfmi@teleport.com
Web: www.sfmiusa.org
P.O. Box 144, Bend, OR 97709
Mr. Larry Montgomery, President
A nondenominational sending agency of evangelical tradition engaged in evangelism, church planting and missionary training. Statistical information from 1996.
Year Founded in USA 1953
Income for Overseas Mins $126,045
Fully Supported USA Personnel Overseas:
Expecting to serve more than 4 years 17
Other Personnel:
Bivocational/Tentmaker from USA 3
Home ministry & office staff in USA 2
Countries: Brazil 2, Cote d'Ivoire 2, Mexico 7, Pakistan 1, Romania 2, Russia 2, Turkey 1

SIM USA
(704)588-4300 Fax: (704)587-1518
E-Mail: Info@sim.org
Web: www.sim.org/usa/index.html
P.O. Box 7900, Charlotte, NC 28241-7900
Dr. Larry D. Fehl, U.S. Director
An interdenominational sending agency of evangelical tradition engaged in church planting, broadcasting, development, theological education, medical work and support of national churches. Includes merger of Africa Evangelical Fellowship.
Purpose: "...planting, strengthening and partnering with churches around the world as we evangelize the unreached, minister to human need, disciple believers into churches and equip churches to fulfill Christ's Commission."
Year Founded in USA 1893
Income for Overseas Mins $21,812,357
Gifts-in-Kind $295,784
Fully Supported USA Personnel Overseas:
Expecting to serve more than 4 years 527
Expecting to serve 1 to 4 years 42
Nonresidential mission personnel 2
Other Personnel:
Non-USA serving in own/other country 501
Short-Term less than 1 year from USA 245
Home ministry & office staff in USA 119
Countries: Angola 7, Bangladesh 5, Benin 13, Bolivia 57, Botswana 10, Brazil 2, Burkina Faso 14, Cen

Africa Rep 1, Chile 7, Cote d'Ivoire 21, Djibouti 2, Ecuador 8, Eritrea 3, Ethiopia 84, Ghana 12, Guinea 14, India 7, Italy 2, Kenya 20, Korea-S 1, Liberia 7, Malawi 4, Mauritius 1, Mongolia 3, Mozambique 10, Niger 75, Nigeria 68, Pakistan 2, Paraguay 16, Peru 7, Philippines 3, Portugal 4, Senegal 9, S Africa 17, Sudan 6, Tanzania 4, Togo 2, Uruguay 4, Zambia 34, Zimbabwe 3

Slavic Gospel Association

(815)282-8900 **Fax: (815)282-8901**
E-Mail: sga@sga.org
Web: www.sga.org
6151 Commonwealth Dr., Loves Park, IL 61111
Dr. Robert W. Provost, President

An interdenominational agency of evangelical tradition engaged in support of national church planters and workers, Bible distribution, church construction, church planting, theological education and literature distribution. Personnel totals from 1996.

Purpose: "To serve evangelical churches, helping make disciples of the people in the lands of Russia."

Year Founded in USA 1934
Income for Overseas Mins $4,724,982
Gifts-in-Kind $936,477
Fully Supported USA Personnel Overseas:
Nonresidential mission personnel 2
Other Personnel:
Non-USA serving in own/other country 91
Home ministry & office staff in USA 46
Countries: Belarus, Kazakhstan, Russia, Ukraine

Slavic Missionary Service

(732)873-8981 **Fax: (732)873-1625**
E-Mail: smsusa@aol.com
P.O. Box 307, South River, NJ 08882
Rev. Alex Leonovich, Exec. Director

An interdenominational support agency of evangelical tradition engaged in support of national churches, broadcasting, church planting and literature distribution.

Year Founded in USA 1933
Income for Overseas Mins .... NR
Fully Supported USA Personnel Overseas:
Nonresidential mission personnel 3
Other Personnel:
Short-Term less than 1 year from USA 2
Home ministry & office staff in USA 5

Society for Europe's Evangelization

(941)747-6870 **Fax: (941)750-8701**
P.O. Box 1868, Bradenton, FL 34206-1868
Rev. T. M. Frye, President

A denominational sending agency of Baptist tradition engaged in evangelism, Bible distribution, theological education and leadership development. Statistical information from 1996.

Year Founded in USA 1956
Income for Overseas Mins $117,333
Fully Supported USA Personnel Overseas:
Expecting to serve more than 4 years 5
Other Personnel:
Short-Term less than 1 year from USA 3
Home ministry & office staff in USA 3
Countries: France 5

Society of St. Margaret

(617)445-8961
Web: www.ssmbos.com
17 Highland Park St., Boston, MA 02119
Sister Adele Marie, Mother Superior

A denominational service agency of Episcopal tradition engaged in Christian education, childrens programs, development, leadership development, literacy work, providing medical supplies and support of national churches.

Year Founded in USA 1873
Income for Overseas Mins .... NA
Fully Supported USA Personnel Overseas:
Expecting to serve more than 4 years 2
Other Personnel:
Non-USA serving in own/other country 3
Short-Term less than 1 year from USA 4
Countries: Haiti 2

Son Shine Ministries International

(817)444-3777 **Fax: (817)270-0199**
P.O. Box 456, Azle, TX 76098-0456
Rev. Edward G. Platt, Co-Director
Rev. Lewis F. Shaffer, Co-Director

An interdenominational sending agency of evangelical tradition engaged in evangelism, correspondence courses and Christian education.

Year Founded in USA 1977
Income for Overseas Mins .... NR
Personnel:
Non-USA serving in own/other country 4
Home ministry & office staff in USA 8

Source of Light Ministries Intl.

(706)342-0397 **Fax: (706)342-9072**
E-Mail: sol1usa@aol.com
Web: www.sourcelight.org
1011 Mission Rd., Madison, GA 30650
Dr. Glenn E. Dix, Gen. Director

A nondenominational sending agency of evangelical and fundamental tradition engaged in correspondence courses, church planting, theological education, literature distribution, literature production and support of national workers.

Year Founded in USA 1953
Income for Overseas Mins $726,000
Fully Supported USA Personnel Overseas:
Expecting to serve more than 4 years 7
Nonresidential mission personnel...................... 2
Other Personnel:
Non-USA serving in own/other country 129
Short-Term less than 1 year from USA 5
Home ministry & office staff in USA 50
Countries: Bolivia 2, Brazil 2, Cote d'Ivoire 2, Mexico 1

South America Mission

(561)965-1833 **Fax: (561)439-8950**
E-Mail: samusa@samlink.org
Web: www.samlink.org
5217 S. Military Trail, Lake Worth, FL 33463-6099
Rev. William K. Ogden, Exec. Director

An interdenominational sending agency of evangelical tradition engaged in church planting, aviation services, leadership development and training.

Purpose: "...to establish the church of Jesus Christ in South America by planting and nurturing churches, training church leaders, [and] developing church associations."

Year Founded in USA 1914
Income for Overseas Mins $2,757,094
Fully Supported USA Personnel Overseas:
Expecting to serve more than 4 years 84
Expecting to serve 1 to 4 years 6
Nonresidential mission personnel..................... 1
Other Personnel:
Non-USA serving in own/other country 90
Short-Term less than 1 year from USA 12
Home ministry & office staff in USA 10
Countries: Bolivia 38, Brazil 13, Colombia 9, Peru 30

South American Missionary Society

(724)266-0669 **Fax: (724)266-5681**
E-Mail: SAMS@episcopalian.org
Web: www.sams-usa.org
P.O. Box 399, 1013 Merchant Street, Ambridge, PA 15003
Rev. Thomas M. Prichard, Exec. Director

A denominational sending agency of Episcopal tradition engaged in church planting, development, Christian education, evangelism, leadership development and support of national churches.

Purpose: "To be witnesses and make disciples for Jesus Christ in fellowship with the Episcopal/Anglican Church in Latin America."

Year Founded in USA 1976
Income for Overseas Mins $1,023,799
Fully Supported USA Personnel Overseas:
Expecting to serve more than 4 years 38
Other Personnel:
Non-USA serving in own/other country 8
Short-Term less than 1 year from USA 2
Home ministry & office staff in USA 12
Countries: Bolivia 1, Chile 3, Costa Rica 3, Dominican Rep 4, Honduras 19, Mexico 2, Peru 2, Spain 2, Uruguay 2

Southern Baptist Convention International Mission Board

(804)353-0151 **Fax: (804)254-8982**
E-Mail: IMBResourceCenter@imb.org
Web: www.imb.org
P.O. Box 6767, Richmond, VA 23233
Dr. Jerry Rankin, President

A denominational sending agency of Baptist tradition engaged in church planting, TEE, evangelism, leadership development, medical work, support of national churches, relief and/or rehabilitation and mission-related research.

Purpose: "...to lead Southern Baptists in international missions efforts to evangelize the lost, disciple believers, develop churches and minister to people in need..."
Year Founded in USA 1845
Income for Overseas Mins $270,562,000
Fully Supported USA Personnel Overseas:
Expecting to serve more than 4 years 3610
Expecting to serve 1 to 4 years 952
Nonresidential mission personnel 8
Other Personnel:
Short-Term less than 1 year from USA ... 19943
Home ministry & office staff in USA 472
Countries: Africa 845, Asia 1904, Europe 549, Latin America 1264

Sowers International, The

(310)325-0950 Fax: (310)325-9593
E-Mail: gwynn@sower.org
Web: www.sower.org
26347 Governor Ave., Harbor City, CA 90710-3617
Mr. Gwynn Lewis, Exec. Director

A transdenominational support agency of evangelical tradition engaged in funds transmission for support of national and short-term workers engaged in evangelism, development, and childrens ministries.
Year Founded in USA 1992
Income for Overseas Mins $350,000
Fully Supported USA Personnel Overseas:
Expecting to serve more than 4 years 2
Expecting to serve 1 to 4 years 1
Nonresidential mission personnel 3
Other Personnel:
Non-USA serving in own/other country 10
Bivocational/Tentmaker from USA 2
Short-Term less than 1 year from USA 50
Home ministry & office staff in USA 2
Countries: China (PRC) 1, Colombia, Ecuador 2, Guatemala, Philippines, Taiwan, Thailand

Spanish World Gospel Mission

(219)267-8821 Fax: (219)267-3524
E-Mail: spanish_world@kconline.com
P.O. Box 542, Winona Lake, IN 46590
Mr. Cornelius Rivera, Exec. Director

A nondenominational support agency of evangelical and fundamental tradition engaged in broadcasting, Bible distribution, correspondence courses, evangelism, literature distribution and support of national workers.
Purpose: "To assist local churches in the Spanish speaking world to carry out the ministry of communicating the Gospel of the Lord Jesus Christ and making disciples."
Year Founded in USA 1959
Income for Overseas Mins $140,000
Fully Supported USA Personnel Overseas:
Nonresidential mission personnel 2
Other Personnel:
Non-USA serving in own/other country 23
Bivocational/Tentmaker from USA 2
Home ministry & office staff in USA 11
Countries: Argentina, Chile, Colombia, Honduras, Mexico, Peru, Spain, Venezuela

Spiritual Growth Resources, Inc.

(209)536-1544 Fax: (408)848-4198
P.O. Box 1014, Downey, CA 90240
Rev. Royal L. Peck, President

An interdenominational support agency of Baptist and Presbyterian tradition engaged in support of national churches, correspondence courses, evangelism, leadership development and support of national workers.
Year Founded in USA 1984
Income for Overseas Mins $87,000
Fully Supported USA Personnel Overseas:
Nonresidential mission personnel 2
Other Personnel:
Non-USA serving in own/other country 7
Home ministry & office staff in USA 1
Countries: Italy, Albania

Spiritual Overseers Service International Corp.

(707)451-9830 Fax: (707)451-2827
E-Mail: RevHEJones@email.msn.com
P.O. Box 2756, Vacaville, CA 95696
Rev. Henry E. Jones, President

An agency of evangelical tradition engaged in leadership development, church planting, management consulting/training, support of national churches and support of national workers. Financial data from 1992.
Year Founded in USA 1979

Income for Overseas Mins $327,373
Personnel:
Home ministry & office staff in USA 3

STEER, Inc.

(701)258-4911 **Fax: (701)258-7684**
P.O. Box 1236, Bismarck, ND 58502
Rev. LaRue Goetz, Exec. Director

A nondenominational support agency of evangelical tradition engaged in a three-way partnership program to help raise funds, agricultural programs and services for other agencies.

Purpose: "...raising money to help existing missionary societies get the Gospel to the ends of the earth in the shortest possible time..."

Year Founded in USA 1957
Income for Overseas Mins $359,000
Personnel:
Home ministry & office staff in USA 9

STEM (Short-Term Evangelical Missions) Ministries

1-877-stemmin **Fax: (952)996-1386**
E-Mail: STEMmin@aol.com
Web: www.stemmin.com
P.O. Box 386001, Minneapolis, MN 55438-6001
Rev. Roger P. Peterson, Exec. Director

A transdenominational specialized agency of evangelical tradition engaged in short-term programs, Bible distribution, church construction, evangelism, mobilization for mission and mission-related research.

Purpose: "...Using mutually-beneficial short-term mission in Caribbean and Latin American nations, STEM mobilizes the North American church into lifetime strategies for world evangelization."

Year Founded in USA 1984
Income for Overseas Mins $302,125
Fully Supported USA Personnel Overseas:
Expecting to serve 1 to 4 years 3
Other Personnel:
Short-Term less than 1 year from USA 242
Home ministry & office staff in USA 6
Countries: Belize, Dominican Rep., Haiti 3, Honduras, Jamaica, Paraguay, Trinidad & Tobg.

Strategic Ventures Network

(719)687-6818 **Fax: (719)687-3694**
E-Mail: 74211.2162@compuserve.com
P.O. Box 220, Woodland Park, CO 80866-0220
Mr. Gary Taylor, President

A nondenominational service agency of evangelical tradition engaged in mobilization for mission through entrepreneurial tentmaking, and providing for-profit creative access platforms through its international telecommunications parent company.

Year Founded in USA 1986
Income for Overseas Mins .... NA
Personnel:
Home ministry & office staff in USA 3

TAM-ICCC (The Associated Missions of the International Council of Christian Churches)

(856)858-7175
1115 Haddon Ave., Collingswood, NJ 08108
Dr. Earl White, President

An inter-mission agency of fundamental tradition serving its constituents in the International Council of Christian Churches.

Year Founded in USA 1948
Income for Overseas Mins .... NA

TCM International

(317)299-0333 **Fax: (317)290-8607**
E-Mail: tcm@tcmi.org
Web: www.tcmi.org
P.O. Box 24560, Indianapolis, IN 46224
Dr. Tony Twist, President

A nondenominational agency of Christian (Restoration Movement) tradition engaged in theological education, benevolence and support of national churches in Eastern Europe.

Purpose: "...to assist, disciple, encourage and equip Eastern and Central European Christians to reach their own people for Christ."

Year Founded in USA 1957
Income for Overseas Mins $1,476,136
Gifts-in-Kind $3,022
Fully Supported USA Personnel Overseas:
Expecting to serve more than 4 years 9
Nonresidential mission personnel 2

Other Personnel:
Short-Term less than 1 year from USA 6
Home ministry & office staff in USA 7
Countries: Europe-E 9

TEAM (The Evangelical Alliance Mission)

(630)653-5300 Fax: (630)653-1826
E-Mail: TEAM@teamworld.org
Web: www.teamworld.org
P.O. Box 969, Wheaton, IL 60189-0969
Dr. Charles Davis, Exec. Dir.

A nondenominational sending agency of evangelical and Baptist tradition engaged in evangelism, church planting, TEE, medical work, mobilization for mission and short-term programs.

Purpose: "...to help churches send missionaries to establish reproducing churches among the nations..."

Year Founded in USA 1890
Income for Overseas Mins $28,418,000
Fully Supported USA Personnel Overseas:
Expecting to serve more than 4 years 561
Expecting to serve 1 to 4 years 77
Nonresidential mission personnel 5
Other Personnel:
Non-USA serving in own/other country 13
Short-Term less than 1 year from USA 146
Home ministry & office staff in USA 83
Countries: Austria 22, Brazil 6, Chad 27, Colombia 24, Czech Rep 12, France 40, Germany 16, Hong Kong 6, India 2, Indonesia 20, Ireland 5, Italy 22, Japan 83, Macao 7, Mexico 16, Mozambique 3, Nepal 18, Neth Antilles 5, Pakistan 36, Peru 8, Philippines 18, Poland 4, Portugal 9, Russia 13, S Africa 22, Spain 27, Sri Lanka 1, Taiwan (ROC) 20, Trinidad & Tobg 4, Turkey 2, United Arab Emr 34, UK 2, Venezuela 86, Zimbabwe 18

Team Expansion, Inc.

(800)447-0800
E-Mail: info@teamexpansion.org
Web: www.teamexpansion.org
3700 Hopewell Road, Louisville, KY 40299
Mr. Doug Lucas, Coordinator of Intl. Services

A nondenominational sending agency of Christian (Restoration Movement) tradition engaged in church planting, Christian education, mobilization for mission, short-term programs, support of national workers and translation work.

Purpose: "...to pioneer with local churches to send and sustain teams of interdependent missionaries to plant indigenous churches among unreached people groups worldwide."

Year Founded in USA 1978
Income for Overseas Mins .... NR
Fully Supported USA Personnel Overseas:
Expecting to serve more than 4 years 73
Other Personnel:
Bivocational/Tentmaker from USA 25
Short-Term less than 1 year from USA 150
Home ministry & office staff in USA 20
Countries: Africa 1, Argentina 1, Bosnia 5, China (PRC) 5, Colombia 3, Ecuador 4, Ethiopia 1, France 1, Ireland 6, Italy 3, Kazakhstan 1, Laos 3, Mongolia 3, Taiwan (ROC) 8, Tanzania 3, Ukraine 14, Venezuela 11

Teen Missions International

(321)453-0350 Fax: (321)452-7988
E-Mail: info@teenmissions.org
Web: www.teenmissions.org
885 East Hall Rd., Merritt Island, FL 32953
Rev. Robert M. Bland, President/Director

An interdenominational sending agency of evangelical tradition engaged in short-term programs, camping programs, evangelism, literature production, missionary training and youth programs.

Purpose: "...to challenge, train, and disciple young people, exposing them to worldwide missions."

Year Founded in USA 1970
Income for Overseas Mins $4,791,154
Fully Supported USA Personnel Overseas:
Expecting to serve more than 4 years 13
Expecting to serve 1 to 4 years 7
Other Personnel:
Non-USA serving in own/other country 2
Short-Term less than 1 year from USA 3000
Home ministry & office staff in USA 72
Countries: Brazil 1, Ecuador 2, Honduras 3, Madagascar 2, Malawi 3, Mozambique 3, S Africa 3, Thailand 1, Zimbabwe 2

Teen World Outreach

(716)582-2792 Fax: (716)624-1229
E-Mail: jkporter@compuserve.com

Web: www.t-w-o.org
P.O. Box57A, Lima, NY 14485
Rev. James Porter, Director
A transdenominational service agency of Pentecostal tradition engaged in short-term programs, evangelism, medical work, support of national churches and youth programs. An affiliate of Elim Fellowship.
Year Founded in USA 1981
Income for Overseas Mins $670,000
Personnel:
Short-Term less than 1 year from USA 240
Home ministry & office staff in USA 3

The Master's Harvest

(956)782-0316 **Fax: (956)782-1864**
E-Mail: harvestbdr@aol.com
P.O. Box 955, Alamo, TX 78516
Mr. Kenny Ingram, Director
A transdenominational sending agency of Baptist and charismatic tradition engaged in short-term programs, evangelism, support of national churches and youth programs.
Year Founded in USA 1992
Income for Overseas Mins .... NA
Fully Supported USA Personnel Overseas:
Expecting to serve more than 4 years 4
Other Personnel:
Bivocational/Tentmaker from USA 2
Countries: Mexico 4

The Master's Mission, Inc.

(828)479-6873 **Fax: (828)479-2471**
E-Mail: tmmpaulteasdale@juno.com
Web: www.mastersmission.org
P.O. Box 547, Robbinsville, NC 28771
Rev. Paul Teasdale, Exec. Director
An interdenominational sending agency of evangelical tradition engaged in missionary education, church planting, medical work and technical assistance. Statistical information from 1996.
Year Founded in USA 1980
Income for Overseas Mins $730,000
Fully Supported USA Personnel Overseas:
Expecting to serve more than 4 years 20
Other Personnel:
Non-USA serving in own/other country 9
Short-Term less than 1 year from USA 3
Home ministry & office staff in USA 12
Countries: Congo/Zaire 2, Kenya 16, Mexico 2

Things To Come Mission, Inc.

(317)262-8806 **Fax: (317)262-8852**
E-Mail: tcmusa@compuserve.com
Web: www.tcmusa.org
2200 English Ave., Indianapolis, IN 46201
Rev. Joseph W. Watkins, Exec. Director
A nondenominational sending agency of fundamental tradition engaged in church planting, theological education, evangelism and training.
Purpose: "...preaching of the gospel of salvation through faith in the shed blood of Jesus Christ, training believers for ministry and leadership and establishing indigenous, local churches..."
Year Founded in USA 1955
Income for Overseas Mins $800,000
Fully Supported USA Personnel Overseas:
Expecting to serve more than 4 years 12
Expecting to serve 1 to 4 years 3
Other Personnel:
Non-USA serving in own/other country 39
Bivocational/Tentmaker from USA 1
Short-Term less than 1 year from USA 10
Home ministry & office staff in USA 3
Countries: Australia 1, Brazil 4, Cameroon 2, Kenya 5, Senegal 1, S Africa 2

Third World Baptist Missions

(517)547-5516 **Fax: (517)547-4188**
E-Mail: Cturbeville@dmci.net
Web: www.3rdworld.org
175 Manitou Road, Manitou Beach, MI 49253
Dr. Caroll D. Turbeville, Director
A sending agency of fundamental and Independent Baptist tradition engaged in church planting, Bible distribution, camping programs, church construction, theological education and support of national workers.
Year Founded in USA 1991
Income for Overseas Mins $700,000
Gifts-in-Kind $600,000
Fully Supported USA Personnel Overseas:
Expecting to serve more than 4 years 4
Nonresidential mission personnel 1
Other Personnel:
Non-USA serving in own/other country 88
Bivocational/Tentmaker from USA 20

Short-Term less than 1 year from USA 12
Home ministry & office staff in USA 2

Countries: India 2, Philippines 2

TMA Ministries

(901)367-2677 Fax: (901)367-2677
E-Mail: 74241.332@compuserve.com
P.O. Box 38366, Memphis, TN 38183
Dr. John L. Langston, III, President

A nondenominational service agency of evangelical tradition engaged in technical assistance, theological education, evangelism, support of national churches and services for other agencies.

Purpose: "To bring the Gospel to all peoples around the world and globally provide consultative architectural services to national/domestic missionaries and mission agencies and train others to carry the Gospel in the world."

Year Founded in USA 1982
Income for Overseas Mins $4,000
Fully Supported USA Personnel Overseas:
Expecting to serve more than 4 years 2
Nonresidential mission personnel...................... 2
Other Personnel:
Non-USA serving in own/other country 2
Short-Term less than 1 year from USA 1
Home ministry & office staff in USA 4

Countries: Belize 1, Ghana 1

Touch the World Ministries

(888)281-4887
E-Mail: info@touchtheworld.org
Web: www.touchtheworld.org
P.O. Box 7, Bergenfield, NJ 07621
Mr. Jeff Boucher, President

A nondenominational sending agency of evangelical tradition engaged in short-term programs, camping programs, leadership development, evangelism and youth/children's programs. Formerly High School Evangelism Fellowship, Inc.

Purpose: "...to evangelize high school students by discipling Christian students in their spiritual growth and training them to share Christ..."

Year Founded in USA 1944
Income for Overseas Mins $830,000
Fully Supported USA Personnel Overseas:
Expecting to serve more than 4 years 5
Expecting to serve 1 to 4 years 1
Nonresidential mission personnel...................... 2
Other Personnel:
Non-USA serving in own/other country 19
Short-Term less than 1 year from USA 190
Home ministry & office staff in USA 33

Countries: Japan 5, Russia 1

Training Evangelistic Leadership

(940)382-8365
P.O. Drawer E, Denton, TX 76202
Rev. Roy Robertson, International Director

A nondenominational sending agency of evangelical tradition engaged in training, evangelism, literature distribution and support of national churches. Personnel information from 1996.

Year Founded in USA 1970
Income for Overseas Mins $392,000
Fully Supported USA Personnel Overseas:
Expecting to serve more than 4 years 8
Nonresidential mission personnel...................... 1
Other Personnel:
Non-USA serving in own/other country 2
Bivocational/Tentmaker from USA.................. 4
Short-Term less than 1 year from USA 35
Home ministry & office staff in USA 2

Countries: China (PRC) 3, Hong Kong 4, Indonesia 1

Trans World Missions

(818)830-3437 Fax: (818)830-2787
P.O. Box 10, Glendale, CA 91209
Rev. Luis R. Mejia, President

An interdenominational support agency of evangelical and Pentecostal tradition engaged in church planting, Bible distribution, childcare/orphanage programs, childrens programs, evangelism and leadership development.

Purpose: "...ministering to the whole man spiritually, physically, emotionally and mentally..."

Year Founded in USA 1949
Income for Overseas Mins $331,648
Personnel:
Non-USA serving in own/other country 52
Home ministry & office staff in USA 3

Trans World Radio

(919)460-3700 **Fax: (919)460-3702**
E-Mail: info@twr.org
Web: www.twr.org
P.O. Box 8700, Cary, NC 27512
Mr. Thomas J. Lowell, President

An interdenominational specialized agency of evangelical tradition engaged in broadcasting, audio recording/distribution, church planting, correspondence courses, evangelism and technical assistance.

Purpose: "...to assist the Church to fulfill the command of Jesus Christ to make disciples of all peoples and to do so by using and making available mass media..."

Year Founded in USA 1952
Income for Overseas Mins $15,430,221
Gifts-in-Kind $647,963
Fully Supported USA Personnel Overseas:
Expecting to serve more than 4 years 143
Expecting to serve 1 to 4 years 21
Nonresidential mission personnel 5
Other Personnel:
Non-USA serving in own/other country 151
Bivocational/Tentmaker from USA 5
Short-Term less than 1 year from USA 24
Home ministry & office staff in USA 82
Countries: Africa 26, Asia 65, Europe 37, Latin America 36

Tribes and Nations Outreach, USA

(626)964-4742 **Fax: (626)964-4742**
E-Mail: tnousa@aol.com
19271 E. Colima Rd., Suite H, Rowland Heights, CA 91748
Pastor Fred Cheock, USA Director

A nondenominational support agency of evangelical and independent tradition engaged in training and Bible distribution.

Purpose: "...to build the body of Christ in Asia through training of nationals and provision of Bibles."

Year Founded in USA 1985
Income for Overseas Mins .... NR

Turkish World Outreach

(970)434-1942 **Fax: (970)434-1461**
E-Mail: TWO@onlinecol.com
508 Fruitvale Court, Grand Junction, CO 81504
Rev. Steven E. Hagerman, U.S. Director

A nondenominational support agency of evangelical tradition engaged in church planting, Bible distribution, literature distribution, mobilization for prayer, services for other agencies and video/film production/distribution.

Purpose: "...to evangelize Turks by any means possible."

Year Founded in USA 1969
Income for Overseas Mins $151,291
Fully Supported USA Personnel Overseas:
Expecting to serve more than 4 years 9
Other Personnel:
Non-USA serving in own/other country 3
Bivocational/Tentmaker from USA 6
Home ministry & office staff in USA 12
Countries: Central Asia 2, Germany 2, Turkey 5

UFM International

(610)667-7660 **Fax: (610)660-9068**
E-Mail: bala@ufm.org
Web: www.ufm.org
P.O. Box 306, Bala-Cynwyd, PA 19004
Rev. D. James O'Neill, Gen. Director

An interdenominational sending agency of evangelical tradition engaged in church planting, Christian education, theological education, evangelism, leadership development and medical work.

Purpose: "...helps churches start new churches by evangelizing the unreached, discipling believers and training leaders."

Year Founded in USA 1931
Income for Overseas Mins .... NR
Fully Supported USA Personnel Overseas:
Expecting to serve more than 4 years 268
Expecting to serve 1 to 4 years 21
Other Personnel:
Non-USA serving in own/other country 40
Short-Term less than 1 year from USA 82
Home ministry & office staff in USA 74
Countries: Austria 6, Bosnia 2, Brazil 65, Congo/Zaire 5, Dominican Rep 22, France 26, Germany 23, Guyana 13, Haiti 32, Indonesia 24, Ireland 7, Italy 15, Mexico 15, Neth Antilles 2, Philippines 10, Puerto Rico 2, Romania 2, Slovakia 3, S Africa 5, Spain 8, Sweden 2

United Board for Christian Higher Education in Asia

(212)870-2609 **Fax: (212)870-2322**
E-Mail: staff@ubchea.org
475 Riverside Dr. Rm. 1221, New York, NY 10115
Dr. David W. Vikner, President

An interdenominational service agency of ecumenical tradition engaged in leadership development, technical assistance and training. Statistical information from 1996.

Purpose: "...to contribute to higher education and to the exchange of resources in and with Asia for the pursuit of truth and knowledge...and full human development understood from the perspective of Christian faith."

Year Founded in USA 1932
Income for Overseas Mins $5,700,000
Personnel:
Short-Term less than 1 year from USA 38
Home ministry & office staff in USA 11

United Church Board for World Ministries

(216)736-3202 **Fax: (216)736-3259**
E-Mail: bishopd@ucc.org
700 Prospect Ave. E., Cleveland, OH 44115
Dr. Dale Bishop, Exec. Vice-President

A denominational sending agency of Congregational, Reformed and ecumenical tradition engaged in support of national churches, development, Christian education, theological education, leadership development and medical work.

Year Founded in USA 1812
Income for Overseas Mins $13,379,044
Fully Supported USA Personnel Overseas:
Expecting to serve 1 to 4 years 126
Other Personnel:
Home ministry & office staff in USA 48
Countries: Argentina 2, Asia 1, Australia 2, Botswana 2, Brazil 1, Chile 1, China (PRC) 2, Dominican Rep 1, Ecuador 2, El Salvador 2, Fiji 2, Germany 2, Guatemala 1, Haiti 2, Honduras 2, Hong Kong 1, Hungary 2, India 4, Indonesia 2, Israel 2, Jamaica 2, Japan 15, Kenya 1, Korea-S 1, Lebanon 2, Lesotho 12, Marshall Isls 2, Mexico 2, Namibia 2, Nepal 10, Nicaragua 1, Paraguay 2, Philippines 4, S Africa 7, Sri Lanka 3, Swaziland 2, Taiwan (ROC) 5, Thailand 6, Turkey 6, Vietnam 1, Zimbabwe 4

United Evangelical Churches

(800)228-2289 **Fax: (831)635-0909**
E-Mail: uec@uecol.org
Web: www.uecol.org
P.O. Box 1000, S. Juan Batista, CA 95045-1000
Dr. Charles J. Hardin, President

A transdenominational sending agency of charismatic tradition engaged in evangelism and support of national churches.

Year Founded in USA 1964
Income for Overseas Mins $40,138
Fully Supported USA Personnel Overseas:
Expecting to serve more than 4 years 4
Other Personnel:
Non-USA serving in own/other country 4
Home ministry & office staff in USA 4
Countries: Bolivia 2, Philippines 2

United Methodist Church, General Board of Global Ministries

(212)870-3606 **Fax: (212)870-3748**
Web: www.gbgm-umc.org
475 Riverside Dr., Rm. 1400, New York, NY 10115
Dr. Randolph Nugent, Gen. Secretary

A denominational sending agency of Methodist tradition responding to program and personnel needs through relationships to partner churches and ecumenical organizations all over the world, including evangelism, community development, support of national churches, relief aid, and missionary training.

Year Founded in USA 1820
Income for Overseas Mins $78,240,936
Fully Supported USA Personnel Overseas:
Expecting to serve more than 4 years 413
Other Personnel:
Short-Term less than 1 year from USA 72
Home ministry & office staff in USA 324
Countries: Unspecified 413

United Methodist Committee on Relief

See: United Methodist Church, General Board of Global Mins.

United Pentecostal Church Intl., Foreign Missions Division

(314)837-7300 Fax: (314)837-2387
E-Mail: UPCIMAIN@aol.com
Web: www.upci.org
8855 Dunn Rd., Hazelwood, MO 63042
Rev. Harry E. Scism, Gen. Director

A denominational sending agency of Pentecostal tradition engaged in evangelism, church planting, theological education, leadership development, literature distribution and literature production. Overseas personnel information from 1992 report.

Year Founded in USA 1924
Income for Overseas Mins $18,061,036
Fully Supported USA Personnel Overseas:
Expecting to serve more than 4 years 267
Countries: Argentina 8, Asia 21, Australia 4, Austria 4, Bahamas 2, Belgium 2, Belize 2, Bolivia 4, Botswana 2, Brazil 12, Cameroon 2, Chile 6, Colombia 4, Costa Rica 2, Cote d'Ivoire 2, Dominican Rep 6, Ecuador 4, Egypt 2, El Salvador 4, Europe 6, France 4, Germany 4, Ghana 5, Greece 4, Guatemala 2, Haiti 4, Honduras 4, Hong Kong 4, Hungary 2, Indonesia 4, Japan 2, Kenya 6, Korea-S 3, Liberia 2, Madagascar 10, Malawi 4, Malaysia 2, Mexico 12, Micronesia 4, Namibia 2, Netherlands 2, Neth Antilles 4, New Zealand 2, Nigeria 6, Norway 2, Pakistan 4, Panama 4, Paraguay 2, Peru 4, Philippines 8, Portugal 2, Puerto Rico 2, Russia 2, Sierra Leone 2, Singapore 2, S Africa 2, Spain 2, Sri Lanka 4, Swaziland 6, Tanzania 6, Trinidad & Tobg 2, UK 4, Uruguay 2, Venezuela 4, Zambia 4

United States Center for World Mission
See: Frontier Mission Fellowship

United World Mission, Inc.

(704)357-3355 Fax: (704)357-6389
Web: www.uwm.org
P.O. Box 668767, Charlotte, NC 28266-8767
Rev. Eugene W. Phillips, Jr., President

A nondenominational sending agency of evangelical tradition engaged in church planting, theological education, leadership development, support of national churches and missionary training. Statistical information from 1992.

Year Founded in USA 1946
Income for Overseas Mins $1,812,226
Fully Supported USA Personnel Overseas:
Expecting to serve more than 4 years 53
Expecting to serve 1 to 4 years 10
Other Personnel:
Non-USA serving in own/other country 9
Short-Term less than 1 year from USA 86
Home ministry & office staff in USA 57
Countries: Belgium 5, Bolivia 11, Brazil 2, Congo 6, Guatemala 4, Mali 5, Nigeria 2, Romania 1, Senegal 15, Spain 2, UK 6, Venezuela 4

VELA Ministries International

(408)995-5090 Fax: (408)995-5092
Web: www.vela.org
1100 Shasta Ave., San Jose, CA 95126-2621
Mr. Galo Vasquez, President
Mr. Ken Briden, Operations Director

An interdenominational support agency of evangelical tradition engaged in leadership development, funds transmission, mobilization for mission, mission-related research, support of national workers and training.

Year Founded in USA 1990
Income for Overseas Mins $200,000
Fully Supported USA Personnel Overseas:
Expecting to serve 1 to 4 years 1
Nonresidential mission personnel 1
Other Personnel:
Home ministry & office staff in USA 3
Countries: Mexico 1

Vellore Christian Medical College Board (USA), Inc.

(212)870-2640 Fax: (212)870-2173
E-Mail: usaboard@vellorecmc.org
Web: www.vellorecmc.org
475 Riverside Dr. Rm. 243, New York, NY 10115
Rev. William Salmond, President

An interdenominational specialized agency of ecumenical tradition engaged in medical work, funds transmission, providing medical supplies and training.

Purpose: "...to provide a focus for excellence and integrity through the support of the wide range of programs of Vellore Christian Medical College and Hospital, Vellore, India."

Year Founded in USA 1948
Income for Overseas Mins $1,089,057

Gifts-in-Kind $184,153
Personnel:
Home ministry & office staff in USA 5

Venture International

(800)421-2159 **Fax: (480)730-2720**
E-Mail: info@ventureftf.org
Web: www.fni.net/vme
P.O. Box 7396, Tempe, AZ 85281
Mr. Leonard H. Rodgers, President

An interdenominational service agency of evangelical tradition engaged in support of nurturing families via local churches, childrens programs, development, disability assistance programs, medical work and relief aid. Changed name from Venture Middle East in 2000.

Purpose: "...serves as a bridge between those in need and those who want to help God's people in the Middle East; empowering and enhancing their work through strategic partnerships, emergency relief, small business creation and people development."

Year Founded in USA 1986
Income for Overseas Mins $546,673
Gifts-in-Kind $223,365
Fully Supported USA Personnel Overseas:
Expecting to serve more than 4 years 2
Expecting to serve 1 to 4 years 2
Nonresidential mission personnel 1
Other Personnel:
Non-USA serving in own/other country 5
Bivocational/Tentmaker from USA 6
Home ministry & office staff in USA 5
Countries: Central Asia 1, Egypt 1, Israel 1, Jordan 1

Village Ministries International, Inc.

(830)997-7111 **Fax: (830)997-0952**
E-Mail: information@villageministries.org
Web: www.villageministries.org
P.O. Box 873, Fredericksburg, TX 78624
Rev. Dan R. Hawkins, Chief Exec. Officer

A nondenominational service agency of independent and evangelical tradition engaged in theological education, evangelism and short-term programs.

Purpose: "...to take the Gospel and the teaching of God's Word to people...in villages and remote cities that ordinarily are not exposed to missionary activity or Bible teaching."

Year Founded in USA 1990
Income for Overseas Mins $172,000
Personnel:
Non-USA serving in own/other country 40
Short-Term less than 1 year from USA 26
Home ministry & office staff in USA 4
Countries: Belarus, Ghana, Mexico, Nigeria, Sri Lanka

Vineyard International Consortium

(714)765-5530 **Fax: (714)765-5535**
E-Mail: info@vineyardinternational.org
Web: www.vineyardinternational.org
P.O. Box 17580, Anaheim, CA 92817
Mr. Bob Fulton, Intl. Coordinator

A consortium of 8 different associations of charismatic and evangelical tradition in Canada, England, the Netherlands, New Zealand, South Africa, Sweden, Switzerland and the U.S., engaged in church planting, evangelism, leadership development and support of national churches. There are 380 Vineyard Churches outside the USA in 52 countries. The 8 associations oversee the work being done in the different areas of the world.

Purpose: "...to equip the saints for the advancement of the Kingdom of God through evangelizing and church planting."

Year Founded in USA 1982
Income for Overseas Mins .... NA

Virginia Mennonite Board of Missions

(540)434-9727 **Fax: (540)434-7627**
E-Mail: vmbm1@aol.com
901 Parkwood Dr., Harrisonburg, VA 22801
Mr. David D. Yoder, President

A denominational sending agency of Mennonite tradition engaged in leadership development, theological education, evangelism, humantarian services and support of national church outreach.

Purpose: "...[to] meet human needs, extend an invitation to a relationship with Jesus Christ, promote communities of faith that continue God's work in the world..."

Year Founded in USA 1919
Income for Overseas Mins $800,000
Gifts-in-Kind $10,000
Fully Supported USA Personnel Overseas:
Expecting to serve more than 4 years 6
Expecting to serve 1 to 4 years 8
Nonresidential mission personnel 2
Other Personnel:
Non-USA serving in own/other country 3
Bivocational/Tentmaker from USA 2
Home ministry & office staff in USA 15
Countries: Albania 4, Italy 4, Jamaica 2, Trinidad & Tobg 4

Voice of the Martyrs, The

(918)337-8015 **Fax: (918)337-9287**
E-Mail: thevoice@vom-usa.org
Web: www.persecution.com
P.O. Box 443, Bartlesville, OK 74005-0443
Rev. Richard Wurmbrand, Founder & President
Mr. Tom White, USA Director

An interdenominational support agency of evangelical tradition engaged in literature distribution, Bible distribution and evangelism. Statistical information from 1996.

Year Founded in USA 1967
Income for Overseas Mins $1,355,466

Walk Thru The Bible Ministries

(770)458-9300 **Fax: (770)454-9313**
Web: www.walkthru.com
4201 N. Peachtree Rd., Atlanta, GA 30341-1207
Mr. Terry Sparks, VP of Int'l. Division
Mr. William Watson, Exec. VP

A transdenominational service agency of evangelical tradition engaged in Christian education, leadership development, literature distribution, literature production and video/film production/distribution. Personnel information from 1996.

Purpose: "...to contribute to the spiritual growth of Christians worldwide through Bible teaching, tools, and training."

Year Founded in USA 1977
Income for Overseas Mins $285,672
Personnel:
Non-USA serving in own/other country .. 1522
Short-Term less than 1 year from USA 110
Home ministry & office staff in USA 85
Countries: Argentina, Australia, Belarus, Brazil, Costa Rica, Cote d'Ivoire, Ecuador, El Salvador, Estonia, France, Germany, Greece, Guatemala, Guyana, Hong Kong, India, Indonesia, Kazakhstan, Kenya, Korea-S, Kyrgyzstan, Latvia, Lithuania, Mali, Mexico, Moldava, Netherlands, New Zealand, Nigeria, Norway, Papua New Guinea, Philippines, Poland, Romania, Russia, Senegal, Singapore, S Africa, Spain, Sweden, Taiwan, Tajikistan, Tanzania, Thailand, Uganda, Ukraine, UK, Uruguay, Uzbekistan, Zambia

WEC International

(215)646-2322
E-Mail: jjraymo@aol.com
P.O. Box 1707, 709 Pennsylvania Ave.
Fort Washington, PA 19034-8707
Mr. James Raymo, U.S.A. Director

An interdenominational sending agency of evangelical tradition engaged in evangelism, childcare/orphanage programs, church planting, medical work, support of national churches and missionary training.

Purpose: "...[to] see viable churches formed among unreached peoples and to disciple, train and equip believers for evangelism, church planting and involvement in worldwide mission..."

Year Founded in USA 1939
Income for Overseas Mins $2,744,054
Fully Supported USA Personnel Overseas:
Expecting to serve more than 4 years 156
Expecting to serve 1 to 4 years 9
Other Personnel:
Non-USA serving in own/other country 1
Home ministry & office staff in USA 35
Countries: Asia 46, Brazil 4, Chad 2, Cote d'Ivoire 13, France 4, Gambia 3, Germany 1, Ghana 2, Guinea 1, Guinea Bissau 3, Indonesia 8, Italy 5, Mexico 14, Nepal 2, New Zealand 2, Romania 1, Russia 3, Senegal 2, S Africa 1, Spain 5, Thailand 8, UK 7, Unspecified 25, Venezuela 3

Wesleyan World Missions

(317)570-5160 **Fax: (317)570-5256**
E-Mail: WWM@wesleyan.org
Web: www.wesleyan.org/wwm/wmission.htm
P.O. Box 50434, Indianapolis, IN 46250

Dr. Donald L. Bray, Gen. Director

A denominational sending agency of Wesleyan tradition engaged in church planting, Christian education, theological education, evangelism, leadership development and support of national churches.

Purpose: "...calling Wesleyans to evangelism, church planting, leadership development, and ministries of compassion for the establishing of a flourishing international church."

Year Founded in USA 1889

Income for Overseas Mins $6,771,000

Fully Supported USA Personnel Overseas:

Expecting to serve more than 4 years 112

Other Personnel:

Non-USA serving in own/other country 39

Short-Term less than 1 year from USA 717

Home ministry & office staff in USA 19

Countries: Albania 2, Australia 4, Brazil 10, Central Asia 4, Colombia 4, Croatia 3, Czech Rep 4, Guyana 1, Haiti 9, Honduras 6, India 2, Indonesia 2, Japan 2, Kenya 2, Mexico 5, Mozambique 2, Papua New Guin 6, Peru 6, Philippines 4, Puerto Rico 4, Russia 9, S Africa 8, Suriname 4, UK 2, Zambia 7

Westminister Biblical Missions

(916)273-4673

E-Mail: Mathatas@nccn.net

Web: www.nccn.net/~wbminc

17355 Alexandra Way, Grass Valley, CA 95949

Rev. Dennis E. Roe, Gen. Secretary

A transdenominational sending agency of Presbyterian tradition engaged in theological education, literature production and support of national churches.

Year Founded in USA 1974

Income for Overseas Mins $375,000

Fully Supported USA Personnel Overseas:

Expecting to serve more than 4 years 3

Nonresidential mission personnel 2

Other Personnel:

Non-USA serving in own/other country 51

Short-Term less than 1 year from USA 4

Home ministry & office staff in USA 3

Countries: Europe 1, Korea-S 1, Pakistan 1

Wisconsin Evangelical Lutheran Synod, Bd. for World Missions

(414)256-3233 **Fax: (414)256-6480**

E-Mail: bwm@sab.wels.net

Web: www.wels.net

2929 N. Mayfair Road, Milwaukee, WI 53222

Rev. Daniel H. Koelpin, Administrator

A denominational sending board of Lutheran tradition engaged in church planting, broadcasting, theological education, literature production, support of national churches and relief aid.

Purpose: "...to make disciples throughout the world...using the gospel to win the lost for Christ and to nurture believers for lives of Christian service..."

Year Founded in USA 1955

Income for Overseas Mins $2,969,807

Fully Supported USA Personnel Overseas:

Expecting to serve more than 4 years 66

Expecting to serve 1 to 4 years 13

Other Personnel:

Short-Term less than 1 year from USA 6

Home ministry & office staff in USA 24

Countries: Albania 2, Antigua 1, Brazil 4, Bulgaria 6, Cameroon 3, Colombia 3, Cuba 1, Dominican Rep 2, Hong Kong 2, India 3, Indonesia 1, Japan 6, Malawi 10, Mexico 5, Puerto Rico 5, Russia 6, Sweden 2, Taiwan (ROC) 3, Thailand 3, Zambia 11

Witnessing Ministries of Christ

(559)226-7349 **Fax: (559)226-0558**

E-Mail: wmc@presbymin.org

4717 N. Barton Ave., Fresno, CA 93726

Rev. Philip A. Prasad, President

An interdenominational service agency of Presbyterian tradition engaged in church planting, Christian education, leadership development, literacy work and medical work. Statistical information from 1996.

Year Founded in USA 1983

Income for Overseas Mins $535,640

Personnel:

Non-USA serving in own/other country 287

Short-Term less than 1 year from USA 4

Home ministry & office staff in USA 2

Countries: India

Word of Life Fellowship

(518)532-7111 **Fax: (518)532-7421**

Web: www.wol.org

P.O. Box 600, Schroon Lake, NY 12870

Mr. Donald H. Lough, Jr., VP Intl. Mins.

A nondenominational sending agency of independent tradition engaged in evangelism, broadcasting, and youth camping in 46 countries. Statistical information from 1996.

Year Founded in USA 1940

Income for Overseas Mins $5,700,000

Fully Supported USA Personnel Overseas:

Expecting to serve more than 4 years 118

Other Personnel:

Non-USA serving in own/other country 543

Short-Term less than 1 year from USA 25

Home ministry & office staff in USA 507

Countries: Unspecified 118

Word To Russia

(916)372-4610 **Fax: (916)371-2077**

P.O. Box 1521, 1240 Merkley Ave., Suite 106, West Sacramento, CA 95691

Mr. Michael D. Lokteff, President

A nondenominational support agency of evangelical tradition engaged in audio recording/distribution, literature distribution, and radio outreach to Russian-speaking immigrants. Financial information from 1996.

Year Founded in USA 1972

Income for Overseas Mins $66,450

Personnel:

Non-USA serving in own/other country 2

Short-Term less than 1 year from USA 2

Home ministry & office staff in USA 5

World Baptist Fellowship Mission Agency

(817)274-7161 **Fax: (817)861-1992**

E-Mail: wbfraley@onramp.net

Web: www.wbfi.net

P.O. Box 13459, Arlington, TX 76094

Rev. Thomas M. Raley, Missions Director

A denominational sending agency of Baptist and fundamental tradition engaged in church planting, evangelism, funds transmission and literature distribution.

Year Founded in USA 1928

Income for Overseas Mins $4,082,797

Fully Supported USA Personnel Overseas:

Expecting to serve more than 4 years 102

Expecting to serve 1 to 4 years 28

Other Personnel:

Home ministry & office staff in USA 14

Countries: Australia 2, Belarus 2, Brazil 30, Cambodia 2, Caribbean Isls 8, Colombia 8, Ecuador 14, France 2, Guatemala 4, Honduras 8, Indonesia 5, Ireland 4, Latvia 2, Mexico 26, New Zealand 6, Singapore 2, Spain 4, Thailand 1

World Bible Translation Center

(817)595-1664 **Fax: (817)589-7013**

E-Mail: info@wbtc.com

Web: www.wbtc.com

P.O. Box 820648, Fort Worth, TX 76182

Mr. Dale Randolph, President

A nondenominational agency of evangelical tradition supporting Bible translation/ distribution in 33 languages.

Year Founded in USA 1973

Income for Overseas Mins $1,710,000

Personnel:

Non-USA serving in own/other country 80

Home ministry & office staff in USA 13

Countries: Bulgaria, China, Hungary, India, Jordan, Korea-S, Myanmar, Romania, Russia, Thailand, Ukraine, Yugoslavia

World Concern

(206)546-7201 **Fax: (206)546-7269**

E-Mail: wconcern@crista.org

Web: www.worldconcern.org

19303 Fremont Ave. North, Seattle, WA 98133

Mr. Paul Kennell, President

A nondenominational sending agency of evangelical tradition engaged in development, agricultural programs, camping programs, evangelism, providing medical supplies, medical work, support of national churches and relief and/or rehabilitation.

Purpose: "To overcome human suffering through emergency relief, rehabilitation and long-term development programs so that families and individuals can be in right relationship with God, with one another and with creation."

Year Founded in USA 1973

Income for Overseas Mins $19,339,518

Gifts-in-Kind $10,244,400

Fully Supported USA Personnel Overseas:

Expecting to serve more than 4 years 9

Expecting to serve 1 to 4 years 25

Other Personnel:
Non-USA serving in own/other country 650
Short-Term less than 1 year from USA 103
Home ministry & office staff in USA 44
Countries: Bolivia 2, Cambodia 1, Ethiopia 1, Georgia 1, Haiti 2, India 1, Kenya 8, Laos 2, Malaysia 1, Myanmar/Burma 2, Nepal 2, Peru 1, Tanzania 1, Thailand 5, Uganda 1, Uzbekistan 1, Vietnam 2

World Evangelization Research Center and Global Evangelization Movement

(804)355-1646 **Fax: (804)355-2016**
E-Mail: GEM@xc.org
Web: www.gem-werc.org
P.O. Box 6628, Richmond, VA 23230
Mr. David B. Barrett, President

A multidenominational specialized service agency initiating, promoting, publishing, and disseminating research related to all varieties of global Christian evangelization and mission.

Purpose: "...to document world Christianity and its progress in completing the Great Commission, communicate this information to the global body of Christ and advocate the unevangelized as the leading priority of world mission."

Year Founded in USA 1965
Income for Overseas Mins .... NA
Personnel:
Home ministry & office staff in USA 7

World Gospel Mission

(765)664-7331 **Fax: (765)671-7230**
E-Mail: WGM@wgm.org
Web: www.wgm.org
P.O. Box 948, Marion, IN 46952-0948
Dr. Thomas H. Hermiz, President

An interdenominational sending agency of Wesleyan and Holiness tradition engaged in church planting, aviation services, theological education, TEE, evangelism, leadership development, medical work and support of national churches.

Purpose: "...to lead men and women into a personal relationship with Christ as Savior and Lord; to gather converts into self-propagating, self-supporting and self-governing congregations; and to lead them into a lifestyle of Christian holiness..."

Year Founded in USA 1910
Income for Overseas Mins $13,287,519
Gifts-in-Kind $728,584
Fully Supported USA Personnel Overseas:
Expecting to serve more than 4 years 189
Expecting to serve 1 to 4 years 2
Other Personnel:
Non-USA serving in own/other country 10
Bivocational/Tentmaker from USA 2
Short-Term less than 1 year from USA 552
Home ministry & office staff in USA 84
Countries: Argentina 9, Bolivia 34, Haiti 2, Honduras 29, Hungary 5, India 2, Japan 4, Kenya 52, Mexico 15, Papua New Guin 8, Paraguay 5, Taiwan (ROC) 2, Tanzania 12, Uganda 4, Ukraine 6, Virgin Isls USA 2

World Harvest Mission

(215)885-1811 **Fax: (215)885-4762**
E-Mail: info@whm.org
Web: www.whm.org
100 West Ave., Suite W960, Jenkintown, PA 19046-2697
Rev. Stephen Smallman, Chief Exec. Officer

A nondenominational sending agency of evangelical tradition engaged in church planting, leadership development, medical work and renewal of the local church.

Purpose: "...[to see] local churches revived, mobilized and...sending teams of trained men and women to plant churches overseas."

Year Founded in USA 1983
Income for Overseas Mins $2,609,032
Fully Supported USA Personnel Overseas:
Expecting to serve more than 4 years 33
Expecting to serve 1 to 4 years 2
Other Personnel:
Short-Term less than 1 year from USA 150
Home ministry & office staff in USA 24
Countries: India 2, Netherlands 6, Russia 3, Spain 2, Uganda 14, UK 8

World Harvest Now, Inc.

(940)891-4400 **Fax: (940)484-6097**
E-Mail: WHN@whn.org
Web: www.whn.org
P.O. Box 911, Denton, TX 76202
Mr. Lamont Brown, President/Founder

A nondenominational sending agency of evangelical tradition engaged in church planting, evangelism, leadership development, support of national churches and missionary training.

Purpose: "…to facilitate the planting of cell group churches among the least evangelized people in or near the 10/40 Window."

Year Founded in USA 1992
Income for Overseas Mins $687,400
Gifts-in-Kind $430,000
Fully Supported USA Personnel Overseas:
Expecting to serve more than 4 years 2
Expecting to serve 1 to 4 years 7
Nonresidential mission personnel 1
Other Personnel:
Non-USA serving in own/other country 11
Bivocational/Tentmaker from USA 3
Short-Term less than 1 year from USA 2
Home ministry & office staff in USA 8
Countries: Asia 2, Central Asia 3, Russia 4

World Help

(804)525-4657 **Fax: (804)525-4727**
E-Mail: Info@worldhelp.net
Web: www.worldhelp.net
P.O. Box 501, Forest, VA 24551
Mr. Vernon Brewer, President

An interdenominational service agency of evangelical tradition engaged in Bible distribution, childcare/orphanage programs, church planting, providing medical supplies, support of national churches and relief and/or rehabilitation.

Purpose: "...to fulfill the Great Commission and the Great Commandment through partnering, training, helping and serving, especially in the unreached areas of the world."

Year Founded in USA 1992
Income for Overseas Mins $3,895,752
Gifts-in-Kind $544,725
Personnel:
Short-Term less than 1 year from USA 160
Home ministry & office staff in USA 37

World Horizons

(804)353-9155 **Fax: (804)353-9155**
E-Mail: worldhorizons@compuserve.com
Web: www.whorizons.org
P.O. Box 17721, Richmond, VA 23226
Mr. Andrew Fuller, Operations Director

A transdenominational support agency of charismatic and evangelical tradition engaged in church planting, support of national churches, mobilization for mission and short-term programs. The US arm of an international ministry with more than 300 field personnel drawn from more than 20 nations.

Year Founded in USA 1992
Income for Overseas Mins $60,000
Fully Supported USA Personnel Overseas:
Expecting to serve more than 4 years 2
Other Personnel:
Non-USA serving in own/other country 2
Short-Term less than 1 year from USA 37
Home ministry & office staff in USA 1
Countries: Morocco 1, Turkey 1

World In Need - USA

(708)524-5070 **Fax: (708)524-9119**
E-Mail: worldin@juno.com
237 Harrison, Oak Park, IL 60304

An interdenominational support agency of evangelical tradition engaged in funds transmission, development, missions information service, mobilization for mission, relief and/or rehabilitation and support of national workers.

Year Founded in USA 1992
Income for Overseas Mins $100,549
Personnel:
Short-Term less than 1 year from USA 2
Home ministry & office staff in USA 2

World Indigenous Missions

(830)629-0863 **Fax: (830)629-0357**
E-Mail: wimplant@sat.net
Web: www.worldim.com/
P.O. Box 310627, New Braunfels, TX 78131
Mr. Charles E. Hall, President

A nondenominational sending agency of charismatic tradition engaged in church planting, evangelism and short-term programs.

Year Founded in USA 1981
Income for Overseas Mins $1,196,104
Fully Supported USA Personnel Overseas:
Expecting to serve more than 4 years 45

Expecting to serve 1 to 4 years 2
Nonresidential mission personnel 5

Other Personnel:

Bivocational/Tentmaker from USA 4
Short-Term less than 1 year from USA 30
Home ministry & office staff in USA 9

Countries: Bolivia 4, Hungary 2, India 1, Indonesia 4, Mexico 28, Russia 6, Spain 2

World Mission Associates

(717)898-2281 Fax: (717)898-3993
E-Mail: wmausa@msn.com
Web: www.wmausa.org
825 Darby Lane, Lancaster, PA 17601-2009
Rev. Glenn J. Schwartz, Exec. Director

A nondenominational service agency of evangelical tradition engaged in national church support and mobilization for mission through seminars, training, and video production/distribution.

Year Founded in USA 1983
Income for Overseas Mins $53,850
Fully Supported USA Personnel Overseas:
Expecting to serve more than 4 years 2
Other Personnel:
Home ministry & office staff in USA 4
Countries: Kenya 2

World Mission Prayer League Inc.

(612)871-6843 Fax: (612)871-6844
E-Mail: WMPL@wmpl.org
Web: www.wmpl.org
232 Clifton Ave., Minneapolis, MN 55403-3497
Rev. Charles Lindquist, Gen. Director

A denominational sending agency of Lutheran tradition engaged in church planting, development, TEE, evangelism, medical work and support of national churches.

Year Founded in USA 1937
Income for Overseas Mins $2,446,619
Fully Supported USA Personnel Overseas:
Expecting to serve more than 4 years 55
Expecting to serve 1 to 4 years 13
Other Personnel:
Non-USA serving in own/other country 2
Home ministry & office staff in USA 13
Countries: Bangladesh 7, Bolivia 9, Ecuador 10, Eritrea 1, India 2, Kenya 9, Mexico 7, Mongolia 2, Nepal 5, Pakistan 5, Peru 5, Philippines 4, Romania 2

World Missionary Press, Inc.

(219)831-2111 Fax: (219)831-2161
E-Mail: mailroom@wmpress.org
Web: www.wmpress.org
P.O. Box 120, New Paris, IN 46553
Mr. Jay E. Benson, President

A nondenominational specialized agency of evangelical tradition engaged in production/distribution of free topical Scripture and Bible study booklets in more than 300 languages.

Year Founded in USA 1961
Income for Overseas Mins $1,650,532
Personnel:
Home ministry & office staff in USA 38

World Missions Far Corners, Inc.

(562)402-4400 Fax: (562)402-9039
Web: www.wmfcinc.com
P.O. Box 2611, Long Beach, CA 90801
Dr. J. Leonard Bell, President/Director

A nondenominational mission organization of evangelical tradition engaged in medical work, church planting, evangelism, literature distribution, relief and training carried out by national workers in 21 countries on five continents.

Year Founded in USA 1958
Income for Overseas Mins $1,455,864
Fully Supported USA Personnel Overseas:
Expecting to serve more than 4 years 36
Other Personnel:
Non-USA serving in own/other country 59
Countries: Bangladesh 2, China (PRC) 4, Cote d'Ivoire 2, Cuba 2, Ecuador 6, Mexico 8, Peru 6, S Africa 1, UK 2, Vietnam 3

World Missions Fellowship

(503)655-5152 Fax: (503)557-2338
E-Mail: wmf@teleport.com
P.O. Box 5148, Oregon City, OR 97045
Mr. George A. Bradley, Gen. Director

A nondenominational sending agency of evangelical and independent tradition engaged in church planting, camping programs and childcare/orphanage programs.

Year Founded in USA 1946
Income for Overseas Mins $257,912

Fully Supported USA Personnel Overseas:
Expecting to serve more than 4 years 7
Nonresidential mission personnel 14
Other Personnel:
Non-USA serving in own/other country 9
Short-Term less than 1 year from USA 35
Home ministry & office staff in USA 3
Countries: Austria 2, Ireland 5

World Neighbors

(405)752-9700 **Fax: (405)752-9393**
E-Mail: info@wn.org
Web: www.wn.org
4127 NW 122nd St., Oklahoma City, OK 73120
Mr. Ron Burkard, Exec. Director

A nondenominational service agency engaged in development and agricultural programs.
Year Founded in USA 1951
Income for Overseas Mins $2,795,072
Fully Supported USA Personnel Overseas:
Expecting to serve more than 4 years 4
Countries: Asia 2, Latin America 2

World Opportunities Intl.

(323)466-7187 **Fax: (323)871-1546**
E-Mail: worldop@msn.com
Web: www.childrenscharities.org/helpthechildren.html
1415 Cahuenga Blvd., Hollywood, CA 90028
Dr. Roy B. McKeown, President

An interdenominational service agency of evangelical tradition engaged in relief, childcare/orphanage programs, disability assistance programs, literature distribution, providing medical supplies and services for other agencies. Overseas income from 1992.
Year Founded in USA 1961
Income for Overseas Mins $1,000,000
Gifts-in-Kind $871,000
Personnel:
Home ministry & office staff in USA 20

World Outreach Ministries

(770)424-1545 **Fax: (770)424-1545**
Web: www.worldoutreach.org
P.O. Box B, Marietta, GA 30061
Mr. Jason R. Peebles, Founder/President

An interdenominational agency of charismatic and evangelical tradition performing a variety of home office duties for independent missionaries engaged in church planting, evangelism and missionary training.
Year Founded in USA 1979
Income for Overseas Mins $1,200,000

World Partners USA

(219)747-2027 **Fax: (219)747-5331**
E-Mail: WorldPartners@compuserve.com
P.O. Box 9127, Fort Wayne, IN 46899-9127
Rev. David Mann, Director

A denominational sending agency of evangelical tradition engaged in church planting, agricultural programs, camping programs, extension education, support of national churches and Bible translation.
Purpose: "...[to] communicate the gospel to under-evangelized peoples and establish the converts...in a mature national church in a continuing process of world outreach..."
Year Founded in USA 1969
Income for Overseas Mins $3,391,858
Fully Supported USA Personnel Overseas:
Expecting to serve more than 4 years 74
Nonresidential mission personnel 3
Other Personnel:
Bivocational/Tentmaker from USA 2
Short-Term less than 1 year from USA 150
Home ministry & office staff in USA 8
Countries: Asia 6, Brazil 4, Chad 2, China (PRC) 2, Cyprus 2, Dominican Rep 4, Ecuador 12, France 2, Guinea Bissau 9, Indonesia 2, Jamaica 2, Nigeria 3, Portugal 4, Russia 6, Spain 9, Thailand 3, Vietnam 2

World Radio Missionary Flwshp.
See: HCJB World Radio

World Reach, Inc.

(205)979-2400 **Fax: (205)979-6289**
E-Mail: 70451.236@compuserve.com
Web: www.world-reach.org
P.O. Box 26155, Birmingham, AL 35260-6155
Rev. Timothy Q. Prewitt, Gen. Director

An interdenominational sending agency of evangelical tradition engaged in church planting, correspondence courses, evangelism, leadership development, support of national churches and short-term programs.
Purpose: "...targeting unreached peoples in both

remote and urban areas for the purpose of evangelizing and discipling."

Year Founded in USA 1982

Income for Overseas Mins $933,825

Fully Supported USA Personnel Overseas:

Expecting to serve more than 4 years 11

Expecting to serve 1 to 4 years 1

Nonresidential mission personnel 4

Other Personnel:

Non-USA serving in own/other country 23

Short-Term less than 1 year from USA 8

Home ministry & office staff in USA 5

Countries: El Salvador 3, Honduras 6, Romania 1, Russia 2

World Relief Corporation

(630)665-0235 **Fax: (630)665-4473**

E-Mail: WorldRelief@wr.org

Web: www.wr.org

P.O. Box WRC, Wheaton, IL 60189

Dr. Clive Calver, President

An interdenominational service agency of evangelical tradition engaged in relief and/or rehabilitation, development and technical assistance. Ongoing programs in 14 countries.

Purpose: "...to work with the church in alleviating human suffering worldwide in the name of Christ."

Year Founded in USA 1944

Income for Overseas Mins $5,690,249

Fully Supported USA Personnel Overseas:

Expecting to serve more than 4 years 4

Expecting to serve 1 to 4 years 6

Nonresidential mission personnel 7

Other Personnel:

Non-USA serving in own/other country 4

Home ministry & office staff in USA 544

Countries: Cambodia 4, Mozambique 3, Nicaragua 1, Pakistan 1, Rwanda 1

World Servants

(612)866-0010 **Fax: (612)866-0078**

E-Mail: LordYes@worldservants.org

Web: www.worldservants.org

7130 Portland Ave. S., Richfield, MN 55423

Rev. Timothy N. Gibson, Exec. Director

A nondenominational specialized agency of evangelical tradition engaged in short-term support of national churches, cross-cultural orientation, and mobilization and training for individuals, groups, and churches for mission.

Purpose: "To mobilize a global network of people who will impact the world for Jesus Christ through responding to physical and spiritual need."

Year Founded in USA 1986

Income for Overseas Mins $518,916

Gifts-in-Kind $10,000

Personnel:

Short-Term less than 1 year from USA 2000

Home ministry & office staff in USA 16

World Team

(215)491-4900 **Fax: (215)491-4910**

E-Mail: WT-USA@worldteam.org

Web: www.worldteam.org

1431 Stuckert Rd., Warrington, PA 18976

Rev. Lee Maliska, USA Director

Rev. Albert Ehmann, Intl. President

A nondenominational sending agency of evangelical tradition engaged in church planting, evangelism, leadership development, support of national churches, mobilization for mission and missionary training. Statistical information from 1996.

Year Founded in USA 1928

Income for Overseas Mins $6,036,455

Fully Supported USA Personnel Overseas:

Expecting to serve more than 4 years 174

Expecting to serve 1 to 4 years 1

Other Personnel:

Non-USA serving in own/other country 56

Bivocational/Tentmaker from USA 7

Home ministry & office staff in USA 19

Countries: Brazil 12, Cameroon 17, Chile 5, Dominican Rep 4, Europe-E 4, France 12, Guadeloupe 4, Haiti 9, Indonesia 24, Italy 4, Mexico 1, Peru 10, Philippines 18, Russia 14, Spain 15, St Vincent 2, Suriname 9, Trinidad & Tobg 7, UK 4

World Thrust International, Inc.

(770)923-5215 **Fax: (770)923-3933**

E-Mail: wthrustint@aol.com

Web: www.worldthrust.com

3545 Cruse Rd., Suite 309B, Lawrenceville, GA 30044

Dr. Bill H. Boerop, President

A nondenominational support agency of evangelical tradition engaged in mobilization for mission and leadership development with seminars, conferences or trips to more than 40 countries.

Purpose: "...to serve...as a catalyst to help mobilize the local church toward a more effective involvement in the evangelization of the world."

Year Founded in USA 1984
Income for Overseas Mins $40,000
Personnel:
Short-Term less than 1 year from USA 3
Home ministry & office staff in USA 3

World Vision Inc.

(253)815-1000 Fax: (253)815-3343
Web: www.worldvision.org
34834 Weyerhaeuser Way South, Federal Way, WA 98001
Mr. Richard E. Stearns, President

An interdenominational service agency of evangelical tradition engaged in development, agricultural programs, childcare/orphanage programs, evangelism, funds transmission and relief and/or rehabilitation.

Purpose: "...working with the poor and oppressed to promote human transformation, seek justice and bear witness to the good news of the Kingdom of God."

Year Founded in USA 1950
Income for Overseas Mins $233,391,000
Gifts-in-Kind $111,971,000
Fully Supported USA Personnel Overseas:
Expecting to serve more than 4 years 13
Expecting to serve 1 to 4 years 33
Other Personnel:
Home ministry & office staff in USA 556

Countries: Albania 1, Armenia 1, Asia 2, Azerbaijan 2, Bosnia 5, Burundi 3, Cambodia 6, Georgia 1, Honduras 1, Indonesia 2, Laos 1, Liberia 1, Mali 1, Mauritania 2, Mongolia 1, Mozambique 8, Myanmar/Burma 1, Niger 1, Senegal 1, Sierra Leone 1, Sudan 1, Vietnam 2, Yugoslavia 1

World Vision International

(626)303-8811 Fax: (626)301-7786
Web: http://www.wvi.org
800 W. Chestnut Ave., Monrovia, CA 91016-3198
Dean R. Hirsch, International President

The international coordination office for the regional and national offices and other entities of the World Vision Partnership engaged in childcare/orphanage programs, development, evangelism, leadership development and training. North American personnel serving overseas, income for overseas ministries, and countries of activity included in World Vision (USA) and World Vision Canada.

Purpose: "...working with the poor and oppressed to promote human transformation, seek justice and bear witness to the good news of the Kingdom of God."

Year Founded in USA 1978
Income for Overseas Mins .... NA
Personnel:
Home ministry & office staff in USA 130

World Witness, the Board of Foreign Missions of the Associate Reformed Presbyterian Church

(864)233-5226 Fax: (864)233-5326
E-Mail: WorldWitness@worldwitness.org
Web: www.worldwitness.org
1 Cleveland St., Suite 220, Greenville, SC 29601
Mr. John E. Mariner, Exec. Director

A denominational sending agency of Reformed and Presbyterian tradition engaged in church planting, TEE, evangelism, medical work, support of national workers and youth programs.

Purpose: "To glorify God through Jesus Christ through evangelism among unreached peoples, urban church planting and a demonstration of the compassion of Jesus Christ..."

Year Founded in USA 1876
Income for Overseas Mins $2,598,124
Gifts-in-Kind $50,230
Fully Supported USA Personnel Overseas:
Expecting to serve more than 4 years 35
Nonresidential mission personnel 4
Other Personnel:
Non-USA serving in own/other country 450
Home ministry & office staff in USA 7

Countries: Asia 4, Germany 6, Mexico 9, Pakistan 10, Russia 4, Turkey 2

World-Wide Missions

(909)793-2009 **Fax: (909)793-6880**
E-Mail: wwmiss@gte.net
P.O. Box 2300, Redlands, CA 92373
Rev. Fred M. Johnson, Exec. Director

An interdenominational support agency of evangelical tradition engaged in support of national workers, childcare/orphanage programs, Christian education, evangelism, medical work and relief aid.

Year Founded in USA 1950
Income for Overseas Mins $560,000
Gifts-in-Kind $5,600
Fully Supported USA Personnel Overseas:
Expecting to serve 1 to 4 years 4
Nonresidential mission personnel 9
Other Personnel:
Non-USA serving in own/other country 267
Home ministry & office staff in USA 3
Countries: Bolivia, Brazil 4, Cameroon, Chile, Colombia, Congo/Zaire, Egypt, El Salvador, Guatemala, Haiti, Honduras, India, Kenya, Korea-S, Liberia, Malawi, Mexico, Nepal, Nigeria, Papua New Guinea, Paraguay, Philippines, Syria, Taiwan, Turkey

Worldwide Discipleship Assoc.

(770)460-1337 **Fax: (770)460-1339**
E-Mail: Headquarters@wdausa.org
110 Carnegie Place #100, Fayetteville, GA 30214
Mr. Bob Dukes, President

An interdenominational support agency of evangelical tradition engaged in training, evangelism and missions information service. Statistical information from 1996.

Year Founded in USA 1974
Income for Overseas Mins $134,126
Fully Supported USA Personnel Overseas:
Expecting to serve more than 4 years 4
Nonresidential mission personnel 2
Other Personnel:
Short-Term less than 1 year from USA 18
Home ministry & office staff in USA 8
Countries: Korea-S 3, Romania 1

Wycliffe Associates USA

(714)639-9950 **Fax: (714)771-5262**
E-Mail: wa@wycliffe.org
Web: www.wycliffeassociates.org
P.O. Box 2000, Orange, CA 92859
Mr. Martin Huyett, President

A nondenominational service agency of evangelical tradition engaged in short-term programs, mobilization for mission, supplying equipment and technical assistance.

Purpose: "...supports Wycliffe Bible Translators through programs and services that enable God's people to become involved in Bible translation through their prayers and resources."

Year Founded in USA 1967
Income for Overseas Mins $2,959,290
Gifts-in-Kind $64,862
Fully Supported USA Personnel Overseas:
Expecting to serve 1 to 4 years 10
Nonresidential mission personnel 2
Other Personnel:
Short-Term less than 1 year from USA 7
Home ministry & office staff in USA 59
Countries: Guatemala 2, Indonesia 2, Kenya 2, Papua New Guin 2, Senegal 2

Wycliffe Bible Translators International

(972)708-7400 **Fax: (972)708-7350**
E-Mail: corporation_secretary@sil.org
Web: www.wycliffe.net
7500 W. Camp Wisdom Rd., Dallas, TX 75236
Mr. John Watters, Exec. Director

An interdenominational agency of evangelical tradition that is the international coordination center for 31 Wycliffe national sending agencies and 14 affiliates around the world. Wycliffe is engaged in Bible translation, linguistics, literacy work and other activities needed to support these primary ministries. Income and overseas personnel totals from the USA and Canada shown under Wycliffe USA and Wycliffe Canada.

Purpose: "…to integrate Scripture translation, scholarship and service so that all people will have access to God's Word in their own language."

Year Founded in USA 1934
Income for Overseas Mins .... NA

Wycliffe Bible Translators USA

(407)852-3600 **Fax: (407)852-3601**
E-Mail: hq@wycliffe.org
Web: www.wycliffe.org
P.O. Box 628200, Orlando, FL 32862-8200
Mr. Roy Peterson, Exec. Director

Mr. James Swartzentruber, Exec. V.P.

A nondenominational sending agency of evangelical and independent tradition engaged in Bible translation, linguistics, literacy work and translation work.

Purpose: "...to integrate Scripture translation, scholarship and service so that all people will have access to God's Word in their own language."

Year Founded in USA 1934

Income for Overseas Mins $83,591,000

Fully Supported USA Personnel Overseas:

Expecting to serve more than 4 years 2930

Nonresidential mission personnel 2

Other Personnel:

Short-Term less than 1 year from USA 109

Home ministry & office staff in USA 140

Countries: Africa 198, Asia 256, Australia 15, Brazil 117, Burkina Faso 32, Cameroon 135, Cen Africa Rep 5, Chad 24, Colombia 107, Congo 23, Cote d'Ivoire 69, Ethiopia 23, Europe 7, France 3, Germany 1, Ghana 22, Indonesia 185, Latin America 125, Malaysia 18, Mexico 207, Mozambique 28, New Zealand 1, Niger 33, Nigeria 20, Oceania 3, Papua New Guin 405, Peru 147, Philippines 196, Senegal 28, Solomon Isls 29, S Africa 2, Sudan 38, Suriname 27, Togo 30, UK 14, Unspecified 349, Vanuatu 8

Young Life

(719)381-1800 **Fax: (719)381-1750**

Web: www.younglife.org

P.O. Box 520, Colorado Springs, CO 80901

Mr. Denny Rydberg, President

A nondenominational sending agency of evangelical tradition engaged in evangelism, camping programs and youth programs in 40 countries. Personnel information from 1992.

Year Founded in USA 1941

Income for Overseas Mins $4,330,000

Fully Supported USA Personnel Overseas:

Expecting to serve more than 4 years 34

Expecting to serve 1 to 4 years 29

Other Personnel:

Bivocational/Tentmaker from USA 12

Short-Term less than 1 year from USA 2

Countries: Austria 15, Belgium 3, Czech Rep 4, Dominican Rep 4, Germany 17, Hungary 2, Kenya 6, Nicaragua 3, Poland 1, Russia 4, S Africa 4

Youth for Christ / USA, World Outreach Division

(303)843-9000 **Fax: (303)843-6793**

E-Mail: info@yfc.org

Web: www.yfc.org/worldoutreach

P.O. Box 228822, Denver, CO 80222

Mr. Lawrence Russell, Division Director

A nondenominational sending agency of evangelical tradition engaged in evangelism and youth programs. Statistical information from 1992.

Purpose: "...helping teens and adults from the USA find opportunities to minister to young people around the world."

Year Founded in USA 1945

Income for Overseas Mins $2,460,910

Fully Supported USA Personnel Overseas:

Expecting to serve more than 4 years 38

Expecting to serve 1 to 4 years 21

Other Personnel:

Short-Term less than 1 year from USA 1780

Home ministry & office staff in USA 9

Countries: Am Samoa 1, Austria 1, Brazil 5, Colombia 2, Cyprus 2, Ecuador 2, France 1, Kenya 2, Lebanon 2, Liberia 2, Mexico 2, Myanmar/Burma 2, Portugal 3, Singapore 3, S Africa 11, Spain 2, Sweden 1, Switzerland 8, Uganda 1, UK 4, Zimbabwe 2

Youth With A Mission (YWAM), North American Office

(503)364-3837 **Fax: (503)378-7026**

E-Mail: YWAMNAO@compuserve.com

Web: www.ywam.org

7085 Battlecreek Rd. SE, Salem, OR 97301

Mr. Peter Iliyn, N. American Regional Dir.

An interdenominational sending agency of evangelical tradition engaged in evangelism, church planting, relief aid, missionary training and youth programs. See also Mercy Ships.

Year Founded in USA 1960

Income for Overseas Mins .... NA

Fully Supported USA Personnel Overseas:

Expecting to serve more than 4 years 817

Expecting to serve 1 to 4 years 1000

Nonresidential mission personnel 15

Other Personnel:

Short-Term less than 1 year from USA ... 10057

Home ministry & office staff in USA 1267

Countries: Albania 4, Australia 56, Austria 10, Bangladesh 2, Barbados 8, Belarus 7, Belize 6, Bolivia 2, Brazil 25, Bulgaria 1, Burkina Faso 2, Cambodia 5, Chile 12, Colombia 5, Costa Rica 5, Cote d'Ivoire 1, Croatia 2, Cyprus 1, Czech Rep 3, Dominican Rep 12, Estonia 1, Fiji 5, France 7, Germany 13, Greece 1, Greenland 3, Guatemala 4, Haiti 8, Honduras 5, Hong Kong 15, Hungary 15, India 57, Indonesia 7, Israel 2, Jamaica 2, Japan 27, Kenya 6, Latvia 4, Lebanon 1, Madagascar 1, Malaysia 5, Mali 2, Mexico 38, Mozambique 4, Nepal 9, Netherlands 38, New Zealand 16, Nicaragua 2, Niger 1, N Mariana Isls 1, Norway 4, Oceania 13, Panama 2, Paraguay 1, Philippines 16, Poland 4, Puerto Rico 1, Romania 10, Russia 8, Senegal 4, Singapore 8, Slovakia 3, Solomon Isls 2, S Africa 3, Spain 9, Sweden 8, Switzerland 26, Taiwan (ROC) 5, Tanzania 1, Thailand 18, Tonga 2, Ukraine 12, UK 103, Unspecified 1078, Venezuela 3, Zambia 2, Zimbabwe 2

YUGO Ministries

(909)592-6621 Fax: (909)394-1210
E-Mail: Outreach@yugo.org
Web: http://www.yugo.org
P.O. Box 25, San Dimas, CA 91773-0025
Mr. Leonard K. Janssen, Exec. Director

A nondenominational sending agency of evangelical tradition engaged in short-term programs, church planting, evangelism and youth programs. Personnel information from 1996.

Year Founded in USA 1964
Income for Overseas Mins $231,000
Fully Supported USA Personnel Overseas:
Expecting to serve more than 4 years 13
Nonresidential mission personnel 2
Other Personnel:
Short-Term less than 1 year from USA 5
Home ministry & office staff in USA 13
Countries: Mexico 13

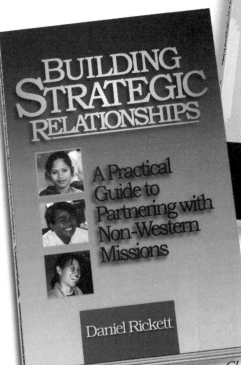

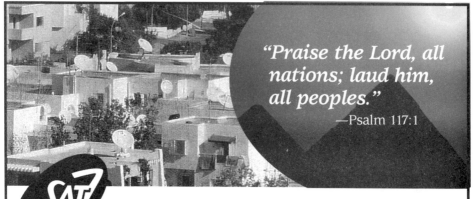

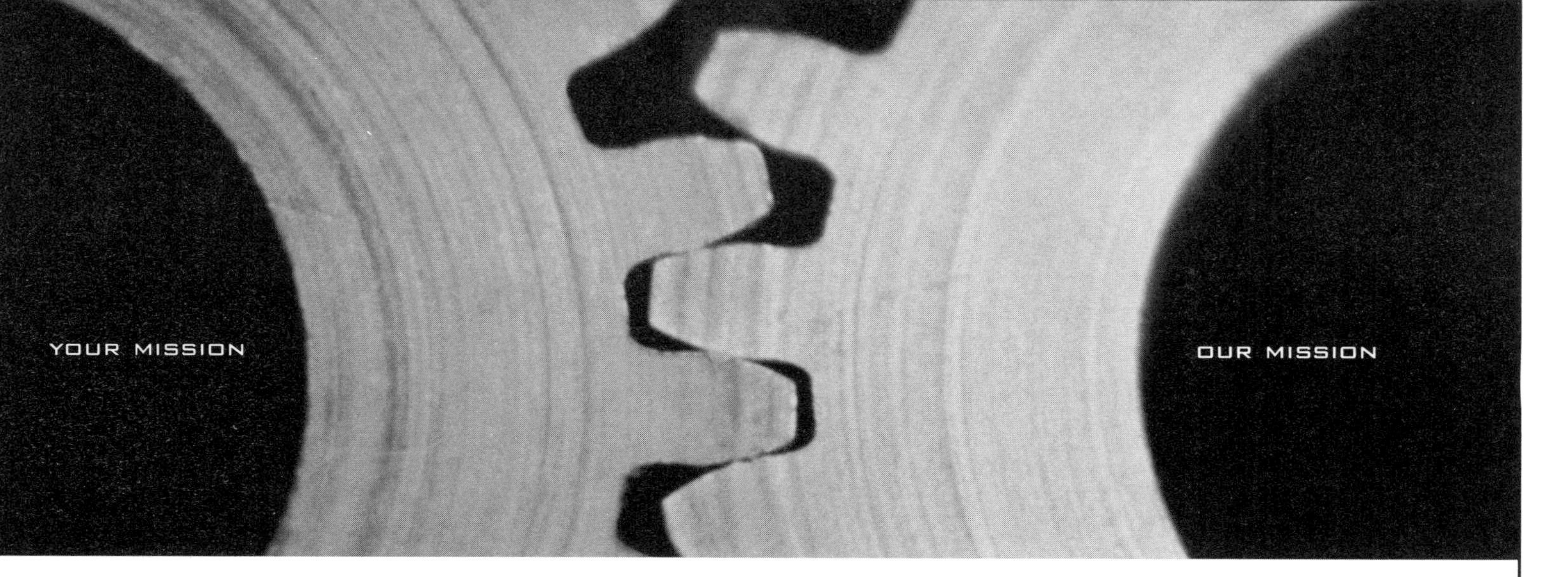
YOUR MISSION
OUR MISSION

team

Chapter 6

Indices to U.S. Protestant Agencies

Many *Handbook* users find it valuable to locate agencies by particular categories of church tradition or ministry activity. This chapter provides the user with those indices. Agency responses on the *Mission Handbook* survey questionnaire helped define the listed categories. The organizations in each category appear in alphabetical order by organization name.

Index by Church Tradition

If an agency needed more than one generic or denominational category to describe its traditional doctrinal and/or ecclesiastical stance, the agency may appear under as many as two of the given categories. We have arranged the list alphabetically by category and within each category by agency name. See question #7 of the survey questionnaire reproduced in the Appendix for the actual wording of the question and the check-off list of choices.

Index by Ministry Activity

Almost all agencies are involved in several types of ministry activities. Each agency may be listed under as many as six primary categories of activity. We asked those with more than six primary activities to indicate the six activities toward which they had committed the largest amount of resources.

We have divided the broad activities of education and evangelism into subcategories. For example, the evangelism category appears as "evangelism, mass" and "evangelism, student," and so on. See question #8 of the survey questionnaire in the Appendix for the actual wording of the question and the check-off list of activities.

Agencies sometimes have written in new categories under the "other" choice in previous surveys. Some of these may be included in the check-off list of the next survey questionnaire. Sometimes categories are dropped because of lack of use. The most used categories, however, have remained the same over the years. Three new categories added during this edition (which will appear as options on the next survey) are Association of Missions, Member Care, and Partnership Development.

Adventist

Advent Christian World Msns.
International Children's Care
Seventh-day Adventists

Anglican

Reformed Episcopal Bd Missions

Baptist

ABWE
American Baptist Association
American Baptist Churches USA
Anis Shorrosh Evan. Assoc.
Baptist Bible Fellowship Intl.
Baptist Faith Missions
Baptist General Conference
Baptist International Missions
Baptist International Outreach
Baptist Medical & Dental
Baptist Mid-Missions
Baptist Missionary Assoc.
Baptist Missions to Forgotten
Baptist World Mission
Barnabas Ministries, Inc.
Biblical Ministries Worldwide
Bridge Builders International
Carver International Missions
CBInternational
Cedar Lane Missionary Homes
Childcare International
Christ to the Nations Missions
Cooperative Baptist Fellowship
Donetsk Christian University
East-West Ministries Intl.
Evangelical Baptist Missions
Evangelize China Fellowship
Free Will Baptist, Inc.
Frontier Mission Fellowship
Fundamental Bapt. Msn Trinidad
Galcom International
General Assoc Regular Baptists
General Baptists International
Gospel Furthering Fellowship
Gospel Mission of S. America
Gospel Missionary Union
Grace Baptist Missions Intl.
Handclasp International, Inc.
Have Christ Will Travel Mins.
In Touch Mission Intl.
Independent Faith Mission
Independent Gospel Missions
International Crusades, Inc.
International Partnership Mins
International Street Kids Mins
Intl. Board of Jewish Missions
Intl. Discipleship Mission
Lott Carey Baptist Mission
Macedonia World Baptist Msns.
Macedonian Missionary Service
Maranatha Baptist Mission
Medical Missions Philippines
Mexican Christian Mission
Middle Eastern Outreach
Mission O.N.E., Inc.
Mission to the Americas
Missionary Flights Intl.
Missions to Military
National Baptist Conv. of Am.
National Baptist Conv. USA
North American Baptist Conf.
Open Door Baptist Missions
Outreach To Asia Nationals
Pan American Missions
Prakash Association USA
Priority One International
Progressive Natl Bapt Conv USA
Reformed Baptist Mission Svcs.
Romanian Missionary Society
Russian Bible Society, Inc.
Seventh Day Baptist Msny. Soc.
Society for Europe's Evang.
Southern Baptist Intl. Mission
Spiritual Growth Resources
TEAM
The Master's Harvest
Third World Baptist Missions
World Baptist Fellowship Msn.

Brethren

Brethren Church Missionary Bd.
Church of The Brethren
Church of the United Brethren
Grace Brethren Intl. Missions
India Evangelical Mission

Charismatic

Advancing Indigenous Missions
Agape Gospel Mission
AIMS
Apostolic Team Ministries Intl
Bethel Christian Ministries
Big World Ventures Inc.

Blessings International
Calvary Commission, Inc.
Calvary International
China Campus Outreach
Christ for India, Inc.
Christ for the Nations, Inc.
Christian Church of North Am.
Christian Fellowship Union
Christian Laymen's Msny Evang
Christian Ministries Intl.
Cornerstone Intl.
Covenant Celebration Church
Elim Fellowship World Missions
European Missions Outreach
Foundation For His Ministry
Global Strategy Mission Assoc.
Globe Missionary Evangelism
Good News for India
Gospel Outreach
Harvesting In Spanish
Hope for the Hungry
International Gospel Outreach
International Leadership Smnrs
International Outreach Mins.
Intl. Pentecostal Ch of Christ
Lion and Lamb Outreach
Mahesh Chavda Ministries Intl.
Marriage Ministries Intl.
Messenger Films, Inc.
Ministry of Jesus, Inc.
Ministry to Eastern Europe
Mission of Mercy
Mission Possible Foundation
Missionary Revival Crusade
Omega World Missions
Open Bible Standard Churches
ORA International
Oriental Missionary Crusade
Pass the Torch Ministries
Precious Seed Ministries
SAND Institutes International
Sentinel Group, The
Shield of Faith Ministries
The Master's Harvest
United Evangelical Churches
Vineyard Intl. Consortium
World Horizons
World Indigenous Missions
World Outreach Ministries

Christian (Restoration Movement)

ACM International
African Mission Evangelism
AMOR Ministries
Christian Chs. /Chs. of Christ
Churches of Christ
CMF International
European Evangelistic Society
Fellowship of Assoc. Medical
Good News Productions Intl.
Key Communications
Liberia Christian Mission
Mission Services Association
Missions Resource Center
Muslim Hope
Pioneer Bible Translators
TCM International
Team Expansion, Inc.

Christian/Plymouth Brethren

Brethren Assemblies
Christian Mission for the Deaf
Christian Msns. in Many Lands
Grace and Truth, Inc.
Ireland Outreach Intl., Inc.
MSC Canada
Overcomer Press, Inc.

Congregational

Armenian Missionary Assoc.
Congregational Christian Chs.
Conservative Cong. Christian
Evangelical Covenant Church
Mazahua Mission
Mission Ministries, Inc.
United Church Board World Mins

Ecumenical

American Waldensian Society
Bread for the World
Carpenter's Tools Intl.
Celebrant Singers
Christian Blind Mission Intl.
Christian Literacy Associates
Christian Ministries Intl.
Church World Service & Witness
East Gates Ministries Intl.
Floresta USA, Inc.

Friendship Mins.
Habitat for Humanity Intl.
Health Teams International
Heifer Project International
Hosanna
Interchurch Medical Assistance
International Students, Inc
Intl. Foundation for EWHA
ISOH/Impact
Japan - North American Comm
Latin America Assistance
Ludhiana Christian Medical Col
MAP International
Middle East Media - USA
Overseas Ministries Study Ctr.
Progressive Vision
United Board for Christian Ed.
United Church Board World Mins
Vellore Christian Medical Col.

Episcopal

Anglican Frontier Missions
Episcopal Church Msnry Commun.
Episcopal Church, Msny. Soc.
Episcopal World Mission
Society of St. Margaret
South American Missionary Soc.

Evangelical

ACMC
Action International Mins.
ACTS International Ministries
AD2000 & Beyond Movement
Adopt-A-People Clearinghouse
Advancing Indigenous Missions
Advancing Native Missions
Africa Inland Mission Intl.
African Bible Colleges
African Enterprise, Inc.
African Leadership
Alberto Mottesi Evang. Assoc.
Ambassadors for Christ Intl.
Ambassadors for Christ, Inc.
American Leprosy Missions
American Missionary Fellowship
American Scripture Gift Msn.
AmeriTribes
AMF International
AMG International
Anglican Frontier Missions
Anis Shorrosh Evan. Assoc.
Arab World Ministries
ARISE International
Armenian Missionary Assoc.
Artists In Christian Testimony
Asian Outreach U.S.A.
ASSIST - Aid to Special Saints
Audio Scripture Ministries
Awana Clubs International
Back to the Bible Intl.
Barnabas International
Bethany Fellowship Missions
Bible League, The
Bible Literature International
Bibles For The World
Biblical Literature Fellowship
BILD International
Billy Graham Center, The
Blossoming Rose
Bridge Builders International
Bright Hope International
Cadence International
Caleb Project
Calvary Evangelistic Mission
CAM International
Campus Crusade for Christ
Caring Partners International
Carpenter's Tools Intl.
Carver International Missions
Cedar Lane Missionary Homes
CEIFA Ministries International
Child Evangelism Fellowship
Children of Promise Int'l.
Children's Haven International
Children's Hunger Relief Fund
China Campus Outreach
China Connection
China Ministries International
China Partner
Chosen People Ministries
CHOSEN, Inc.
Christ Community Church
Christ for the City Intl.
Christ for the Lost World
Christar
Christian Aid Mission
Christian and Msny. Alliance
Christian Associates Intl.
Christian Broadcasting Network
Christian Business Men's Comte
Christian Dental Society

HCJB World Radio
Heart of God Mins.
Heart to Heart Intl. Mins.
Hellenic Ministries
Help for Christian Nationals
Helps International Ministries
Hermano Pablo Ministries
High Adventure Ministries
Holt Intl. Children's Services
HOPE Bible Mission, Inc.
Hope for the Hungry
ICI University
IFMA
Impact International
In Touch Mission Intl.
India Gospel Outreach
India Rural Evangelical Flwshp
Institute Intl Christian Comm
Institute of Chinese Studies
Institute of Hindu Studies
INTENT
InterAct Ministries
INTERCOMM
Intercristo
INTERDEV
International Aid
International Bible Institute
International Bible Society
International Child Care
International Cooperating Mins
International Family Missions
International Gospel League
International Health Services
International Messengers
International Needs - USA
International Students, Inc
International Teams, U.S.A.
International Urban Associates
InterServe/USA
InterVarsity Mission
Intl. Christian Leprosy Msn.
Intl. Christian Lit. Distrib.
Intl. Inst. Christian Studies
Iranian Christians Intl.
Island Missionary Society
Issachar Frontier Missions
JAARS, Inc.
Japanese Evangelical Msnry Soc
Japanese Evangelization Center
Jews for Jesus
Joni and Friends
Kids Alive International
Kingdom Building Ministries
Larry Jones International Mins
Latin America Assistance
Latin America Mission
Latin American Indian Mins.
Liberty Corner Mission
Liebenzell Mission USA
LIFE Ministries
Lifewater International
LIGHT International, Inc.
Link Care Center
Literacy & Evangelism Intl.
Living Water Teaching Intl.
Luis Palau Evangelistic Assoc.
Luke Society, The
Lutheran Brethren World Msns.
M/E International
MATS International
Mazahua Mission
MBMS International
Media Associates International
Medical Ambassadors Intl.
Men for Missions Intl.
Mercy Ships
Message of Life, Inc.
Messenger Films, Inc.
Mexican Medical, Inc.
Middle East Christian Outreach
Middle East Media - USA
Ministries In Action
Ministry to Eastern Europe
Mission 21 India
Mission Aides, Inc.
Mission Aviation Fellowship
Mission Ministries, Inc.
Mission O.N.E., Inc.
Mission of Mercy
Mission Possible
Mission Safety International
Mission To Unreached Peoples
Mission Training International
Mission Trng. & Resource Ctr.
Mission: Moving Mountains
Missionaire International
Missionary Athletes Intl.
Missionary Flights Intl.
Missionary Gospel Fellowship
Missionary Retreat Fellowship
Missionary Revival Crusade
Missionary Ventures Intl.

Missions Outreach Intl.
Missions To Japan, Inc.
MMS Aviation
Moody Institute of Science
Morelli Ministries Intl.
Mustard Seed, Inc.
Narramore Christian Foundation
National Religious Broadcaster
Navigators, The
NEED, Inc.
Network of Intl Christian Schs
New Hope International
New Life League International
No Greater Love Ministries
OC International, Inc.
OMF International
OMS Intl., Inc.
On The Go Ministries
Open Air Campaigners
Open Doors with Brother Andrew
Operation Blessing Intl.
Operation Mobilization
Overseas Council Intl.
Overseas Ministries Study Ctr.
Overseas Radio & Television
Pan American Missions
Paraclete Mission Group, Inc.
Partners International
People International
Peoples Mission International
Peter Deyneka Russian Mins.
Pioneer Clubs
Pioneers
Pocket Testament League
Presb. Order for World Evang.
Priority One International
Project AmaZon
Project Care
Project Mercy, Inc.
Project Partner with Christ
Providence Mission Homes, Inc.
Ramabai Mukti Mission
Ramesh Richard Evangelism
Ravi Zacharias Int. Mins.
RBC Ministries
Reach Ministries International
Reciprocal Ministries Intl.
Red Sea Team International
Rio Grande Bible Institute
Ripe for Harvest, Inc.
Samaritan's Purse
SAND Institutes International
SAT-7 North America
Scripture Union, USA
SEND International
Sentinel Group, The
Share International
Shield of Faith Ministries
Shield of Faith Mission Intl.
SIM USA
Slavic Gospel Association
Slavic Missionary Service
Son Shine Ministries Intl.
Source of Light Ministries
South America Mission
Sowers International, The
Spanish World Gospel Mission
Spiritual Overseers Service
STEER, Inc.
STEM Ministries
Strategic Ventures Network
TEAM
Teen Missions International
The Master's Mission, Inc.
TMA Ministries
Touch the World Ministries
Training Evangelistic Leadership
Trans World Missions
Trans World Radio
Tribes and Nations Outreach
Turkish World Outreach
UFM International
United World Mission
VELA Ministries International
Venture Middle East
Village Ministries Intl.
Vineyard Intl. Consortium
Voice of the Martyrs, The
Walk Thru The Bible Ministries
WEC International
Word To Russia
World Bible Translation Center
World Concern
World Harvest Mission
World Harvest Now
World Help
World Horizons
World In Need - USA
World Mission Associates
World Missionary Press, Inc.
World Missions Far Corners
World Missions Fellowship

World Neighbors
World Opportunities Intl.
World Outreach Ministries
World Partners USA
World Reach, Inc.
World Relief Corporation
World Servants
World Team
World Thrust Int.
World Vision Inc.
World Vision International
Worldwide Discipleship Assoc.
Wycliffe Associates USA
Wycliffe Bible Translators
Young Life
Youth for Christ / USA
Youth With A Mission (YWAM)
YUGO Ministries

Friends

Central Yearly Mtg. of Friends
Evangelical Friends Mission
Friends Church Southwest
Friends United Meeting

Fundamental

Baptist International Missions
Baptist International Outreach
Baptist Mid-Missions
Baptist World Mission
Berean Mission, Inc.
Brazil Gospel Fellowship Msn.
Christian Fellowship Union
Final Frontiers Foundation
FOM
Fundamental Bapt. Msn Trinidad
Good Shepherd Ministries
Gospel Fellowship Association
Gospel Mission of S. America
Helps International Ministries
India National Inland Mission
International Partnership Mins
Intl. Discipleship Mission
Missionary Athletes Intl.
Missionary TECH Team
New Tribes Mission
Open Bible Ministries
Open Door Baptist Missions
Pilgrim Fellowship, Inc.
Project Christ International
Russian Bible Society, Inc.
Source of Light Ministries
Spanish World Gospel Mission
TAM-ICCC
Things To Come Mission, Inc.
Third World Baptist Missions
World Baptist Fellowship Msn.

Holiness

Allegheny Wesleyan Meth. Msns.
Church of God (Anderson, IN)
Church of the Nazarene
Congregational Holiness Church
Evangelical Bible Mission
Evangelistic Faith Missions
Free Gospel Church Msns. Dept.
Heart of God Mins.
Intl. Pentecostal Holiness Ch.
OMS Intl., Inc.
Pentecostal Free Will Bapt.Ch.
Pillar of Fire Missions Intl.
World Gospel Mission

Independent

American Tract Society
Aurora Mission, Inc.
Barnabas Ministries, Inc.
BCM International
Berean Mission, Inc.
Bethany Missionary Association
Biblical Ministries Worldwide
Chosen People Ministries
Christ to the Nations Missions
Christian Union Mission
Church Missions Link
Church of God (Holiness) Msn.
David Livingstone Kure Fndtn
Evangelical Baptist Missions
Fellowship International Msn.
Final Frontiers Foundation
Galcom International
Global Outreach Mission
Grand Old Gospel Fellowship
Have Christ Will Travel Mins.
Independent Gospel Missions
Intl. Board of Jewish Missions
Mailbox Club International
Mexican Border Missions
Missions to Military
Mutual Faith Ministries Intl.
New Tribes Mission

Lutheran

Mennonite

Methodist

Pentecostal

Presbyterian

Presb. Evangelistic Fellowship
Presbyterian Church (USA)
Presbyterian Missionary Union
Reformed Church In America
Spiritual Growth Resources
Westminister Biblical Missions
Witnessing Mins. of Christ
World Witness

Reformed

Christian Reformed Relief Comm
Christian Reformed World Msns.
Church Planting International
Cities for Christ Worldwide
Evangelical Presbyterian Ch.
International Outreach Mins.
LOGOI/FLET
Ministries In Action
Orthodox Presbyterian Church
Outreach, Inc.
Presb. Evangelistic Fellowship
Prison Mission Association
Reformation Translation Fellowship
Reformed Church In America
Reformed Presbyterian Church
World Witness

Wesleyan

Bible Missionary Church
Brethren in Christ World Msns.
China Outreach Ministries
Congregational Methodist Ch.
Cornerstone Intl.
Evangelical Congregational Ch.
Evangelistic Faith Missions
Free Methodist World Missions
GO International
Harvest Intl. Christian Outrch
International Gospel Outreach
Primitive Methodist Church
Salvation Army, U.S.A.
Wesleyan World Missions
World Gospel Mission

Agricultural Programs

China Connection
Christian Blind Mission Intl.
Church World Service & Witness
ECHO
Emmanuel Intl. Mission (U.S.)
Equip, Inc.
FARMS International, Inc.
Floresta USA, Inc.
General Baptists International
Heifer Project International
Latin American Indian Mins.
Lifewater International
Lott Carey Baptist Mission
Lutheran World Relief
Mazahua Mission
Medical Ambassadors Intl.
Mennonite Central Committee
Ministry of Jesus, Inc.
Mission To Unreached Peoples
Mission: Moving Mountains
Prakash Association USA
Project Mercy, Inc.
Red Sea Team International
SAND Institutes International
Self-Help Foundation
STEER, Inc.
World Concern
World Neighbors
World Partners USA
World Vision Inc.

Association of Missions

EFMA
FOM
IFMA
TAM-ICCC

Audio Recording/Distribution

Anis Shorrosh Evan. Assoc.
Assemblies of God
Audio Scripture Ministries
Back to the Bible Intl.
Celebrant Singers
Derek Prince Ministries, Intl.
East Gates Ministries Intl.
Emmaus Road, International
European Missions Outreach
Free Will Baptist, Inc.
Friendship International
Gospel Recordings

Aviation Services

Bible Distribution

Outreach To Asia Nationals
Pentecostal Church of God
Pioneer Bible Translators
Pocket Testament League
Prakash Association USA
Presbyterian Missionary Union
Progressive Natl Bapt Conv USA
Project Christ International
Red Sea Team International
Ripe for Harvest, Inc.
Romanian Mission of Chicago
Russian Bible Society, Inc.
Slavic Gospel Association
Society for Europe's Evang.
Spanish World Gospel Mission
STEM Ministries
Third World Baptist Missions
Trans World Missions
Tribes and Nations Outreach
Turkish World Outreach
Voice of the Martyrs, The
World Bible Translation Center
World Help

Broadcasting, Radio and/or TV

African Bible Colleges
Alberto Mottesi Evang. Assoc.
Anis Shorrosh Evan. Assoc.
Arab World Ministries
Asian Outreach U.S.A.
Assemblies of God
Back to the Bible Intl.
Baptist International Missions
Calvary Evangelistic Mission
CAM International
China Outreach Ministries
Christian Aid Mission
Christian and Msny. Alliance
Christian Broadcasting Network
Christian Church of North Am.
Congregational Methodist Ch.
Correll Missionary Ministries
Derek Prince Ministries, Intl.
European Christian Mission
Evangelistic Faith Missions
Far East Broadcasting Company
Friends of Israel Gospel Min.
Global Outreach Mission
Go Ye Fellowship
Good News Productions Intl.
Gospel for Asia
Gospel Mission of S. America
Gospel Missionary Union
Grace and Truth, Inc.
Grand Old Gospel Fellowship
HBI Global Partners
HCJB World Radio
Hermano Pablo Ministries
High Adventure Ministries
Impact International
India Gospel Outreach
International Cooperating Mins
Intl. Board of Jewish Missions
Intl. Lutheran Laymen's League
Joni and Friends
Key Communications
Liberia Christian Mission
Luis Palau Evangelistic Assoc.
Macedonian Missionary Service
Mission Aides, Inc.
Mission to the Americas
Missionary Gospel Fellowship
Missionary Revival Crusade
Mutual Faith Ministries Intl.
National Religious Broadcaster
Open Doors with Brother Andrew
Overseas Radio & Television
Pan American Missions
Ramesh Richard Evangelism
RBC Ministries
Romanian Missionary Society
SAT-7 North America
Seventh-day Adventists
SIM USA
Slavic Missionary Service
Spanish World Gospel Mission
Trans World Radio
Wisconsin Evang. Lutheran Syn.
Word of Life Fellowship
Word To Russia

Camping Programs

Action International Mins.
Awana Clubs International
Baptist Faith Missions
BCM International
Berean Mission, Inc.
Brazil Gospel Fellowship Msn.
Calvary Commission, Inc.
Child Evangelism Fellowship
CityTeam Ministries
Congregational Methodist Ch.

Fellowship International Msn.
Friends in the West
Gospel Fellowship Association
Gospel Missionary Union
Grand Old Gospel Fellowship
Greater Europe Mission
Heart to Heart Intl. Mins.
InterAct Ministries
International Messengers
International Street Kids Mins
Latin America Assistance
Latin America Mission
Mazahua Mission
Missionary Gospel Fellowship
Navigators, The
Peter Deyneka Russian Mins.
Pioneer Clubs
Presb. Evangelistic Fellowship
Salvation Army, U.S.A.
Third World Baptist Missions
Touch the World Ministries
Word of Life Fellowship
World Concern
World Missions Fellowship
World Partners USA
Young Life

Childcare/Orphanage

All God's Children Intl.
AMG International
Apostolic Christian Church
Armenian Missionary Assoc.
Assemblies of God
Assoc of Free Lutheran Congs
Baptist Medical & Dental
Barnabas Ministries, Inc.
Bibles For The World
Brethren Church Missionary Bd.
Calvary Commission, Inc.
Calvary International
CEIFA Ministries International
Childcare International
Children of India Foundation
Children's Haven International
China Connection
Christian Dynamics
Christians In Action, Inc.
Compassion International, Inc.
Congregational Christian Chs.
Eastern European Outreach
Evangelistic Faith Missions
Evangelize China Fellowship
Food for the Hungry, Inc.
Foundation For His Ministry
Free Methodist World Missions
Friends in the West
General Baptists International
Global Fellowship
Go Ye Fellowship
Harvesting In Spanish
HBI Global Partners
Heart to Heart Intl. Mins.
Holt Intl. Children's Services
Hope for the Hungry
Independent Gospel Missions
India Evangelical Mission
India National Inland Mission
India Rural Evangelical Flwshp
International Children's Care
International Street Kids Mins
International Teams, U.S.A.
Intl. Pentecostal Ch of Christ
Kids Alive International
Larry Jones International Mins
Latin America Mission
Mission of Mercy
Mission Possible Foundation
Mustard Seed, Inc.
Mutual Faith Ministries Intl.
New Life League International
Open Air Campaigners
ORA International
Precious Seed Ministries
Project Christ International
Project Partner with Christ
Ramabai Mukti Mission
Trans World Missions
WEC International
World Help
World Missions Fellowship
World Opportunities Intl.
World Vision Inc.
World Vision International
World-Wide Missions

Children's Programs

Action International Mins.
African Methodist Episcopal Ch
Awana Clubs International
BCM International
Christ to the Nations Missions
Christian Advance Intl.

Christian Services, Inc.
Church of God in Christ, Menn.
Cornerstone Intl.
East-West Ministries Intl.
Evangelical Baptist Missions
Every Child Ministries, Inc.
FOCAS
Globe Missionary Evangelism
GO International
Heart to Heart Intl. Mins.
Holt Intl. Children's Services
International Family Missions
ISOH/Impact
Larry Jones International Mins.
Latin American Indian Mins.
Ministry to Eastern Europe
Mission 21 India
Mission Ministries, Inc.
Missionary Ventures Intl.
Open Air Campaigners
Operation Blessing Intl.
Pan American Missions
Pioneer Clubs
Progressive Natl Bapt Conv USA
Project Mercy, Inc.
Romanian Mission of Chicago
Salvation Army, U.S.A.
Samaritan's Purse
Society of St. Margaret
Sowers International, The
Touch the World Ministries
Trans World Missions
Venture Middle East

Church Construction

African Leadership
African Methodist Episcopal Ch
Assemblies of God
Baptist Medical & Dental
Brethren in Christ World Msns.
China Connection
Christ for the Nations, Inc.
Christian Aid Ministries
Christian and Msny. Alliance
Christian Church of North Am.
Christian Union Mission
Church Ministries Intl.
Church of God Apostolic Faith
Church of God World Missions
Congregational Holiness Church
Correll Missionary Ministries
East Gates Ministries Intl.
Evangel Bible Translators
Evangelical Free Church Msn.
Evangelistic Faith Missions
Free Will Baptist, Inc.
Full Gospel Evangelistic Assoc
International Cooperating Mins
Macedonian Missionary Service
Men for Missions Intl.
Mexican Border Missions
Mexican Christian Mission
Mission of Mercy
Missions Outreach Intl.
National Baptist Conv. USA
North American Baptist Conf.
Open Bible Standard Churches
Oriental Missionary Crusade
Pentecostal Church of God
Pentecostal Free Will Bapt.Ch.
Peter Deyneka Russian Mins.
Pillar of Fire Missions Intl.
Progressive Natl Bapt Conv USA
Reciprocal Ministries Intl.
Romanian Mission of Chicago
Slavic Gospel Association
STEM Ministries
Third World Baptist Missions
United Methodist Church

Church Establishing/Planting

ABWE
ACM International
Action International Mins.
Advent Christian World Msns.
Africa Inland Mission Intl.
Africa Inter-Mennonite Mission
African Mission Evangelism
Agape Gospel Mission
Allegheny Wesleyan Meth. Msns.
American Assoc. Lutheran Chs.
American Baptist Association
American Missionary Fellowship
AmeriTribes
AMG International
Anglican Frontier Missions
Apostolic Christian Church
Apostolic Team Ministries Intl
Arab World Ministries
Armenian Missionary Assoc.
Assemblies of God

Assoc of Free Lutheran Congs.
Aurora Mission, Inc.
Baptist Bible Fellowship Intl.
Baptist Faith Missions
Baptist General Conference
Baptist International Missions
Baptist International Outreach
Baptist Medical & Dental
Baptist Mid-Missions
Baptist Missionary Assoc.
Baptist Missions to Forgotten
Baptist World Mission
BCM International
Berean Mission, Inc.
Bethany Fellowship Missions
Bethel Christian Ministries
Bible League, The
Bible Missionary Church
Biblical Ministries Worldwide
BILD International
Brazil Gospel Fellowship Msn.
Brethren Assemblies
Brethren Church Missionary Bd.
Brethren in Christ World Msns.
Calvary Commission, Inc.
Calvary International
CAM International
CBInternational
Central Missionary Fellowship
Central Yearly Mtg. of Friends
Childcare International
Children of Promise Int'l.
China Campus Outreach
Christ Community Church
Christ for India, Inc.
Christ for the City Intl.
Christ to the Nations Missions
Christar
Christian Aid Mission
Christian and Msny. Alliance
Christian Associates Intl.
Christian Chs. /Chs. of Christ
Christian Church of North Am.
Christian Fellowship Union
Christian Ministries Intl.
Christian Reformed World Msns.
Christians In Action, Inc.
Church Ministries Intl.
Church of God (Anderson, IN)
Church of God (Holiness) Msn.
Church of God of Prophecy
Church of God World Missions
Church of the Nazarene
Church of the United Brethren
Church Planting International
Church Resource Ministries
Churches of Christ
Churches of God General Conf.
CMF International
Congregational Methodist Ch.
Cooperative Baptist Fellowship
Cornerstone Intl.
Covenant Celebration Church
Crossover Communications Intl.
Cumberland Presbyterian Church
Dawn Ministries
Dayspring Enterprises Intl.
Eastern European Outreach
Eastern Mennonite Missions
Elim Fellowship World Missions
European Evangelistic Society
European Missions Outreach
Evangelical Baptist Missions
Evangelical Bible Mission
Evangelical Congregational Ch.
Evangelical Covenant Church
Evangelical Free Church Msn.
Evangelical Friends Mission
Evangelical Greenhouse Mins.
Evangelical Lutheran Synod
Evangelical Mennonite Church
Evangelical Methodist Church
Evangelical Presbyterian Ch.
Evangelistic Faith Missions
Every Home for Christ
Faith Christian Fellowship
Fellowship International Msn.
Final Frontiers Foundation
Foundation For His Ministry
Foursquare Missions Intl.
Franconia Mennonite Conf.
Free Gospel Church Msns. Dept.
Free Methodist World Missions
Free Will Baptist, Inc.
Friends Church Southwest
Frontiers
Full Gospel Grace Fellowship
Fundamental Bapt. Msn Trinidad
General Baptists International
General Conf. Mennonite Church
Global Fellowship
Global Outreach Mission

Global Strategy Mission Assoc.
Globe Missionary Evangelism
GO International
Good News for India
Gospel Fellowship Association
Gospel for Asia
Gospel Furthering Fellowship
Gospel Mission of S. America
Gospel Missionary Union
Gospel Outreach
Gospel Outreach Mins. Intl.
Grace Baptist Missions Intl.
Grace Brethren Intl. Missions
Grace Ministries International
Grand Old Gospel Fellowship
Great Commission Center Intl.
Great Commission Ministries
Greater Europe Mission
Greater Grace World Outreach
Harvesting In Spanish
HBI Global Partners
Hellenic Ministries
Impact International
Independent Faith Mission
Independent Gospel Missions
India Evangelical Mission
India Gospel Outreach
India National Inland Mission
India Rural Evangelical Flwshp
InterAct Ministries
International Gospel Outreach
International Messengers
International Outreach Mins.
International Partnership Mins
International Teams, U.S.A.
InterServe/USA
Intl. Board of Jewish Missions
Intl. Pentecostal Holiness Ch.
Iranian Christians Intl.
Ireland Outreach Intl., Inc.
Island Missionary Society
Latin America Mission
Latin American Indian Mins.
Liebenzell Mission USA
LIFE Ministries
Lutheran Brethren World Msns.
Lutheran Church-Missouri Synod
M/E International
Macedonia World Baptist Msns.
Maranatha Baptist Mission
MBMS International
Mexican Border Missions
Mexican Christian Mission
Ministry of Jesus, Inc.
Mission 21 India
Mission O.N.E., Inc.
Mission Possible Foundation
Mission Soc. for United Meth.
Mission to the Americas
Mission to the World
Mission To Unreached Peoples
Mission: Moving Mountains
Missionary Gospel Fellowship
Missionary Revival Crusade
Missionary Ventures Intl.
Missions to Military
Morelli Ministries Intl.
MSC Canada
Mustard Seed, Inc.
National Baptist Conv. of Am.
National Baptist Conv. USA
New Tribes Mission
North American Baptist Conf.
Omega World Missions
OMF International
OMS Intl., Inc.
Open Bible Ministries
Open Bible Standard Churches
Open Door Baptist Missions
Operation Mobilization
ORA International
Orthodox Presbyterian Church
Outreach To Asia Nationals
Pan American Missions
Partners in Asian Missions
Partners International
Pass the Torch Ministries
Pentecostal Church of God
Pentecostal Free Will Bapt.Ch.
People International
Perimeter Ch., Global Outreach
Peter Deyneka Russian Mins.
Pilgrim Fellowship, Inc.
Pioneers
PNMC Missions
Prakash Association USA
Precious Seed Ministries
Presb. Order for World Evang.
Presbyterian Church (USA)
Primitive Methodist Church
Project AmaZon
Project Christ International

Correspondence Courses

Development, Community/Other

Engineering Ministries Intl.
Episcopal Church, Msny. Soc.
Equip, Inc.
Evangelical Covenant Church
Evangelical Lutheran Church
Faith Christian Fellowship
FARMS International, Inc.
Floresta USA, Inc.
FOCAS
Food for the Hungry, Inc.
For Haiti with Love Inc.
Friends United Meeting
General Conf. Mennonite Church
Global Outreach, Ltd.
GO International
Habitat for Humanity Intl.
Harvest
Heart to Heart Intl. Mins.
Heifer Project International
INTERDEV
International Child Care
International Outreach Mins.
InterServe/USA
Larry Jones International Mins
Lifewater International
Luke Society, The
Lutheran Brethren World Msns.
Lutheran World Relief
MAP International
MBMS International
Medical Ambassadors Intl.
Medical Missions Philippines
Mennonite Central Committee
Mercy Ships
Middle East Christian Outreach
Ministries In Action
Ministry of Jesus, Inc.
Mission 21 India
Mission Ministries, Inc.
Mission of Mercy
Mission Training International
Mission: Moving Mountains
Operation Blessing Intl.
Opportunity International
Partners International
People International
Presbyterian Church (USA)
Project Mercy, Inc.
Salvation Army, U.S.A.
Self-Help Foundation
Servants in Faith & Technology
SIM USA
Society of St. Margaret
South American Missionary Soc.
Sowers International, The
United Church Board World Mins
United Methodist Church
Venture Middle East
Virginia Mennonite Bd. of Msns
World Concern
World In Need - USA
World Mission Prayer League
World Neighbors
World Relief Corporation
World Servants
World Vision Inc.
World Vision International

Disability Assistance Programs

American Leprosy Missions
Baptist International Outreach
Christian Blind Mission Intl.
ComCare International
Deaf Missions International
Evangelize China Fellowship
Holt Intl. Children's Services
InterAct Ministries
International Child Care
Joni and Friends
Venture Middle East
World Opportunities Intl.

Education, Church/School General Christian

Africa Inland Mission Intl.
African Bible Colleges
African Leadership
Allegheny Wesleyan Meth. Msns.
Armenian Missionary Assoc.
Assemblies of God
Baptist Faith Missions
Barnabas Ministries, Inc.
Bethany Missionary Association
Bibles For The World
CAM International
Campus Crusade for Christ
Carver International Missions
Christian Church of North Am.
Christian Mission for the Deaf
Christian Reformed Relief Comm
Christian Services, Inc.

Education, Extension (Other)

Education, Missionary (Certificate/Degree)

Education, Theological

Advent Christian World Msns.
Africa Inland Mission Intl.
African Leadership
African Mission Evangelism
American Baptist Association
American Baptist Churches USA
AMG International
Arabic Communication Center
Assemblies of God
Assoc of Free Lutheran Congs
Baptist Bible Fellowship Intl.
Baptist General Conference
Baptist International Missions
Baptist International Outreach
Baptist Medical & Dental
Baptist Mid-Missions
Baptist Missionary Assoc.
Baptist World Mission
Berean Mission, Inc.
Bethany Fellowship Missions
Bible Missionary Church
Bibles For The World
Biblical Ministries Worldwide
BILD International
Brazil Gospel Fellowship Msn.
Calvary International
CAM International
CBInternational
China Ministries International
China Partner
Christar
Christian and Msny. Alliance
Christian Fellowship Union
Christian Leadership Dev.
Christian Mission for the Deaf
Christian Reformed World Msns.
Church of God (Holiness) Msn.
Church of God Apostolic Faith
Daystar U.S.
Donetsk Christian University
East-West Ministries Intl.
Eastern Mennonite Missions
Elim Fellowship World Missions
European Evangelistic Society
Evangelical Free Church Msn.
Evangelical Friends Mission
Evangelical Greenhouse Mins.
Evangelical Lutheran Synod
Evangelical Methodist Church
Evangelistic Faith Missions
Free Methodist World Missions
Friends Church Southwest
General Conf. Mennonite Church
Global Youth Min. Network
Good News for India
Gospel Fellowship Association
Gospel Furthering Fellowship
Gospel Mission of S. America
Gospel Missionary Union
Greater Europe Mission
Greater Grace World Outreach
HBI Global Partners
HCJB World Radio
ICI University
India Gospel Outreach
India Rural Evangelical Fellowship
International Cooperating Mins
International Urban Associates
Intl. Inst. Christian Studies
Intl. Pentecostal Ch of Christ
Intl. Pentecostal Holiness Ch.
Latin America Mission
Liebenzell Mission USA
Living Water Teaching Intl.
Lutheran Church-Missouri Synod
Macedonia World Baptist Msns.
Mazahua Mission
MBMS International
Mennonite Board of Missions
Ministry to Eastern Europe
Mission to the Americas
Mission to the World
Moravian Church North America
Mustard Seed, Inc.
North American Baptist Conf.
OMF International
OMS Intl., Inc.
Orthodox Presbyterian Church
Outreach To Asia Nationals
Outreach, Inc.
Overseas Council Intl.
Pillar of Fire Missions Intl.
Presbyterian Church (USA)
Primitive Methodist Church
Ramesh Richard Evangelism
Ravi Zacharias Int. Mins.
Reformed Church In America
Rehoboth Ministries, Inc
Rio Grande Bible Institute
Romanian Missionary Society
SEND International
SIM USA

Education, Theological by Extension (TEE)

Evangelism, Mass

Every Home for Christ
Final Frontiers Foundation
FOCAS
Foursquare Missions Intl.
Friendship International
Globe Missionary Evangelism
Gospel Outreach Mins. Intl.
Gospel Revival Ministries
Grand Old Gospel Fellowship
Harvest Evangelism, Inc.
Harvest Intl. Christian Outrch
Hermano Pablo Ministries
High Adventure Ministries
ICI University
Impact International
Independent Faith Mission
India Evangelical Mission
India Gospel Outreach
India Rural Evangelical Fellowship
INTERCOMM
International Gospel Outreach
Intl. Board of Jewish Missions
Intl. Lutheran Laymen's League
Iranian Christians Intl.
Kingdom Building Ministries
Larry Jones International Mins
Lott Carey Baptist Mission
Luis Palau Evangelistic Assoc.
M/E International
Mahesh Chavda Ministries Intl.
Mexican Medical, Inc.
Middle East Media - USA
Ministry of Jesus, Inc.
Missionary Athletes Intl.
Missionary Revival Crusade
Morelli Ministries Intl.
Mutual Faith Ministries Intl.
National Baptist Conv. of Am.
No Greater Love Ministries
On The Go Ministries
Open Air Campaigners
Operation Mobilization
Orthodox Presbyterian Church
Overseas Radio & Television
Pentecostal Church of God
Pocket Testament League
Presb. Evangelistic Fellowship
Ramesh Richard Evangelism
Samaritan's Purse
SAT-7 North America
Seventh-day Adventists
Shield of Faith Ministries
Southern Baptist Intl. Mission
Spiritual Growth Resources
STEM Ministries
Things To Come Mission, Inc.
Training Evangelistic Ldrshp.
Trans World Radio
United Evangelical Churches
United Pentecostal Church Intl
Village Ministries Intl.
Word of Life Fellowship
World Indigenous Missions
World Missions Far Corners
World Outreach Ministries
World Reach, Inc.
Youth for Christ / USA

Evangelism, Personal and Small Group

ABWE
Action International Mins.
Africa Inland Mission Intl.
Africa Inter-Mennonite Mission
African Bible Colleges
African Enterprise, Inc.
African Methodist Epis. Zion
Agape Gospel Mission
Allegheny Wesleyan Meth. Msns.
American Baptist Association
American Baptist Churches USA
American Scripture Gift Msn.
AMF International
Apostolic Christian Church
Arab World Ministries
Arabic Communication Center
Artists In Christian Testimony
Assemblies of God
ASSIST - Aid to Special Saints
Aurora Mission, Inc.
Awana Clubs International
Baptist Bible Fellowship Intl.
Baptist Faith Missions
Baptist International Outreach
Baptist Missionary Assoc.
Baptist Missions to Forgotten
Barnabas Ministries, Inc.
BCM International
Berean Mission, Inc.
Bethany Fellowship Missions
Bible League, The
Biblical Ministries Worldwide

Big World Ventures Inc.
Brazil Gospel Fellowship Msn.
Brethren Church Missionary Bd.
Brethren in Christ World Msns.
Cadence International
Calvary Evangelistic Mission
CAM International
Campus Crusade for Christ
CBInternational
Central Yearly Mtg. of Friends
Child Evangelism Fellowship
Children of Promise Int'l.
China Campus Outreach
China Ministries International
Chosen People Ministries
Christ Community Church
Christ for India, Inc.
Christ for the City Intl.
Christ for the Lost World
Christar
Christian and Msny. Alliance
Christian Business Men's Comte
Christian Medical & Dental Soc
Christian Mission for the Deaf
Christian Outreach Intl.
Christian Reformed World Msns.
Christian Union Mission
Christians In Action, Inc.
Church of God (Holiness) Msn.
Church of God in Christ, Menn.
Church of God World Missions
Church of the United Brethren
Church Planting International
Church Resource Ministries
Churches of God General Conf.
CityTeam Ministries
CMF International
ComCare International
Congregational Methodist Ch.
Cooperative Baptist Fellowship
Cornerstone Intl.
Crossover Communications Intl.
Cumberland Presbyterian Church
Eastern European Outreach
Episcopal World Mission
Equip, Inc.
European Christian Mission
European Evangelistic Society
Evangelical Baptist Missions
Evangelical Covenant Church
Evangelical Free Church Msn.
Evangelical Friends Mission
Evangelical Greenhouse Mins.
Evangelical Lutheran Synod
Evangelical Methodist Church
Evangelical Presbyterian Ch.
Evangelism Explosion Intl.
Evangelism Resources
Evangelistic Faith Missions
Every Home for Christ
FARMS International, Inc.
Fellowship International Msn.
Fellowship of Assoc. Medical
Final Frontiers Foundation
For Haiti with Love Inc.
Forward Edge International
Foundation For His Ministry
Franconia Mennonite Conf.
Free Gospel Church Msns. Dept.
Free Methodist World Missions
Free Will Baptist, Inc.
Friends Church Southwest
Friends of Israel Gospel Min.
Friends United Meeting
Friendship International
Frontiers
Full Gospel Grace Fellowship
Fundamental Bapt. Msn Trinidad
General Conf. Mennonite Church
Gideons International, The
Global Fellowship
Global Outreach Mission
Global Outreach, Ltd.
Global Strategy Mission Assoc.
GO International
Go Ye Fellowship
Gospel Fellowship Association
Gospel for Asia
Gospel Furthering Fellowship
Gospel Missionary Union
Gospel Recordings
Grace Brethren Intl. Missions
Great Commission Center Intl.
Great Commission Ministries
Greater Europe Mission
Greater Grace World Outreach
Harvest Evangelism, Inc.
Have Christ Will Travel Mins.
HBI Global Partners
Health Teams International
Heart to Heart Intl. Mins.
Hellenic Ministries

HOPE Bible Mission, Inc.
Hope for the Hungry
ICI University
Impact International
In Touch Mission Intl.
Independent Faith Mission
India Evangelical Mission
InterAct Ministries
INTERCOMM
International Bible Society
International Crusades, Inc.
International Family Missions
International Gospel League
International Health Services
International Messengers
International Outreach Mins.
International Teams, U.S.A.
InterServe/USA
InterVarsity Mission
Intl. Discipleship Mission
Ireland Outreach Intl., Inc.
Island Missionary Society
Jews for Jesus
Latin America Assistance
Latin America Lutheran Mission
Latin America Mission
Liberty Corner Mission
Liebenzell Mission USA
LIFE Ministries
Literacy & Evangelism Intl.
Living Water Teaching Intl.
Lutheran Church-Missouri Synod
M/E International
Macedonia World Baptist Msns.
Mahesh Chavda Ministries Intl.
Medical Missions Philippines
Mercy Ships
Mexican Border Missions
Mexican Christian Mission
Mexican Medical, Inc.
Middle East Christian Outreach
Middle Eastern Outreach
Mission Ministries, Inc.
Mission O.N.E., Inc.
Mission Possible
Mission Soc. for United Meth.
Mission to the Americas
Mission: Moving Mountains
Missionary Athletes Intl.
Missions To Japan, Inc.
MSC Canada
Muslim Hope
National Baptist Conv. of Am.
Navigators, The
Network of Intl Christian Schs
New Life League International
No Greater Love Ministries
OC International, Inc.
OMF International
OMS Intl., Inc.
Open Bible Ministries
Open Door Baptist Missions
Operation Mobilization
ORA International
Orthodox Presbyterian Church
Pan American Missions
Partners in Asian Missions
Pass the Torch Ministries
Pentecostal Church of God
Pentecostal Free Will Bapt.Ch.
People International
Perimeter Ch., Global Outreach
Pioneers
Precious Seed Ministries
Presb. Evangelistic Fellowship
Presb. Order for World Evang.
Presbyterian Church (USA)
Prison Mission Association
Project AmaZon
Project Mercy, Inc.
Ramabai Mukti Mission
Reach Ministries International
Red Sea Team International
Reformed Church In America
Reformed Presbyterian Church
Rehoboth Ministries, Inc
Ripe for Harvest, Inc.
Salvation Army, U.S.A.
SEND International
Seventh Day Baptist Msny. Soc.
Shield of Faith Ministries
Shield of Faith Mission Intl.
Society for Europe's Evang.
Son Shine Ministries Intl.
South American Missionary Soc.
Southern Baptist Intl. Mission
Sowers International, The
Spanish World Gospel Mission
Spiritual Growth Resources
TEAM
Teen Missions International
Teen World Outreach

Evangelism, Student

Funds Transmission

Harvest
Hope for the Hungry
Independent Gospel Missions
India National Inland Mission
Intl. Foundation for EWHA
Living Water Teaching Intl.
Luke Society, The
Maranatha Baptist Mission
Mazahua Mission
Mission Ministries, Inc.
Moravian Church North America
NEED, Inc.
Outreach, Inc.
Perimeter Ch., Global Outreach
Pilgrim Fellowship, Inc.
Presbyterian Missionary Union
Ramesh Richard Evangelism
Reciprocal Ministries Intl.
Red Sea Team International
Reformed Baptist Mission Svcs.
Ripe for Harvest, Inc.
Seventh Day Baptist Msny. Soc.
Seventh-day Adventists
Sowers International, The
STEER, Inc.
VELA Ministries International
Vellore Christian Medical Col.
World Baptist Fellowship Msn.
World In Need - USA
World Outreach Ministries
World Vision Inc.
Wycliffe Associates USA

Furloughed Missionary Support

Bible Missionary Church
Biblical Literature Fellowship
Cedar Lane Missionary Homes
Intl. Pentecostal Holiness Ch.
Mission Training International
Missionary Retreat Fellowship
Missionary TECH Team
Open Bible Standard Churches
Overseas Ministries Study Ctr.
Providence Mission Homes, Inc.
Wycliffe Associates USA

Information Services

AD2000 & Beyond Movement
Adopt-A-People Clearinghouse
Billy Graham Center, The
Cadence International
China Connection
ChinaSource
Christian Msns. in Many Lands
Church Missions Link
Episcopal Church Msnry Commun.
Episcopal Church, Msny. Soc.
Evangelism & Missions Info
FOM
General Assoc Regular Baptists
General Baptists International
Global Mapping International
Grace Baptist Missions Intl.
In Touch Mission Intl.
Institute of Hindu Studies
INTENT
Issachar Frontier Missions
Japanese Evangelization Center
Lifewater International
Middle Eastern Outreach
Mission Aviation Fellowship
Mission Services Association
Mission Trng. & Resource Ctr.
Missions Resource Center
OC International, Inc.
Overcomer Press, Inc.
Reformed Baptist Mission Svcs.
World Evangelization Research
World In Need - USA
Worldwide Discipleship Assoc.

Leadership Development

ACM International
ACMC
ACTS International Ministries
Advancing Native Missions
Africa Inland Mission Intl.
Africa Inter-Mennonite Mission
African Bible Colleges
African Enterprise, Inc.
African Leadership
Alberto Mottesi Evang. Assoc.
Asian Outreach U.S.A.
Assemblies of God
Awana Clubs International
Baptist General Conference
Barnabas International
Bethany Fellowship Missions
Bible League, The
Big World Ventures Inc.
BILD International
Billy Graham Center, The

Overseas Council Intl.
Overseas Ministries Study Ctr.
Partners in Asian Missions
Partners International
Perimeter Ch., Global Outreach
Pioneers
Presbyterian Church (USA)
Progressive Vision
Project Care
Project Partner with Christ
Ravi Zacharias Int. Mins.
Reach Ministries International
Reformed Church In America
Rehoboth Ministries, Inc
Romanian Missionary Society
Rosedale Mennonite Missions
SEND International
Shield of Faith Ministries
Society for Europe's Evang.
Society of St. Margaret
South America Mission
South American Missionary Soc.
Southern Baptist Intl. Mission
Spiritual Growth Resources
Spiritual Overseers Service
TCM International
Teen Missions International
Touch the World Ministries
Trans World Missions
UFM International
United Board for Christian Ed.
United Church Board World Mins
United Pentecostal Church Intl
United World Mission
VELA Ministries International
Vineyard Intl. Consortium
Virginia Mennonite Bd. of Msns
Walk Thru The Bible Ministries
Wesleyan World Missions
Witnessing Mins. of Christ
World Gospel Mission
World Harvest Mission
World Harvest Now
World Reach, Inc.
World Servants
World Team
World Vision International

Linguistics

Africa Inter-Mennonite Mission
Christian Reformed World Msns.
Evangel Bible Translators
Evangelical Mennonite Church
Evangelical Presbyterian Ch.
Link Care Center
Lutheran Bible Translators
New Tribes Mission
Overseas Radio & Television
Pioneer Bible Translators
Wycliffe Bible Translators

Literacy

Anglican Frontier Missions
Christian Dynamics
Christian Literacy Associates
Christian Literature Crusade
Christian Mission for the Deaf
Christian Reformed World Msns.
Evangel Bible Translators
General Baptists International
InterServe/USA
Literacy & Evangelism Intl.
Lutheran Bible Translators
Mission 21 India
New Tribes Mission
Omega World Missions
Pioneer Bible Translators
Society of St. Margaret
Witnessing Mins. of Christ
Wycliffe Bible Translators

Literature Distribution

ABWE
ACMC
ACTS International Ministries
Advancing Renewal Ministries
Advent Christian World Msns.
African Methodist Epis. Zion
All God's Children Intl.
Allegheny Wesleyan Meth. Msns.
American Scripture Gift Msn.
American Tract Society
AMF International
Anis Shorrosh Evan. Assoc.
Arabic Communication Center
Assemblies of God
ASSIST - Aid to Special Saints
Aurora Mission, Inc.
Baptist International Missions
Bible Literature International
Biblical Literature Fellowship
Calvary Evangelistic Mission

World Missions Far Corners
World Opportunities Intl.

Literature Production

ABWE
ACMC
ACTS International Ministries
American Scripture Gift Msn.
American Tract Society
American Waldensian Society
Asian Outreach U.S.A.
Assemblies of God
Back to the Bible Intl.
Baptist Mid-Missions
Bethany Fellowship Missions
BILD International
CEIFA Ministries International
Christ Community Church
Christian Leadership Dev.
Christian Literature Crusade
Christian Union Mission
Christian World Publishers
Cook Communications Ministries
Derek Prince Ministries, Intl.
East Gates Ministries Intl.
Eastern European Outreach
Evangelical Lutheran Synod
Evangelism Explosion Intl.
Friends of Israel Gospel Min.
Frontier Mission Fellowship
Global Harvest Ministries
Gospel Mission of S. America
Grace and Truth, Inc.
Hands for Christ
Harvest
Institute of Chinese Studies
INTENT
International Leadership Smnrs
InterVarsity Mission
Ireland Outreach Intl., Inc.
Jews for Jesus
Literacy & Evangelism Intl.
Luis Palau Evangelistic Assoc.
Lutheran Brethren World Msns.
Lutheran Lit. Soc. for Chinese
Macedonia World Baptist Msns.
Mahesh Chavda Ministries Intl.
MAP International
Men for Missions Intl.
Mennonite Board of Missions
Message of Life, Inc.
Middle East Media - USA
Ministry to Eastern Europe
Mission Possible Foundation
Narramore Christian Foundation
Navigators, The
New Hope International
New Life League International
OMF International
Orthodox Presbyterian Church
Overcomer Press, Inc.
Project Care
RBC Ministries
Reformation Translation Flwshp
Romanian Missionary Society
Russian Bible Society, Inc.
Scripture Union, USA
Seventh-day Adventists
Source of Light Ministries
United Pentecostal Church Intl
Walk Thru The Bible Ministries
Westminister Biblical Missions
Wisconsin Evang. Lutheran Syn.
World Missionary Press, Inc.

Management Consulting/Training

Artists In Christian Testimony
ChinaSource
Christian Information Service
Church Missions Link
Cities for Christ Worldwide
Cook Communications Ministries
Crisis Consulting
Daystar U.S.
Development Associates Intl.
Enterprise Development Intl.
Faith Christian Fellowship
Great Commission Ministries
Intercristo
Lifewater International
LIGHT International, Inc.
Media Associates International
OC International, Inc.
Overseas Council Intl.
Paraclete Mission Group, Inc.
Partners International
Project Partner with Christ
Shelter Now International
Spiritual Overseers Service
TCM International
World Mission Associates

Medical Supplies

All God's Children Intl.
American Leprosy Missions
Baptist International Outreach
Barnabas Ministries, Inc.
Blessings International
Caring Partners International
Central Missionary Fellowship
Children of India Foundation
Children's Medical Ministries
CHOSEN, Inc.
Christian Aid Ministries
Christian Pilots Association
Christian Service Intl.
Church of God in Christ, Menn.
Church of the Nazarene
Congregational Christian Chs.
Congregational Holiness Church
Correll Missionary Ministries
Flying Doctors of America
For Haiti with Love Inc.
Global Health Ministries
In Touch Mission Intl.
International Aid
International Child Care
Intl. Christian Leprosy Msn.
ISOH/Impact
Ludhiana Christian Medical Col
MAP International
Medical Missions Philippines
Mission of Mercy
National Baptist Conv. of Am.
National Baptist Conv. USA
Presb. Order for World Evang.
Samaritan's Purse
Society of St. Margaret
Vellore Christian Medical Col.
World Concern
World Help
World Opportunities Intl.

Medicine, incl. Dental and Public Health

ABWE
ACM International
Africa Inland Mission Intl.
AmeriTribes
Armenian Missionary Assoc.
Assemblies of God
Assoc of Free Lutheran Congs
Baptist Medical & Dental
Baptist Mid-Missions
Blessings International
Brethren Church Missionary Bd.
Caring Partners International
Carver International Missions
CBInternational
China Connection
CHOSEN, Inc.
Christ for India, Inc.
Christ for the City Intl.
Christar
Christian Advance Intl.
Christian Blind Mission Intl.
Christian Dental Society
Christian Medical & Dental Soc
Christian Service Intl.
Church of God World Missions
Churches of God General Conf.
CMF International
Congregational Methodist Ch.
Crossover Communications Intl.
Emmanuel Intl. Mission (U.S.)
Equip, Inc.
Evangelical Covenant Church
Evangelical Lutheran Church
Evangelical Methodist Church
Fellowship of Assoc. Medical
Flying Doctors of America
FOCAS
Foundation For His Ministry
Free Will Baptist, Inc.
Global Health Ministries
Global Outreach Mission
Global Outreach, Ltd.
Grace Ministries International
HCJB World Radio
Health Teams International
Interchurch Medical Assistance
International Child Care
International Health Services
InterServe/USA
ISOH/Impact
Kids Alive International
Lott Carey Baptist Mission
Ludhiana Christian Medical Col
Luke Society, The
Macedonian Missionary Service
MAP International
Medical Ambassadors Intl.
Medical Missions Philippines
Mennonite Board of Missions

Mennonite Central Committee
Mercy Ships
Mexican Medical, Inc.
Mission Soc. for United Meth.
Mission: Moving Mountains
Moravian Church North America
Mustard Seed, Inc.
National Baptist Conv. of Am.
NEED, Inc.
North American Baptist Conf.
Operation Blessing Intl.
Orthodox Presbyterian Church
Perimeter Ch., Global Outreach
Presbyterian Church (USA)
Primitive Methodist Church
Project AmaZon
Project Christ International
Ramabai Mukti Mission
Reformed Church In America
Reformed Episcopal Bd Missions
Samaritan's Purse
Seventh-day Adventists
SIM USA
Southern Baptist Intl. Mission
TEAM
Teen World Outreach
The Master's Mission, Inc.
UFM International
United Church Board World Mins
Vellore Christian Medical Col.
Venture Middle East
WEC International
Witnessing Mins. of Christ
World Concern
World Gospel Mission
World Harvest Mission
World Mission Prayer League
World Missions Far Corners
World Witness
World-Wide Missions

Member Care

Barnabas International
Marriage Ministries Intl.

National Church Nurture/Support

ACTS International Ministries
Advancing Indigenous Missions
Advancing Native Missions
Africa Inter-Mennonite Mission
African Mission Evangelism
AIMS
American Baptist Churches USA
American Waldensian Society
AmeriTribes
AMOR Ministries
Apostolic Christian Church
Asian Outreach U.S.A.
Assemblies of God
Baptist Bible Fellowship Intl.
Barnabas International
Bible League, The
Bible Missionary Church
Bibles For The World
BILD International
Brethren Church Missionary Bd.
Brethren in Christ World Msns.
Bridge Builders International
CAM International
Central Missionary Fellowship
China Partner
Christ Community Church
Christ to the Nations Missions
Christian Associates Intl.
Christian Church of North Am.
Christian Fellowship Union
Christian Leadership Dev.
Christians In Action, Inc.
Church of God (Holiness) Msn.
Church of God (Seventh Day)
Church of God in Christ, Menn.
Church of God of Prophecy
Church of God World Missions
Church of God, The
Church of The Brethren
Church of the United Brethren
Church Resource Ministries
Churches of God General Conf.
Congregational Holiness Church
Conservative Cong. Christian
Covenant Celebration Church
Cumberland Presbyterian Church
East Gates Ministries Intl.
East-West Ministries Intl.
Eastern European Outreach
Emmanuel Intl. Mission (U.S.)
Episcopal Church, Msny. Soc.
Episcopal World Mission
European Christian Mission
Evangelical Congregational Ch.
Evangelical Covenant Church
Evangelical Lutheran Church

Evangelical Presbyterian Ch.
Every Home for Christ
Final Frontiers Foundation
Forward Edge International
Foursquare Missions Intl.
Free Gospel Church Msns. Dept.
Friends United Meeting
Friendship Mins.
Full Gospel Evangelistic Assoc
General Baptists International
General Conf. Mennonite Church
Global Advance
Global Fellowship
Globe Missionary Evangelism
Gospel Furthering Fellowship
Grace Baptist Missions Intl.
Harvest Evangelism, Inc.
Have Christ Will Travel Mins.
Help for Christian Nationals
Hope for the Hungry
In Touch Mission Intl.
Independent Gospel Missions
India Gospel Outreach
InterServe/USA
Intl. Pentecostal Ch of Christ
Intl. Pentecostal Holiness Ch.
Iranian Christians Intl.
Island Missionary Society
Japanese Evangelical Msnry Soc
Kingdom Building Ministries
Latin America Lutheran Mission
Latin America Mission
Latin American Indian Mins.
Liberia Christian Mission
Liberty Corner Mission
LIFE Ministries
Lott Carey Baptist Mission
Lutheran Brethren World Msns.
Mahesh Chavda Ministries Intl.
MBMS International
Middle East Christian Outreach
Ministries In Action
Ministry of Jesus, Inc.
Mission Soc. for United Meth.
Mission to the Americas
Mission to the World
Missionary Ventures Intl.
Missions To Japan, Inc.
Morelli Ministries Intl.
New Hope International
OC International, Inc.
Open Door Baptist Missions
ORA International
Pan American Missions
Partners in Asian Missions
Pentecostal Church of God
Pentecostal Free Will Bapt.Ch.
PNMC Missions
PNMC Missions
Presbyterian Church (USA)
Presbyterian Missionary Union
Primitive Methodist Church
Project AmaZon
Reciprocal Ministries Intl.
Reformed Church In America
Ripe for Harvest, Inc.
Rosedale Mennonite Missions
Samaritan's Purse
SAT-7 North America
SEND International
Seventh Day Baptist Msny. Soc.
SIM USA
Slavic Missionary Service
Society of St. Margaret
South American Missionary Soc.
Southern Baptist Intl. Mission
Spiritual Growth Resources
Spiritual Overseers Service
TCM International
Teen World Outreach
The Master's Harvest
TMA Ministries
Training Evangelistic Ldrshp.
United Church Board World Mins
United Evangelical Churches
United Methodist Church
United World Mission
Venture Middle East
Vineyard Intl. Consortium
WEC International
Wesleyan World Missions
Westminister Biblical Missions
Wisconsin Evang. Lutheran Syn.
World Concern
World Gospel Mission
World Harvest Now
World Help
World Horizons
World Mission Prayer League
World Partners USA
World Reach, Inc.
World Team

Psychological Counseling

Barnabas International
Holt Intl. Children's Services
Link Care Center
Narramore Christian Foundation

Purchasing Services

Christian Dental Society
Equipping the Saints
Galcom International
Interchurch Medical Assistance
MATS International

Recruiting/Mobilizing

ACMC
Action International Mins.
AD2000 & Beyond Movement
AIMS
Ambassadors for Christ, Inc.
American Baptist Churches USA
AMF International
ARISE International
Baptist General Conference
Berean Mission, Inc.
Cadence International
Caleb Project
Central Missionary Fellowship
Christ for the City Intl.
Christian Ministries Intl.
Christian Outreach Intl.
Church Resource Ministries
Cornerstone Intl.
Crossover Communications Intl.
Emmaus Road, International
Engineering Ministries Intl.
Episcopal Church Msnry Commun.
Episcopal World Mission
Food for the Hungry, Inc.
Forward Edge International
Friendship International
Frontiers
Global Opportunities
Global Strategy Mission Assoc.
Grace Brethren Intl. Missions
Harvest Evangelism, Inc.
Harvest Intl. Christian Outrch
Heart of God Mins.
Institute of Hindu Studies
INTENT
Intercristo
International Gospel Outreach
International Messengers
International Students, Inc
InterVarsity Mission
Intl. Pentecostal Holiness Ch.
Issachar Frontier Missions
Kids Alive International
Kingdom Building Ministries
Middle Eastern Outreach
Mission Soc. for United Meth.
Mission To Unreached Peoples
Missions Outreach Intl.
OC International, Inc.
Operation Mobilization
Pioneer Bible Translators
Presb. Center for Msn. Studies
Priority One International
Share International
STEM Ministries
Strategic Ventures Network
TEAM
Team Expansion, Inc.
Turkish World Outreach
VELA Ministries International
World Horizons
World In Need - USA
World Team
World Thrust Int.
Wycliffe Associates USA

Relief and/or Rehabilitation

African Enterprise, Inc.
All God's Children Intl.
American Assoc. Lutheran Chs.
AMG International
AMOR Ministries
Armenian Missionary Assoc.
Assemblies of God
Baptist Mid-Missions
Blessings International
Bright Hope International
Calvary Commission, Inc.
Childcare International
Children's Hunger Relief Fund
Christ for the City Intl.
Christian Aid Ministries
Christian Blind Mission Intl.
Christian Reformed Relief Comm
Christians In Action, Inc.
Church of God in Christ, Menn.
Church of The Brethren
Church of the Nazarene

Research

Services for Other Agencies

Blessings International
Caleb Project
Calvary Evangelistic Mission
Carpenter's Tools Intl.
ChinaSource
Christian Dental Society
Christian Information Service
Christian Ministries Intl.
Church Ministries Intl.
Congregational Christian Chs.
Crisis Consulting
Door of Hope International
ECHO
Evangelism Resources
Frontier Mission Fellowship
Galcom International
Global Mapping International
Gospel Literature Intl.
Gospel Recordings
Grace Baptist Missions Intl.
Greater Europe Mission
Handclasp International, Inc.
Health Teams International
Helps International Ministries
Institute of Chinese Studies
INTERDEV
Issachar Frontier Missions
Literacy & Evangelism Intl.
Mission Services Association
Mission To Unreached Peoples
Missionaire International
Missionary Retreat Fellowship
Missionary TECH Team
Peoples Mission International
Priority One International
Sentinel Group, The
STEER, Inc.
Teen Missions International
TMA Ministries
Turkish World Outreach
World Mission Associates
World Opportunities Intl.

Short-Term Programs Coordination

AMF International
AMOR Ministries
Berean Mission, Inc.
Biblical Literature Fellowship
Big World Ventures Inc.
Blossoming Rose
Caleb Project
Calvary Commission, Inc.
Calvary International
Caring Partners International
Celebrant Singers
Childcare International
China Campus Outreach
Christ for the Nations, Inc.
Christian Advance Intl.
Christian Information Service
Christian Medical & Dental Soc
Christian Outreach Intl.
Christian Service Intl.
Church of God (Anderson, IN)
ComCare International
Conservative Cong. Christian
Cornerstone Intl.
Crossover Communications Intl.
East-West Ministries Intl.
Evangelical Lutheran Church
Fellowship of Assoc. Medical
Flying Doctors of America
Forward Edge International
Friends United Meeting
Friendship International
GO International
Greater Grace World Outreach
Habitat for Humanity Intl.
Harvest Evangelism, Inc.
Harvest Intl. Christian Outrch
Harvesting In Spanish
Heart to Heart Intl. Mins.
Hope for the Hungry
Impact International
Independent Gospel Missions
International Crusades, Inc.
International Family Missions
International Gospel Outreach
International Messengers
Japanese Evangelical Msnry Soc
Kids Alive International
Kingdom Building Ministries
Larry Jones International Mins
Latin America Lutheran Mission
Macedonian Missionary Service
Men for Missions Intl.
Mexican Medical, Inc.
Missionary Athletes Intl.
Missionary Ventures Intl.
Missions Outreach Intl.
MSC Canada
Mutual Faith Ministries Intl.
New Tribes Mission

Supplying Equipment

Support of National Workers

Gospel for Asia
Gospel Outreach Mins. Intl.
Gospel Recordings
Gospel Revival Ministries
Harvest
HBI Global Partners
Help for Christian Nationals
HOPE Bible Mission, Inc.
Independent Gospel Missions
India Evangelical Mission
India Gospel Outreach
International Gospel League
International Needs - USA
International Partnership Mins
Latin America Lutheran Mission
Lion and Lamb Outreach
M/E International
MBMS International
Medical Ambassadors Intl.
Medical Missions Philippines
Mexican Border Missions
Mexican Christian Mission
Mission O.N.E., Inc.
Mission Possible
Missionaire International
Missionary Ventures Intl.
Navigators, The
New Hope International
New Life League International
Omega World Missions
Open Bible Standard Churches
ORA International
Outreach To Asia Nationals
Pan American Missions
Partners in Asian Missions
Partners International
Pentecostal Church of God
Perimeter Ch., Global Outreach
Peter Deyneka Russian Mins.
Pillar of Fire Missions Intl.
Prakash Association USA
Precious Seed Ministries
Presb. Evangelistic Fellowship
Project AmaZon
Project Care
Project Christ International
Project Partner with Christ
Ramabai Mukti Mission
Romanian Mission of Chicago
Share International
Slavic Gospel Association
Source of Light Ministries
Sowers International, The
Spanish World Gospel Mission
Spiritual Growth Resources
Spiritual Overseers Service
Team Expansion, Inc.
Teen Missions International
Third World Baptist Missions
VELA Ministries International
World In Need - USA
World Witness
World-Wide Missions

Technical Assistance

Big World Ventures Inc.
CHOSEN, Inc.
ECHO
Engineering Ministries Intl.
Enterprise Development Intl.
Equip, Inc.
FARMS International, Inc.
Galcom International
Global Mapping International
Gospel Recordings
Habitat for Humanity Intl.
Heifer Project International
Helps International Ministries
Interchurch Medical Assistance
International Aid
International Child Care
JAARS, Inc.
Joni and Friends
Lifewater International
Media Associates International
Men for Missions Intl.
Mennonite Central Committee
Middle East Media - USA
Mission Aides, Inc.
Missionary TECH Team
MMS Aviation
SAND Institutes International
Self-Help Foundation
Servants in Faith & Technology
Shelter Now International
The Master's Mission, Inc.
TMA Ministries
Trans World Radio
United Board for Christian Ed.
World Relief Corporation
Wycliffe Associates USA

Training, Other

Agape Gospel Mission
AIMS
Ambassadors for Christ Intl.
AMF International
Artists In Christian Testimony
Asian Outreach U.S.A.
Baptist International Missions
BCM International
Billy Graham Center, The
Campus Crusade for Christ
Carver International Missions
Child Evangelism Fellowship
Childcare International
China Outreach Ministries
China Partner
CHOSEN, Inc.
Christ for India, Inc.
Christian Blind Mission Intl.
Christian Leadership Dev.
Christian Ministries Intl.
Church Ministries Intl.
Cities for Christ Worldwide
Crisis Consulting
ECHO
Educational Services Intl.
Enterprise Development Intl.
Every Child Ministries, Inc.
Friendship International
Global Advance
Global Harvest Ministries
Global Opportunities
Global Youth Min. Network
Habitat for Humanity Intl.
Heifer Project International
Help for Christian Nationals
Holt Intl. Children's Services
Institute of Hindu Studies
International Aid
International Crusades, Inc.
International Street Kids Mins
International Students, Inc
International Urban Associates
Joni and Friends
Kingdom Building Ministries
Latin American Indian Mins.
Marriage Ministries Intl.
Media Associates International
Medical Missions Philippines
Mennonite Central Committee
MMS Aviation
National Religious Broadcaster
On The Go Ministries
Open Air Campaigners
Oriental Missionary Crusade
Pass the Torch Ministries
Pioneer Bible Translators
Pioneer Clubs
PNMC Missions
Progressive Vision
Ramesh Richard Evangelism
Ravi Zacharias Int. Mins.
Reciprocal Ministries Intl.
Rio Grande Bible Institute
SAND Institutes International
Scripture Union, USA
Self-Help Foundation
Sentinel Group, The
Servants in Faith & Technology
Seventh-day Adventists
Share International
South America Mission
Things To Come Mission, Inc.
Training Evangelistic Leadership
Tribes and Nations Outreach
United Board for Christian Ed.
VELA Ministries International
Vellore Christian Medical Col.
World Missions Far Corners
World Thrust Int.
World Vision International
Worldwide Discipleship Assoc.

Training/Orientation, Missionary

ACM International
African Enterprise, Inc.
AMOR Ministries
Apostolic Team Ministries Intl
Assemblies of God
Baptist Bible Fellowship Intl.
Bethany Fellowship Missions
Bethany Missionary Association
BILD International
Caleb Project
Calvary International
Central Missionary Fellowship
China Campus Outreach
China Ministries International
ChinaSource
Chosen People Ministries
Christ to the Nations Missions
Christian Information Service

Christian Literature Crusade
Christians In Action, Inc.
Church Missions Link
Church of the Nazarene
CityTeam Ministries
CMF International
Daystar U.S.
Deaf Missions International
Emmaus Road, International
Episcopal Church Msnry Community
Episcopal Church, Msny. Soc.
Equip, Inc.
Evangelical Covenant Church
Evangelical Lutheran Church
Faith Christian Fellowship
Frontier Mission Fellowship
Global Fellowship
Global Mapping International
Global Strategy Mission Assoc.
Gospel for Asia
Grace Baptist Missions Intl.
Great Commission Center Intl.
Greater Grace World Outreach
Harvest Evangelism, Inc.
Heart of God Mins.
Hope for the Hungry
Institute Intl Christian Comm.
International Family Missions
International Gospel Outreach
International Messengers
International Teams, U.S.A.
InterVarsity Mission
Japanese Evangelical Msnry Soc
Japanese Evangelization Center
Jews for Jesus
Larry Jones International Mins
Liebenzell Mission USA
Link Care Center
Lion and Lamb Outreach
Living Water Teaching Intl.
Lutheran Youth Encounter
Mennonite Board of Missions
Mercy Ships
Mexican Medical, Inc.
Middle Eastern Outreach
Mission O.N.E., Inc.
Mission Soc. for United Meth.
Mission Training International
Mission Trng. & Resource Ctr.
Narramore Christian Foundation
Navigators, The
New Tribes Mission
OC International, Inc.
Operation Mobilization
ORA International
Overseas Ministries Study Ctr.
Paraclete Mission Group, Inc.
Peoples Mission International
Project AmaZon
Project Christ International
Project Partner with Christ
Reach Ministries International
Shield of Faith Mission Intl.
Teen Missions International
United Methodist Church
United World Mission
WEC International
World Harvest Now
World Mission Associates
World Outreach Ministries
World Servants
World Team
Youth With A Mission (YWAM)

Translation, Bible

ABWE
Africa Inter-Mennonite Mission
American Assoc. Lutheran Chs.
American Bible Society
Baptist Mid-Missions
Evangel Bible Translators
Evangelical Baptist Missions
International Bible Society
Lutheran Bible Translators
Lutheran Brethren World Msns.
New Tribes Mission
Pioneer Bible Translators
Reach Ministries International
Reformed Church In America
Reformed Episcopal Bd Missions
Romanian Missionary Society
Russian Bible Society, Inc.
World Bible Translation Center
World Partners USA
Wycliffe Bible Translators

Translation, Other

Anis Shorrosh Evan. Assoc.
Arabic Communication Center

Video/Film Production/Distribution

Youth Programs

Young Life
Youth for Christ / USA
Youth With A Mission (YWAM)
YUGO Ministries

CHAPTER 7

Countries of Activity for U.S. Protestant Agencies

In this chapter you will find the countries where agencies reported field personnel in answer to question #12 of the Survey Questionnaire (see the Appendix for details). The few exceptions to this are agencies whose whole program supports (with funds raised in Canada, but which may not be designated to specific personnel on a regular basis) churches or other initiatives in a country.

All countries are listed in alphabetical order according to the name most commonly recognized in North America. Countries that are part of the Commonwealth of Independent States (most of the former Soviet Union) have been listed separately. Examples of this include Armenia, Kyrgyzstan and Belarus. In a few cases we have listed a territory or other administrative district of a country because it is commonly viewed as a separate entity and mission agencies report it that way. An example would be the Azores, located in the Atlantic Ocean 900 miles west of mainland Portugal.

We have separated the personnel totals for all agencies into five categories. Under the "personnel from U.S." heading, the term of expected service has been divided into three categories: 4+ years, 2-4 years and 1-2 years for fully supported personnel. For non-U.S. personnel in the "other countries" heading, the categories are those who are citizens of that ministry country and those who are not citizens, and are fully or partially supported by funds raised in the U.S. by the associated agency. For example, a Korean with specific mission/ministry duties serving in Korea would be included in an agency's "citizens" column of the Korea section. A Korean serving in Russia would be listed in the "not citizen" column of the Russian Federation section.

At the end of each country section, totals of each category for that country are given. Please note that the totals for the "other countries" heading do not necessarily reflect all non-U.S. mission personnel who draw support from U.S. agencies. Some agencies give grants for ongoing institutions and other programs without specifying individual recipients. This may be in addition to U.S. mission personnel based in that country or the agency may not have U.S. personnel living in that country.

Please note also that the totals will be minimum numbers only because of the bigger number of large agencies in this edition that reported their personnel only by general regions and not by specific countries. Therefore, their numbers are not included in this "countries of activity" chapter.

COUNTRY Agency	Year Began	Personnel from U. S.			Other Countries	
		4+yrs	2-4 yrs	1-2 yrs	Citizens	Not Citiz.
Afghanistan						
InterServe/USA	1964	10	-	-	-	-
Shelter Now International	1982	-	1	-	-	-
	Totals:	10	1	-	-	-
Albania						
AMG International	1994	2	-	-	-	-
Apostolic Team Ministries Intl		5	-	-	3	-
Assemblies of God	1991	8	-	3	-	-
Baptist Bible Fellowship Intl.	1995	2	-	-	-	-
Baptist International Missions	1996	1	-	-	-	-
Baptist World Mission	1998	4	-	-	-	-
Bethany Fellowship Missions	1993	3	-	-	-	1
Bible League, The	1997	-	-	-	2	-
Brethren Assemblies		6	-	-	-	-
CAM International	1995	1	-	-	-	1
Campus Crusade for Christ	1991	8	-	1	29	1
CBInternational	1992	2	-	-	-	-
Child Evangelism Fellowship	1992	1	-	-	-	-
Christar	1993	8	-	-	-	-
Christian Aid Mission		-	-	-	12	-
Church of God World Missions	1993	-	-	-	-	1
Church of the Nazarene	1993	5	-	-	-	2
Door of Hope International	1992	4	-	-	-	-
Eastern European Outreach		1	-	-	3	-
Eastern Mennonite Missions	1998	8	-	-	-	-
Every Home for Christ	1992	-	-	-	6	-
Final Frontiers Foundation	1996	-	-	-	1	-
Foursquare Missions Intl.	1996	2	-	-	-	-
Globe Missionary Evangelism	1994	-	3	-	-	-
Gospel Fellowship Association	1997	2	-	-	-	2
International Teams, U.S.A.	1992	2	-	-	-	1
Larry Jones International Mins	1999	-	-	-	2	2
Mission Aviation Fellowship	1991	5	-	-	-	-
Mission Possible Foundation		-	-	-	5	-
Operation Mobilization	1991	5	-	1	-	-
Perimeter Ch., Global Outreach	1996	-	2	-	-	1
Pioneers	1992	3	-	-	-	1
Presbyterian Church (USA)		7	-	-	-	-
Seventh-day Adventists	1992	2	-	-	4	-
Spiritual Growth Resources	1994	-	-	-	2	2
Virginia Mennonite Bd. of Msns	1994	-	3	1	-	1
Wesleyan World Missions	1992	2	-	-	-	-
Wisconsin Evang. Lutheran Syn.	1995	-	2	-	-	-
World Vision Inc.	1998	-	-	1	-	-
Youth With A Mission		4	-	-	-	-
	Totals:	103	10	7	69	16
Algeria						
Anglican Frontier Missions	1998	2	-	-	-	-
	Totals:	2	-	-	-	-

COUNTRY Agency	Year Began	Personnel from U. S.			Other Countries	
		4+yrs	2-4 yrs	1-2 yrs	Citizens	Not Citiz.
American Samoa						
American Baptist Association		2	-	-	-	-
Assemblies of God	1926	2	-	-	-	-
Church of God of Prophecy	1981	2	-	-	1	-
Faith Christian Fellowship	1994	-	2	-	-	-
Youth for Christ / USA		-	1	-	-	-
	Totals:	6	3	-	1	-
Andorra						
Elim Fellowship World Missions	1989	2	-	-	-	-
Faith Christian Fellowship	1993	-	2	-	-	-
	Totals:	2	2	-	-	-
Angola						
Assemblies of God	1985	2	-	-	-	-
Campus Crusade for Christ	1997	-	-	-	10	-
Christ Community Church	1978	2	-	-	-	-
Christian Aid Mission		-	-	-	4	-
Larry Jones International Mins	1995	-	-	-	7	-
SIM USA	1914	7	-	-	2	-
	Totals:	11	-	-	23	-
Antigua						
Habitat for Humanity Intl.	1996	-	1	-	-	-
Independent Faith Mission	1950	2	-	-	-	-
Salvation Army, U.S.A.	1887	1	-	-	-	-
Seventh-day Adventists	1889	2	-	-	-	-
Wisconsin Evang. Lutheran Syn.	1998	-	-	1	-	-
	Totals:	5	1	1	-	-
Argentina						
ABWE	1978	15	-	-	-	-
Apostolic Christian Church	1969	1	-	-	11	-
Assemblies of God	1910	24	-	1	-	-
Baptist Bible Fellowship Intl.	1959	31	-	-	-	-
Baptist General Conference	1957	14	-	-	-	-
Baptist International Missions	1983	10	-	-	-	-
Baptist Mid-Missions	1987	5	-	-	-	-
Baptist World Mission	1977	4	-	-	-	-
Biblical Ministries Worldwide	1979	3	-	-	1	5
Brethren Assemblies		8	-	-	-	-
Brethren Church Missionary Bd.	1911	1	-	-	-	-
Campus Crusade for Christ	1963	4	-	6	14	1
CBInternational	1947	13	-	-	-	-
Central Missionary Fellowship	1990	1	-	-	-	-
Child Evangelism Fellowship	1944	-	-	-	2	1
Christian Aid Mission		-	-	-	1563	-
Christian and Msny. Alliance	1897	12	2	-	-	-
Christian Chs. /Chs. of Christ		6	-	-	-	-
Christian Church of North Am.	1996	-	-	-	400	-

COUNTRY Agency	Year Began	Personnel from U. S.			Other Countries	
		4+yrs	2-4 yrs	1-2 yrs	Citizens	Not Citiz.
Church of God of Prophecy	1955	-	-	-	-	1
Church of the Nazarene	1909	14	-	-	-	4
Elim Fellowship World Missions	1956	2	-	-	-	-
Evangelical Baptist Missions	1974	8	-	-	-	-
Evangelical Covenant Church	1999	-	-	-	-	2
Evangelical Lutheran Church	1948	2	-	-	-	-
Evangelical Presbyterian Ch.	1991	5	-	-	-	-
Every Home for Christ	1958	-	-	-	3	-
Full Gospel Grace Fellowship		3	-	-	-	-
Gospel Mission of S. America	1970	8	-	-	1	7
Gospel Missionary Union	1956	8	-	1	1	2
Grace Brethren Intl. Missions	1909	9	-	1	-	-
Greater Grace World Outreach	1996	-	-	-	-	2
Harvest Evangelism, Inc.	1988	2	1	-	2	-
HCJB World Radio	1998	-	-	-	-	2
Impact International	1959	-	-	-	2	-
Latin America Mission	1982	3	-	-	1	1
Luis Palau Evangelistic Assoc.		-	-	-	3	-
Maranatha Baptist Mission	1975	4	-	-	-	-
Medical Ambassadors Intl.	1995	-	-	-	6	-
Mennonite Board of Missions	1917	8	-	-	-	-
Mission to the World	1983	2	-	-	-	-
Missionary Revival Crusade	1991	3	-	-	-	-
Navigators, The	1973	6	2	-	-	-
Network of Intl Christian Schs	1998	-	1	10	1	-
OC International, Inc.	1987	2	-	-	-	1
Presbyterian Church (USA)		13	-	-	-	-
Seventh-day Adventists	1890	4	-	-	3	-
Spanish World Gospel Mission	1988	-	-	-	2	-
Team Expansion, Inc.	1986	1	-	-	-	-
United Church Board World		-	2	-	-	-
United Pentecostal Church Intl	1967	8	-	-	-	-
Walk Thru The Bible Ministries	1988	-	-	-	23	-
World Gospel Mission	1970	9	-	-	-	1
	Totals:	276	8	19	2039	30
Armenia						
Armenian Missionary Assoc.	1994	2	-	-	-	4
Bible League, The	1998	-	-	-	2	-
Christian Aid Mission		-	-	-	2	-
InterVarsity Mission	1996	-	1	-	-	-
Seventh-day Adventists	1886	2	-	-	-	-
World Vision Inc.	1997	-	-	1	-	-
	Totals:	4	1	1	4	4
Aruba						
Church of God World Missions	1968	2	-	-	-	-
	Totals:	2	-	-	-	-

COUNTRY Agency	Year Began	Personnel from U. S.			Other Countries	
		4+yrs	2-4 yrs	1-2 yrs	Citizens	Not Citiz.
Australia						
ABWE	1970	12	-	-	-	-
American Baptist Association	1968	1	-	-	-	-
Apostolic Christian Church	1978	2	-	-	-	-
Awana Clubs International	1975	2	-	-	28	-
Back to the Bible Intl.	1957	-	-	-	6	-
Baptist Bible Fellowship Intl.	1954	31	-	-	-	-
Baptist International Missions	1970	30	-	-	-	-
Baptist Mid-Missions	1968	24	-	4	-	-
Baptist World Mission	1984	4	-	-	-	-
Biblical Ministries Worldwide	1981	2	-	-	-	-
Campus Crusade for Christ	1967	4	-	1	87	-
Child Evangelism Fellowship	1944	2	-	-	1	-
Christ to the Nations Missions	1998	2	-	-	-	2
Christian Chs. /Chs. of Christ		14	-	-	-	-
Church of God of Prophecy	1956	1	-	-	-	-
Church of God World Missions	1976	2	-	-	-	4
Church of the Nazarene	1946	6	-	-	-	10
Church Resource Ministries	1986	2	-	-	-	-
Eastern Mennonite Missions	1980	2	-	-	-	-
Elim Fellowship World Missions	1991	2	-	-	-	-
Fellowship International Msn.	1984	8	-	-	-	-
Global Outreach Mission	1994	2	-	-	-	-
Gospel Fellowship Association	1973	4	-	-	-	4
Gospel Recordings	1953	-	-	-	23	-
Grace Baptist Missions Intl.	1991	2	-	-	-	-
Grace Ministries International	1976	6	-	1	-	-
Hope for the Hungry	1991	1	-	-	-	-
International Gospel Outreach	1998	-	1	-	-	-
International Teams, U.S.A.	1991	-	-	1	-	9
Intl. Pentecostal Holiness Ch.	1995	2	-	-	-	-
Jews for Jesus	1998	1	-	-	-	-
Maranatha Baptist Mission	1964	8	-	-	-	-
Mission to the World	1984	14	9	-	-	-
Navigators, The	1964	5	-	-	-	-
Presbyterian Church (USA)		2	-	-	-	-
Seventh-day Adventists	1885	4	-	-	3	-
SIM USA		-	-	-	25	-
Things To Come Mission, Inc.	1995	1	-	-	1	-
United Church Board World		-	2	-	-	-
United Pentecostal Church Intl	1956	4	-	-	-	-
Walk Thru The Bible Ministries	1980	-	-	-	8	-
Wesleyan World Missions	1945	4	-	-	-	-
World Baptist Fellowship Msn.	1995	-	2	-	-	-
Wycliffe Bible Translators	1950	15	-	-	-	-
Youth With A Mission		56	-	-	-	-
	Totals:	284	14	7	182	29
Austria						
Apostolic Team Ministries Intl		-	-	-	2	-
Assemblies of God	1967	8	-	-	-	-

COUNTRY Agency	Year Began	Personnel from U. S.			Other Countries	
		4+yrs	2-4 yrs	1-2 yrs	Citizens	Not Citiz.
Baptist Bible Fellowship Intl.		2	-	-	-	-
Baptist International Missions	1982	2	-	-	-	-
Baptist Mid-Missions	1965	2	-	1	-	-
BCM International	1975	1	-	-	-	-
Biblical Ministries Worldwide	1964	2	-	-	-	-
Brethren Assemblies		6	-	-	1	-
Campus Crusade for Christ	1974	3	-	-	-	-
CBInternational	1969	12	-	1	-	-
Child Evangelism Fellowship	1955	1	-	-	-	-
Christian Chs. /Chs. of Christ	1983	-	2	-	-	-
Elim Fellowship World Missions	1991	1	-	-	-	-
Evangelical Free Church Msn.	1971	2	-	2	-	-
Every Home for Christ		-	-	-	2	-
Global Outreach Mission		1	-	-	-	-
Gospel Fellowship Association	1997	4	-	-	-	4
Gospel Missionary Union	1966	3	-	3	-	8
International Teams, U.S.A.	1973	29	9	-	-	12
Mission to the World	1991	6	6	-	-	-
Navigators, The	1973	-	1	-	-	-
Network of Intl Christian Schs	1995	1	-	15	-	-
Pocket Testament League	1987	1	-	-	-	-
TEAM	1932	18	4	-	-	-
UFM International	1984	6	-	-	-	-
United Pentecostal Church Intl	1971	4	-	-	-	-
World Missions Fellowship	1991	2	-	-	-	-
Young Life	1974	6	9	-	-	-
Youth for Christ / USA		1	-	-	-	-
Youth With A Mission		10	-	-	-	-
	Totals:	134	31	22	5	24
Azerbaijan						
Greater Grace World Outreach	1991	-	-	-	-	3
World Vision Inc.	1998	-	-	2	-	-
	Totals:	-	-	2	-	3
Azores						
Baptist Bible Fellowship Intl.	1993	2	-	-	-	-
Baptist Missions to Forgotten		2	-	-	-	-
Gospel Fellowship Association	1978	4	-	-	-	4
	Totals:	8	-	-	-	4
Bahamas						
Assemblies of God	1942	8	-	1	-	-
Baptist Bible Fellowship Intl.		2	-	-	-	-
Christian Chs. /Chs. of Christ	1952	2	-	-	-	-
Gospel Missionary Union	1956	4	-	-	-	2
Island Missionary Society	1989	-	-	-	2	-
National Baptist Conv. USA	1946	2	-	-	168	-
United Pentecostal Church Intl	1988	2	-	-	-	-
	Totals:	20	-	1	170	2

COUNTRY Agency	Year Began	Personnel from U. S.			Other Countries	
		4+yrs	2-4 yrs	1-2 yrs	Citizens	Not Citiz.
Bahrain						
Arab World Ministries		2	-	-	-	2
Church of God World Missions	1984	-	-	-	-	2
Marriage Ministries Intl.	1993	-	-	-	-	2
Navigators, The		-	1	-	-	-
Reformed Baptist Mission Svcs.		2	-	-	-	1
	Totals:	4	1	-	-	7
Bangladesh						
ABWE	1954	63	-	-	-	-
American Baptist Churches USA	1976	1	-	-	-	-
Baptist Mid-Missions	1979	2	-	1	-	2
Campus Crusade for Christ	1975	-	-	-	216	-
Christian Aid Mission		-	-	-	49	-
Christian Chs. /Chs. of Christ	1990	-	2	-	-	-
Christian Reformed Relief	1972	1	1	-	1	-
Churches of God General Conf.	1971	-	-	-	55	-
Evangelical Lutheran Church	1993	2	-	-	-	-
Every Home for Christ	1973	-	-	-	15	-
FARMS International, Inc.	1996	-	-	-	-	-
Food for the Hungry, Inc.	1972	2	1	-	125	1
Global Fellowship		-	-	-	5	2
Global Outreach Mission		-	-	-	6	-
Gospel for Asia	1997	-	-	-	20	-
Gospel Recordings	1975	-	-	-	5	-
InterServe/USA	1971	6	-	-	-	-
Intl. Inst. Christian Studies	1999	-	-	2	-	-
Medical Ambassadors Intl.	1988	-	-	-	13	-
Operation Mobilization		2	-	-	-	-
Partners International	1975	-	-	-	62	-
Presbyterian Church (USA)		6	-	-	-	-
Rosedale Mennonite Missions	1995	1	-	-	-	-
Seventh-day Adventists	1906	4	-	-	5	-
SIM USA	1957	5	-	-	2	-
World Concern	1978	-	-	-	128	-
World Mission Prayer League	1972	6	-	1	-	-
World Missions Far Corners	1972	2	-	-	-	-
Youth With A Mission		2	-	-	-	-
	Totals:	105	4	4	707	5
Barbados						
Christian Chs. /Chs. of Christ	1953	2	-	-	-	-
National Baptist Conv. USA	1975	-	2	-	3	-
Youth With A Mission		8	-	-	-	-
	Totals:	10	2	-	3	-
Belarus						
Assemblies of God		5	-	4	-	-
Baptist International Missions	1993	1	-	-	-	-
Baptist International Outreach	1994	4	-	-	-	-
Baptist Mid-Missions	1986	2	-	-	-	-

COUNTRY Agency	Year Began	Personnel from U. S.			Other Countries	
		4+yrs	2-4 yrs	1-2 yrs	Citizens	Not Citiz.
Baptist World Mission	1998	4	-	-	-	-
Bible League, The	1993	-	-	-	14	-
Cadence International	1997	-	-	-	10	-
Campus Crusade for Christ	1992	2	-	9	4	3
Christian Aid Mission		-	-	-	44	-
Church of God of Prophecy	1995	-	-	-	1	-
Every Home for Christ	1993	-	-	-	5	-
Greater Grace World Outreach	1996	-	-	-	-	1
InterVarsity Mission	1992	1	-	-	-	-
Mission Ministries, Inc.	1992	-	-	-	-	-
Peter Deyneka Russian Mins.	1992	-	-	-	10	-
Rosedale Mennonite Missions	1994	2	-	-	-	-
Slavic Gospel Association	1945	-	-	-	8	-
Village Ministries Intl.	1992	-	-	-	1	-
Walk Thru The Bible Ministries	1993	-	-	-	97	-
World Baptist Fellowship Msn.	1995	-	2	-	-	-
Youth With A Mission		7	-	-	-	-
	Totals:	28	2	13	194	4
Belau(Palau)						
Assemblies of God	1983	4	-	-	-	-
High Adventure Ministries	1991	1	-	-	7	2
Liebenzell Mission USA	1941	3	-	-	2	-
	Totals:	8	-	-	9	2
Belgium						
Arab World Ministries		2	-	-	-	2
Assemblies of God	1949	16	-	38	-	-
Baptist Bible Fellowship Intl.	1962	9	-	-	-	-
Baptist International Missions	1978	1	-	-	-	-
Biblical Literature Fellowship	1958	10	1	-	1	-
CBInternational	1989	10	-	-	-	-
Child Evangelism Fellowship	1955	2	-	-	3	-
Christian Chs. /Chs. of Christ	1956	2	-	-	-	-
Church of God of Prophecy	1983	-	-	-	1	-
Church of God World Missions	1973	4	-	-	-	2
Church of the Nazarene		-	-	-	-	4
Elim Fellowship World Missions	1991	1	-	-	-	-
Evangelical Free Church Msn.	1977	15	-	-	-	-
Every Home for Christ		-	-	-	1	-
Fellowship International Msn.	1991	1	-	-	-	-
Global Outreach Mission		2	-	-	-	-
Gospel Missionary Union	1974	3	-	1	2	3
Gospel Recordings	1983	-	-	-	1	-
InterVarsity Mission	1997	-	-	1	-	-
Mennonite Board of Missions	1950	2	-	-	-	-
Operation Mobilization		8	-	2	-	-
Pilgrim Fellowship, Inc.	1990	1	-	-	1	-
Presbyterian Church (USA)		3	-	-	-	-
United Pentecostal Church Intl	1983	2	-	-	-	-
United World Mission	1970	3	2	-	4	-

COUNTRY Agency	Year Began	Personnel from U. S.			Other Countries	
		4+yrs	2-4 yrs	1-2 yrs	Citizens	Not Citiz.
Young Life	1984	2	1	-	-	-
	Totals:	99	4	42	14	11
Belize						
Assemblies of God	1956	6	-	2	-	-
Baptist Bible Fellowship Intl.	1979	6	-	-	-	-
BCM International		-	-	-	1	-
Calvary Commission, Inc.	1982	2	-	-	5	-
Child Evangelism Fellowship	1997	2	-	-	-	-
Christian Aid Mission		-	-	-	4	-
Christian Reformed World	1980	1	-	-	-	-
Church of God (Anderson, IN)		2	-	-	-	-
Church of the Nazarene	1934	-	-	-	-	2
Eastern Mennonite Missions	1960	4	-	-	-	-
Foursquare Missions Intl.	1990	2	-	-	-	-
Friends United Meeting	1976	2	-	-	-	-
Global Outreach Mission		2	-	-	-	-
Global Outreach, Ltd.	1978	5	1	-	-	-
Gospel Missionary Union		2	-	-	3	5
Hope for the Hungry	1991	2	-	-	-	-
International Gospel Outreach	1995	-	2	-	-	-
Living Water Teaching Intl.	1996	-	-	-	5	-
Macedonia World Baptist Msns.	1994	2	-	-	-	-
Mission to the Americas	1960	1	-	-	1	-
Mission to the World	1996	3	2	-	-	-
Pentecostal Church of God	1957	2	-	-	-	-
Pioneers	1986	3	1	-	-	-
STEM Ministries	1996	-	-	-	-	-
TMA Ministries	1973	1	-	-	-	-
United Pentecostal Church Intl	1985	2	-	-	-	-
Youth With A Mission		6	-	-	-	-
	Totals:	58	6	2	19	7
Benin						
Assemblies of God	1937	2	-	-	-	-
Baptist World Mission	1991	5	-	-	-	-
Campus Crusade for Christ	1988	-	-	-	11	-
Christian Aid Mission		-	-	-	22	-
Christian Chs. /Chs. of Christ	1992	-	4	-	-	-
Church of God of Prophecy	1985	-	-	-	1	-
CMF International	1991	-	-	2	-	2
Evangel Bible Translators	1989	-	-	-	1	-
Evangelical Baptist Missions	1966	1	-	-	-	-
Every Home for Christ	1991	-	-	-	9	-
Mennonite Board of Missions	1986	4	-	-	-	-
Ministry of Jesus, Inc.	1995	2	-	-	-	-
Pioneers	1998	2	-	-	4	-
Seventh-day Adventists	1967	-	-	-	1	-
SIM USA	1946	13	-	-	37	-
	Totals:	29	4	2	86	2

COUNTRY Agency	Year Began	Personnel from U. S.			Other Countries	
		4+yrs	2-4 yrs	1-2 yrs	Citizens	Not Citiz.
Bermuda						
Church of God (Anderson, IN)	1905	2	-	-	-	-
	Totals:	2	-	-	-	-
Bhutan						
Global Fellowship		-	-	-	5	5
Good News for India	1997	-	-	-	-	1
Gospel for Asia	1991	-	-	-	57	-
New Life League International	1975	-	-	-	2	-
	Totals:	-	-	-	64	6
Bolivia						
American Baptist Churches USA	1986	2	-	-	-	-
Apostolic Team Ministries Intl		2	-	-	-	-
Assemblies of God	1946	12	-	2	-	-
Baptist Bible Fellowship Intl.	1978	6	-	-	-	-
Baptist International Missions	1969	10	-	-	-	-
Baptist Missionary Assoc.	1965	3	-	-	-	-
Brethren Assemblies		17	-	-	-	1
Campus Crusade for Christ	1965	-	-	-	10	1
Central Yearly Mtg. of Friends	1925	5	2	-	-	-
Christian Aid Mission		-	-	-	27	-
Christian and Msny. Alliance	1981	4	-	-	-	-
Church of God (Anderson, IN)	1974	2	-	-	-	-
Church of God (Holiness) Msn.	1945	3	-	-	-	3
Church of God of Prophecy	1974	-	-	-	1	-
Church of the Nazarene	1945	4	-	-	-	-
Compassion International, Inc.	1975	-	-	-	18	-
Equip, Inc.	1998	-	2	-	-	-
Evangelical Friends Mission	1982	2	-	-	-	1
Evangelical Methodist Church	1978	4	-	-	-	-
Evangelistic Faith Missions	1977	-	2	-	-	-
Every Home for Christ	1971	-	-	-	1	-
Food for the Hungry, Inc.	1978	5	4	-	148	-
Globe Missionary Evangelism	1997	2	-	-	-	-
Gospel Missionary Union	1937	18	-	2	1	32
Grace Ministries International	1952	6	-	1	-	-
Habitat for Humanity Intl.	1984	-	2	-	22	-
International Teams, U.S.A.	1977	-	-	2	-	-
ISOH/Impact	1991	-	1	-	-	-
Latin America Mission	1990	1	-	-	1	1
MAP International	1989	-	-	-	18	-
Maranatha Baptist Mission	1963	8	-	-	-	-
New Tribes Mission	1942	97	-	8	2	3
Partners International	1976	-	-	-	18	-
Pentecostal Church of God	1997	2	-	-	-	-
Pioneers	1984	8	-	-	-	-
Seventh-day Adventists	1907	-	-	-	8	-
Shield of Faith Ministries	1995	-	-	-	6	-
SIM USA	1907	53	-	4	28	-
Source of Light Ministries	1996	2	-	-	-	-

COUNTRY Agency	Year Began	Personnel from U. S.			Other Countries	
		4+yrs	2-4 yrs	1-2 yrs	Citizens	Not Citiz.
South America Mission	1922	35	-	3	-	38
South American Missionary Soc.	1996	1	-	-	-	1
United Evangelical Churches		2	-	-	-	2
United Pentecostal Church Intl	1974	4	-	-	-	-
United World Mission	1948	11	-	-	2	-
World Concern	1997	-	2	-	15	-
World Gospel Mission	1944	34	-	-	-	3
World Indigenous Missions	1987	4	-	-	-	-
World Mission Prayer League	1938	8	-	1	-	-
World-Wide Missions	1963	-	-	-	38	-
Youth With A Mission		2	-	-	-	-
	Totals:	379	15	23	364	86
Bophuthatswana						
Christian Chs. /Chs. of Christ		4	-	-	-	-
	Totals:	4	-	-	-	-
Bosnia						
Christian Aid Mission		-	-	-	8	-
Christian and Msny. Alliance	1998	9	-	-	-	-
Eastern Mennonite Missions	1998	1	-	-	-	-
Perimeter Ch., Global Outreach	1996	-	-	-	2	-
Pioneers	1992	15	-	-	4	-
Team Expansion, Inc.		5	-	-	-	-
UFM International	1996	2	-	-	-	-
World Vision Inc.	1998	-	-	5	-	-
	Totals:	32	-	5	14	-
Botswana						
Africa Inter-Mennonite Mission	1975	5	-	-	-	4
Assemblies of God	1963	2	-	-	-	-
Baptist International Outreach	1996	-	-	-	-	1
Baptist Mid-Missions	1999	2	-	-	-	-
Campus Crusade for Christ	1993	-	-	-	4	1
Child Evangelism Fellowship	1996	1	-	-	-	-
Christian Aid Mission		-	-	-	8	-
Christian Chs. /Chs. of Christ	1984	2	-	-	-	-
Church of God of Prophecy	1965	-	-	-	-	1
Church of God World Missions	1951	2	-	-	-	-
Church of the Nazarene	1984	1	-	-	-	-
Faith Christian Fellowship	1994	2	-	-	-	1
General Conf. Mennonite	1975	3	-	-	-	3
Habitat for Humanity Intl.	1992	-	6	-	12	-
Lutheran Bible Translators	1993	6	-	1	5	-
Lutheran Church-Missouri	1984	4	-	-	-	-
Mission Aviation Fellowship		4	-	-	-	-
Seventh-day Adventists	1921	-	-	-	6	-
SIM USA	1973	10	-	-	5	-
United Church Board World		-	2	-	-	-
United Pentecostal Church Intl	1980	2	-	-	-	-
	Totals:	46	8	1	40	11

COUNTRY Agency	Year Began	Personnel from U. S.			Other Countries	
		4+yrs	2-4 yrs	1-2 yrs	Citizens	Not Citiz.
Brazil						
ABWE	1942	103	-	-	-	-
Action International Mins.	1991	4	-	-	-	-
Apostolic Christian Church	1961	17	-	-	3	2
Apostolic Team Ministries Intl		2	-	-	-	-
Assemblies of God	1925	13	-	-	-	-
Assoc of Free Lutheran Congs	1964	8	1	-	13	2
Baptist Bible Fellowship Intl.	1952	38	-	-	-	-
Baptist Faith Missions	1923	18	-	-	-	-
Baptist General Conference	1955	8	-	-	-	-
Baptist International Missions	1967	43	-	-	-	-
Baptist International Outreach	1993	3	-	-	-	-
Baptist Mid-Missions	1935	146	-	9	-	-
Baptist Missionary Assoc.	1953	2	-	-	-	-
Baptist World Mission	1970	22	-	-	-	-
BCM International	1987	-	-	-	4	-
Berean Mission, Inc.	1967	9	-	-	-	-
Bethany Fellowship Missions	1963	22	-	-	-	1
Brazil Gospel Fellowship Msn.	1939	64	-	-	-	-
Brethren Assemblies		7	-	-	1	1
Campus Crusade for Christ	1968	4	-	7	35	1
CBInternational	1946	30	-	1	-	-
Central Missionary Fellowship	1994	2	-	-	-	-
Child Evangelism Fellowship	1941	2	-	-	-	2
Christian Aid Mission		-	-	-	62	-
Christian and Msny. Alliance	1962	25	1	-	-	-
Christian Chs. /Chs. of Christ	1948	49	-	-	-	-
Christian Ministries Intl.	1984	2	-	-	16	2
Christians In Action, Inc.	1960	5	-	-	-	5
Church of God (Anderson, IN)	1923	4	-	-	-	-
Church of God of Prophecy	1965	-	-	-	1	-
Church of God World Missions	1951	5	-	2	-	-
Church of the Nazarene	1958	10	-	-	-	3
Churches of God General Conf.	1994	2	-	-	6	-
CMF International	1957	5	-	-	-	5
Compassion International, Inc.	1974	-	-	-	15	-
Cornerstone Intl.	1986	2	-	-	-	-
Crossover Communications Intl.	1994	-	-	-	3	1
Cumberland Presbyterian		2	1	-	-	-
Eastern Mennonite Missions	1996	2	-	-	-	-
Equip, Inc.	1995	8	-	-	-	-
Evangelical Bible Mission		-	4	-	-	-
Evangelical Free Church Msn.	1986	4	-	-	-	-
Evangelical Lutheran Church	1958	5	-	-	-	-
Every Home for Christ	1963	-	-	-	6	-
Fellowship International Msn.	1964	30	-	-	-	-
Food for the Hungry, Inc.	1997	-	-	-	-	2
Foursquare Missions Intl.	1946	2	-	-	-	-
Free Methodist World Missions	1928	4	-	-	-	-
Free Will Baptist, Inc.	1958	18	2	-	-	-
General Conf. Mennonite	1964	1	-	-	1	6

COUNTRY Agency	Year Began	Personnel from U. S.			Other Countries	
		4+yrs	2-4 yrs	1-2 yrs	Citizens	Not Citiz.
Global Outreach Mission	1973	2	-	-	-	-
Global Outreach, Ltd.	1990	-	1	-	-	-
Gospel Fellowship Association	1965	8	-	-	-	8
Gospel Missionary Union	1911	22	-	2	1	4
Gospel Recordings	1972	-	-	-	2	-
Grace Brethren Intl. Missions	1949	4	-	1	-	-
Grace Ministries International	1957	2	-	-	-	-
Greater Grace World Outreach	1983	-	-	-	1	-
Habitat for Humanity Intl.	1987	-	2	-	7	-
Harvest	1999	-	-	-	1	1
HCJB World Radio	1986	-	-	-	-	2
International Street Kids Mins	1992	1	-	-	1	-
Japanese Evangelical Msnry Soc	1961	1	-	-	-	-
Latin America Mission	1985	2	-	-	2	2
Lutheran Church-Missouri	1900	-	-	1	-	-
Macedonia World Baptist Msns.	1971	14	-	-	-	-
Maranatha Baptist Mission	1969	8	-	-	-	-
MBMS International	1946	-	2	-	-	-
Mennonite Board of Missions	1955	7	-	-	-	-
Mission Aviation Fellowship	1957	6	-	-	-	-
Mission to the World	1993	4	1	-	-	-
Navigators, The	1963	4	1	-	-	-
Network of Intl Christian Schs	1997	3	1	4	-	-
New Life League International	1984	1	-	-	-	-
New Tribes Mission	1946	160	-	5	3	11
North American Baptist Conf.	1966	6	-	-	-	-
OC International, Inc.	1963	13	-	-	-	1
OMS Intl., Inc.	1950	5	-	-	-	2
Open Air Campaigners	1990	-	-	-	1	-
Partners International	1969	-	-	-	159	-
Pilgrim Fellowship, Inc.	1948	5	-	-	-	1
Pocket Testament League	1965	-	-	-	2	2
Presbyterian Church (USA)	1859	14	23	7	-	-
Project AmaZon	1976	33	-	2	-	-
Reformed Episcopal Bd	1975	1	-	-	-	-
Salvation Army, U.S.A.	1922	4	-	-	-	-
Seventh-day Adventists	1894	-	-	-	5	-
Shield of Faith Ministries	1998	-	-	-	-	1
Shield of Faith Mission Intl.	1970	2	-	-	-	-
SIM USA	1994	2	-	-	-	-
Source of Light Ministries	1982	2	-	-	-	-
South America Mission	1913	11	-	2	-	13
TEAM	1972	6	-	-	-	-
Teen Missions International		1	-	-	-	-
Things To Come Mission, Inc.	1958	4	-	-	5	4
UFM International	1931	62	-	3	-	8
United Church Board World Mins	1922	-	1	-	-	-
United Pentecostal Church Intl	1956	12	-	-	-	-
United World Mission	1996	2	-	-	-	-
Walk Thru The Bible Ministries	1988	-	-	-	1	-
WEC International	1957	4	-	-	-	-

COUNTRY Agency	Year Began	Personnel from U. S.			Other Countries	
		4+yrs	2-4 yrs	1-2 yrs	Citizens	Not Citiz.
Wesleyan World Missions	1958	10	-	-	-	-
Wisconsin Evang. Lutheran Syn.	1987	4	-	-	-	-
World Baptist Fellowship Msn.	1960	28	2	-	-	-
World Partners USA	1955	4	-	-	-	-
World Team	1957	12	-	-	-	-
World-Wide Missions	1965	-	-	4	-	-
Wycliffe Bible Translators	1956	117	-	-	-	-
Youth for Christ / USA	1950	3	2	-	-	-
Youth With A Mission		25	-	-	-	-
	Totals:	1393	45	50	357	93
Bulgaria						
All God's Children Intl.	1992	-	-	-	2	-
AMG International	1991	-	-	-	10	-
Armenian Missionary Assoc.	1998	-	-	-	-	1
Baptist Bible Fellowship Intl.	1995	2	-	-	-	-
Baptist General Conference	1994	1	-	-	-	-
Bible League, The	1994	-	-	-	5	-
Campus Crusade for Christ	1991	11	-	1	12	-
Christian Aid Mission		-	-	-	102	-
Church of God of Prophecy	1991	-	-	-	1	-
Church of God World Missions	1982	2	-	-	-	-
Church of the Nazarene	1994	4	-	-	-	11
Congregational Christian Chs.	1992	-	-	-	2	-
Every Home for Christ	1991	-	-	-	2	-
Foursquare Missions Intl.	1992	-	-	2	-	-
International Teams, U.S.A.	1973	-	3	-	-	1
Ministry to Eastern Europe	1990	-	1	-	7	-
Mission Possible Foundation		-	-	-	7	-
Mission to the World	1994	7	-	-	-	-
Navigators, The		4	-	1	-	-
ORA International	1992	2	-	-	7	-
Partners International	1994	-	-	-	27	-
Presb. Evangelistic Fellowship		2	-	-	8	-
SEND International	1992	4	-	-	-	-
Wisconsin Evang. Lutheran Syn.	1992	6	-	-	-	-
World Bible Translation Center	1990	-	-	-	3	-
Youth With A Mission		1	-	-	-	-
	Totals:	46	4	4	195	13
Burkina Faso						
Africa Inter-Mennonite Mission	1978	5	-	4	-	8
Assemblies of God	1919	9	-	-	-	-
Baptist Bible Fellowship Intl.	1994	2	-	-	-	-
Campus Crusade for Christ	1991	2	-	-	9	-
Child Evangelism Fellowship	1982	-	-	-	2	-
Christian and Msny. Alliance	1923	18	2	-	-	-
Eastern Mennonite Missions	1997	2	-	-	-	-
Evangelical Covenant Church	1998	2	-	-	-	-
Every Home for Christ	1995	-	-	-	4	-
General Conf. Mennonite	1977	3	-	-	-	4

COUNTRY Agency	Year Began	Personnel from U. S.			Other Countries	
		4+yrs	2-4 yrs	1-2 yrs	Citizens	Not Citiz.
Gospel Recordings	1995	-	-	-	9	-
MBMS International	1994	-	2	-	-	-
Seventh-day Adventists	1972	-	-	-	4	-
SIM USA	1930	14	-	-	18	-
World Horizons	1990	-	-	-	-	1
Wycliffe Bible Translators	1980	32	-	-	-	-
Youth With A Mission		2	-	-	-	-
	Totals:	91	4	4	46	13
Burundi						
Brethren Assemblies		4	-	-	-	-
Campus Crusade for Christ	1980	-	-	-	25	-
Child Evangelism Fellowship	1952	-	-	-	1	-
Christian Aid Mission		-	-	-	298	-
Covenant Celebration Church		-	-	-	1	-
Free Methodist World Missions	1935	2	-	-	-	-
Seventh-day Adventists	1925	-	-	-	4	-
World Vision Inc.	1998	-	-	3	-	-
	Totals:	6	-	3	329	-
Cambodia						
ABWE	1998	9	-	-	-	-
American Baptist Churches USA	1996	2	-	-	-	-
Assemblies of God		25	-	8	-	-
Baptist Bible Fellowship Intl.		8	-	-	-	-
Baptist International Missions	1996	5	-	-	-	-
Baptist Mid-Missions	1998	2	-	-	-	-
Baptist World Mission	1979	8	-	-	-	-
Bible League, The	1996	-	-	-	6	-
Christian Aid Mission		-	-	-	146	-
Christian and Msny. Alliance	1923	18	7	-	-	-
Christian Reformed Relief	1995	-	1	-	-	2
Church of the Nazarene	1992	2	-	-	-	1
Church Resource Ministries	1994	5	-	-	-	-
Church World Service &	1950	1	-	-	10	4
Eastern Mennonite Missions	1998	5	-	-	-	-
Elim Fellowship World Missions	1995	1	-	-	-	-
Far East Broadcasting Company	1993	-	-	-	20	-
Final Frontiers Foundation	1987	-	-	-	14	-
Food for the Hungry, Inc.	1991	3	4	-	43	3
Friends Church Southwest	1995	4	-	-	-	-
Gospel Fellowship Association		2	-	-	-	2
Grace Brethren Intl. Missions		-	1	-	-	-
Intl. Pentecostal Holiness Ch.	1996	-	-	-	-	2
Mission To Unreached Peoples	1989	5	-	-	1	-
Partners International	1993	-	-	-	50	-
Seventh-day Adventists	1937	8	1	-	1	-
Wesleyan World Missions	1994	-	-	-	-	4
World Baptist Fellowship Msn.		-	-	2	-	-
World Concern	1985	-	1	-	61	-
World Relief Corporation	1991	2	1	1	-	1

COUNTRY Agency	Year Began	Personnel from U. S.			Other Countries	
		4+yrs	2-4 yrs	1-2 yrs	Citizens	Not Citiz.
World Vision Inc.	1992	3	1	2	-	-
Youth With A Mission		5	-	-	-	-
	Totals:	123	17	13	352	19
Cameroon						
Assemblies of God	1976	4	-	2	-	-
Baptist General Conference	1982	6	-	-	-	-
Bible League, The	1993	-	-	-	2	1
Campus Crusade for Christ	1992	-	-	-	30	2
Child Evangelism Fellowship	1995	-	-	-	4	-
Christian Blind Mission Intl.	1982	-	1	-	-	-
Church of God of Prophecy	1985	-	-	-	1	-
Evangelical Covenant Church	1998	2	2	-	-	-
Evangelical Lutheran Church	1923	16	-	3	-	-
Evangelism Resources	1999	-	2	-	-	-
Gospel Fellowship Association	1987	14	-	3	-	17
Gospel Recordings	1994	-	-	-	1	-
Gospel Revival Ministries	1998	-	-	-	1	-
Lutheran Bible Translators	1980	6	-	-	6	-
Navigators, The	1990	2	-	-	-	-
North American Baptist Conf.	1891	21	-	1	-	-
Presbyterian Church (USA)		4	-	-	-	-
Prison Mission Association	1992	-	-	-	1	-
Seventh-day Adventists	1928	4	-	-	8	-
Things To Come Mission, Inc.	1995	-	2	-	1	-
United Pentecostal Church Intl	1971	2	-	-	-	-
Wisconsin Evang. Lutheran Syn.	1997	-	2	1	-	-
World Team	1985	17	-	-	-	5
World-Wide Missions	1966	-	-	-	22	-
Wycliffe Bible Translators	1968	135	-	-	-	-
	Totals:	233	9	10	77	25
Canary Isls						
Assemblies of God	1973	4	-	-	-	-
	Totals:	4	-	-	-	-
Cape Verde Isls						
Seventh-day Adventists	1935	-	-	-	2	-
	Totals:	-	-	-	2	-
Caribbean Isls						
Brethren Assemblies		3	-	-	-	1
Calvary Evangelistic Mission	1953	4	-	6	-	2
Church of God World Missions	1924	1	-	-	-	-
Church of the Nazarene		7	-	-	-	-
Macedonia World Baptist Msns.	1983	2	-	-	-	-
Wesleyan World Missions	1904	-	-	-	4	-
World Baptist Fellowship Msn.	1991	8	-	-	-	-
	Totals:	25	-	6	4	3

COUNTRY Agency	Year Began	Personnel from U. S.			Other Countries	
		4+yrs	2-4 yrs	1-2 yrs	Citizens	Not Citiz.
Cayman Isls						
Christian Chs./Chs. of Christ		5	-	-	-	-
Church of God (Holiness) Msn.	1954	2	-	-	2	2
	Totals:	7	-	-	2	2
Central Africa Republic						
Africa Inland Mission Intl.	1924	2	-	-	-	-
Baptist Mid-Missions	1920	19	-	-	-	-
Campus Crusade for Christ	1987	-	-	-	29	-
Evangelical Covenant Church	1997	12	-	-	-	-
Evangelical Free Church Msn.	1997	12	-	1	-	-
Evangelical Lutheran Church	1974	10	1	-	-	-
Grace Brethren Intl. Missions	1918	9	-	8	-	-
Habitat for Humanity Intl.	1991	-	3	-	9	-
Missionary Ventures Intl.	1991	-	-	-	2	-
SIM USA	1978	1	-	-	-	-
Wycliffe Bible Translators		5	-	-	-	-
	Totals:	70	4	9	40	-
Chad						
Africa Inland Mission Intl.	1986	3	-	-	-	-
Brethren Assemblies		-	1	-	-	-
Campus Crusade for Christ	1996	-	-	-	6	-
Central Missionary Fellowship	1997	-	1	-	-	-
Child Evangelism Fellowship	1997	-	-	-	-	1
Christian Mission for the Deaf		-	-	-	2	-
Gospel Recordings	1995	-	-	-	9	-
Gospel Revival Ministries	1997	-	-	-	5	-
Lutheran Brethren World Msns.	1920	6	-	-	-	-
Navigators, The		-	1	-	-	-
TEAM	1969	25	-	2	-	2
WEC International	1962	2	-	-	-	-
World Partners USA	1996	2	-	-	-	-
Wycliffe Bible Translators	1977	24	-	-	-	-
	Totals:	62	3	2	22	3
Chile						
ABWE	1953	32	-	-	-	-
American Baptist Churches USA	1993	4	-	-	-	-
Assemblies of God	1941	23	-	-	-	-
Baptist Bible Fellowship Intl.	1954	11	-	-	-	-
Baptist International Missions	1996	2	-	-	-	-
Baptist Mid-Missions	1992	8	-	-	-	-
Brethren Assemblies		1	-	-	2	1
Campus Crusade for Christ	1963	-	-	-	11	-
Christian Aid Mission		-	-	-	13	-
Christian and Msny. Alliance	1897	21	-	-	-	-
Christian Chs./Chs. of Christ	1949	32	-	-	-	-
Church of God of Prophecy	1975	-	-	-	1	-
Church of God World Missions	1954	-	-	-	-	2
Church of the Nazarene	1962	4	-	-	-	-

COUNTRY Agency	Year Began	Personnel from U. S.			Other Countries	
		4+yrs	2-4 yrs	1-2 yrs	Citizens	Not Citiz.
CMF International	1988	6	-	-	-	6
Evangelical Lutheran Church	1982	3	-	-	-	-
Evangelical Lutheran Synod	1992	-	2	-	-	-
Final Frontiers Foundation	1998	-	-	-	1	-
Foursquare Missions Intl.	1947	1	-	-	-	-
Free Methodist World Missions	1986	2	-	-	-	-
Global Outreach, Ltd.	1995	-	2	-	-	-
Gospel Fellowship Association	1963	6	-	-	-	6
Gospel Mission of S. America	1923	20	-	-	-	20
International Gospel Outreach	1988	1	-	-	2	1
International Partnership Mins	1991	-	-	-	1	-
Macedonia World Baptist Msns.	1996	2	-	-	-	-
Maranatha Baptist Mission	1963	4	-	-	-	-
Mennonite Board of Missions	1970	2	-	-	-	-
Mission to the World	1977	16	-	-	-	-
Navigators, The	1985	2	1	-	-	-
Presb. Evangelistic Fellowship		1	-	-	-	-
Presbyterian Church (USA)	1845	7	-	-	-	-
Salvation Army, U.S.A.	1909	6	-	-	-	-
Seventh-day Adventists	1895	4	-	-	1	-
SIM USA	1986	7	-	-	2	-
Source of Light Ministries	1980	-	-	-	2	-
South American Missionary Soc.	1979	3	-	-	-	2
Spanish World Gospel Mission	1988	-	-	-	2	-
United Church Board World Mins		-	1	-	-	-
United Pentecostal Church Intl	1964	6	-	-	-	-
World Team	1982	5	-	-	-	-
World-Wide Missions	1964	-	-	-	14	-
Youth With A Mission		12	-	-	-	-
	Totals:	254	6	-	52	38
China (PRC)						
ABWE	1998	6	-	-	-	-
All God's Children Intl.	1995	-	-	-	1	-
American Baptist Churches USA	1843	1	-	2	-	-
Anglican Frontier Missions	1995	4	-	-	-	-
Back to the Bible Intl.	1994	-	-	-	7	-
Baptist Bible Fellowship Intl.	1950	4	-	-	-	-
Baptist International Outreach	1993	4	-	-	-	-
Bible League, The	1980	-	-	-	3	3
Central Missionary Fellowship	1991	2	-	-	-	-
China Connection	1989	1	-	-	-	-
Christian Aid Mission		-	-	-	986	-
Christian and Msny. Alliance	1897	19	-	-	-	-
Christian Chs. /Chs. of Christ	1990	1	-	4	-	-
Christian Ministries Intl.	1987	2	2	8	-	10
Church of God World Missions	1992	6	-	-	-	-
Church of The Brethren		-	2	-	-	-
Church of the Nazarene		8	-	-	-	3
East Gates Ministries Intl.	1990	-	-	-	1	-
Evangelical Free Church Msn.	1994	15	-	3	-	-

COUNTRY Agency	Year Began	Personnel from U. S.			Other Countries	
		4+yrs	2-4 yrs	1-2 yrs	Citizens	Not Citiz.
Evangelical Lutheran Church	1986	-	2	6	-	-
Evangelize China Fellowship	1947	-	-	-	3	-
Every Home for Christ	1995	-	-	-	1	-
Final Frontiers Foundation	1988	-	-	-	18	-
Food for the Hungry, Inc.	1992	4	1	-	-	-
General Conf. Mennonite	1909	2	-	-	-	2
Global Outreach, Ltd.	1992	8	4	-	-	-
Global Strategy Mission Assoc.	1996	-	-	4	-	-
Gospel for Asia	1991	-	-	-	31	-
Holt Intl. Children's Services	1990	-	-	-	6	1
Hope for the Hungry	1991	2	1	-	-	-
InterServe/USA	1989	1	-	-	-	-
Lutheran Church-Missouri	1913	7	-	3	-	-
Macedonia World Baptist Msns.	1996	6	-	-	-	-
Mennonite Board of Missions	1947	2	-	-	-	-
Mission Possible Foundation		-	-	-	1	-
Mission Soc. for United Meth.	1994	1	-	2	-	-
Mission To Unreached Peoples	1986	6	-	-	-	-
Missions To Japan, Inc.		1	-	-	-	-
Overseas Radio & Television		-	-	-	-	2
Partners International	1943	-	-	-	289	-
Presbyterian Church (USA)		4	-	20	-	-
Project Partner with Christ	1984	-	-	-	1	-
Seventh-day Adventists	1902	4	2	-	1	-
SIM USA		-	-	-	2	-
Sowers International, The	1995	-	1	-	1	-
Team Expansion, Inc.		5	-	-	-	-
Training Evangelistic Ldrshp.	1985	3	-	-	-	-
United Church Board World Mins		-	2	-	-	-
World Bible Translation Center	1991	-	-	-	4	-
World Missions Far Corners	1988	4	-	-	-	-
World Partners USA	1955	2	-	-	-	-
	Totals:	135	17	52	1356	21
Colombia						
ABWE	1939	16	-	-	-	-
Action International Mins.	1990	4	-	-	-	1
American Baptist Association	1971	1	-	-	-	-
Assemblies of God	1962	23	-	8	-	-
Baptist Bible Fellowship Intl.	1971	4	-	-	-	-
Baptist International Missions	1990	2	-	-	-	-
Baptist Missions to Forgotten		2	-	-	-	-
Bible League, The	1990	-	-	-	40	-
Brethren Assemblies		19	-	-	-	1
Brethren in Christ World Msns.	1984	2	1	1	-	-
Campus Crusade for Christ	1963	-	-	-	4	-
Child Evangelism Fellowship	1943	-	-	-	1	-
Christ for the City Intl.	1988	2	-	-	11	-
Christian Aid Mission		-	-	-	42	-
Christian and Msny. Alliance	1923	20	-	-	-	-
Christian Chs. /Chs. of Christ	1962	14	-	-	-	-

COUNTRY Agency	Year Began	Personnel from U. S. 4+yrs	 2-4 yrs	 1-2 yrs	Other Countries Citizens	 Not Citiz.
Christian Church of North Am.	1965	1	-	-	-	-
Christian Literature Crusade	1973	2	-	-	-	-
Christians In Action, Inc.	1970	3	-	-	-	3
Church of God of Prophecy	1973	-	-	-	1	-
Church of God World Missions	1954	3	-	-	-	-
Compassion International, Inc.	1976	-	-	-	20	-
Cumberland Presbyterian	1929	2	1	-	-	-
Deaf Missions International	1970	1	-	-	-	-
Elim Fellowship World Missions	1964	6	-	-	-	-
Evangelical Covenant Church	1968	9	2	-	-	-
Evangelical Lutheran Church	1944	2	-	-	-	-
Fellowship International Msn.	1991	2	-	-	-	-
General Conf. Mennonite	1947	-	-	2	1	4
Gospel Missionary Union	1908	4	-	-	-	1
Habitat for Humanity Intl.	1994	-	3	-	2	-
Hope for the Hungry	1991	1	-	1	-	-
Impact International	1990	2	-	-	3	-
International Teams, U.S.A.	1995	2	-	-	-	-
Latin America Mission	1932	13	-	-	4	4
Macedonia World Baptist Msns.	1994	2	-	-	-	-
Maranatha Baptist Mission	1983	4	-	-	-	-
MBMS International	1945	-	1	-	-	-
Mission to the World	1979	13	-	-	-	-
Missionary Revival Crusade	1974	4	-	-	2	-
Navigators, The		2	-	-	-	-
New Tribes Mission	1944	55	-	2	3	4
OMS Intl., Inc.	1943	12	-	-	-	4
Presbyterian Church (USA)	1856	7	-	-	-	-
Reformed Baptist Mission Svcs.	1985	2	-	-	-	1
Seventh-day Adventists	1921	2	-	-	3	-
South America Mission	1934	9	-	-	-	9
Sowers International, The	1993	-	-	-	1	1
Spanish World Gospel Mission	1988	-	-	-	2	-
TEAM	1923	24	-	-	-	-
Team Expansion, Inc.	1989	3	-	-	-	-
United Pentecostal Church Intl	1936	4	-	-	-	-
Wesleyan World Missions	1941	4	-	-	-	2
Wisconsin Evang. Lutheran Syn.	1974	3	-	-	-	-
World Baptist Fellowship Msn.	1968	4	2	2	-	-
World-Wide Missions	1964	-	-	-	1	-
Wycliffe Bible Translators	1962	107	-	-	-	-
Youth for Christ / USA		2	-	-	-	-
Youth With A Mission		5	-	-	-	-
	Totals:	430	10	16	141	35
Comoros Isls						
Africa Inland Mission Intl.	1975	6	-	-	-	-
	Totals:	6	-	-	-	-
Congo						
Africa Inland Mission Intl.	1912	3	-	2	-	-
African Enterprise, Inc.	1994	-	-	-	3	-

COUNTRY Agency	Year Began	Personnel from U. S.			Other Countries	
		4+yrs	2-4 yrs	1-2 yrs	Citizens	Not Citiz.
Assemblies of God	1988	2	-	-	-	-
Brethren Assemblies		8	-	-	-	2
Campus Crusade for Christ	1990	-	-	-	15	3
Christian and Msny. Alliance	1992	6	-	-	-	-
Christian Blind Mission Intl.	1991	-	1	-	-	-
Evangelical Covenant Church	1937	2	-	-	-	-
Evangelical Free Church Msn.	1922	6	-	-	-	-
Every Child Ministries, Inc.		-	-	-	4	-
Every Home for Christ	1993	-	-	-	65	-
Global Outreach Mission	1974	5	-	-	-	-
International Outreach Mins.	1986	8	-	5	-	-
Medical Ambassadors Intl.	1987	-	-	-	26	-
United World Mission	1948	6	-	-	-	-
Wycliffe Bible Translators		23	-	-	-	-
	Totals:	69	1	7	113	5
Congo/Zaire						
Africa Inter-Mennonite Mission	1912	2	-	-	-	-
American Baptist Churches USA	1884	19	-	-	-	1
Assemblies of God	1921	4	-	-	-	-
Baptist Bible Fellowship Intl.	1957	6	-	-	-	-
Berean Mission, Inc.	1938	9	-	-	-	-
Campus Crusade for Christ	1979	-	-	-	159	2
CBInternational	1946	4	-	-	-	-
Child Evangelism Fellowship	1952	-	-	-	4	-
Christian Aid Mission		-	-	-	36	-
Christian and Msny. Alliance	1884	2	-	-	-	-
Christian Chs. /Chs. of Christ	1948	34	-	-	-	-
Church of God of Prophecy	1979	-	-	-	1	-
Compassion International, Inc.	1980	-	-	-	23	-
Episcopal World Mission	1994	3	-	-	-	-
Evangelism Resources	1980	2	-	-	-	2
Every Child Ministries, Inc.	1985	-	-	-	11	-
Every Home for Christ	1965	-	-	-	206	-
Food for the Hungry, Inc.	1994	-	2	-	22	1
General Conf. Mennonite	1906	1	-	-	-	1
Grace Ministries International	1928	12	-	1	15	-
Habitat for Humanity Intl.	1974	-	1	-	58	-
Independent Faith Mission	1988	8	-	-	-	-
Mahesh Chavda Ministries Intl.	1985	-	-	-	6	-
Mission Aviation Fellowship	1960	24	-	2	-	2
Navigators, The	1982	2	-	-	-	-
Presbyterian Church (USA)	1891	12	10	-	-	-
The Master's Mission, Inc.	1980	2	-	-	-	-
UFM International	1931	5	-	-	-	1
World-Wide Missions	1960	-	-	-	12	-
	Totals:	151	13	3	553	10
Costa Rica						
ABWE	1998	4	-	-	-	-
American Baptist Association	1940	3	-	-	-	-

COUNTRY Agency	Year Began	Personnel from U. S.			Other Countries	
		4+yrs	2-4 yrs	1-2 yrs	Citizens	Not Citiz.
American Baptist Churches USA	1980	3	-	-	-	-
Assemblies of God	1943	22	-	3	-	-
Baptist Bible Fellowship Intl.	1968	13	-	-	-	-
Baptist International Missions	1968	14	-	-	-	-
Baptist International Outreach	1990	-	-	-	2	-
Baptist Missionary Assoc.	1961	2	-	-	-	-
Calvary International	1983	7	-	-	-	-
CAM International	1891	15	2	-	-	3
Campus Crusade for Christ	1976	2	-	1	4	2
Christ for the City Intl.	1985	2	-	-	28	6
Christian Aid Mission		-	-	-	18	-
Christian and Msny. Alliance	1975	1	-	-	-	-
Christian Chs. /Chs. of Christ		6	-	-	-	-
Christian Leadership Dev.	1973	2	-	-	-	1
Christian Reformed World	1981	5	3	1	-	-
Church of God (Anderson, IN)	1920	2	-	-	-	-
Church of God of Prophecy	1932	-	-	-	-	1
Church of the Nazarene	1964	9	-	-	-	2
Evangelical Lutheran Church	1998	2	-	-	-	-
Final Frontiers Foundation	1991	-	-	-	4	-
Foursquare Missions Intl.	1953	-	-	-	-	2
Gospel Fellowship Association	1991	2	-	-	1	1
Grace Ministries International	1984	5	-	-	-	-
Habitat for Humanity Intl.	1987	-	3	-	-	-
Hope for the Hungry	1991	2	-	-	-	-
Impact International		1	-	-	2	-
International Children's Care	1988	-	1	-	-	-
International Outreach Mins.	1995	3	-	-	-	-
International Teams, U.S.A.	1994	4	-	2	-	7
Intl. Pentecostal Holiness Ch.	1951	2	-	-	-	-
Latin America Assistance	1963	-	-	-	1	3
Latin America Mission	1921	53	-	2	9	9
Living Water Teaching Intl.	1994	-	-	-	-	2
Macedonia World Baptist Msns.	1994	2	-	-	-	-
Mission Soc. for United Meth.	1986	-	5	-	-	-
Mission to the Americas	1967	1	-	-	-	-
Mutual Faith Ministries Intl.	1985	1	-	-	-	-
Presb. Evangelistic Fellowship		1	-	-	-	-
Presbyterian Church (USA)	1970	4	8	2	-	-
Project Partner with Christ	1979	-	-	-	1	-
Rosedale Mennonite Missions	1961	4	-	-	-	-
Salvation Army, U.S.A.	1907	7	-	-	-	-
Seventh-day Adventists	1903	4	1	-	-	-
South American Missionary Soc.	1982	3	-	-	-	2
United Pentecostal Church Intl	1975	2	-	-	-	-
Walk Thru The Bible Ministries	1993	-	-	-	1	-
Youth With A Mission		5	-	-	-	-
	Totals:	220	23	11	71	41

Cote d'Ivoire

Advancing Renewal Ministries	1992	-	-	-	1	-

COUNTRY Agency	Year Began	Personnel from U. S. 4+yrs	2-4 yrs	1-2 yrs	Other Countries Citizens	Not Citiz.
Africa Inter-Mennonite Mission	1997	-	-	2	-	-
Assemblies of God	1968	2	-	-	-	-
Baptist Bible Fellowship Intl.	1988	2	-	-	-	-
Baptist General Conference	1977	8	-	-	-	1
Baptist International Missions	1970	3	-	-	-	-
Baptist Mid-Missions	1974	23	-	5	-	-
Campus Crusade for Christ	1975	-	-	-	32	-
CBInternational	1947	60	-	4	-	-
Child Evangelism Fellowship	1976	-	-	-	1	-
Christian Aid Mission		-	-	-	12	-
Christian and Msny. Alliance	1930	42	15	-	-	-
Christian Chs. /Chs. of Christ	1985	10	-	-	-	-
Church of God (Anderson, IN)		2	-	-	-	-
Church of God of Prophecy	1978	-	-	-	1	-
Church of God World Missions	1992	2	-	-	-	-
Church of the Nazarene	1987	10	-	-	-	-
CMF International	1998	2	-	-	-	2
Evangelical Baptist Missions	1971	10	-	2	-	-
Evangelical Free Church Msn.	1997	4	-	-	-	-
Every Home for Christ	1991	-	-	-	4	-
Final Frontiers Foundation	1994	-	-	-	7	-
Free Will Baptist, Inc.	1958	26	1	2	-	-
Global Fellowship		-	-	-	5	-
International Partnership Mins		-	-	-	2	-
Intl. Pentecostal Holiness Ch.	1993	2	-	-	-	-
Liberia Christian Mission	1991	2	-	-	-	-
Lion and Lamb Outreach	1974	1	-	-	-	-
Lutheran Bible Translators	1996	7	-	-	4	-
Lutheran Church-Missouri	1991	4	-	4	-	-
Macedonia World Baptist Msns.	1980	2	-	-	-	-
MAP International	1995	-	-	-	3	-
Mission to the World	1985	12	-	-	-	-
Navigators, The	1984	6	1	-	-	-
New Tribes Mission	1982	61	-	7	-	7
Partners International	1990	-	-	-	232	-
Pioneers		-	-	-	8	-
Seventh-day Adventists	1946	4	-	-	7	-
Shield of Faith Mission Intl.	1995	2	-	-	-	-
SIM USA	1968	19	-	2	5	-
Source of Light Ministries	1979	2	-	-	-	-
United Pentecostal Church Intl	1972	2	-	-	-	-
Walk Thru The Bible Ministries	1994	-	-	-	2	-
WEC International	1934	13	-	-	-	-
World Missions Far Corners	1992	2	-	-	-	-
Wycliffe Bible Translators	1970	69	-	-	-	-
Youth With A Mission		1	-	-	-	-
	Totals:	417	17	28	326	10
Croatia						
Advent Christian World Msns.	1996	-	-	-	1	-
Assemblies of God		2	-	-	-	-

COUNTRY Agency	Year Began	Personnel from U. S. 4+yrs	 2-4 yrs	 1-2 yrs	Other Countries Citizens	 Not Citiz.
Baptist Bible Fellowship Intl.		2	-	-	-	-
Campus Crusade for Christ	1993	8	-	9	11	-
Child Evangelism Fellowship	1989	2	-	-	2	-
Christian Aid Mission		-	-	-	22	-
Every Home for Christ		-	-	-	3	-
InterVarsity Mission	1997	-	-	2	-	-
Ministry to Eastern Europe	1998	-	-	-	3	-
Navigators, The		2	-	-	-	-
Pioneers	1992	2	-	-	-	-
Presbyterian Church (USA)		2	-	-	-	-
SEND International		3	-	-	-	-
Wesleyan World Missions	1992	3	-	-	-	-
Youth With A Mission		2	-	-	-	-
	Totals:	28	-	11	42	-
Cuba						
ABWE	1998	4	-	-	-	-
American Baptist Churches USA	1898	1	-	-	-	-
Baptist Bible Fellowship Intl.	1955	4	-	-	-	-
Baptist World Mission	1997	4	-	-	-	-
BCM International		1	-	-	-	-
Child Evangelism Fellowship	1949	-	-	-	2	-
Christ to the Nations Missions	1995	10	-	-	6	4
Church of God of Prophecy	1935	-	-	-	1	-
Final Frontiers Foundation	1998	-	-	-	1	-
International Gospel Outreach	1998	1	-	-	-	-
International Partnership Mins		-	-	-	11	-
Marriage Ministries Intl.	1993	-	-	-	2	-
Wisconsin Evang. Lutheran Syn.	1995	1	-	-	-	-
World Missions Far Corners	1990	2	-	-	-	-
	Totals:	28	-	-	23	4
Cyprus						
AMG International	1984	2	-	-	2	-
Arab World Ministries		-	-	-	-	3
Biblical Ministries Worldwide	1963	4	-	-	-	-
Child Evangelism Fellowship	1952	8	-	-	-	-
Church of God of Prophecy	1965	-	-	-	1	-
Episcopal World Mission	1984	-	-	-	2	-
Globe Missionary Evangelism	1999	2	-	-	-	-
InterServe/USA	1984	2	-	-	-	-
Macedonia World Baptist Msns.	1989	2	-	-	-	-
Middle East Christian Outreach	1975	-	-	-	-	19
Orthodox Presbyterian Church	1984	2	-	-	-	-
Reformed Presbyterian Church	1992	-	1	-	-	-
SAT-7 North America	1996	-	-	-	5	-
World Partners USA	1966	2	-	-	-	-
Youth for Christ / USA		-	2	-	-	-
Youth With A Mission		1	-	-	-	-
	Totals:	25	3	-	10	22

COUNTRY Agency	Year Began	Personnel from U. S.			Other Countries	
		4+yrs	2-4 yrs	1-2 yrs	Citizens	Not Citiz.
Czech Rep						
American Baptist Churches USA	1995	6	-	-	-	-
Apostolic Christian Church	1998	1	-	-	-	-
Assemblies of God	1981	4	-	1	-	-
Baptist International Missions	1994	1	-	-	-	-
Baptist Missionary Assoc.		1	-	-	-	-
Calvary International		2	-	-	-	-
Campus Crusade for Christ	1981	6	-	3	8	-
CBInternational	1991	4	-	-	-	-
Child Evangelism Fellowship	1966	1	-	-	-	-
Christian Aid Mission		-	-	-	36	-
Christian Outreach Intl.	1992	2	5	-	1	2
Evangelical Covenant Church	1999	2	-	-	-	-
Evangelical Free Church Msn.	1991	11	-	2	-	-
Evangelical Lutheran Synod	1990	-	3	-	-	-
Every Home for Christ	1991	-	-	-	4	-
Faith Christian Fellowship	1997	-	2	-	-	-
Gospel Missionary Union		1	-	-	-	-
Grace Brethren Intl. Missions	1993	4	-	-	-	-
Greater Grace World Outreach	1991	-	-	-	-	2
HCJB World Radio	1992	-	-	-	-	2
International Messengers	1989	-	-	1	2	-
International Teams, U.S.A.	1973	11	2	-	-	6
Intl. Inst. Christian Studies	1992	8	-	-	1	-
Mission to the World	1989	4	8	-	-	-
Missionary Athletes Intl.	1993	2	-	-	-	-
New Hope International	1992	-	-	-	6	-
Operation Mobilization		4	-	1	-	-
Salvation Army, U.S.A.	1990	2	-	-	-	-
SEND International	1994	4	-	2	-	-
Seventh-day Adventists	1901	-	-	-	1	-
TEAM	1994	11	-	1	-	-
Wesleyan World Missions	1992	4	-	-	-	-
Young Life	1990	4	-	-	-	-
Youth With A Mission		3	-	-	-	-
	Totals:	103	20	11	59	12
Denmark						
Baptist Bible Fellowship Intl.		2	-	-	-	-
Bethany Missionary Association		1	-	-	-	-
Child Evangelism Fellowship	1947	3	-	-	-	-
Christian Chs. /Chs. of Christ	1992	-	-	2	-	-
Elim Fellowship World Missions	1995	2	-	-	-	-
Evangelical Lutheran Church	1995	2	-	-	-	-
Global Outreach Mission	1995	2	-	-	-	-
	Totals:	12	-	2	-	-
Djibouti						
Campus Crusade for Christ	1994	3	-	-	-	-
Project Mercy, Inc.	1977	-	-	-	-	23
SIM USA	1996	2	-	-	1	-
	Totals:	5	-	-	1	23

COUNTRY Agency	Year Began	Personnel from U. S.			Other Countries	
		4+yrs	2-4 yrs	1-2 yrs	Citizens	Not Citiz.
Dominica						
Berean Mission, Inc.	1973	1	-	-	-	-
Church of the Nazarene	1974	-	-	-	-	4
Gospel Fellowship Association	1994	2	-	-	-	2
	Totals:	3	-	-	-	6
Dominican Rep						
American Baptist Churches USA	1980	6	-	-	-	-
Assemblies of God	1922	12	-	2	-	-
Baptist Bible Fellowship Intl.	1996	4	-	-	-	-
BCM International		-	-	-	2	-
Bethany Fellowship Missions	1978	2	-	-	-	-
Bible League, The	1991	-	-	-	20	-
Brethren Assemblies		2	-	-	-	-
Campus Crusade for Christ	1977	-	-	-	13	-
Christian Aid Mission		-	-	-	4	-
Christian and Msny. Alliance	1969	14	-	-	-	-
Christian Blind Mission Intl.	1985	-	-	1	-	-
Christian Chs. /Chs. of Christ		6	-	-	-	-
Christian Reformed Relief	1982	1	-	-	-	-
Christian Reformed World	1979	17	6	2	-	-
Church of God of Prophecy	1940	-	-	-	1	-
Church of the Nazarene	1974	6	-	-	-	4
Compassion International, Inc.	1970	-	-	-	18	-
Floresta USA, Inc.	1984	-	-	-	11	-
Food for the Hungry, Inc.	1979	1	4	-	24	1
Foursquare Missions Intl.	1996	2	-	-	-	-
Free Methodist World Missions	1889	4	-	-	-	-
Habitat for Humanity Intl.	1987	-	4	-	5	-
Harvest	1981	-	-	-	5	-
International Children's Care	1987	-	2	-	-	-
Kids Alive International	1989	1	9	-	25	-
Medical Ambassadors Intl.	1988	-	-	-	6	-
Ministries In Action	1995	-	-	-	-	1
Mission Possible	1987	-	-	-	14	-
Mission to the Americas	1981	-	-	-	1	-
Presbyterian Church (USA)		3	-	-	-	-
Primitive Methodist Church	1997	2	-	-	-	-
Seventh-day Adventists	1908	2	-	-	4	-
South American Missionary Soc.	1987	4	-	-	-	1
STEM Ministries	1994	-	-	-	-	-
UFM International	1949	18	-	4	-	-
United Church Board World		-	1	-	-	-
United Pentecostal Church Intl	1965	6	-	-	-	-
Wisconsin Evang. Lutheran Syn.	1993	2	-	-	-	-
World Partners USA	1945	4	-	-	-	-
World Team		4	-	-	-	-
Young Life	1989	4	-	-	-	-
Youth With A Mission		12	-	-	-	-
	Totals:	139	26	9	153	7

COUNTRY Agency	Year Began	Personnel from U. S.			Other Countries	
		4+yrs	2-4 yrs	1-2 yrs	Citizens	Not Citiz.
Ecuador						
Assemblies of God	1962	26	-	5	-	-
Back to the Bible Intl.	1970	-	-	-	6	-
Baptist Bible Fellowship Intl.	1975	12	-	-	-	-
Baptist International Missions	1990	8	-	-	-	-
Baptist Mid-Missions	1998	15	-	11	-	-
Berean Mission, Inc.	1959	19	-	-	-	-
Brethren Assemblies		14	-	-	-	-
Campus Crusade for Christ	1965	-	-	-	42	-
Child Evangelism Fellowship	1941	-	-	-	3	-
Christian Aid Mission		-	-	-	21	-
Christian and Msny. Alliance	1897	31	29	-	-	-
Christian Blind Mission Intl.	1980	-	1	-	-	-
Christian Chs. /Chs. of Christ		6	-	-	-	-
Christian Reformed Relief	1983	-	-	-	-	1
Christian Reformed World	1991	1	-	-	-	-
Christians In Action, Inc.	1979	2	-	-	-	2
Church of God (Anderson, IN)		4	-	-	-	-
Church of God of Prophecy	1982	-	-	-	-	1
Church of God World Missions	1971	7	-	-	-	2
Church of the Nazarene	1972	6	-	-	-	5
Compassion International, Inc.	1974	-	-	-	16	1
Evangelical Covenant Church	1947	9	1	-	-	-
FARMS International, Inc.		-	-	-	-	-
Fellowship International Msn.	1967	4	-	-	-	-
Foursquare Missions Intl.	1956	2	-	-	-	-
Free Methodist World Missions	1981	2	-	-	-	-
Global Outreach, Ltd.	1990	4	-	-	-	-
Gospel Missionary Union	1896	36	-	6	4	11
HCJB World Radio	1931	179	-	4	8	34
Holt Intl. Children's Services	1990	-	-	-	10	-
International Teams, U.S.A.	1997	2	2	2	-	4
InterVarsity Mission	1992	2	-	-	-	-
Latin America Mission	1975	1	-	-	-	3
Liebenzell Mission USA	1989	1	-	-	-	-
Lutheran Bible Translators	1982	-	-	-	-	-
MAP International	1981	-	-	-	10	-
Mission Aviation Fellowship	1948	28	1	5	-	1
Mission to the World	1975	19	7	-	-	-
OMS Intl., Inc.	1952	16	2	-	-	4
Reformed Church In America	1989	-	-	-	1	-
Rosedale Mennonite Missions	1982	7	-	-	-	2
SIM USA	1989	8	-	-	9	-
Sowers International, The	1980	2	-	-	-	-
Team Expansion, Inc.	1989	4	-	-	-	-
Teen Missions International		-	2	-	-	-
United Church Board World Mins	1945	-	2	-	-	-
United Pentecostal Church Intl	1964	4	-	-	-	-
Walk Thru The Bible Ministries	1993	-	-	-	7	-
World Baptist Fellowship Msn.	1972	12	2	-	-	-
World Mission Prayer League	1951	6	-	4	-	-

COUNTRY Agency	Year Began	Personnel from U. S.			Other Countries	
		4+yrs	2-4 yrs	1-2 yrs	Citizens	Not Citiz.
World Missions Far Corners	1984	6	-	-	-	-
World Partners USA	1945	12	-	-	-	-
Youth for Christ / USA	1982	2	-	-	-	-
	Totals:	519	49	37	137	71
Egypt						
Arab World Ministries	1984	10	-	-	-	4
Back to the Bible Intl.	1998	-	-	-	5	-
Bible League, The	1980	-	-	-	5	-
Campus Crusade for Christ	1972	5	-	-	53	1
Christ Community Church	1983	2	-	-	-	-
Christian Aid Mission		-	-	-	57	-
Church of God of Prophecy	1935	-	-	-	1	-
Evangelical Lutheran Church	1967	2	-	2	-	-
Evangelistic Faith Missions	1905	-	-	-	25	-
Global Outreach Mission		-	-	-	6	-
Habitat for Humanity Intl.	1989	-	1	-	1	-
Marriage Ministries Intl.	1992	-	-	-	1	1
Partners International	1989	-	-	-	17	-
Presbyterian Church (USA)	1954	13	10	-	-	-
SAT-7 North America	1997	-	-	-	7	-
Seventh-day Adventists	1879	6	-	-	-	-
United Pentecostal Church Intl	1955	2	-	-	-	-
Venture Middle East	1995	1	-	-	2	-
World Horizons	1990	-	-	-	-	1
World-Wide Missions	1961	-	-	-	10	-
	Totals:	41	11	2	190	7
El Salvador						
American Baptist Churches USA	1911	2	-	-	-	-
Assemblies of God	1925	13	-	27	-	-
Brethren Assemblies		6	-	-	-	-
CAM International	1896	7	-	-	-	-
Campus Crusade for Christ	1966	-	-	-	27	-
Child Evangelism Fellowship	1942	-	-	-	1	-
Christian Reformed Relief	1976	-	1	-	-	-
Christian Reformed World	1996	2	-	-	-	-
Church of God of Prophecy	1954	-	-	-	1	-
Evangelistic Faith Missions	1964	-	-	-	5	-
Final Frontiers Foundation	1991	-	-	-	4	-
Greater Grace World Outreach	1974	-	-	-	2	-
Habitat for Humanity Intl.	1992	-	-	-	13	-
Harvesting In Spanish	1977	3	-	5	-	-
Larry Jones International Mins	1983	-	-	-	6	-
Living Water Teaching Intl.	1989	4	-	-	-	-
Medical Ambassadors Intl.	1983	-	-	-	6	1
Mission to the Americas	1994	-	-	-	1	-
Open Bible Standard Churches	1975	2	-	-	-	-
Partners International	1989	-	-	-	11	-
Ripe for Harvest, Inc.	1993	-	1	-	-	-
United Church Board World Mins	1983	-	2	-	-	-

COUNTRY Agency	Year Began	Personnel from U. S.			Other Countries	
		4+yrs	2-4 yrs	1-2 yrs	Citizens	Not Citiz.
United Pentecostal Church Intl	1975	4	-	-	-	-
Walk Thru The Bible Ministries	1993	-	-	-	1	-
World Reach, Inc.	1996	3	-	-	-	-
World-Wide Missions	1964	-	-	-	14	-
	Totals:	46	4	32	92	1
Equatorial Guinea						
Assemblies of God	1987	8	-	-	-	-
Evangelical Covenant Church	1999	2	-	-	-	-
Every Home for Christ	1994	-	-	-	6	-
Gospel Fellowship Association		2	-	-	-	2
	Totals:	12	-	-	6	2
Eritrea						
Assemblies of God		6	-	-	-	-
Evangelistic Faith Missions	1950	-	2	-	75	-
Lutheran Church-Missouri	1975	2	-	-	-	-
SIM USA	1952	3	-	-	-	-
World Mission Prayer League	1994	-	-	1	-	-
	Totals:	11	2	1	75	-
Estonia						
Baptist General Conference		2	-	-	-	-
Campus Crusade for Christ	1994	1	-	4	1	-
Navigators, The		-	2	-	-	-
Operation Mobilization		-	-	2	-	-
Reformed Church In America	1994	2	-	-	-	-
Walk Thru The Bible Ministries	1993	-	-	-	21	-
Youth With A Mission		1	-	-	-	-
	Totals:	6	2	6	22	-
Ethiopia						
ACM International	1996	1	-	-	-	-
African Enterprise, Inc.	1995	-	-	-	1	-
Assemblies of God	1968	23	-	-	-	-
Baptist Bible Fellowship Intl.	1960	8	-	-	-	-
Baptist General Conference	1950	8	-	-	-	-
Baptist International Outreach	1985	-	-	-	40	-
Baptist Mid-Missions	1993	5	-	-	-	1
Bible League, The	1991	-	-	-	1	-
Campus Crusade for Christ	1980	-	-	-	107	-
Christian Mission for the Deaf		-	-	-	2	-
Church of God of Prophecy	1996	-	-	-	1	-
Church of the Nazarene	1992	2	-	-	-	1
CMF International	1963	11	-	2	-	13
Compassion International, Inc.	1993	-	-	-	17	-
Eastern Mennonite Missions	1948	6	-	-	-	-
Elim Fellowship World Missions	1995	1	-	-	-	-
Equip, Inc.	1995	4	-	-	-	-
Evangelical Lutheran Church	1957	2	-	-	-	-
Evangelistic Faith Missions	1950	-	-	-	5	-

COUNTRY Agency	Year Began	Personnel from U. S.			Other Countries	
		4+yrs	2-4 yrs	1-2 yrs	Citizens	Not Citiz.
Every Home for Christ	1991	-	-	-	6	-
Food for the Hungry, Inc.	1984	2	-	-	200	4
Habitat for Humanity Intl.	1990	-	5	-	5	-
Helps International Ministries	1988	-	-	-	-	1
Larry Jones International Mins	1983	-	-	-	12	-
Medical Ambassadors Intl.	1993	-	-	-	2	-
Mission to the World	1982	2	2	-	-	-
Mission: Moving Mountains	1994	4	-	-	-	-
ORA International	1998	1	-	1	30	-
Orthodox Presbyterian Church	1994	2	-	-	-	-
Presbyterian Church (USA)	1820	4	18	2	-	-
Project Mercy, Inc.	1977	2	-	-	17	-
Reformed Church In America	1975	4	-	-	-	-
Seventh-day Adventists	1907	6	-	-	10	-
SIM USA	1927	71	-	13	34	-
Team Expansion, Inc.		1	-	-	-	-
World Concern	1993	1	-	-	16	-
Wycliffe Bible Translators	1975	23	-	-	-	-
	Totals:	194	25	18	506	20
Fiji						
Assemblies of God	1914	6	-	-	-	-
Baptist Bible Fellowship Intl.	1976	6	-	-	-	-
Baptist International Missions	1994	4	-	-	-	-
Biblical Ministries Worldwide	1990	4	-	-	-	4
Campus Crusade for Christ	1974	-	-	-	5	-
Child Evangelism Fellowship	1953	3	-	-	1	-
Church of the Nazarene	1995	4	-	-	-	-
Every Home for Christ		-	-	-	12	-
Fellowship International Msn.	1995	1	-	-	-	-
Final Frontiers Foundation	1997	-	-	-	1	-
Habitat for Humanity Intl.	1991	-	2	2	2	4
Mustard Seed, Inc.	1998	-	-	-	2	-
Presbyterian Church (USA)	1974	2	-	-	-	-
United Church Board World Mins		-	2	-	-	-
World Missions Far Corners	1993	-	-	-	2	-
Youth With A Mission		5	-	-	-	-
	Totals:	35	4	2	25	8
Finland						
Baptist International Missions		2	-	-	-	-
Baptist Mid-Missions	1980	2	-	-	-	-
BCM International	1968	-	-	-	2	-
Evangelical Lutheran Church	1978	-	2	-	-	-
Greater Grace World Outreach	1975	-	-	-	12	-
Mission Possible Foundation	1985	-	-	-	3	-
Salvation Army, U.S.A.	1889	5	-	-	-	-
	Totals:	9	2	-	17	-
French Polynesia						
Baptist Bible Fellowship Intl.	1977	4	-	-	-	-
	Totals:	4	-	-	-	-

COUNTRY Agency	Year Began	Personnel from U. S. 4+yrs	2-4 yrs	1-2 yrs	Other Countries Citizens	Not Citiz.
France						
ABWE	1984	10	-	-	-	-
Africa Inland Mission Intl.	1987	2	-	-	-	-
American Baptist Association	1973	1	-	-	-	-
Apostolic Team Ministries Intl		4	-	-	1	-
Arab World Ministries	1963	36	-	-	-	29
Artists In Christian Testimony	1998	2	-	-	-	2
Assemblies of God	1952	11	-	5	-	-
Baptist Bible Fellowship Intl.	1970	10	-	-	-	-
Baptist General Conference	1989	6	-	-	-	-
Baptist International Missions	1969	4	-	-	-	-
Baptist Mid-Missions	1948	23	-	2	-	-
Baptist World Mission	1969	20	-	-	-	-
BCM International	1988	2	-	-	-	-
Bethany Fellowship Missions	1980	4	-	-	-	-
Biblical Ministries Worldwide	1996	2	-	-	-	-
Brethren Assemblies		15	-	-	-	3
Campus Crusade for Christ	1970	22	-	20	-	3
CBInternational	1962	19	-	1	-	-
Child Evangelism Fellowship	1949	2	-	-	-	-
Christar	1988	12	-	-	-	-
Christian Aid Mission		-	-	-	4	-
Christian and Msny. Alliance	1962	18	-	-	-	-
Christian Chs./Chs. of Christ		6	-	-	-	-
Christian Outreach Intl.	1993	1	-	-	1	-
Christian Reformed World Msns	1989	2	-	-	-	-
Christian World Publishers	1985	2	-	-	-	-
Church of God of Prophecy	1985	-	-	-	1	-
Church of God World Missions	1960	-	-	1	-	-
Church of the Nazarene	1977	4	-	-	-	3
Church Resource Ministries	1995	4	-	-	-	-
Cornerstone Intl.	1984	2	-	-	-	-
Development Associates Intl.	1997	-	-	-	-	1
European Missions Outreach	1989	2	-	-	-	-
Evangel Bible Translators	1978	2	-	-	-	-
Evangelical Baptist Missions	1956	26	-	-	-	-
Evangelical Covenant Church	1996	3	-	-	-	-
Evangelical Free Church Msn.	1988	14	-	-	-	-
Evangelical Greenhouse Mins.	1996	6	1	-	5	-
Evangelical Presbyterian Ch.	1992	2	-	-	-	-
Every Home for Christ	1992	-	-	-	4	-
Fellowship International Msn.	1987	1	-	-	-	-
Final Frontiers Foundation	1997	-	-	-	2	-
Foursquare Missions Intl.	1982	2	-	-	-	-
Free Will Baptist, Inc.	1966	8	-	-	-	-
General Conf. Mennonite	1974	2	-	-	-	-
Global Outreach Mission	1946	30	-	-	10	-
Globe Missionary Evangelism	1996	2	-	-	-	-
Gospel Missionary Union	1960	7	-	7	1	-
Grace Brethren Intl. Missions	1951	21	-	-	-	-
Greater Grace World Outreach	1982	-	-	-	4	2

COUNTRY Agency	Year Began	Personnel from U. S.			Other Countries	
		4+yrs	2-4 yrs	1-2 yrs	Citizens	Not Citiz.
Hope for the Hungry	1991	2	1	-	-	-
International Teams, U.S.A.	1969	16	4	-	-	2
InterVarsity Mission	1987	1	-	1	-	-
Jews for Jesus	1992	-	-	-	1	1
Lion and Lamb Outreach	1991	2	-	-	-	-
Maranatha Baptist Mission	1983	8	-	-	-	-
Mennonite Board of Missions	1953	3	-	1	-	-
Mission Soc. for United Meth.	1994	6	3	-	-	-
Mission to the World	1978	29	5	-	-	-
Missionary Revival Crusade	1983	4	-	-	-	2
Missions to Military	1971	5	-	-	-	-
Mutual Faith Ministries Intl.	1997	-	-	-	1	-
Navigators, The	1972	4	2	-	-	-
OC International, Inc.	1980	4	-	-	-	-
Operation Mobilization		2	-	1	-	-
Partners International	1983	-	-	-	2	-
Pocket Testament League	1988	-	-	-	2	-
Presb. Evangelistic Fellowship		5	-	-	-	-
Presbyterian Church (USA)		2	-	-	-	-
Reformed Baptist Mission Svcs.	1992	2	-	-	-	1
Reformed Episcopal Bd	1970	2	-	-	-	-
SIM USA		-	-	-	7	-
Society for Europe's Evang.	1956	5	-	-	-	-
TEAM	1938	40	-	-	-	-
Team Expansion, Inc.	1991	1	-	-	-	-
UFM International	1962	26	-	-	-	3
United Pentecostal Church Intl	1973	4	-	-	-	-
Walk Thru The Bible Ministries	1990	-	-	-	2	-
WEC International	1950	4	-	-	-	-
World Baptist Fellowship Msn.	1954	-	-	2	-	-
World Partners USA	1979	2	-	-	-	-
World Team	1980	12	-	-	-	-
Wycliffe Bible Translators		3	-	-	-	-
Youth for Christ / USA	1949	1	-	-	-	-
Youth With A Mission		7	-	-	-	-
	Totals:	576	16	41	48	52
French Guiana						
Brethren Assemblies		2	-	-	-	-
	Totals:	2	-	-	-	-
Gabon						
Campus Crusade for Christ	1989	-	-	-	7	-
Christian and Msny. Alliance	1934	26	8	-	-	-
InterVarsity Mission	1994	2	-	-	-	-
Medical Ambassadors Intl.	1993	-	-	-	1	-
	Totals:	28	8	-	8	-
Gambia						
ABWE	1978	23	-	-	-	-
Child Evangelism Fellowship	1986	2	-	-	-	-
Christian Aid Mission		-	-	-	6	-

COUNTRY Agency	Year Began	Personnel from U. S.			Other Countries	
		4+yrs	2-4 yrs	1-2 yrs	Citizens	Not Citiz.
General Conf. Mennonite	1995	2	-	-	-	1
WEC International	1957	3	-	-	-	-
	Totals:	30	-	-	6	1
Georgia						
Assemblies of God		4	-	1	-	-
Salvation Army, U.S.A.	1991	6	-	-	-	-
World Concern	1998	-	-	1	1	-
World Vision Inc.	1997	-	-	1	-	-
	Totals:	10	-	3	1	-
Germany						
ABWE	1989	12	-	-	-	-
Africa Inland Mission Intl.	1997	-	-	2	-	-
American Baptist Association		1	-	-	-	-
Apostolic Team Ministries Intl		-	-	-	2	-
Arab World Ministries	1986	4	-	-	-	2
Assemblies of God	1950	29	-	-	-	-
Baptist Bible Fellowship Intl.	1970	25	-	-	-	-
Baptist International Missions	1969	5	-	-	-	-
Baptist Mid-Missions	1959	23	-	3	-	-
Baptist Missions to Forgotten		11	-	-	-	-
Baptist World Mission	1968	13	-	-	-	-
BCM International		3	-	-	-	-
Bible Missionary Church	1995	2	-	-	-	-
Biblical Ministries Worldwide	1958	7	-	-	-	-
Brethren Assemblies		3	-	-	-	-
Cadence International	1973	19	-	18	-	1
Campus Crusade for Christ	1966	23	-	10	-	6
Child Evangelism Fellowship	1949	3	-	-	-	-
Chosen People Ministries	1995	-	-	-	-	2
Christar	1989	4	-	-	-	-
Christian and Msny. Alliance	1975	9	3	-	-	-
Christian Associates Intl.	1996	4	-	-	1	-
Christian Chs. /Chs. of Christ	1956	10	-	-	-	-
Christians In Action, Inc.	1972	4	-	-	1	3
Church of God (Anderson, IN)		2	-	-	-	-
Church of God of Prophecy	1959	7	-	-	-	-
Church of God World Missions	1936	5	-	-	-	-
Church of The Brethren	1946	-	5	-	-	-
Church of the Nazarene	1958	2	-	-	-	-
Eastern Mennonite Missions	1957	4	-	-	-	1
European Evangelistic Society	1991	2	-	-	-	-
Evangelical Baptist Missions	1977	6	-	-	-	-
Evangelical Covenant Church	1991	3	2	-	-	-
Evangelical Free Church Msn.	1958	14	-	2	-	-
Evangelical Lutheran Church	1972	1	2	-	-	-
Every Home for Christ		-	-	-	8	-
Fellowship International Msn.	1984	2	-	-	-	-
Foursquare Missions Intl.	1981	4	-	-	-	-
General Conf. Mennonite	1994	-	-	-	-	4
Global Outreach Mission	1946	7	-	-	8	-

COUNTRY Agency	Year Began	Personnel from U. S.			Other Countries	
		4+yrs	2-4 yrs	1-2 yrs	Citizens	Not Citiz.
Globe Missionary Evangelism	1985	2	-	-	-	-
Gospel Fellowship Association	1963	18	-	1	3	16
Gospel Missionary Union	1961	4	-	3	-	1
Gospel Recordings	1965	-	-	-	7	-
Grace Baptist Missions Intl.	1990	1	-	-	-	-
Grace Brethren Intl. Missions	1969	12	-	1	-	-
Great Commission Ministries		2	-	-	-	-
Greater Grace World Outreach	1983	-	-	-	-	2
International Messengers	1992	2	-	-	-	-
International Teams, U.S.A.	1972	2	2	1	-	2
Intl. Discipleship Mission	1990	2	-	-	-	-
Intl. Pentecostal Holiness Ch.	1987	3	-	-	-	-
Liebenzell Mission USA	1941	2	1	-	-	-
Macedonia World Baptist Msns.	1987	4	-	-	-	-
Maranatha Baptist Mission	1981	4	-	-	-	-
MBMS International	1953	-	2	-	-	-
Mission to the World	1991	10	-	-	-	-
Missionary Revival Crusade		3	-	-	-	2
New Tribes Mission	1991	2	-	-	-	-
OC International, Inc.	1981	13	-	-	-	-
Operation Mobilization		-	-	1	-	-
Pocket Testament League	1986	2	-	-	-	-
Presbyterian Church (USA)		2	8	-	-	-
Reformed Episcopal Bd	1950	2	-	-	-	3
Rosedale Mennonite Missions	1979	3	-	1	-	-
Salvation Army, U.S.A.	1886	2	-	-	-	-
Seventh-day Adventists	1875	-	-	-	2	-
TEAM	1910	10	6	-	-	-
Turkish World Outreach	1988	2	-	-	2	-
UFM International	1976	18	-	5	-	3
United Church Board World Mins		-	2	-	-	-
United Pentecostal Church Intl	1968	4	-	-	-	-
Walk Thru The Bible Ministries	1988	-	-	-	1	1
WEC International	1948	1	-	-	-	-
Wesleyan World Missions	1987	-	-	-	2	-
World Reach, Inc.	1988	-	-	-	2	-
World Witness	1993	6	-	-	-	-
Wycliffe Bible Translators		1	-	-	-	-
Young Life	1975	2	8	7	-	-
Youth With A Mission		13	-	-	-	-
	Totals:	427	41	55	39	49
Ghana						
ABWE	1993	4	-	-	-	-
African Enterprise, Inc.	1995	-	-	-	3	-
African Methodist Epis. Zion	1896	1	-	-	-	-
African Mission Evangelism	1966	11	-	1	12	-
Agape Gospel Mission	1994	-	-	-	8	3
American Baptist Churches USA	1994	1	-	-	-	-
Apostolic Christian Church	1975	-	-	-	2	-
Assemblies of God	1931	2	-	-	-	-

COUNTRY Agency	Year Began	Personnel from U. S. 4+yrs	 2-4 yrs	 1-2 yrs	Other Countries Citizens	 Not Citiz.
Baptist International Missions	1976	2	-	-	-	-
Baptist Mid-Missions	1946	15	-	6	-	-
Baptist World Mission	2000	2	-	-	-	-
BCM International	1985	-	-	-	2	-
Bethany Fellowship Missions	1995	2	-	-	-	1
Bible League, The	1985	-	-	-	2	-
Bible Missionary Church	1984	2	-	-	-	-
Campus Crusade for Christ	1969	-	-	-	46	-
Child Evangelism Fellowship	1971	-	-	-	14	-
Christ to the Nations Missions	1999	2	-	-	2	-
Christian Aid Ministries		-	2	-	-	-
Christian Aid Mission		-	-	-	23	-
Christian Chs. /Chs. of Christ	1965	7	-	-	-	-
Christians In Action, Inc.	1994	3	-	-	-	3
Church of God of Prophecy	1977	-	-	-	1	-
Church of God World Missions	1965	-	-	-	-	2
Church of the Nazarene	1990	2	-	-	-	-
East West Ministries		-	-	-	1	-
Evangel Bible Translators	1992	2	-	-	-	-
Every Child Ministries, Inc.	1999	-	-	-	1	-
Every Home for Christ	1976	-	-	-	2	-
Final Frontiers Foundation	1992	-	-	-	15	-
Full Gospel Grace Fellowship		1	-	-	-	-
Globe Missionary Evangelism	1998	2	-	-	-	-
Gospel Recordings	1990	-	-	-	8	-
Gospel Revival Ministries	1996	-	-	-	4	-
Grace Baptist Missions Intl.	1990	-	-	-	1	-
Greater Grace World Outreach	1988	-	-	-	10	-
Habitat for Humanity Intl.	1987	-	3	-	16	-
Hope for the Hungry	1991	-	-	-	3	-
International Partnership Mins	1987	2	-	-	11	-
Intl. Pentecostal Holiness Ch.	1992	2	-	-	-	-
Ireland Outreach Intl., Inc.	1997	-	-	-	1	-
Lutheran Church-Missouri	1960	11	-	5	-	-
Mennonite Board of Missions	1957	6	-	-	-	-
Mission Soc. for United Meth.	1985	4	2	-	-	-
Mutual Faith Ministries Intl.	1985	-	-	-	-	1
National Baptist Conv. of Am.	1984	-	-	-	14	-
Navigators, The	1967	2	-	-	-	-
Partners International	1973	-	-	-	42	-
Presbyterian Church (USA)	1964	4	-	-	-	-
Self-Help Foundation	1990	-	1	-	12	-
Seventh-day Adventists	1894	-	1	-	-	-
SIM USA	1956	12	-	-	11	-
Source of Light Ministries	1995	-	-	-	5	-
TMA Ministries	1990	1	-	-	-	-
United Pentecostal Church Intl	1969	5	-	-	-	-
Village Ministries Intl.	1991	-	-	-	6	-
WEC International		2	-	-	-	-
Wycliffe Bible Translators	1962	22	-	-	-	-
	Totals:	134	9	12	278	10

COUNTRY Agency	Year Began	Personnel from U. S.			Other Countries	
		4+yrs	2-4 yrs	1-2 yrs	Citizens	Not Citiz.
Greece						
AMG International	1945	16	-	-	11	-
Baptist Bible Fellowship Intl.	1993	2	-	-	-	-
BCM International	1995	-	-	-	1	-
Brethren Assemblies		3	-	-	-	-
Campus Crusade for Christ	1978	5	-	-	-	-
Child Evangelism Fellowship	1971	2	-	-	2	-
Church of God of Prophecy	1931	-	-	-	1	-
Congregational Christian Chs.	1962	-	-	-	4	-
European Christian Mission	1987	7	-	-	-	-
Every Home for Christ	1981	-	-	-	1	-
Free Methodist World Missions	1998	2	-	-	-	-
Global Outreach Mission	1994	2	-	-	-	-
Gospel Missionary Union	1959	1	-	-	4	1
Greater Grace World Outreach	1984	-	-	-	2	-
Hellenic Ministries	1981	5	-	1	3	1
International Teams, U.S.A.	1990	8	6	-	-	8
OC International, Inc.	1967	2	-	-	-	-
Presb. Evangelistic Fellowship		1	-	-	-	-
Seventh-day Adventists	1907	-	-	-	1	-
United Pentecostal Church Intl	1975	4	-	-	-	-
Walk Thru The Bible Ministries	1990	-	-	-	2	-
Youth With A Mission		1	-	-	-	-
	Totals:	61	6	1	32	10
Greenland						
New Tribes Mission	1988	1	-	-	-	10
Youth With A Mission		3	-	-	-	-
	Totals:	4	-	-	-	10
Grenada						
Baptist Missions to Forgotten	1979	2	-	-	-	-
Berean Mission, Inc.	1956	2	-	-	-	-
Christian Chs./Chs. of Christ		4	-	-	-	-
Final Frontiers Foundation	1996	-	-	-	1	-
Macedonia World Baptist Msns.	1986	2	-	-	-	-
Maranatha Baptist Mission	1987	2	-	-	-	-
Ministries In Action	1974	1	-	-	-	-
	Totals:	13	-	-	1	-
Guadeloupe						
World Team	1947	4	-	-	-	-
	Totals:	4	-	-	-	-
Guam						
Assemblies of God	1961	6	-	7	-	-
Biblical Ministries Worldwide	1981	4	-	-	-	-
Christian Reformed World	1962	4	3	-	-	-
Church of God (Anderson, IN)		2	-	-	-	-
Church of the Nazarene	1971	4	-	-	-	-
Liebenzell Mission USA	1962	9	1	-	-	-

COUNTRY Agency	Year Began	Personnel from U. S.			Other Countries	
		4+yrs	2-4 yrs	1-2 yrs	Citizens	Not Citiz.
Mission to the World	1996	2	-	-	-	-
Seventh-day Adventists	1930	83	12	-	4	-
	Totals:	114	16	7	4	-
Guatemala						
Africa Inland Mission Intl.		1	-	-	-	-
American Assoc. Lutheran Chs.	1998	-	-	-	-	2
AMG International	1976	2	-	-	5	-
Assemblies of God	1937	16	-	2	-	-
Baptist International Missions	1971	6	-	-	-	-
Baptist Missionary Assoc.		3	-	-	-	-
BILD International		-	-	-	1	-
Brethren Assemblies		4	-	-	-	-
Calvary International	1986	27	-	-	-	-
CAM International	1899	47	4	2	4	4
Campus Crusade for Christ	1963	2	-	1	50	2
Child Evangelism Fellowship	1943	-	-	-	2	-
Children of Promise Int'l.		-	4	-	-	-
Christian Aid Mission		-	-	-	1075	-
Christian Chs. /Chs. of Christ	1991	2	4	-	-	-
Christian Reformed Relief	1976	-	-	-	1	-
Christians In Action, Inc.	1970	5	-	-	3	2
Church of God of Prophecy	1951	-	-	-	-	1
Church of God World Missions	1934	2	-	-	-	-
Church of the Nazarene	1904	23	-	-	-	8
Compassion International, Inc.	1976	-	-	-	17	-
Correll Missionary Ministries	1979	2	-	-	-	-
Eastern Mennonite Missions	1967	8	3	-	-	-
Evangel Bible Translators	1999	2	-	-	-	-
Evangelical Lutheran Church	1990	1	-	-	-	-
Evangelistic Faith Missions	1959	-	-	2	-	-
Faith Christian Fellowship	1991	6	-	-	-	-
Final Frontiers Foundation	1992	-	-	-	25	-
Food for the Hungry, Inc.	1976	-	2	-	22	2
Friends Church Southwest	1902	2	-	-	-	-
Global Fellowship		-	-	-	-	2
Global Outreach Mission		-	-	-	10	-
Globe Missionary Evangelism	1980	15	-	-	-	-
Habitat for Humanity Intl.	1979	-	2	-	15	-
Help for Christian Nationals	1994	-	-	-	3	1
Holt Intl. Children's Services	1986	-	-	-	25	-
Impact International	1970	2	-	-	4	-
International Children's Care	1990	-	6	-	-	-
Intl. Pentecostal Holiness Ch.	1995	2	-	-	-	-
Kids Alive International	1997	-	2	-	5	-
Larry Jones International Mins	1984	-	-	-	11	-
Living Water Teaching Intl.	1979	9	2	15	-	-
Luis Palau Evangelistic Assoc.		-	-	-	4	-
Lutheran Bible Translators	1996	8	1	-	7	-
Lutheran Church-Missouri	1947	9	-	4	-	-
Maranatha Baptist Mission	1991	2	-	-	-	-
MBMS International	1992	-	2	-	-	-

COUNTRY Agency	Year Began	Personnel from U. S.			Other Countries	
		4+yrs	2-4 yrs	1-2 yrs	Citizens	Not Citiz.
Medical Ambassadors Intl.	1983	-	-	-	13	-
Mission Aviation Fellowship	1977	8	-	-	-	-
Mission to the Americas	1990	1	-	-	1	-
Missionary Ventures Intl.	1983	-	-	-	3	-
Mutual Faith Ministries Intl.	1985	1	-	-	-	-
Navigators, The		-	2	-	-	-
New Life League International	1976	5	-	-	-	-
OC International, Inc.	1979	12	-	-	-	-
Partners International	1964	-	-	-	25	-
Pentecostal Free Will Bapt.Ch.	1987	2	-	-	-	-
Perimeter Ch., Global Outreach	1991	-	2	-	5	-
Presbyterian Church (USA)	1822	14	-	20	-	-
Primitive Methodist Church	1922	4	-	-	-	-
Shield of Faith Ministries	1994	-	-	-	7	-
Sowers International, The	1992	-	-	-	-	1
United Church Board World Mins		-	1	-	-	-
United Pentecostal Church Intl	1977	2	-	-	-	-
United World Mission	1952	4	-	-	-	-
Walk Thru The Bible Ministries	1993	-	-	-	1	-
World Baptist Fellowship Msn.		2	-	2	-	-
World-Wide Missions	1963	-	-	-	12	-
Wycliffe Associates USA	1998	-	2	-	-	-
Youth With A Mission		4	-	-	-	-
	Totals:	267	39	48	1356	25
Guinea						
Christian Reformed Relief	1986	-	-	-	-	-
Gospel Recordings	1997	-	-	-	7	-
Seventh-day Adventists	1987	-	-	-	2	-
SIM USA	1986	14	-	-	1	-
WEC International	1986	1	-	-	-	-
	Totals:	15	-	-	10	-
Guinea Bissau						
Assemblies of God	1990	4	-	-	-	-
Campus Crusade for Christ	1977	-	-	-	24	-
Christian and Msny. Alliance	1919	26	9	-	-	-
Christian Chs. /Chs. of Christ	1990	1	-	-	-	-
Christian Reformed World	1984	3	2	2	-	-
Every Home for Christ		-	-	-	5	-
Lutheran Church-Missouri	1990	2	-	-	-	-
National Baptist Conv. USA	1990	-	2	-	11	-
New Tribes Mission	1986	40	-	1	-	8
Open Bible Standard Churches	1960	2	-	-	-	-
Pioneer Bible Translators	1988	18	-	-	15	-
Seventh-day Adventists	1975	-	-	-	2	-
WEC International	1939	3	-	-	-	-
World Partners USA	1995	9	-	-	-	-
	Totals:	108	13	3	57	8

COUNTRY Agency	Year Began	Personnel from U. S.			Other Countries	
		4+yrs	2-4 yrs	1-2 yrs	Citizens	Not Citiz.
Guyana						
African Methodist Epis. Zion	1911	1	-	-	-	-
Baptist International Missions	1994	4	-	-	-	-
Baptist Mid-Missions	1954	4	-	-	-	-
BCM International		-	-	-	2	-
Bible Missionary Church	1958	4	-	-	-	-
Campus Crusade for Christ	1977	-	-	-	6	-
Christian Chs. /Chs. of Christ	1959	2	-	-	-	-
Church of God of Prophecy	1956	-	-	-	1	-
Habitat for Humanity Intl.	1995	-	4	-	-	-
Lott Carey Baptist Mission	1975	-	-	-	25	-
Seventh Day Baptist Msny. Soc.	1995	-	1	-	-	-
Seventh-day Adventists	1887	-	-	-	2	-
Source of Light Ministries	1971	-	-	-	1	-
UFM International	1949	13	-	-	-	1
Walk Thru The Bible Ministries	1994	-	-	-	-	1
Wesleyan World Missions	1913	1	-	-	-	-
	Totals:	29	5	-	37	2
Haiti						
Allegheny Wesleyan Meth. Msns.	1969	9	-	-	-	-
American Baptist Churches USA	1923	7	-	-	-	2
Assemblies of God	1945	6	-	2	-	-
Baptist Bible Fellowship Intl.	1982	4	-	-	-	-
Baptist Mid-Missions	1934	6	-	-	-	-
Baptist World Mission	1986	2	-	-	-	-
Barnabas Ministries, Inc.	1993	-	-	-	16	-
Campus Crusade for Christ	1977	-	-	-	7	-
Child Evangelism Fellowship	1946	2	-	-	1	-
Christian Aid Ministries	1991	-	14	-	24	-
Christian Aid Mission		-	-	-	48	-
Christian Chs./Chs. of Christ		29	-	-	-	-
Christian Reformed Relief	1975	1	-	-	1	2
Christian Reformed World	1985	6	2	2	-	-
Christian Service Intl.	1963	2	2	-	-	-
Church of God of Prophecy	1931	-	-	-	1	-
Church of God World Missions	1933	4	-	-	-	-
Church of The Brethren		-	2	-	-	-
Church of the Nazarene	1950	8	-	-	-	7
Churches of God General Conf.	1967	2	3	-	27	-
Compassion International, Inc.	1968	-	-	-	30	-
East West Ministries		-	-	-	1	-
ECHO	1993	-	2	-	-	-
Elim Fellowship World Missions	1986	2	-	-	-	-
Evangelical Bible Mission	1943	-	6	-	-	-
FARMS International, Inc.		-	-	-	-	-
Floresta USA, Inc.	1995	-	-	-	31	-
FOCAS	1986	-	-	-	5	-
Foursquare Missions Intl.	1981	2	-	-	-	-
Free Methodist World Missions	1964	9	-	-	-	-
Global Outreach, Ltd.	1989	5	3	-	-	-

COUNTRY Agency	Year Began	Personnel from U. S. 4+yrs	2-4 yrs	1-2 yrs	Other Countries Citizens	Not Citiz.
Global Strategy Mission Assoc.	1988	2	-	-	-	-
Globe Missionary Evangelism	1990	4	2	-	-	-
Good Shepherd Ministries	1973	-	-	-	49	-
Habitat for Humanity Intl.	1981	-	3	-	-	-
Harvest	1981	-	-	-	3	-
Have Christ Will Travel Mins.	1966	-	-	-	-	10
Hope for the Hungry	1982	2	1	1	4	-
International Child Care	1966	2	-	-	-	-
International Partnership Mins	1982	-	-	-	34	-
Intl. Pentecostal Holiness Ch.	1976	4	2	-	-	-
ISOH/Impact		-	1	-	-	-
Larry Jones International Mins	1979	-	-	-	7	-
Macedonia World Baptist Msns.	1967	2	-	-	-	-
Medical Ambassadors Intl.	1981	1	-	-	13	1
Ministries In Action	1974	1	-	-	2	3
Mission Aviation Fellowship	1981	9	2	2	-	-
Mission Possible	1979	1	-	-	123	1
Mission to the Americas	1992	-	-	-	2	-
Missionary Ventures Intl.	1992	2	-	-	-	-
Missions Outreach Intl.		3	-	-	-	-
National Baptist Conv. of Am.	1975	-	-	-	25	-
New Life League International	1976	2	-	-	-	-
OMS Intl., Inc.	1958	5	-	1	-	3
Open Door Baptist Missions	1995	4	-	-	-	-
Pentecostal Church of God	1952	2	-	-	-	-
Presbyterian Church (USA)	1974	6	-	-	-	-
Reciprocal Ministries Intl.	1988	3	-	-	3	-
Rehoboth Ministries, Inc	1985	2	-	-	-	-
Seventh-day Adventists	1905	8	-	-	2	-
Society of St. Margaret	1927	2	-	-	2	1
STEM Ministries	1985	-	2	1	-	-
UFM International	1943	32	-	-	-	1
United Church Board World Mins		-	2	-	-	-
United Pentecostal Church Intl	1966	4	-	-	-	-
Wesleyan World Missions	1948	9	-	-	-	1
World Concern	1977	1	1	-	21	-
World Gospel Mission	1962	2	-	-	-	-
World Team	1936	9	-	-	-	6
World-Wide Missions	1962	-	-	-	1	-
Youth With A Mission		8	-	-	-	-
	Totals:	238	50	9	483	38
Honduras						
Assemblies of God	1940	17	-	1	-	-
Baptist Bible Fellowship Intl.	1974	3	-	-	-	-
Baptist International Missions	1970	10	-	-	-	-
Baptist Medical & Dental	1974	-	-	-	32	14
Baptist Mid-Missions	1959	9	-	-	-	-
Baptist Missionary Assoc.	1976	4	-	-	-	-
Biblical Ministries Worldwide	1949	4	-	-	-	-
Brethren Assemblies		10	-	-	-	-

COUNTRY Agency	Year Began	Personnel from U. S.			Other Countries	
		4+yrs	2-4 yrs	1-2 yrs	Citizens	Not Citiz.
Brethren in Christ World Msns.	1990	-	2	-	1	-
CAM International	1896	13	-	1	-	-
Campus Crusade for Christ	1966	-	-	-	31	4
Child Evangelism Fellowship	1964	1	-	-	-	-
Christian Aid Mission		-	-	-	226	-
Christian Chs. /Chs. of Christ		7	-	-	-	-
Christian Reformed Relief	1974	1	1	-	1	2
Christian Reformed World	1971	8	5	-	-	-
Church of God of Prophecy	1952	-	-	-	1	-
Church of God World Missions	1944	7	-	-	-	2
Church of the Nazarene	1970	2	-	-	-	1
Congregational Christian Chs.	1976	-	-	-	2	-
Congregational Methodist Ch.	1960	1	-	-	-	-
Eastern Mennonite Missions	1950	2	-	2	-	-
Evangelistic Faith Missions	1968	-	7	-	-	-
Every Home for Christ	1982	-	-	-	1	-
Final Frontiers Foundation	1991	-	-	-	10	-
Food for the Hungry, Inc.	1994	-	1	-	-	2
Friends Church Southwest	1960	2	-	-	-	-
General Baptists International	1995	5	-	-	-	-
Global Outreach Mission		2	-	-	1	-
Global Outreach, Ltd.	1990	2	1	-	-	-
Globe Missionary Evangelism	1979	2	-	-	-	-
Great Commission Ministries		-	-	-	-	2
Habitat for Humanity Intl.	1988	-	3	-	13	-
Harvest	1981	-	-	-	2	-
Impact International	1975	2	-	-	1	-
International Gospel Outreach	1993	1	-	-	-	-
Larry Jones International Mins	1983	-	-	-	7	-
Latin America Mission	1998	1	-	-	-	-
Living Water Teaching Intl.	1991	5	-	-	-	-
Lutheran Church-Missouri	1961	-	-	2	-	-
Mission to the Americas	1951	5	-	-	4	-
Missionary Ventures Intl.	1987	4	-	-	-	-
Moravian Church North	1930	1	-	-	1	-
Pentecostal Church of God	1980	2	-	-	-	-
Presbyterian Church (USA)	1973	9	-	-	-	-
Reformed Church In America	1990	-	-	-	6	-
Ripe for Harvest, Inc.	1993	-	5	-	-	-
Seventh-day Adventists	1891	4	-	-	-	-
Shelter Now International	1998	-	1	-	-	-
Shield of Faith Ministries	1990	-	-	-	10	-
South American Missionary Soc.	1981	19	-	-	-	2
Spanish World Gospel Mission	1993	-	-	-	2	-
STEM Ministries	1996	-	-	-	-	-
Teen Missions International		2	-	1	-	-
United Church Board World Mins	1921	-	2	-	-	-
United Pentecostal Church Intl	1977	4	-	-	-	-
Wesleyan World Missions	1957	6	-	-	-	-
World Baptist Fellowship Msn.	1969	6	-	2	-	-
World Gospel Mission	1944	29	-	-	-	-

COUNTRY Agency	Year Began	Personnel from U. S. 4+yrs	2-4 yrs	1-2 yrs	Other Countries Citizens	Not Citiz.
World Reach, Inc.	1982	6	-	-	7	-
World Vision Inc.	1974	1	-	-	-	-
World-Wide Missions	1965	-	-	-	1	-
Youth With A Mission		5	-	-	-	-
	Totals:	224	28	9	360	29
Hong Kong						
ABWE	1950	16	-	-	-	-
Advancing Renewal Ministries	1994	-	-	-	-	1
American Baptist Churches USA	1842	4	-	-	1	-
Baptist Bible Fellowship Intl.	1950	7	-	-	-	-
Baptist Mid-Missions	1958	-	-	-	-	1
Baptist World Mission	1994	2	-	-	-	-
Biblical Ministries Worldwide	1988	5	-	-	-	1
Brethren Assemblies		2	-	-	-	-
Campus Crusade for Christ	1972	-	-	-	100	-
CBInternational	1963	8	-	1	-	-
Child Evangelism Fellowship	1948	1	-	-	-	2
Children of Promise Int'l.		2	-	-	-	-
Christian Aid Mission		-	-	-	4	-
Christian Chs./Chs. of Christ	1963	18	-	-	-	-
Christian Literature Crusade	1976	2	-	-	-	-
Church of God (Anderson, IN)	1953	1	-	-	-	-
Cumberland Presbyterian	1949	1	-	-	-	-
East Gates Ministries Intl.	1990	-	-	-	3	-
Eastern Mennonite Missions	1965	4	2	-	-	-
Elim Fellowship World Missions	1986	4	-	-	-	-
Evangelical Free Church Msn.	1987	6	-	1	-	-
Evangelical Lutheran Church	1890	11	-	-	-	-
Evangelize China Fellowship	1949	-	-	-	20	-
Free Methodist World Missions	1951	9	-	-	-	-
General Conf. Mennonite	1980	2	-	-	-	2
Holt Intl. Children's Services	1986	-	1	-	3	1
Intl. Pentecostal Holiness Ch.	1911	2	-	-	-	-
Lutheran Church-Missouri	1950	40	-	-	-	-
Mission to the World	1982	2	-	-	-	-
OMF International	1950	4	-	-	-	-
OMS Intl., Inc.	1954	9	-	1	-	-
Partners International	1950	-	-	-	60	-
Presbyterian Church (USA)	1844	9	-	-	-	-
Reach Ministries International		1	-	-	1	-
SEND International		4	-	-	-	-
Seventh-day Adventists	1888	16	1	-	5	-
SIM USA		-	-	-	3	-
TEAM	1988	6	-	-	-	-
Training Evangelistic Ldrshp.	1987	4	-	-	-	-
United Church Board World Mins	1950	-	1	-	-	-
United Pentecostal Church Intl	1976	4	-	-	-	-
Walk Thru The Bible Ministries	1982	-	-	-	1	-
Wisconsin Evang. Lutheran Syn.	1964	2	-	-	-	-
Youth With A Mission		15	-	-	-	-
	Totals:	223	5	3	201	8

COUNTRY Agency	Year Began	Personnel from U. S.			Other Countries	
		4+yrs	2-4 yrs	1-2 yrs	Citizens	Not Citiz.
Hungary						
ABWE	1990	23	-	-	-	-
Assemblies of God	1926	8	-	-	-	-
Baptist Bible Fellowship Intl.	1990	12	-	-	-	-
Baptist International Missions	1990	2	-	-	-	-
Baptist World Mission	1993	4	-	-	-	-
BCM International	1994	-	-	-	-	2
Brethren Assemblies		1	-	-	-	-
Campus Crusade for Christ	1978	58	-	17	63	1
CBInternational	1991	8	-	3	-	-
Child Evangelism Fellowship	1989	1	-	-	14	2
Christ to the Nations Missions	1999	2	-	-	2	-
Christian Aid Mission		-	-	-	18	-
Christian Reformed World	1990	3	2	2	-	-
Church of God of Prophecy	1998	-	-	-	1	-
Church of the Nazarene	1996	2	-	-	-	-
Church Resource Ministries	1986	12	-	-	-	-
Eastern Mennonite Missions	1997	3	-	-	-	-
Evangelical Free Church Msn.	1997	4	-	-	-	-
Final Frontiers Foundation	1996	-	-	-	1	-
Free Methodist World Missions	1998	3	-	-	-	-
General Conf. Mennonite	1993	2	-	-	-	-
Greater Grace World Outreach	1990	-	-	-	1	8
Habitat for Humanity Intl.	1994	2	1	-	-	3
Heart to Heart Intl. Mins.	1999	-	-	2	-	-
International Health Services	1996	2	1	-	4	-
International Messengers	1988	4	-	-	2	-
International Teams, U.S.A.	1973	-	5	-	-	-
Intl. Pentecostal Holiness Ch.	1989	2	-	-	-	-
Lutheran Church-Missouri	1991	-	-	5	-	-
Ministry to Eastern Europe	1997	2	2	1	1	-
Mission to the World	1991	2	2	-	-	-
Mission To Unreached Peoples	1996	-	4	-	-	-
Navigators, The		-	2	-	-	-
New Hope International	1998	-	-	-	1	-
OMS Intl., Inc.	1992	-	3	-	-	1
Operation Mobilization		2	1	-	-	-
Pioneers	1992	5	-	-	4	-
Reformed Church In America	1996	2	-	-	-	-
Ripe for Harvest, Inc.	1996	-	1	-	-	-
SEND International	1994	6	-	-	-	-
United Church Board World Mins		-	2	-	-	-
United Pentecostal Church Intl	1972	2	-	-	-	-
World Bible Translation Center	1990	-	-	-	5	-
World Gospel Mission	1992	5	-	-	-	-
World Indigenous Missions	1998	2	-	-	-	-
Young Life	1988	2	-	-	-	-
Youth With A Mission		15	-	-	-	-
	Totals:	203	26	30	117	17

COUNTRY Agency	Year Began	Personnel from U. S.			Other Countries	
		4+yrs	2-4 yrs	1-2 yrs	Citizens	Not Citiz.
Iceland						
Assemblies of God		2	-	-	-	-
Baptist Bible Fellowship Intl.		2	-	-	-	-
Baptist Missions to Forgotten		2	-	-	-	-
Navigators, The	1967	-	2	-	-	-
	Totals:	6	2	-	-	-
India						
Action International Mins.	1986	4	-	-	-	-
Advancing Renewal Ministries	1989	-	-	-	5	-
Advent Christian World Msns.	1882	4	-	-	50	-
American Baptist Churches USA	1836	4	-	-	2	-
AMG International	1970	2	-	-	869	-
Anglican Frontier Missions	1993	1	-	-	-	-
Anis Shorrosh Evan. Assoc.	1971	-	-	-	1	-
Assoc of Free Lutheran Congs	1979	-	-	-	32	-
Back to the Bible Intl.	1970	-	-	-	25	-
Baptist Bible Fellowship Intl.	1952	4	-	-	-	-
Baptist International Missions	1978	6	-	-	-	-
Baptist International Outreach	1993	-	-	-	2	-
Baptist Mid-Missions	1935	8	-	5	2	-
BCM International	1972	-	-	-	100	-
Bethany Fellowship Missions	1996	-	-	-	-	2
Bible League, The	1980	-	-	-	6	-
Bibles For The World	1959	-	-	-	400	-
BILD International	1986	-	-	-	2	-
Brethren Assemblies		7	-	-	-	-
Brethren Church Missionary Bd.	1969	-	-	-	2	-
Brethren in Christ World Msns.	1904	-	-	-	103	-
Campus Crusade for Christ	1963	2	-	-	2608	5
CBInternational	1945	8	2	2	-	-
Children of India Foundation	1977	-	-	-	2	-
Christ for India, Inc.	1986	-	-	-	500	-
Christian Aid Mission		-	-	-	2432	-
Christian Chs. /Chs. of Christ	1928	23	-	-	-	-
Christian Church of North Am.	1965	4	-	-	1000	-
Christian Dynamics	1976	-	-	-	-	25
Christian Reformed Relief	1965	-	-	-	-	-
Christians In Action, Inc.	1972	2	-	-	2	-
Church of God of Prophecy	1957	-	-	-	1	-
Church of the Nazarene	1898	4	-	-	-	2
Church of the United Brethren	1978	-	1	-	-	1
Churches of God General Conf.	1898	1	-	-	5	-
Compassion International, Inc.	1968	-	-	-	27	-
Congregational Christian Chs.	1962	-	-	-	2	-
Cornerstone Intl.	1997	1	-	-	-	-
Dayspring Enterprises Intl.	1979	-	-	-	-	-
Development Associates Intl.	1998	-	-	-	-	1
East West Ministries		-	-	-	7	-
Eastern Mennonite Missions	1998	1	-	-	-	-
Engineering Ministries Intl.	1998	-	-	3	3	-

COUNTRY Agency	Year Began	Personnel from U. S.			Other Countries	
		4+yrs	2-4 yrs	1-2 yrs	Citizens	Not Citiz.
Enterprise Development Intl.	1992	-	-	-	1	-
Evangel Bible Translators	1978	6	-	-	8	-
Evangelical Free Church Msn.	1995	3	-	1	-	-
Evangelical Friends Mission	1992	2	-	-	-	1
Evangelical Presbyterian Ch.	1996	2	-	-	-	-
Evangelism Resources	1991	1	-	-	-	-
Every Home for Christ	1965	-	-	-	510	-
FARMS International, Inc.		-	-	-	-	-
Final Frontiers Foundation	1988	-	-	-	277	-
Food for the Hungry, Inc.	1998	1	-	-	-	-
Free Gospel Church Msns. Dept.	1932	-	-	-	3	-
Free Will Baptist, Inc.	1935	1	-	-	-	-
Frontier Mission Fellowship	1997	2	-	-	-	-
General Conf. Mennonite	1900	2	-	-	-	2
Global Fellowship		-	-	-	290	-
Global Outreach Mission		-	-	-	16	-
Global Outreach, Ltd.	1977	2	-	-	-	-
Globe Missionary Evangelism	1993	5	4	-	-	-
Good News for India	1986	-	-	-	53	-
Gospel for Asia	1979	-	-	-	10075	-
Gospel Outreach Mins. Intl.	1988	-	-	-	250	-
Gospel Recordings	1957	-	-	-	13	-
Gospel Revival Ministries	1995	-	-	-	187	-
Grace Ministries International	1969	-	-	-	-	2
Greater Grace World Outreach	1984	-	-	-	8	1
Habitat for Humanity Intl.	1983	-	3	-	11	3
Harvest	1996	-	-	-	2	-
Have Christ Will Travel Mins.	1995	-	-	-	-	18
HBI Global Partners	1952	2	-	-	-	-
Help for Christian Nationals	1996	-	-	-	3	1
Holt Intl. Children's Services	1979	-	-	-	60	-
Hope for the Hungry	1988	-	-	-	3	-
India Evangelical Mission	1966	-	-	-	525	-
India National Inland Mission	1962	3	-	-	330	-
India Rural Evangelical Flwshp	1950	-	-	-	127	-
International Bible Institute	1998	-	-	1	1	-
International Gospel Outreach	1989	1	-	-	-	-
International Partnership Mins	1988	-	-	-	37	-
InterServe/USA	1952	4	-	-	-	-
Intl. Christian Leprosy Msn.	1948	-	-	-	3	-
Intl. Pentecostal Ch of Christ	1940	1	-	-	-	-
Intl. Pentecostal Holiness Ch.	1911	2	-	-	-	-
Lott Carey Baptist Mission	1963	-	-	-	300	-
Lutheran Church-Missouri	1895	1	-	-	-	-
M/E International	1985	-	-	-	60	-
Medical Ambassadors Intl.	1982	-	-	-	74	-
Mennonite Board of Missions	1899	4	-	-	-	-
Mission Soc. for United Meth.	1995	2	-	-	-	-
Mission to the World	1973	7	1	-	-	-
Mission To Unreached Peoples	1987	6	-	-	3	-
Mustard Seed, Inc.	1998	2	-	1	13	-

COUNTRY Agency	Year Began	Personnel from U. S.			Other Countries	
		4+yrs	2-4 yrs	1-2 yrs	Citizens	Not Citiz.
Mutual Faith Ministries Intl.	1986	-	-	-	-	3
New Life League International	1972	-	-	-	2	-
New Tribes Mission	1945	1	-	-	-	-
OMS Intl., Inc.	1941	-	-	-	-	2
Open Air Campaigners	1987	-	-	-	11	-
Open Door Baptist Missions	1995	-	-	-	2	-
Operation Mobilization	1964	7	1	-	-	-
Partners International	1969	-	-	-	669	-
Pentecostal Church of God	1934	2	-	-	-	-
Prakash Association USA	1968	-	-	-	35	-
Presb. Evangelistic Fellowship		-	-	-	5	-
Presbyterian Church (USA)	1834	-	-	21	-	-
Project Christ International	1984	-	-	-	120	-
Project Partner with Christ	1982	-	-	-	1	-
Ramabai Mukti Mission	1889	-	-	-	125	-
Ravi Zacharias Int. Mins.	1984	2	-	-	2	-
Reach Ministries International		2	-	-	1	1
Reformed Church In America	1840	5	-	-	-	-
Reformed Episcopal Bd	1890	-	-	-	-	2
Ripe for Harvest, Inc.	1993	2	-	-	-	-
Salvation Army, U.S.A.	1882	2	-	-	-	-
Seventh-day Adventists	1895	8	-	-	2	-
Shield of Faith Ministries	1995	-	-	-	12	7
SIM USA	1893	6	-	1	2	-
Source of Light Ministries	1979	-	-	-	100	-
TEAM	1892	2	-	-	-	-
Third World Baptist Missions	1996	2	-	-	35	-
United Church Board World Mins	1813	-	4	-	-	-
Vellore Christian Medical Col.	1948	-	-	-	-	-
Walk Thru The Bible Ministries	1990	-	-	-	82	-
Wesleyan World Missions	1910	2	-	-	-	-
Wisconsin Evang. Lutheran Syn.	1970	3	-	-	-	-
Witnessing Mins. of Christ	1983	-	-	-	287	-
World Bible Translation Center	1973	-	-	-	30	-
World Concern	1995	-	1	-	-	-
World Gospel Mission	1937	2	-	-	-	-
World Harvest Mission	1998	2	-	-	-	-
World Indigenous Missions	1997	1	-	-	-	-
World Mission Prayer League	1941	2	-	-	-	-
World Missions Fellowship	1965	-	-	-	2	4
World-Wide Missions	1958	-	-	-	4	-
Youth With A Mission		57	-	-	-	-
	Totals:	258	17	35	22962	83
Indonesia						
AMG International	1975	-	-	-	324	-
Apostolic Christian Church	1986	2	-	-	-	-
Assemblies of God	1937	25	-	5	-	-
Baptist Bible Fellowship Intl.	1972	4	-	-	-	-
Baptist International Missions	1971	2	-	-	-	-
Bethany Fellowship Missions	1971	3	-	-	-	-

COUNTRY Agency	Year Began	Personnel from U. S.			Other Countries	
		4+yrs	2-4 yrs	1-2 yrs	Citizens	Not Citiz.
Bethel Christian Ministries	1940	2	-	-	-	-
Bible League, The	1997	-	-	-	6	-
Brethren Assemblies		3	-	-	-	-
Campus Crusade for Christ	1968	2	-	-	389	-
CBInternational	1961	8	2	1	-	-
Christ for the Lost World	1983	-	-	-	101	-
Christ to the Nations Missions	1998	2	-	-	2	-
Christian Aid Mission		-	-	-	74	-
Christian and Msny. Alliance	1929	44	2	-	-	-
Christian Chs. /Chs. of Christ	1968	24	-	-	-	-
Christian Reformed Relief	1984	-	1	-	1	-
Church of God of Prophecy	1971	-	-	-	1	-
Church of God World Missions	1967	2	-	-	-	-
Church of the Nazarene	1973	4	-	-	-	-
Church World Service &	1950	-	1	-	10	-
CMF International	1978	3	1	2	1	5
Compassion International, Inc.	1968	-	-	-	15	-
Evangelical Lutheran Church	1970	4	-	-	-	-
Evangelize China Fellowship	1951	-	-	-	10	-
Far East Broadcasting Company	1951	-	-	-	50	-
Full Gospel Grace Fellowship		1	-	-	-	-
Gospel Recordings	1956	-	-	-	7	-
International Gospel Outreach	1990	1	-	-	-	-
Macedonia World Baptist Msns.	1980	2	-	-	-	-
Mission Aviation Fellowship	1952	62	-	10	-	2
Mission to the World	1977	11	-	-	-	-
Mission To Unreached Peoples	1991	2	-	-	-	-
Mustard Seed, Inc.	1972	2	-	-	230	-
Navigators, The	1967	2	4	1	-	-
Network of Intl Christian Schs	1995	2	11	5	-	2
New Tribes Mission	1970	70	-	-	2	2
OC International, Inc.	1968	18	2	-	-	-
Omega World Missions	1985	2	-	-	-	-
OMF International	1952	10	-	-	-	-
OMS Intl., Inc.	1971	11	2	-	-	3
Partners International	1971	-	-	-	531	-
Pocket Testament League	1976	-	-	-	10	-
Presbyterian Church (USA)	1951	14	-	-	-	-
Reformed Church In America	1997	2	-	-	-	-
Seventh-day Adventists	1900	6	-	-	6	-
TEAM	1952	20	-	-	2	-
Things To Come Mission, Inc.	1971	-	-	-	2	2
Training Evangelistic Ldrshp.	1974	1	-	-	-	-
UFM International	1957	24	-	-	-	4
United Church Board World Mins	1833	-	2	-	-	-
United Pentecostal Church Intl	1938	4	-	-	-	-
Walk Thru The Bible Ministries	1992	-	-	-	1	-
WEC International	1950	8	-	-	-	-
Wesleyan World Missions	1975	2	-	-	-	-
Wisconsin Evang. Lutheran Syn.	1969	1	-	-	-	-
World Baptist Fellowship Msn.	1969	5	-	-	-	-
World Indigenous Missions	1995	4	-	-	-	-

COUNTRY Agency	Year Began	Personnel from U. S.			Other Countries	
		4+yrs	2-4 yrs	1-2 yrs	Citizens	Not Citiz.
World Partners USA	1992	2	-	-	-	-
World Team	1948	24	-	-	-	17
World Vision Inc.	1995	1	-	1	-	-
Wycliffe Associates USA	1997	-	2	-	-	-
Wycliffe Bible Translators		185	-	-	-	-
Youth With A Mission		7	-	-	-	-
	Totals:	640	30	25	1775	37
Iran						
Anglican Frontier Missions	1994	2	-	-	-	-
Christian Aid Mission		-	-	-	6	-
	Totals:	2	-	-	6	-
Iraq						
Partners International	1989	-	-	-	42	-
	Totals:	-	-	-	42	-
Ireland						
Assemblies of God	1949	6	-	2	-	-
Baptist Bible Fellowship Intl.	1977	5	-	-	-	-
Baptist International Missions	1978	6	-	-	-	-
Baptist Mid-Missions	1978	4	-	1	-	-
Baptist World Mission	1992	20	-	-	-	-
BCM International	1965	2	-	-	-	-
Biblical Ministries Worldwide	1975	5	-	-	-	2
Brethren Assemblies		9	2	-	-	2
CBInternational	1991	4	-	1	-	-
Child Evangelism Fellowship	1950	-	-	1	5	-
Christian Chs./Chs. of Christ	1988	4	-	-	-	-
Church of God World Missions	1995	2	-	-	-	-
Church of the Nazarene	1987	2	-	-	-	-
European Christian Mission	1987	1	-	-	-	-
Global Outreach Mission	1965	8	-	-	2	-
Greater Grace World Outreach	1992	-	-	-	1	-
Ireland Outreach Intl., Inc.	1970	6	-	2	-	3
Mennonite Board of Missions	1987	2	-	-	-	-
Mission to the World	1995	2	-	-	-	-
OMS Intl., Inc.	1998	2	-	-	-	-
Seventh-day Adventists	1898	2	-	-	-	-
TEAM		5	-	-	-	-
Team Expansion, Inc.	1988	6	-	-	-	-
UFM International	1980	7	-	-	-	4
World Baptist Fellowship Msn.	1961	2	-	2	-	-
World Missions Fellowship	1994	5	-	-	1	-
	Totals:	117	2	9	9	11
Israel						
ABWE	1998	2	-	-	-	-
AMF International	1930	2	-	1	-	-
Arab World Ministries	1995	3	-	-	-	-
Baptist World Mission	1986	-	-	-	2	-
Child Evangelism Fellowship	1951	2	-	-	2	-

COUNTRY Agency	Year Began	Personnel from U. S.			Other Countries	
		4+yrs	2-4 yrs	1-2 yrs	Citizens	Not Citiz.
Chosen People Ministries	1968	-	-	-	3	-
Christian Aid Mission		-	-	-	7	-
Christian and Msny. Alliance	1890	10	-	-	-	-
Christian Chs./Chs. of Christ		2	-	-	-	-
Church of God World Missions	1964	5	-	2	-	3
Church of The Brethren	1975	-	4	-	-	-
Church of the Nazarene	1921	2	-	-	-	-
Elim Fellowship World Missions	1977	2	-	-	-	-
Episcopal World Mission	1983	2	-	-	-	-
Evangelical Lutheran Church	1967	4	-	1	-	-
Foursquare Missions Intl.	1996	2	-	-	-	-
Friends United Meeting	1869	2	5	-	-	-
General Conf. Mennonite	1954	2	-	-	-	-
High Adventure Ministries	1979	1	-	-	17	-
Hope for the Hungry	1991	-	-	-	-	1
International Students, Inc		-	-	-	-	1
Jews for Jesus	1994	1	-	-	2	-
Maranatha Baptist Mission	1983	2	-	-	-	-
Mennonite Board of Missions	1953	4	-	-	-	-
Open Door Baptist Missions	1997	2	-	-	-	-
Operation Mobilization		4	4	2	-	-
Presbyterian Church (USA)		4	-	-	-	-
Reformed Baptist Mission Svcs.	1985	2	-	-	1	-
Seventh-day Adventists	1898	2	-	-	2	-
United Church Board World Mins		-	2	-	-	-
Venture Middle East	1999	-	1	-	-	1
Youth With A Mission		2	-	-	-	-
	Totals:	66	16	6	36	6
Italy						
ABWE	1989	14	-	-	-	-
Assemblies of God	1949	4	-	-	-	-
Aurora Mission, Inc.	1978	4	-	-	6	-
Back to the Bible Intl.	1961	-	-	-	9	-
Baptist International Missions	1979	1	-	-	-	-
Baptist Mid-Missions	1951	2	-	-	-	-
Baptist Missions to Forgotten		2	-	-	-	-
Baptist World Mission	1987	6	-	-	-	-
BCM International	1967	6	-	-	-	-
Biblical Ministries Worldwide	1962	8	-	-	-	-
Brethren Assemblies		5	-	-	1	-
Cadence International	1980	-	-	4	-	-
Campus Crusade for Christ	1969	1	-	5	-	-
CBInternational	1946	16	-	2	-	-
Child Evangelism Fellowship	1956	-	-	-	-	1
Christian Chs. /Chs. of Christ	1947	7	-	-	-	-
Christian Church of North Am.	1927	1	-	-	-	-
Christian Literature Crusade	1956	2	-	-	-	-
Church of God of Prophecy	1996	-	-	-	1	-
Church of God World Missions	1959	4	-	-	-	-
Church of the Nazarene	1948	2	-	-	-	9

COUNTRY Agency	Year Began	Personnel from U. S.			Other Countries	
		4+yrs	2-4 yrs	1-2 yrs	Citizens	Not Citiz.
European Christian Mission	1987	2	-	-	-	-
Evangelical Baptist Missions	1983	4	-	-	-	-
Every Home for Christ	1958	-	-	-	1	-
Gospel Fellowship Association	1983	2	-	-	-	2
Gospel Missionary Union	1950	2	-	-	2	-
Independent Faith Mission	1950	5	-	-	-	-
International Teams, U.S.A.	1980	4	-	-	-	2
InterVarsity Mission	1984	3	-	2	-	-
Mission to the World	1988	2	-	-	-	-
Navigators, The	1984	1	1	-	-	-
Operation Mobilization		-	-	2	-	-
Presbyterian Church (USA)	1972	2	-	-	-	-
Salvation Army, U.S.A.	1887	1	-	-	-	-
Seventh-day Adventists	1877	2	-	-	1	-
SIM USA	1979	2	-	-	-	-
Spiritual Growth Resources	1984	-	-	-	3	-
TEAM	1950	21	1	-	-	-
Team Expansion, Inc.		3	-	-	-	-
UFM International	1974	15	-	-	-	4
Virginia Mennonite Bd. of Msns	1964	4	-	-	-	2
WEC International	1964	5	-	-	-	-
World Team	1970	4	-	-	-	3
	Totals:	169	2	15	24	23
Jamaica						
African Methodist Epis. Zion	1966	1	-	-	-	-
Assemblies of God	1942	8	-	6	-	-
Back to the Bible Intl.	1958	-	-	-	9	-
Baptist Bible Fellowship Intl.	1972	10	-	-	-	-
Baptist Mid-Missions	1939	-	-	1	-	-
BCM International		-	-	-	2	-
Calvary International		2	-	-	-	-
Campus Crusade for Christ	1990	-	-	-	4	5
Christian Chs. /Chs. of Christ	1858	9	-	-	-	-
Christian Service Intl.	1979	3	4	1	-	-
Evangelical Lutheran Church	1990	2	-	-	-	-
Faith Christian Fellowship	1989	2	-	2	-	-
Friends United Meeting	1901	-	2	-	-	-
Habitat for Humanity Intl.	1993	-	1	-	3	-
International Outreach Mins.	1992	2	-	-	-	-
Island Missionary Society	1984	8	-	-	-	-
Lott Carey Baptist Mission	1995	-	-	-	10	-
Lutheran Church-Missouri	1993	4	-	-	-	-
Macedonia World Baptist Msns.	1981	6	-	-	-	-
Ministries In Action	1974	-	-	-	1	-
Mission to the World	1981	2	1	-	-	-
National Baptist Conv. of Am.	1945	-	-	-	38	-
Open Air Campaigners	1984	-	-	-	2	-
Presbyterian Church (USA)	1981	5	-	-	-	-
Reformed Baptist Mission Svcs.	1985	2	-	-	1	-
Salvation Army, U.S.A.	1887	7	-	-	-	-

COUNTRY Agency	Year Began	Personnel from U. S.			Other Countries	
		4+yrs	2-4 yrs	1-2 yrs	Citizens	Not Citiz.
Seventh-day Adventists	1893	4	2	-	2	-
Source of Light Ministries	1953	-	-	-	5	-
STEM Ministries	1985	-	-	-	-	-
United Church Board World Mins		-	2	-	-	-
Virginia Mennonite Bd. of Msns	1955	-	2	-	-	-
World Partners USA	1946	2	-	-	-	-
Youth With A Mission		2	-	-	-	-
	Totals:	81	14	10	77	5
Japan						
ABWE	1953	18	-	-	-	-
Advancing Renewal Ministries	1997	-	-	-	1	-
Advent Christian World Msns.	1948	2	-	-	-	-
American Baptist Association	1962	1	-	-	-	-
American Baptist Churches USA	1872	11	-	-	-	-
Apostolic Christian Church	1985	2	-	-	-	-
Artists In Christian Testimony	1999	2	-	-	-	2
Assemblies of God	1913	38	-	6	-	-
Baptist Bible Fellowship Intl.	1950	26	-	-	-	-
Baptist General Conference	1948	19	-	-	-	-
Baptist International Missions	1965	35	-	-	-	-
Baptist Mid-Missions	1949	26	-	-	2	-
Baptist Missionary Assoc.	1953	1	-	-	-	-
Baptist World Mission	1970	16	-	-	-	-
Bethany Fellowship Missions	1980	3	-	-	-	-
Bethany Missionary Association	1959	4	-	-	-	-
Bethel Christian Ministries	1950	6	-	-	-	-
Bible Missionary Church	1963	2	-	-	-	-
Biblical Ministries Worldwide	1987	2	-	-	-	-
Brethren Assemblies		7	1	-	-	2
Cadence International	1961	3	-	11	-	-
Calvary International		1	-	-	-	-
Campus Crusade for Christ	1962	15	-	7	18	14
CBInternational	1947	22	-	-	-	-
Child Evangelism Fellowship	1948	-	-	-	1	2
Christ Community Church		2	-	-	-	-
Christar	1950	15	-	-	-	1
Christian and Msny. Alliance	1891	11	-	-	-	-
Christian Chs. /Chs. of Christ	1901	45	-	-	-	-
Christian Reformed World	1951	16	4	2	-	-
Christians In Action, Inc.	1957	2	-	-	-	2
Church of God (Anderson, IN)	1906	6	-	-	-	-
Church of God of Prophecy	1982	4	-	-	-	-
Church of The Brethren		-	2	-	-	-
Church of the Nazarene	1905	9	-	-	-	1
Church Resource Ministries	1997	4	-	-	-	-
Equip, Inc.	1997	-	-	1	-	-
Evangelical Baptist Missions	1981	4	-	-	-	-
Evangelical Covenant Church	1949	9	4	-	-	-
Evangelical Free Church Msn.	1949	23	-	2	-	-
Evangelical Lutheran Church	1892	18	-	10	-	-

COUNTRY Agency	Year Began	Personnel from U. S.			Other Countries	
		4+yrs	2-4 yrs	1-2 yrs	Citizens	Not Citiz.
Evangelical Presbyterian Ch.	1988	2	-	-	-	-
Every Home for Christ		-	-	-	3	-
Fellowship International Msn.	1980	3	-	-	-	-
Foursquare Missions Intl.	1951	2	-	-	-	-
Free Will Baptist, Inc.	1954	10	-	-	-	-
General Conf. Mennonite	1950	3	-	-	-	7
Global Strategy Mission Assoc.	1993	-	2	-	-	-
Globe Missionary Evangelism	1987	2	-	-	-	-
Gospel Fellowship Association	1958	3	-	-	-	3
Grace Brethren Intl. Missions	1984	4	-	-	-	-
Hope for the Hungry	1991	2	-	-	-	-
Intl. Pentecostal Holiness Ch.	1989	2	-	-	-	-
Japan - North American Comm	1973	-	-	-	-	-
Japanese Evangelical Msnry Soc	1953	-	-	2	6	-
Liberty Corner Mission	1951	2	-	-	-	-
LIFE Ministries	1967	29	2	1	44	-
Lutheran Brethren World Msns.	1950	6	-	3	-	-
Lutheran Church-Missouri	1948	10	20	1	-	-
Macedonia World Baptist Msns.	1996	2	-	-	-	-
Maranatha Baptist Mission	1968	2	-	-	-	-
Mennonite Board of Missions	1949	8	-	-	-	-
Mission Soc. for United Meth.	1997	2	-	-	-	-
Mission to the World	1985	32	20	-	-	-
Mission To Unreached Peoples	1990	2	-	-	-	-
Navigators, The	1951	12	6	7	-	-
New Tribes Mission	1949	2	-	-	-	-
North American Baptist Conf.	1951	6	-	2	-	-
OC International, Inc.	1987	6	-	-	-	-
OMF International	1952	29	-	3	-	-
OMS Intl., Inc.	1901	12	-	-	-	2
Orthodox Presbyterian Church	1938	8	-	-	-	-
Pioneers	1988	6	-	-	-	-
Presb. Evangelistic Fellowship		2	-	-	-	-
Presbyterian Church (USA)	1859	4	34	-	-	-
Project AmaZon	1988	2	1	-	-	-
Reformed Church In America	1850	10	-	-	-	-
Reformed Presbyterian Church	1950	3	-	-	-	-
Ripe for Harvest, Inc.	1993	2	-	-	-	-
SEND International	1947	39	-	8	-	-
Seventh-day Adventists	1896	10	-	-	-	-
TEAM	1891	67	16	-	-	-
Touch the World Ministries	1951	4	-	1	10	-
United Church Board World Mins	1869	-	15	-	-	-
United Pentecostal Church Intl	1949	2	-	-	-	-
Wesleyan World Missions	1918	2	-	-	-	-
Wisconsin Evang. Lutheran Syn.	1952	5	1	-	-	-
World Gospel Mission	1952	4	-	-	-	-
World Missions Fellowship	1995	-	-	-	2	-
Youth With A Mission		27	-	-	-	-
	Totals:	822	128	67	87	36

COUNTRY Agency	Year Began	Personnel from U. S.			Other Countries	
		4+yrs	2-4 yrs	1-2 yrs	Citizens	Not Citiz.
Jordan						
Arab World Ministries	1983	14	-	-	-	10
Calvary International	1989	2	-	-	-	-
CBInternational	1956	8	-	2	-	-
Christian Aid Mission		-	-	-	33	-
Christian and Msny. Alliance	1890	1	-	-	-	-
Christian Blind Mission Intl.	1990	-	1	-	-	-
Church of the Nazarene	1950	4	-	-	-	1
Evangelical Friends Mission	1998	2	-	-	-	-
Every Home for Christ		-	-	-	6	-
International Outreach Mins.	1997	-	2	-	-	-
International Teams, U.S.A.	1995	-	2	-	-	-
InterServe/USA		-	-	3	-	-
Partners International	1997	-	-	-	13	-
Venture Middle East	1997	-	1	-	-	2
World Bible Translation Center	1999	-	-	-	7	-
	Totals:	31	6	5	59	13
Kazakhstan						
Advancing Renewal Ministries	1995	-	-	-	1	-
Bible League, The	1993	-	-	-	11	-
Christian Aid Mission		-	-	-	4	-
Church of the Nazarene	1996	3	-	-	-	1
East-West Ministries Intl.	1994	2	1	-	-	-
Evangelical Presbyterian Ch.	1993	4	-	-	-	-
Every Home for Christ	1994	-	-	-	4	-
Great Commission Center Intl.	1995	-	-	-	-	1
Greater Grace World Outreach	1991	-	-	-	-	2
International Teams, U.S.A.	1992	-	2	-	-	-
Lutheran Church-Missouri	1993	6	-	1	-	-
Mission Soc. for United Meth.	1993	10	2	6	-	-
Presb. Evangelistic Fellowship		1	-	-	-	-
Presbyterian Church (USA)		4	-	-	-	-
Slavic Gospel Association	1945	-	-	-	31	-
Team Expansion, Inc.		1	-	-	-	-
Walk Thru The Bible Ministries	1994	-	-	-	28	-
	Totals:	31	5	7	79	4
Kenya						
ABWE	1983	2	-	-	-	-
ACM International	1996	7	-	-	-	-
Africa Inland Mission Intl.	1895	296	-	37	-	-
African Enterprise, Inc.	1970	-	-	-	8	-
American Baptist Association		3	-	-	-	-
Assemblies of God	1967	24	-	10	-	-
Baptist Bible Fellowship Intl.	1962	44	-	-	-	-
Baptist Faith Missions		-	2	-	-	-
Baptist International Missions	1991	2	-	-	-	-
Baptist International Outreach	1985	-	2	-	2	-
Baptist World Mission	1997	5	-	-	-	-
Bible League, The	1980	-	-	-	4	-

COUNTRY Agency	Year Began	Personnel from U. S.			Other Countries	
		4+yrs	2-4 yrs	1-2 yrs	Citizens	Not Citiz.
Brethren Assemblies		1	-	-	-	-
Campus Crusade for Christ	1972	23	-	-	88	8
CBInternational	1972	14	-	4	-	-
Central Missionary Fellowship	1997	-	1	-	-	-
Child Evangelism Fellowship	1966	6	-	-	14	2
Children of Promise Int'l.		-	4	-	-	-
Christ to the Nations Missions	1999	2	-	-	2	-
Christar	1956	6	-	-	-	-
Christian Aid Mission		-	-	-	2397	-
Christian Blind Mission Intl.	1971	-	1	1	-	-
Christian Chs. /Chs. of Christ	1960	69	-	-	-	-
Christian Church of North Am.	1996	-	2	-	-	-
Christian Reformed Relief	1983	2	1	-	1	2
Christian Services, Inc.	1977	1	-	-	-	-
Church of God (Anderson, IN)	1905	7	-	-	-	-
Church of God of Prophecy	1978	-	-	-	-	1
Church of God World Missions	1977	13	-	-	-	-
Church of the Nazarene	1984	19	-	-	-	16
CMF International	1977	31	-	5	-	36
Compassion International, Inc.	1980	-	-	-	23	-
Congregational Christian Chs.	1992	-	-	-	2	-
Daystar U.S.	1973	7	-	-	-	-
Eastern Mennonite Missions	1964	21	2	2	-	-
Elim Fellowship World Missions	1940	25	-	-	-	-
Equip, Inc.	1998	-	-	-	2	-
Evangelical Free Church Msn.	1996	7	-	-	-	-
Evangelical Presbyterian Ch.	1996	2	-	-	-	-
Faith Christian Fellowship	1996	-	2	-	-	-
Final Frontiers Foundation	1995	-	-	-	61	-
Food for the Hungry, Inc.	1976	2	3	-	134	1
Free Methodist World Missions	1994	2	-	-	-	2
Friends in the West	1990	-	-	-	59	-
Friends United Meeting	1902	4	-	-	-	2
General Conf. Mennonite	1990	4	-	-	-	-
Globe Missionary Evangelism	1979	4	1	-	-	-
Gospel Fellowship Association		2	-	-	-	2
Gospel Furthering Fellowship	1935	3	-	-	-	-
Gospel Recordings	1977	-	-	-	6	2
Greater Grace World Outreach	1998	-	-	-	-	2
Habitat for Humanity Intl.	1985	-	4	-	8	1
Hope for the Hungry	1991	-	-	-	1	-
Independent Faith Mission	1973	8	-	-	-	-
International Gospel League	1978	5	-	-	-	-
International Gospel Outreach	1989	-	1	-	-	-
International Outreach Mins.	1988	2	-	-	-	-
InterVarsity Mission	1981	2	-	-	-	-
Intl. Pentecostal Ch of Christ	1938	3	-	-	-	-
Intl. Pentecostal Holiness Ch.	1972	7	2	-	-	-
Larry Jones International Mins	1979	-	-	-	16	1
Lifewater International	1981	-	-	-	1	-
Lott Carey Baptist Mission	1985	-	-	-	20	-

COUNTRY Agency	Year Began	Personnel from U. S.			Other Countries	
		4+yrs	2-4 yrs	1-2 yrs	Citizens	Not Citiz.
Lutheran World Relief	1989	-	-	-	-	2
MAP International	1980	-	-	-	16	-
Medical Ambassadors Intl.	1997	1	-	-	17	-
Mission Aviation Fellowship		6	-	-	-	-
Mission Ministries, Inc.	1990	-	-	-	-	-
Mission to the World	1977	11	-	-	-	-
Mission: Moving Mountains	1985	5	-	-	-	2
Mutual Faith Ministries Intl.	1985	-	-	-	-	1
Navigators, The	1968	2	1	-	-	-
OC International, Inc.	1985	8	-	-	-	-
Orthodox Presbyterian Church	1979	2	-	-	-	-
Partners International	1972	-	-	-	29	-
Presb. Evangelistic Fellowship	1987	2	-	-	-	-
Presbyterian Church (USA)	1955	11	6	4	-	-
Presbyterian Missionary Union	1985	2	-	-	-	-
Reformed Baptist Mission Svcs.	1985	2	-	-	-	1
Reformed Church In America	1948	8	-	-	-	-
Salvation Army, U.S.A.	1896	2	-	-	-	-
Scripture Union, USA		1	-	-	-	-
Seventh-day Adventists	1906	22	4	-	26	-
Share International	1994	-	-	-	4	-
SIM USA	1977	20	-	-	13	-
The Master's Mission, Inc.	1980	16	-	-	-	-
Things To Come Mission, Inc.	1984	5	-	-	-	4
United Church Board World Mins	1974	-	1	-	-	-
United Pentecostal Church Intl	1972	6	-	-	-	-
Walk Thru The Bible Ministries	1990	-	-	-	16	-
Wesleyan World Missions	1997	2	-	-	-	-
World Concern	1984	3	3	2	18	-
World Gospel Mission	1932	52	-	-	-	6
World Mission Associates	1986	2	-	-	-	-
World Mission Prayer League	1968	8	-	1	-	2
World Missions Far Corners	1992	-	-	-	6	-
World Reach, Inc.	1983	-	-	-	9	-
World-Wide Missions	1960	-	-	-	3	-
Wycliffe Associates USA	1999	-	-	2	-	-
Young Life	1984	4	-	2	-	-
Youth for Christ / USA		-	2	-	-	-
Youth With A Mission		6	-	-	-	-
	Totals:	896	45	70	3006	96
Kiribati						
Assemblies of God	1989	2	-	-	-	-
Elim Fellowship World Missions	1991	2	-	-	-	-
	Totals:	4	-	-	-	-
Korea-S						
Assemblies of God	1928	2	-	-	-	-
Baptist Bible Fellowship Intl.	1950	19	-	-	-	-
Baptist World Mission	1977	2	-	-	-	-
Brethren Assemblies		1	-	-	1	-

COUNTRY Agency	Year Began	Personnel from U. S.			Other Countries	
		4+yrs	2-4 yrs	1-2 yrs	Citizens	Not Citiz.
Cadence International	1975	-	-	3	-	-
Campus Crusade for Christ	1958	-	-	-	729	13
CBInternational	1995	2	-	-	-	-
Christian and Msny. Alliance	1980	2	-	-	-	-
Christian Chs. /Chs. of Christ	1925	4	-	-	-	-
Church of God of Prophecy	1969	-	-	-	1	-
Church of the Nazarene	1948	8	-	-	-	2
Church Planting International		-	-	-	1	-
David Livingstone Kure Fndtn		-	-	-	24	-
Evangelistic Faith Missions	1971	-	-	-	-	-
Far East Broadcasting Company	1976	2	-	2	140	-
Free Methodist World Missions	1990	2	-	-	-	-
Global Outreach Mission		-	-	-	2	-
Gospel Fellowship Association	1967	6	-	-	-	6
Habitat for Humanity Intl.	1994	1	-	-	-	1
Holt Intl. Children's Services	1956	-	-	-	300	-
Independent Faith Mission		2	-	-	-	-
International Gospel Outreach	1998	1	-	-	-	-
Lutheran Church-Missouri	1958	6	-	-	-	-
Mission to the World	1976	2	-	-	-	-
Network of Intl Christian Schs	1983	20	24	36	-	3
New Tribes Mission	1993	2	-	-	2	-
OMF International	1960	4	-	4	-	-
OMS Intl., Inc.	1907	6	-	-	-	2
Orthodox Presbyterian Church	1946	2	-	-	-	-
Partners International	1976	-	-	-	67	-
Presbyterian Church (USA)	1884	6	19	-	-	-
Seventh-day Adventists	1904	12	2	-	7	-
SIM USA		1	-	-	2	-
Source of Light Ministries	1985	-	-	-	2	-
United Church Board World Mins	1983	-	1	-	-	-
United Pentecostal Church Intl	1965	3	-	-	-	-
Walk Thru The Bible Ministries	1988	-	-	-	10	-
Westminister Biblical Missions	1973	1	-	-	15	-
World Bible Translation Center		-	-	-	6	-
World Missions Far Corners	1976	-	-	-	8	-
World-Wide Missions	1960	-	-	-	6	-
Worldwide Discipleship Assoc.	1991	3	-	-	-	-
	Totals:	122	46	45	1323	27
Kuwait						
Arab World Ministries		2	-	-	-	2
	Totals:	2	-	-	-	2
Kyrgyzstan						
Bible League, The	1997	-	-	-	2	-
Christian Aid Mission		-	-	-	78	-
Gospel Missionary Union		2	-	-	-	-
Grace Brethren Intl. Missions		2	-	-	-	-
Great Commission Center Intl.	1997	-	-	-	-	2
Greater Grace World Outreach	1992	-	-	-	-	2

COUNTRY Agency	Year Began	Personnel from U. S.			Other Countries	
		4+yrs	2-4 yrs	1-2 yrs	Citizens	Not Citiz.
Habitat for Humanity Intl.	1996	1	-	-	-	1
InterServe/USA	1993	11	-	-	-	-
Presbyterian Church (USA)		6	-	-	-	-
Seventh-day Adventists	1886	2	-	-	-	-
Walk Thru The Bible Ministries	1993	-	-	-	7	-
	Totals:	24	-	-	87	5
Laos						
Advancing Renewal Ministries	1994	-	-	-	-	1
Assemblies of God	1990	-	-	1	-	-
Bible League, The	1990	-	-	-	-	1
Campus Crusade for Christ	1991	-	-	-	5	-
Christian Aid Mission		-	-	-	158	-
Christian and Msny. Alliance	1929	-	9	-	-	-
Church World Service &	1950	1	-	-	3	-
Evangelical Covenant Church	1991	2	-	-	-	-
Final Frontiers Foundation	1987	-	-	-	1	-
Food for the Hungry, Inc.	1990	4	2	-	5	2
Reformed Church In America	1996	1	-	-	-	-
Seventh-day Adventists	1957	-	-	-	3	-
Team Expansion, Inc.		3	-	-	-	-
World Concern	1990	-	2	-	31	-
World Vision Inc.	1992	1	-	-	-	-
	Totals:	12	13	1	206	4
Latvia						
American Assoc. Lutheran Chs.	1998	-	-	-	1	-
Assemblies of God		4	-	3	-	-
Baptist International Missions	1998	2	-	-	-	-
Bridge Builders International	1998	-	-	-	2	-
Calvary International	1989	6	-	-	-	-
Campus Crusade for Christ	1995	5	-	14	1	2
Christian Associates Intl.	1992	-	-	-	-	1
Foursquare Missions Intl.	1997	-	2	-	-	-
Walk Thru The Bible Ministries	1993	-	-	-	29	-
World Baptist Fellowship Msn.	1995	-	2	-	-	-
Youth With A Mission		4	-	-	-	-
	Totals:	21	4	17	33	3
Lebanon						
American Baptist Churches USA	1998	-	-	-	-	2
Arab World Ministries		7	-	-	-	2
Armenian Missionary Assoc.	1993	2	-	1	-	-
Baptist Bible Fellowship Intl.		6	-	-	-	-
Campus Crusade for Christ	1968	-	-	-	14	-
CBInternational	1995	2	-	-	-	-
Christian Aid Mission		-	-	-	4	-
Christian and Msny. Alliance	1891	2	-	-	-	-
Church of God (Anderson, IN)		2	-	-	-	-
International Partnership Mins		-	-	-	2	-
Kids Alive International	1948	-	-	-	9	5

COUNTRY Agency	Year Began	Personnel from U. S.			Other Countries	
		4+yrs	2-4 yrs	1-2 yrs	Citizens	Not Citiz.
Pioneers		6	-	-	-	-
Presbyterian Church (USA)	1823	3	-	-	-	-
SAT-7 North America	1996	-	-	-	13	-
Seventh-day Adventists	1908	8	-	-	10	-
United Church Board World Mins		-	2	-	-	-
Youth for Christ / USA	1960	2	-	-	-	-
Youth With A Mission		1	-	-	-	-
	Totals:	41	2	1	52	9
Lesotho						
Africa Inland Mission Intl.	1986	5	-	-	-	-
Assemblies of God	1950	2	-	-	-	-
Campus Crusade for Christ	1979	2	-	-	3	-
Church of the Nazarene	1993	2	-	-	-	-
General Conf. Mennonite	1973	-	-	-	-	2
Mission Aviation Fellowship	1979	8	-	-	-	-
National Baptist Conv. USA	1961	2	-	-	6	-
Presbyterian Church (USA)	1977	2	-	-	-	-
United Church Board World Mins	1984	-	12	-	-	-
	Totals:	23	12	-	9	2
Liberia						
African Methodist Epis. Zion	1876	1	-	-	-	-
Agape Gospel Mission	1994	-	-	-	2	1
Assemblies of God	1908	2	-	-	-	-
Bible League, The	1990	-	-	-	5	-
Campus Crusade for Christ	1979	-	-	-	12	-
Child Evangelism Fellowship	1955	-	-	-	7	-
Christian Aid Mission		-	-	-	12	-
Christian Chs. /Chs. of Christ	1971	1	-	-	-	-
Christian Reformed Relief	1982	-	-	-	-	-
Christian Reformed World	1978	1	-	-	-	-
Christian Services, Inc.	1967	1	-	-	-	-
Christian Union Mission	1968	3	-	-	-	-
Church of God of Prophecy	1979	-	-	-	1	-
Church of God World Missions	1974	-	-	-	-	2
Equip, Inc.	1997	-	-	-	2	-
Evangel Bible Translators	1986	-	-	-	1	-
Evangelical Lutheran Church	1862	4	-	1	-	-
Final Frontiers Foundation	1995	-	-	-	4	-
Global Fellowship		-	-	-	75	-
Gospel Recordings	1994	-	-	-	6	-
Greater Grace World Outreach	1990	-	-	-	1	-
Have Christ Will Travel Mins.	1966	-	-	-	-	10
International Partnership Mins		-	-	-	2	-
Lott Carey Baptist Mission	1900	-	-	-	125	-
Lutheran Bible Translators	1969	1	-	2	30	-
Lutheran Church-Missouri	1978	-	-	2	-	-
Mennonite Board of Missions	1988	3	-	-	-	-
Mutual Faith Ministries Intl.	1985	-	-	-	-	1
National Baptist Conv. USA	1882	2	-	-	-	-

COUNTRY Agency	Year Began	Personnel from U. S.			Other Countries	
		4+yrs	2-4 yrs	1-2 yrs	Citizens	Not Citiz.
Partners International	1964	-	-	-	179	-
Presb. Evangelistic Fellowship		-	-	-	5	-
Reformed Episcopal Bd	1990	-	-	-	-	2
Scripture Union, USA		-	-	-	2	-
Seventh-day Adventists	1927	2	-	-	2	-
SIM USA	1952	7	-	-	-	-
United Pentecostal Church Intl	1924	2	-	-	-	-
Wesleyan World Missions	1978	-	-	-	10	-
World Vision Inc.	1998	-	-	1	-	-
World-Wide Missions	1963	-	-	-	65	-
Youth for Christ / USA	1978	2	-	-	-	-
	Totals:	32	-	6	548	16
Lithuania						
Assemblies of God		6	-	-	-	-
Baptist Bible Fellowship Intl.	1991	4	-	-	-	-
Campus Crusade for Christ	1991	9	-	-	2	-
CBInternational	1996	2	-	1	-	-
Christ to the Nations Missions	1989	13	-	-	8	5
Eastern Mennonite Missions	1996	4	-	-	-	-
European Evangelistic Society	1990	2	-	-	-	-
Greater Grace World Outreach	1993	-	-	-	-	2
Navigators, The		-	-	2	-	-
Open Door Baptist Missions	1992	4	-	-	-	-
Presbyterian Church (USA)		2	-	-	-	-
Walk Thru The Bible Ministries	1995	-	-	-	3	-
	Totals:	46	-	3	13	7
Luxembourg						
Assemblies of God	1981	4	-	-	-	-
Biblical Ministries Worldwide	1972	2	-	-	-	2
	Totals:	6	-	-	-	2
Macao						
Campus Crusade for Christ	1975	-	-	-	31	3
CBInternational	1986	7	3	-	-	-
Christians In Action, Inc.	1976	2	-	-	-	2
Church of the United Brethren	1985	-	3	-	-	-
Evangelical Free Church Msn.	1993	3	-	-	-	-
Evangelize China Fellowship	1953	-	-	-	8	-
Lutheran Church-Missouri	1988	4	-	-	-	-
TEAM	1994	7	-	-	-	-
	Totals:	23	6	-	39	5
Macedonia						
Campus Crusade for Christ	1996	-	-	2	-	1
Christian Aid Mission		-	-	-	26	-
Door of Hope International	1994	2	-	-	-	-
Partners International	1991	-	-	-	28	-
SEND International	1993	12	-	-	-	-
	Totals:	14	-	2	54	1

COUNTRY Agency	Year Began	Personnel from U. S.			Other Countries	
		4+yrs	2-4 yrs	1-2 yrs	Citizens	Not Citiz.
Madagascar						
Assemblies of God	1990	8	-	1	-	-
Campus Crusade for Christ	1979	-	-	-	17	-
CBInternational	1966	6	-	6	-	-
Christian Blind Mission Intl.	1982	-	1	-	-	-
Church of the Nazarene	1993	6	-	-	-	2
Episcopal World Mission	1991	2	-	-	-	-
Evangelical Lutheran Church	1888	11	-	1	-	-
Presbyterian Church (USA)		3	-	-	-	-
Seventh-day Adventists	1926	2	-	-	-	-
SIM USA		-	-	-	1	-
Teen Missions International		-	2	-	-	-
United Pentecostal Church Intl	1970	10	-	-	-	-
Youth With A Mission		1	-	-	-	-
	Totals:	49	3	8	18	2
Malawi						
African Bible Colleges		16	1	5	-	-
African Enterprise, Inc.	1982	-	-	-	6	-
Assemblies of God	1944	7	-	2	-	-
Brethren in Christ World Msns.	1987	-	-	2	1	-
Campus Crusade for Christ	1979	2	-	-	25	-
Child Evangelism Fellowship	1988	-	-	-	4	-
Christian Aid Mission		-	-	-	62	-
Christian Chs./Chs. of Christ		7	-	-	-	-
Christian Reformed Relief	1989	-	1	-	-	-
Church of God of Prophecy	1977	-	-	-	1	-
Church of God World Missions	1951	-	-	-	-	2
Church of the Nazarene	1957	8	-	-	-	-
Emmanuel Intl. Mission (U.S.)	1980	1	-	-	-	-
Every Home for Christ	1995	-	-	-	4	-
Foursquare Missions Intl.	1984	2	-	-	-	-
Free Methodist World Missions	1973	2	-	-	-	-
Gospel Recordings	1999	1	-	-	-	-
Habitat for Humanity Intl.	1986	-	6	-	65	-
Intl. Pentecostal Holiness Ch.	1950	2	-	-	-	-
National Baptist Conv. USA	1900	-	2	-	52	-
Navigators, The	1986	2	-	-	-	-
Presbyterian Church (USA)		9	20	-	-	-
Salvation Army, U.S.A.	1968	2	-	-	-	-
Seventh-day Adventists	1902	4	-	-	25	-
SIM USA	1906	4	-	-	8	-
Teen Missions International		1	-	2	-	-
United Pentecostal Church Intl	1979	4	-	-	-	-
Wisconsin Evang. Lutheran Syn.	1963	10	-	-	-	-
World-Wide Missions	1958	-	-	-	10	-
	Totals:	84	30	11	263	2
Malaysia						
Advent Christian World Msns.	1960	-	-	-	6	-
Brethren Church Missionary Bd.	1974	-	-	-	2	-

COUNTRY Agency	Year Began	Personnel from U. S. 4+yrs	 2-4 yrs	 1-2 yrs	Other Countries Citizens	 Not Citiz.
Campus Crusade for Christ	1968	2	-	-	125	-
Christian and Msny. Alliance	1966	3	29	-	-	-
Church of God of Prophecy	1983	-	-	-	1	-
Church of God World Missions	1991	2	-	-	-	-
Elim Fellowship World Missions	1983	2	-	-	-	-
Evangel Bible Translators	1989	-	-	-	1	1
Evangelical Free Church Msn.		4	-	-	-	-
Evangelize China Fellowship	1950	-	-	-	4	-
Every Home for Christ	1983	-	-	-	5	-
Globe Missionary Evangelism	1984	4	-	-	-	-
Gospel Revival Ministries	1999	-	-	-	2	-
Mission To Unreached Peoples	1995	4	-	-	-	-
New Tribes Mission	1993	-	-	-	2	-
Overseas Radio & Television		-	-	-	4	-
Partners International	1954	-	-	-	30	-
United Pentecostal Church Intl	1981	2	-	-	-	-
World Concern	1983	1	-	-	-	-
Wycliffe Bible Translators		18	-	-	-	-
Youth With A Mission		5	-	-	-	-
	Totals:	47	29	-	182	1
Mali						
ACM International	1985	2	-	-	-	-
Assemblies of God	1988	6	-	-	-	-
Campus Crusade for Christ	1972	-	-	-	92	4
Child Evangelism Fellowship	1993	-	-	-	1	-
Christian and Msny. Alliance	1923	27	-	-	-	-
Christian Chs./Chs. of Christ	1985	2	-	-	-	-
Christian Reformed Relief	1984	1	2	-	-	1
Christian Reformed World	1984	5	-	-	-	-
Eastern Mennonite Missions	1998	-	2	-	-	-
Evangelical Baptist Missions	1951	18	-	-	-	-
Gospel Missionary Union	1919	15	-	6	-	14
Mission Aviation Fellowship	1985	14	-	2	-	-
Pioneers	1988	-	-	-	5	-
United World Mission	1954	5	-	-	-	-
Walk Thru The Bible Ministries	1994	-	-	-	3	-
World Vision Inc.	1997	-	-	1	-	-
Youth With A Mission		2	-	-	-	-
	Totals:	97	4	9	101	19
Malta						
Assemblies of God	1985	2	-	-	-	-
Baptist Bible Fellowship Intl.	1983	2	-	-	-	-
Church of God of Prophecy	1995	-	-	-	1	-
Partners International	1997	-	-	-	5	-
	Totals:	4	-	-	6	-
Marshall Isls						
Assemblies of God	1964	2	-	-	-	-
Gospel Fellowship Association	1988	6	-	-	-	6

COUNTRY Agency	Year Began	Personnel from U. S.			Other Countries	
		4+yrs	2-4 yrs	1-2 yrs	Citizens	Not Citiz.
United Church Board World Mins		-	2	-	-	-
	Totals:	8	2	-	-	6
Mauritania						
World Vision Inc.	1992	1	1	-	-	-
	Totals:	1	1	-	-	-
Mauritius						
Presbyterian Church (USA)	1982	2	-	-	-	-
SIM USA		1	-	-	2	-
	Totals:	3	-	-	2	-
Mexico						
ABWE	1991	4	-	-	-	-
Action International Mins.	1991	1	-	-	-	1
Advent Christian World Msns.	1958	1	-	-	6	-
American Baptist Churches USA	1870	8	-	-	-	-
AmeriTribes		6	-	-	-	-
AMG International	1978	3	-	-	-	-
AMOR Ministries	1980	12	5	8	6	-
Apostolic Christian Church	1972	1	-	-	1	-
Assemblies of God	1915	59	-	15	-	-
Assoc of Free Lutheran Congs	1979	4	-	-	4	-
Baptist Bible Fellowship Intl.	1950	72	-	-	-	-
Baptist General Conference	1955	7	-	-	-	-
Baptist International Missions	1965	63	-	-	-	-
Baptist International Outreach	1996	-	3	-	-	-
Baptist Mid-Missions	1960	16	-	2	-	-
Baptist Missionary Assoc.	1953	5	-	-	-	-
Baptist Missions to Forgotten		2	-	-	-	-
Baptist World Mission	1971	12	-	-	-	-
BCM International	1960	-	-	-	4	-
Bethany Fellowship Missions	1979	13	-	2	-	1
Bethany Missionary Association	1959	4	-	-	-	-
Bethel Christian Ministries	1994	-	2	-	-	-
Bible League, The	1966	-	-	-	40	-
Bible Missionary Church	1963	2	-	-	-	-
Biblical Ministries Worldwide	1964	11	-	-	1	2
Brethren Assemblies		36	-	-	-	-
Brethren Church Missionary Bd.	1979	2	-	-	-	-
Brethren in Christ World Msns.	1994	-	4	-	-	-
Calvary Commission, Inc.	1980	10	-	15	55	-
Calvary International	1986	14	-	-	-	-
CAM International	1955	49	8	3	4	2
Campus Crusade for Christ	1961	2	-	22	22	-
Central Missionary Fellowship	1994	3	-	-	-	-
Child Evangelism Fellowship	1939	1	-	-	1	-
Children's Haven International	1997	-	-	2	8	-
Christ for the City Intl.	1988	-	-	-	2	4
Christian Advance Intl.	1985	3	-	-	30	-
Christian Aid Mission		-	-	-	22	-
Christian and Msny. Alliance	1954	10	-	-	-	-

COUNTRY Agency	Year Began	Personnel from U. S.			Other Countries	
		4+yrs	2-4 yrs	1-2 yrs	Citizens	Not Citiz.
Christian Chs. /Chs. of Christ	1902	53	-	-	-	-
Christian Leadership Dev.	1998	-	-	-	-	1
Christian Reformed Relief	1969	-	3	-	2	-
Christian Reformed World	1953	13	-	-	-	-
Christian Union Mission	1976	2	-	-	-	-
Christians In Action, Inc.	1972	3	-	-	1	2
Church of God Apostolic Faith	1950	2	2	-	-	-
Church of God of Prophecy	1944	-	-	-	1	-
Church of the Nazarene	1903	16	-	-	-	4
CMF International	1980	8	1	-	-	9
ComCare International	1996	2	-	-	2	-
Congregational Christian Chs.	1994	-	-	-	4	-
Congregational Methodist Ch.	1963	10	-	-	-	-
David Livingstone Kure Fndtn		-	-	-	8	-
Eastern Mennonite Missions	1996	4	-	-	-	-
Elim Fellowship World Missions	1962	15	-	-	-	-
Enterprise Development Intl.	1996	-	-	1	-	-
Equip, Inc.	1996	2	-	-	-	-
Evangelical Covenant Church	1946	13	1	-	-	-
Evangelical Free Church Msn.	1987	10	-	2	-	-
Evangelical Friends Mission	1967	2	-	-	-	-
Evangelical Lutheran Church	1956	2	1	-	-	-
Evangelical Methodist Church	1946	2	-	-	-	-
Every Home for Christ	1963	-	-	-	4	-
Faith Christian Fellowship	1992	6	-	-	-	-
Fellowship International Msn.	1984	8	-	-	-	-
Final Frontiers Foundation	1993	-	-	-	5	-
Floresta USA, Inc.	1995	-	-	-	8	-
Foundation For His Ministry	1967	-	-	-	77	47
Free Methodist World Missions	1917	2	-	-	-	-
Full Gospel Grace Fellowship		2	-	-	-	-
General Conf. Mennonite	1946	-	-	-	-	6
Global Fellowship		-	-	-	5	-
Global Outreach Mission		11	-	-	-	-
Global Strategy Mission Assoc.	1986	4	1	-	1	-
Globe Missionary Evangelism	1969	17	-	-	-	-
Gospel Fellowship Association	1967	15	-	-	-	15
Gospel Recordings	1966	4	-	-	3	4
Grace Brethren Intl. Missions	1951	4	-	-	-	-
Habitat for Humanity Intl.	1987	-	5	-	26	-
Hope for the Hungry	1984	1	1	1	2	-
Impact International	1990	-	-	-	2	-
Independent Faith Mission	1985	2	-	-	-	-
International Gospel Outreach	1990	2	-	-	-	-
International Outreach Mins.	1988	-	-	-	5	-
International Partnership Mins	1991	-	-	-	-	4
International Teams, U.S.A.	1968	-	6	3	-	4
Intl. Discipleship Mission	1951	2	-	-	-	-
Intl. Pentecostal Ch of Christ	1950	1	-	-	-	-
Intl. Pentecostal Holiness Ch.	1930	2	-	-	-	-
Latin America Lutheran Mission	1941	1	-	-	18	-

COUNTRY Agency	Year Began	Personnel from U. S.			Other Countries	
		4+yrs	2-4 yrs	1-2 yrs	Citizens	Not Citiz.
Latin America Mission	1965	27	-	-	4	4
Latin American Indian Mins.	1972	-	-	-	3	-
Living Water Teaching Intl.	1995	-	-	-	1	-
Lutheran Church-Missouri	1940	6	-	-	-	-
Macedonia World Baptist Msns.	1983	10	-	-	-	-
Maranatha Baptist Mission	1966	12	-	-	-	-
Mazahua Mission	1976	-	-	-	35	-
MBMS International	1905	-	2	-	-	-
Medical Ambassadors Intl.	1990	1	-	-	3	-
Mexican Border Missions	1961	2	-	-	5	-
Mexican Christian Mission	1963	3	-	2	5	-
Mexican Medical, Inc.	1963	12	-	-	-	-
Mission Aviation Fellowship	1946	6	-	4	-	-
Mission Soc. for United Meth.	1987	2	-	-	-	2
Mission to the Americas	1951	4	-	-	2	-
Mission to the World	1977	45	7	-	-	-
Missionary Gospel Fellowship	1950	13	-	-	2	-
Missionary Revival Crusade	1949	24	-	-	5	35
Missionary Ventures Intl.	1994	-	-	-	1	-
Navigators, The	1966	5	-	-	-	-
New Tribes Mission	1975	84	-	-	4	1
North American Baptist Conf.	1992	8	-	-	-	-
OC International, Inc.	1967	4	-	-	-	-
OMS Intl., Inc.	1990	15	-	-	-	2
Open Bible Standard Churches	1965	3	-	-	-	-
Pan American Missions	1960	1	1	-	2	-
Pentecostal Church of God	1942	6	-	-	-	-
PNMC Missions		1	-	-	-	-
Pocket Testament League	1988	-	-	-	2	-
Precious Seed Ministries	1985	-	-	-	8	-
Presb. Evangelistic Fellowship	1980	8	-	-	2	-
Presbyterian Church (USA)	1872	4	23	7	-	-
Project Partner with Christ	1969	-	-	-	1	-
Reformed Church In America	1925	8	-	-	2	-
Rio Grande Bible Institute	1946	51	2	6	-	-
Ripe for Harvest, Inc.	1995	-	-	1	-	-
Rosedale Mennonite Missions	1990	2	-	-	-	-
Salvation Army, U.S.A.	1904	5	-	-	-	-
Seventh-day Adventists	1893	30	-	-	16	-
Shield of Faith Mission Intl.		7	-	-	-	-
Source of Light Ministries	1961	1	-	-	1	-
South American Missionary Soc.	1996	2	-	-	-	-
Spanish World Gospel Mission	1985	-	-	-	6	-
TEAM	1988	16	-	-	-	-
The Master's Harvest	1990	4	-	-	-	-
The Master's Mission, Inc.	1995	2	-	-	-	-
UFM International	1971	14	-	1	-	5
United Church Board World Mins		-	2	-	-	-
United Pentecostal Church Intl	1986	12	-	-	-	-
VELA Ministries International	1984	-	1	-	-	-
Village Ministries Intl.	1998	-	-	-	2	-

COUNTRY Agency	Year Began	Personnel from U. S.			Other Countries	
		4+yrs	2-4 yrs	1-2 yrs	Citizens	Not Citiz.
Walk Thru The Bible Ministries	1995	-	-	-	2	-
WEC International	1990	14	-	-	-	1
Wesleyan World Missions	1920	5	-	-	-	-
Westminister Biblical Missions	1991	-	-	-	1	2
Wisconsin Evang. Lutheran Syn.	1968	4	1	-	-	-
World Baptist Fellowship Msn.	1953	24	-	2	-	-
World Gospel Mission	1945	13	-	2	-	-
World Indigenous Missions	1981	26	-	2	-	-
World Mission Prayer League	1945	5	-	2	-	-
World Missions Far Corners	1958	8	-	-	-	-
World Team	1990	-	-	1	-	2
World Witness	1878	9	-	-	-	-
World-Wide Missions	1966	-	-	-	14	-
Wycliffe Bible Translators	1936	207	-	-	-	-
Youth for Christ / USA		2	-	-	-	-
Youth With A Mission		38	-	-	-	-
YUGO Ministries	1964	13	-	-	-	-
	Totals:	1507	82	106	509	160
Micronesia						
Baptist Mid-Missions	1981	9	-	-	-	-
Campus Crusade for Christ	1976	-	-	-	2	-
Child Evangelism Fellowship	1957	2	-	-	1	-
Conservative Cong. Christian	1984	2	-	2	-	-
Global Outreach Mission	1988	2	-	-	-	-
Independent Faith Mission	1990	2	-	-	-	-
Liebenzell Mission USA	1959	-	-	-	-	2
Mission to the World	1985	2	-	-	-	-
United Pentecostal Church Intl	1981	4	-	-	-	-
	Totals:	23	-	2	3	2
Moldava						
Baptist International Missions	1993	1	-	-	-	-
Bible League, The	1993	-	-	-	2	-
Campus Crusade for Christ	1995	-	-	-	10	-
Crossover Communications Intl.	1995	4	-	-	-	-
Macedonia World Baptist Msns.	1992	6	-	-	-	-
Ministry to Eastern Europe	1998	-	-	-	1	-
New Hope International	1997	-	-	-	3	-
Salvation Army, U.S.A.	1913	3	-	-	-	-
Walk Thru The Bible Ministries	1994	-	-	-	16	-
	Totals:	14	-	-	32	-
Mongolia						
ABWE	1998	4	-	-	-	-
Assemblies of God		16	-	1	-	-
CBInternational	1995	1	-	-	-	-
Christar	1992	6	-	-	-	-
Christian Aid Mission		-	-	-	12	-
Christian and Msny. Alliance	1997	2	-	-	-	-
Church of God World Missions		3	-	-	-	-

COUNTRY Agency	Year Began	Personnel from U. S.			Other Countries	
		4+yrs	2-4 yrs	1-2 yrs	Citizens	Not Citiz.
Evangelical Free Church Msn.	1993	8	-	-	-	-
Every Home for Christ	1998	-	-	-	7	-
Mustard Seed, Inc.	1999	1	-	-	6	-
Navigators, The		1	-	-	-	-
New Tribes Mission	1993	7	-	-	-	2
Seventh-day Adventists	1997	4	-	-	5	-
SIM USA	1996	1	-	2	-	-
Team Expansion, Inc.		3	-	-	-	-
World Mission Prayer League	1993	2	-	-	-	-
World Vision Inc.	1995	1	-	-	-	-
	Totals:	60	-	3	30	2
Morocco						
Arab World Ministries		11	-	-	-	18
Christian Aid Mission		-	-	-	4	-
Church of God World Missions		2	-	-	-	-
Fellowship International Msn.	1950	8	-	-	-	-
Gospel Missionary Union		4	-	-	-	-
Navigators, The		-	4	-	-	-
World Horizons	1998	1	-	-	-	-
	Totals:	26	4	-	4	18
Mozambique						
ACM International	1996	1	-	-	-	-
Africa Inland Mission Intl.	1985	26	-	-	-	-
Assemblies of God	1974	5	-	-	-	-
Bible League, The	1995	-	-	-	3	-
Brethren Assemblies		-	2	-	-	-
Child Evangelism Fellowship	1994	-	-	-	1	-
Christian Chs./Chs. of Christ	1992	2	-	4	-	-
Church of God of Prophecy	1979	-	-	-	1	-
Church of the Nazarene	1922	11	-	-	-	-
Elim Fellowship World Missions		2	-	-	-	-
Every Home for Christ	1995	-	-	-	3	-
Food for the Hungry, Inc.	1987	3	5	-	165	6
General Conf. Mennonite	1994	2	-	-	-	-
Heifer Project International	1996	-	1	-	-	-
Intl. Pentecostal Holiness Ch.	1957	2	-	-	-	-
OMS Intl., Inc.	1994	8	-	2	-	1
Presbyterian Church (USA)		2	-	-	-	-
Seventh-day Adventists	1935	4	-	-	2	-
SIM USA	1937	10	-	-	9	-
TEAM	1988	3	-	-	-	1
Teen Missions International		3	-	-	-	-
Wesleyan World Missions	1998	2	-	-	-	-
World Relief Corporation	1988	-	2	1	-	3
World Vision Inc.	1994	1	1	6	-	-
Wycliffe Bible Translators	1994	28	-	-	-	-
Youth With A Mission		4	-	-	-	-
	Totals:	119	11	13	184	11

COUNTRY Agency	Year Began	Personnel from U. S.			Other Countries	
		4+yrs	2-4 yrs	1-2 yrs	Citizens	Not Citiz.
Myanmar/Burma						
Baptist World Mission	1991	2	-	-	-	-
Bible League, The	1985	-	-	-	8	-
Campus Crusade for Christ	1972	-	-	-	85	-
Christian Aid Mission		-	-	-	903	-
Church Planting International	1995	-	-	-	25	-
East West Ministries		-	-	-	1	-
Evangelize China Fellowship	1993	-	-	-	4	-
Every Home for Christ	1981	-	-	-	21	-
Final Frontiers Foundation	1987	-	-	-	40	-
Food for the Hungry, Inc.	1997	-	-	-	-	2
Global Fellowship		-	-	-	-	4
Global Outreach Mission		-	-	-	2	-
Gospel for Asia	1988	-	-	-	533	-
International Partnership Mins		-	-	-	2	-
Kids Alive International	1999	-	-	-	3	-
Partners International	1978	-	-	-	344	-
Pass the Torch Ministries	1986	-	1	-	5	-
World Bible Translation Center	1997	-	-	-	7	-
World Concern	1993	-	2	-	32	-
World Missions Far Corners	1996	-	-	-	10	-
World Vision Inc.	1997	-	-	1	-	-
Youth for Christ / USA		2	-	-	-	-
	Totals:	4	3	1	2025	6
N Mariana Isls						
Baptist International Missions	1998	4	-	-	-	-
Far East Broadcasting Company	1974	6	2	-	-	-
General Baptists International	1947	2	-	-	-	-
Macedonia World Baptist Msns.	1996	2	-	-	-	-
Pioneers	1983	1	-	-	1	-
Youth With A Mission		1	-	-	-	-
	Totals:	16	2	-	1	-
Namibia						
Africa Inland Mission Intl.	1981	4	-	-	-	-
Assemblies of God	1979	4	-	-	-	-
Child Evangelism Fellowship	1994	2	-	-	-	-
Christian Aid Mission		-	-	-	11	-
Church of the Nazarene	1973	2	-	-	-	-
Evangelical Lutheran Church	1983	-	2	4	-	-
Every Home for Christ	1995	-	-	-	1	-
General Conf. Mennonite	1993	-	-	-	-	1
Lutheran Bible Translators	1996	4	-	2	4	-
Reformed Baptist Mission Svcs.		2	-	-	-	1
SIM USA	1970	-	-	-	5	-
United Church Board World Mins		-	2	-	-	-
United Pentecostal Church Intl	1986	2	-	-	-	-
	Totals:	20	4	6	21	2

COUNTRY Agency	Year Began	Personnel from U. S.			Other Countries	
		4+yrs	2-4 yrs	1-2 yrs	Citizens	Not Citiz.
Nepal						
Advancing Renewal Ministries	1992	-	-	-	-	1
Anglican Frontier Missions	1993	2	-	-	-	-
Baptist International Missions	1998	2	-	-	-	-
BCM International	1995	-	-	-	1	-
Brethren in Christ World Msns.	1992	-	-	-	12	-
Calvary International		2	-	-	-	-
Campus Crusade for Christ	1975	-	-	-	327	-
Christian Aid Mission		-	-	-	324	-
Evangelical Friends Mission	1994	-	-	-	-	4
Every Home for Christ	1982	-	-	-	35	-
General Conf. Mennonite	1983	2	-	-	-	-
Global Fellowship		-	-	-	3	2
Good News for India	1999	-	-	-	3	-
Gospel for Asia	1984	-	-	-	227	-
Gospel Recordings	1982	-	-	-	7	-
Greater Grace World Outreach	1994	-	-	-	-	1
International Partnership Mins		-	-	-	-	1
InterServe/USA	1952	8	-	-	-	-
Medical Ambassadors Intl.	1984	-	-	-	6	-
Mennonite Board of Missions	1957	12	-	-	-	-
Mission To Unreached Peoples	1985	-	6	-	-	-
Navigators, The		-	2	1	-	-
New Life League International	1961	-	-	-	2	-
Presbyterian Church (USA)	1954	10	13	-	-	-
Project Christ International	1993	-	-	-	-	7
Seventh-day Adventists	1957	3	2	-	13	-
SIM USA	1996	-	-	-	1	-
TEAM	1892	15	3	-	-	-
United Church Board World Mins	1979	-	10	-	-	-
WEC International		2	-	-	-	-
Wesleyan World Missions	1950	-	-	-	-	3
World Concern	1990	2	-	-	-	-
World Mission Prayer League	1954	3	-	2	-	-
World-Wide Missions	1962	-	-	-	4	-
Youth With A Mission		9	-	-	-	-
	Totals:	72	36	3	965	19
Netherland Antilles						
Assemblies of God	1983	2	-	-	-	-
Child Evangelism Fellowship		2	-	-	-	-
Global Outreach Mission		2	-	-	1	-
TEAM	1931	5	-	-	-	-
UFM International		-	-	2	-	-
United Pentecostal Church Intl	1974	4	-	-	-	-
	Totals:	15	-	2	1	-
Netherlands						
Arab World Ministries		6	-	-	4	-
Assemblies of God	1965	4	-	-	-	-
Baptist Bible Fellowship Intl.	1979	2	-	-	-	-

COUNTRY Agency	Year Began	Personnel from U. S.			Other Countries	
		4+yrs	2-4 yrs	1-2 yrs	Citizens	Not Citiz.
Baptist Mid-Missions	1954	6	-	-	-	-
Baptist World Mission	1995	2	-	-	-	-
BCM International	1948	1	-	-	8	-
Biblical Ministries Worldwide	1958	2	-	-	1	-
Brethren Assemblies		2	-	-	-	-
Campus Crusade for Christ	1969	-	-	4	-	-
CBInternational	1985	2	1	-	-	-
Christar	1976	3	-	-	-	-
Christian Associates Intl.	1987	15	2	2	2	-
Church of God World Missions	1982	1	-	-	-	2
Church of The Brethren		-	2	-	-	-
Eastern Mennonite Missions	1997	3	-	1	-	-
European Missions Outreach	1989	2	-	-	-	-
Evangelical Free Church Msn.	1997	2	-	-	-	-
Faith Christian Fellowship	1993	-	2	-	-	-
Global Outreach Mission		-	-	-	3	-
Gospel Recordings	1966	-	-	-	6	-
Greater Grace World Outreach	1977	-	-	-	-	4
Habitat for Humanity Intl.	1994	1	-	-	1	-
Shield of Faith Ministries	1992	-	-	-	10	4
United Pentecostal Church Intl	1962	2	-	-	-	-
Walk Thru The Bible Ministries	1991	-	-	-	1	-
World Harvest Mission	1989	6	-	-	-	-
Youth With A Mission		38	-	-	-	-
	Totals:	100	7	7	36	10
New Caledonia						
Assemblies of God	1969	2	-	-	-	-
Baptist International Missions	1995	2	-	-	-	-
	Totals:	4	-	-	-	-
New Zealand						
Advent Christian World Msns.	1995	2	-	-	-	-
American Baptist Association		2	-	-	-	-
Baptist Bible Fellowship Intl.	1971	16	-	-	-	-
Baptist International Missions	1979	4	-	-	-	-
Baptist Mid-Missions	1973	6	-	1	-	-
Baptist World Mission	1988	15	-	-	-	-
Berean Mission, Inc.	1978	-	-	-	2	-
Biblical Ministries Worldwide	1967	11	-	-	-	-
Campus Crusade for Christ	1972	8	-	-	26	1
Christian Chs./Chs. of Christ		4	-	-	-	-
Elim Fellowship World Missions	1964	2	-	-	-	-
Fellowship International Msn.	1995	2	-	-	-	-
Gospel Fellowship Association	1998	2	-	-	-	2
Navigators, The	1953	2	-	-	-	-
Presbyterian Church (USA)		4	-	-	-	-
SIM USA		-	-	-	14	-
United Pentecostal Church Intl	1969	2	-	-	-	-
Walk Thru The Bible Ministries	1982	-	-	-	6	-
WEC International		2	-	-	-	-

COUNTRY Agency	Year Began	Personnel from U. S.			Other Countries	
		4+yrs	2-4 yrs	1-2 yrs	Citizens	Not Citiz.
World Baptist Fellowship Msn.	1979	4	-	2	-	-
Wycliffe Bible Translators		1	-	-	-	-
Youth With A Mission		16	-	-	-	-
	Totals:	105	-	3	48	3
Nicaragua						
ABWE	1998	4	-	-	-	-
American Baptist Churches USA	1917	6	-	-	1	1
Assemblies of God	1936	14	-	3	-	-
Baptist Bible Fellowship Intl.		6	-	-	-	-
Baptist International Missions	1965	5	-	-	-	-
Baptist Medical & Dental	1974	-	-	-	7	2
Brethren in Christ World Msns.	1965	-	2	-	8	-
CAM International	1900	4	-	-	1	1
Christian Aid Ministries		-	2	-	-	-
Christian Aid Mission		-	-	-	14	-
Christian Reformed Relief	1973	1	-	-	2	-
Christian Reformed World	1996	2	-	4	-	-
Church of God of Prophecy	1962	-	-	-	-	1
Church of God World Missions	1950	2	-	-	-	-
Church of the Nazarene	1937	2	-	-	-	-
Enterprise Development Intl.	1991	1	-	-	-	-
Equip, Inc.	1998	2	-	2	2	-
Evangelical Lutheran Church	1980	2	-	2	-	-
Every Home for Christ	1965	-	-	-	4	-
Final Frontiers Foundation	1991	-	-	-	23	-
Food for the Hungry, Inc.	1994	2	4	-	1	1
Globe Missionary Evangelism	1998	2	-	-	-	-
Habitat for Humanity Intl.	1984	-	2	-	21	-
Intl. Pentecostal Holiness Ch.	1994	-	1	-	-	-
Larry Jones International Mins	1989	-	-	-	6	-
Living Water Teaching Intl.	1988	-	-	-	1	1
Missionary Ventures Intl.	1987	-	-	-	3	-
National Baptist Conv. USA	1958	2	-	-	3	-
Pentecostal Church of God	1993	2	-	-	-	-
Presbyterian Church (USA)		4	5	6	-	-
Reformed Church In America	1991	-	-	-	2	-
Self-Help Foundation	1997	-	-	-	1	-
Seventh-day Adventists	1912	4	-	-	-	-
Shield of Faith Ministries	1992	-	-	-	8	-
United Church Board World Mins		-	1	-	-	-
World Relief Corporation	1991	1	-	-	-	-
Young Life	1988	3	-	-	-	-
Youth With A Mission		2	-	-	-	-
	Totals:	73	17	17	108	7
Niger						
Agape Gospel Mission	1995	-	-	-	-	2
Assemblies of God		4	-	-	-	-
Baptist International Missions	1966	1	-	-	-	-
Campus Crusade for Christ	1991	-	-	-	10	-

COUNTRY Agency	Year Began	Personnel from U. S.			Other Countries	
		4+yrs	2-4 yrs	1-2 yrs	Citizens	Not Citiz.
Child Evangelism Fellowship	1994	-	-	-	1	-
Christian Aid Mission		-	-	-	6	-
Christian Reformed Relief	1993	-	-	-	-	1
Elim Fellowship World Missions	1991	2	-	-	-	-
Fellowship International Msn.	1971	3	-	-	-	-
Gospel Revival Ministries	1997	-	-	-	5	-
Lutheran World Relief	1990	2	-	-	-	-
Mission to the World	1993	2	-	-	-	-
Seventh-day Adventists	1987	-	-	-	2	-
SIM USA	1924	71	-	4	46	-
World Vision Inc.	1997	-	-	1	-	-
Wycliffe Bible Translators	1980	33	-	-	-	-
Youth With A Mission		1	-	-	-	-
	Totals:	119	-	5	70	3
Nigeria						
ACM International	1953	3	-	-	-	-
Agape Gospel Mission	1984	-	-	-	17	-
Assemblies of God	1939	6	-	2	-	-
Baptist Bible Fellowship Intl.	1987	4	-	-	-	-
Baptist International Missions	1982	3	-	-	-	-
Baptist International Outreach	1988	-	-	-	7	-
Baptist Missions to Forgotten		2	-	-	-	-
Baptist World Mission	1992	-	-	-	2	-
Bible League, The	1980	-	-	-	16	-
Bible Missionary Church	1971	2	-	-	-	-
BILD International		-	-	-	2	-
Brethren Assemblies		6	-	-	-	2
Campus Crusade for Christ	1969	6	-	-	230	8
Child Evangelism Fellowship	1982	-	-	-	5	-
Christian Aid Mission		-	-	-	437	-
Christian Blind Mission Intl.	1997	-	1	-	-	-
Christian Chs. /Chs. of Christ	1955	2	-	-	-	-
Christian Mission for the Deaf	1960	-	-	-	1	-
Christian Reformed Relief	1969	-	-	-	1	1
Christian Reformed World	1940	29	2	5	-	-
Church of God (Holiness) Msn.	1988	2	-	-	-	2
Church of God of Prophecy	1971	-	-	-	1	1
Church of God World Missions	1951	1	-	-	-	-
Church of The Brethren	1922	-	6	2	-	-
Church of the Nazarene	1977	3	-	-	-	-
Congregational Christian Chs.	1990	-	-	-	2	-
Development Associates Intl.	1996	-	-	-	-	1
Elim Fellowship World Missions	1975	3	-	-	-	-
Equip, Inc.	1995	-	-	-	2	-
Evangel Bible Translators	1982	-	-	-	1	-
Evangelical Baptist Missions	1929	10	-	-	-	-
Evangelical Baptist Missions	1985	-	-	-	2	-
Evangelical Lutheran Church	1913	-	1	1	-	-
Evangelism Resources	1991	2	-	-	2	-
Every Home for Christ	1976	-	-	-	3	-

COUNTRY Agency	Year Began	Personnel from U. S. 4+yrs	2-4 yrs	1-2 yrs	Other Countries Citizens	Not Citiz.
Faith Christian Fellowship	1991	-	2	-	-	-
Fellowship International Msn.	1975	4	-	-	-	-
Free Methodist World Missions	1989	4	-	-	-	-
Gospel Recordings	1983	-	-	-	10	-
Gospel Revival Ministries	1990	-	-	-	28	-
Intl. Inst. Christian Studies	1988	8	-	-	15	-
Ireland Outreach Intl., Inc.	1994	-	-	-	3	-
Lott Carey Baptist Mission	1962	-	-	-	100	-
Lutheran Church-Missouri	1936	21	-	3	-	-
Mission to the World	1990	4	-	-	-	-
Mutual Faith Ministries Intl.	1988	-	-	-	-	1
North American Baptist Conf.	1961	4	-	2	-	-
Partners International	1963	-	-	-	114	-
Presb. Evangelistic Fellowship		1	-	-	2	-
Seventh-day Adventists	1914	8	-	-	2	-
SIM USA	1893	65	-	3	37	-
United Pentecostal Church Intl	1970	6	-	-	-	-
United World Mission	1990	2	-	-	-	-
Village Ministries Intl.	1990	-	-	-	25	-
Walk Thru The Bible Ministries	1984	-	-	-	17	-
World Partners USA	1905	3	-	-	-	-
World-Wide Missions	1960	-	-	-	15	-
Wycliffe Bible Translators	1963	20	-	-	-	-
	Totals:	234	12	18	1099	16
Norway						
ABWE	1978	8	-	-	-	-
Baptist International Missions	1973	1	-	-	-	-
Intl. Pentecostal Holiness Ch.	1992	2	1	-	-	-
Maranatha Baptist Mission	1983	2	-	-	-	-
Seventh-day Adventists	1878	2	-	-	-	-
United Pentecostal Church Intl	1978	2	-	-	-	-
Walk Thru The Bible Ministries	1994	-	-	-	8	-
Youth With A Mission		4	-	-	-	-
	Totals:	21	1	-	8	-
Oman						
Arab World Ministries		2	-	-	-	4
	Totals:	2	-	-	-	4
Pakistan						
Baptist Bible Fellowship Intl.	1959	4	-	-	-	-
Campus Crusade for Christ	1960	-	-	-	115	-
CBInternational	1954	9	-	1	-	-
Child Evangelism Fellowship	1955	-	-	-	1	-
Christian Aid Mission		-	-	-	94	-
Christian Blind Mission Intl.	1982	-	1	-	-	-
Church of God of Prophecy	1991	-	-	-	1	-
Church World Service &	1950	-	-	-	7	-
Episcopal World Mission	1990	2	-	-	-	-
Gospel for Asia	1983	-	-	-	1	-

COUNTRY Agency	Year Began	Personnel from U. S.			Other Countries	
		4+yrs	2-4 yrs	1-2 yrs	Citizens	Not Citiz.
Greater Grace World Outreach	1987	-	-	-	-	1
InterServe/USA	1948	10	-	-	-	-
Literacy & Evangelism Intl.	1989	2	-	-	-	-
Presbyterian Church (USA)	1834	20	-	-	-	-
Seventh-day Adventists	1914	2	-	-	2	-
Shield of Faith Mission Intl.	1983	1	-	-	-	-
SIM USA	1957	2	-	-	19	-
TEAM	1946	36	-	-	-	-
United Pentecostal Church Intl	1971	4	-	-	-	-
Wesleyan World Missions	1992	-	-	-	2	-
Westminister Biblical Missions	1973	1	-	-	20	-
World Mission Prayer League	1946	5	-	-	-	-
World Relief Corporation	1985	1	-	-	-	-
World Witness	1905	10	-	-	450	-
	Totals:	109	1	1	712	1
Panama						
Assemblies of God	1967	12	-	2	-	-
Baptist Bible Fellowship Intl.	1976	10	-	-	-	-
Baptist International Missions	1980	2	-	-	-	-
Cadence International	1958	-	-	2	-	-
CAM International	1940	7	-	-	1	-
Campus Crusade for Christ	1965	-	-	-	19	-
Christian Chs./Chs. of Christ		4	-	-	-	-
Church of God of Prophecy	1946	-	-	-	-	1
Evangelical Lutheran Church	1990	2	-	-	-	-
Free Will Baptist, Inc.	1971	8	-	-	-	-
Gospel Missionary Union		4	-	-	1	1
Intl. Pentecostal Holiness Ch.	1988	2	1	-	-	-
Latin America Mission	1978	-	-	-	2	2
Lutheran Church-Missouri	1941	6	-	6	-	-
National Baptist Conv. of Am.	1909	-	-	-	4	-
New Tribes Mission	1953	80	-	1	-	3
United Pentecostal Church Intl	1980	4	-	-	-	-
Youth With A Mission		2	-	-	-	-
	Totals:	143	1	11	27	7
Papua New Guinea						
ABWE	1967	23	-	-	-	-
Apostolic Christian Church	1961	2	-	-	-	-
Baptist Bible Fellowship Intl.	1961	16	-	-	-	-
Baptist International Missions	1968	17	-	-	-	-
Baptist World Mission	1978	2	-	-	-	-
Bible Missionary Church	1963	8	-	-	-	-
Brethren Assemblies		5	-	-	-	1
Campus Crusade for Christ	1978	-	-	-	3	-
Child Evangelism Fellowship	1992	-	-	-	2	-
Christian Aid Mission		-	-	-	9	-
Christian Blind Mission Intl.	1988	-	2	-	-	-
Christian Chs./Chs. of Christ		28	-	-	-	-
Church of the Nazarene	1955	40	-	-	-	15

COUNTRY Agency	Year Began	Personnel from U. S.			Other Countries	
		4+yrs	2-4 yrs	1-2 yrs	Citizens	Not Citiz.
Eastern Mennonite Missions	1996	2	-	-	-	-
Evangelical Bible Mission	1948	-	55	-	-	-
Evangelical Lutheran Church	1886	8	-	1	-	-
Every Home for Christ	1987	-	-	-	25	-
Foursquare Missions Intl.	1956	2	-	-	-	-
Gospel Fellowship Association	1997	2	-	2	-	4
Gospel Recordings	1975	-	-	-	4	-
Habitat for Humanity Intl.	1983	-	9	-	7	9
International Outreach Mins.	1993	2	-	-	-	-
Kids Alive International	1991	1	-	1	34	-
Lutheran Bible Translators	1998	-	1	-	-	-
Lutheran Church-Missouri	1948	9	-	8	-	-
Maranatha Baptist Mission	1975	4	-	-	-	-
Mission to the World	1987	6	-	-	-	-
Mustard Seed, Inc.	1974	2	-	-	15	2
New Tribes Mission	1950	339	-	35	-	52
Open Bible Standard Churches	1976	4	-	-	-	-
Operation Mobilization		2	-	-	-	-
Pioneer Bible Translators	1979	30	-	-	40	2
Pioneers	1980	14	-	-	1	-
Presbyterian Church (USA)		3	-	-	-	-
Seventh-day Adventists	1908	10	-	-	23	-
SIM USA		-	-	-	2	-
Walk Thru The Bible Ministries	1991	-	-	-	3	-
Wesleyan World Missions	1961	6	-	-	-	-
World Gospel Mission	1996	8	-	-	-	-
World-Wide Missions	1973	-	-	-	6	-
Wycliffe Associates USA	1998	-	-	2	-	-
Wycliffe Bible Translators	1956	405	-	-	-	-
	Totals:	1000	67	49	174	85
Paraguay						
ABWE	1976	18	-	-	-	-
Apostolic Christian Church	1978	1	-	-	1	-
Assemblies of God	1945	19	-	7	-	-
Baptist Bible Fellowship Intl.	1980	4	-	-	-	-
Bethany Fellowship Missions	1985	-	-	2	-	-
Brethren Assemblies		12	-	-	-	-
Campus Crusade for Christ	1966	-	-	-	5	2
Christian Aid Mission		-	-	-	28	-
Church of God of Prophecy	1977	1	-	-	1	-
Church of God World Missions	1954	2	-	-	-	-
Church of the Nazarene	1980	4	-	-	-	-
Full Gospel Grace Fellowship		2	-	-	-	-
General Conf. Mennonite	1952	2	-	-	-	-
Global Outreach Mission	1994	2	-	-	-	-
Habitat for Humanity Intl.	1996	-	2	-	-	-
International Partnership Mins	1995	-	-	-	1	1
Living Water Teaching Intl.	1991	-	2	-	-	-
Lutheran Church-Missouri	1938	-	-	2	-	-
Mission Soc. for United Meth.	1988	6	2	-	-	-

COUNTRY Agency	Year Began	Personnel from U. S.			Other Countries	
		4+yrs	2-4 yrs	1-2 yrs	Citizens	Not Citiz.
New Tribes Mission	1946	67	-	2	1	-
Open Air Campaigners	1992	-	-	-	2	-
Seventh-day Adventists	1900	-	-	-	2	-
SIM USA	1987	13	-	3	7	-
STEM Ministries	1992	-	-	-	-	-
United Church Board World Mins		-	2	-	-	-
United Pentecostal Church Intl	1973	2	-	-	-	-
World Gospel Mission	1986	5	-	-	-	-
World-Wide Missions	1965	-	-	-	1	-
Youth With A Mission		1	-	-	-	-
	Totals:	161	8	16	49	3
Peru						
ABWE	1929	54	-	-	-	-
Allegheny Wesleyan Meth. Msns.	1972	2	-	-	-	-
American Baptist Churches USA	1997	-	-	-	1	-
Assemblies of God	1919	14	-	4	-	-
Baptist Bible Fellowship Intl.	1958	11	-	-	-	-
Baptist Faith Missions	1935	2	-	-	-	-
Baptist International Missions	1968	14	-	-	-	-
Baptist International Outreach	1995	6	-	-	-	-
Baptist Mid-Missions	1937	29	-	9	-	-
Baptist World Mission	1997	2	-	-	-	-
BCM International	1995	-	-	-	6	-
Bible Missionary Church	1988	2	-	-	-	-
Brethren Assemblies		16	1	-	-	-
Campus Crusade for Christ	1964	-	-	-	13	-
Christ for the City Intl.	1989	-	-	-	1	-
Christian Aid Mission		-	-	-	993	-
Christian and Msny. Alliance	1925	22	1	-	-	-
Christians In Action, Inc.	1980	2	-	-	-	2
Church of God of Prophecy	1955	-	-	-	-	1
Church of the Nazarene	1914	10	-	-	-	2
Compassion International, Inc.	1977	-	-	-	19	-
Eastern Mennonite Missions	1986	5	-	-	-	1
Elim Fellowship World Missions	1964	2	-	-	-	-
Evangelical Free Church Msn.	1975	8	-	-	-	-
Evangelical Lutheran Synod	1968	-	3	-	-	-
Final Frontiers Foundation	1997	-	-	-	6	-
Food for the Hungry, Inc.	1982	2	5	-	29	3
Global Outreach Mission		-	-	-	2	-
Habitat for Humanity Intl.	1982	-	2	-	46	-
Impact International		-	-	-	2	-
International Partnership Mins		-	-	-	4	-
Kids Alive International	1993	2	6	-	9	-
Latin America Mission	1975	2	-	-	2	2
Literacy & Evangelism Intl.	1998	2	-	-	-	-
Lutheran Church-Missouri	1995	2	-	-	-	-
Lutheran World Relief	1994	-	-	-	2	-
Macedonia World Baptist Msns.	1987	12	-	-	-	-
Maranatha Baptist Mission	1964	2	-	-	-	-

COUNTRY Agency	Year Began	Personnel from U. S.			Other Countries	
		4+yrs	2-4 yrs	1-2 yrs	Citizens	Not Citiz.
MBMS International	1954	-	2	-	-	-
Mission Aides, Inc.	1994	-	-	-	1	-
Mission Soc. for United Meth.	1997	6	4	-	-	-
Mission to the World	1987	20	4	-	-	-
Missionary Ventures Intl.	1998	4	-	-	-	-
Pioneers	1997	8	-	-	-	-
Presb. Evangelistic Fellowship		4	-	-	2	-
Scripture Union, USA		2	-	-	-	-
Seventh-day Adventists	1898	4	-	-	2	-
SIM USA	1965	5	-	2	26	-
Source of Light Ministries	1978	-	-	-	2	-
South America Mission	1926	29	-	1	-	30
South American Missionary Soc.	1979	2	-	-	-	-
Spanish World Gospel Mission	1974	-	-	-	4	-
TEAM	1962	8	-	-	-	-
United Pentecostal Church Intl	1962	4	-	-	-	-
Wesleyan World Missions	1903	6	-	-	-	-
World Concern	1987	-	1	-	1	-
World Mission Prayer League	1985	4	-	1	-	-
World Missions Far Corners	1963	6	-	-	10	-
World Reach, Inc.	1998	-	-	-	-	2
World Team	1906	10	-	-	-	8
Wycliffe Bible Translators		147	-	-	-	-
	Totals:	494	29	17	1183	51
Philippines						
ABWE	1927	41	-	-	-	-
ACM International	1998	2	-	-	-	-
Action International Mins.	1974	25	-	2	-	-
Advent Christian World Msns.	1950	3	-	-	20	-
American Baptist Churches USA	1900	7	-	-	-	-
AMG International	1977	2	-	-	36	-
Artists In Christian Testimony	1991	2	-	-	-	2
Assemblies of God	1925	68	-	20	-	-
Back to the Bible Intl.	1957	-	-	-	19	-
Baptist Bible Fellowship Intl.	1950	56	-	-	-	-
Baptist General Conference	1949	20	-	-	-	-
Baptist International Missions	1970	35	-	-	-	-
Baptist International Outreach	1998	2	-	-	-	-
Baptist Missionary Assoc.	1974	5	-	-	-	-
Baptist Missions to Forgotten		2	-	-	-	-
Baptist World Mission	1998	4	-	-	-	-
BCM International	1981	-	-	-	4	-
Berean Mission, Inc.	1952	2	-	-	-	-
Bethany Fellowship Missions	1981	6	-	-	-	1
Bible League, The	1972	-	-	-	18	-
Bible Missionary Church	1978	2	-	-	-	-
Brethren Assemblies		12	2	-	-	2
Cadence International	1952	-	-	2	1	-
Calvary International	1988	17	-	-	-	-
Campus Crusade for Christ	1965	28	-	-	204	7

COUNTRY Agency	Year Began	Personnel from U. S.			Other Countries	
		4+yrs	2-4 yrs	1-2 yrs	Citizens	Not Citiz.
CBInternational	1955	42	6	1	-	-
Child Evangelism Fellowship	1952	-	-	-	7	-
Christ to the Nations Missions	1993	10	-	-	8	2
Christar	1951	23	-	-	-	5
Christian Aid Mission		-	-	-	3368	-
Christian and Msny. Alliance	1902	32	7	-	-	-
Christian Blind Mission Intl.	1982	-	-	1	-	-
Christian Chs. /Chs. of Christ	1901	46	-	-	-	-
Christian Church of North Am.	1965	-	-	-	300	-
Christian Reformed Relief	1970	-	-	-	-	1
Christian Reformed World	1961	18	6	2	-	2
Christians In Action, Inc.	1977	8	-	-	8	-
Church of God of Prophecy	1952	1	-	-	1	-
Church of God World Missions	1947	15	-	2	-	2
Church of the Nazarene	1946	31	-	-	-	2
Compassion International, Inc.	1979	-	-	-	20	-
Congregational Christian Chs.	1986	-	-	-	4	-
Covenant Celebration Church	1974	-	-	-	2	-
David Livingstone Kure Fndtn		-	-	-	42	-
Emmanuel Intl. Mission (U.S.)	1983	1	-	-	-	-
Equip, Inc.	1995	2	-	-	-	4
Evangel Bible Translators	1981	1	-	-	-	-
Evangelical Free Church Msn.	1951	30	-	-	-	-
Evangelical Friends Mission	1978	-	-	-	-	2
Evangelize China Fellowship	1996	-	-	-	2	-
Every Home for Christ	1960	-	-	-	7	-
Faith Christian Fellowship	1989	2	-	4	-	-
Far East Broadcasting Company	1948	15	-	2	275	-
FARMS International, Inc.	1984	-	-	-	-	-
Final Frontiers Foundation	1990	-	-	-	57	-
Food for the Hungry, Inc.	1982	-	-	-	19	-
Foursquare Missions Intl.	1927	2	-	-	-	-
Free Gospel Church Msns. Dept.	1920	-	6	-	12	-
Free Methodist World Missions	1949	8	-	-	-	-
Frontier Mission Fellowship	1995	2	-	-	-	-
General Baptists International	1957	2	-	-	-	-
Global Fellowship		-	-	-	150	-
Globe Missionary Evangelism	1987	4	-	-	-	-
Gospel Fellowship Association	1978	16	-	-	1	15
Gospel Recordings	1984	-	-	-	8	-
Grace Brethren Intl. Missions	1984	8	-	1	-	-
Habitat for Humanity Intl.	1986	-	2	-	22	2
Harvest Evangelism, Inc.	1997	-	1	-	-	-
Help for Christian Nationals	1987	2	-	-	-	-
Holt Intl. Children's Services	1975	-	-	-	40	-
Hope for the Hungry	1996	-	-	1	-	-
Independent Faith Mission	1991	2	-	-	-	-
International Bible Institute	1979	1	-	-	1	-
International Teams, U.S.A.	1965	-	-	-	-	26
Intl. Christian Leprosy Msn.	1953	-	-	-	4	-
Intl. Pentecostal Holiness Ch.	1975	3	-	-	-	-

COUNTRY Agency	Year Began	Personnel from U. S.			Other Countries	
		4+yrs	2-4 yrs	1-2 yrs	Citizens	Not Citiz.
Larry Jones International Mins	1985	-	-	-	16	-
Liebenzell Mission USA	1998	2	-	-	-	-
Literacy & Evangelism Intl.	1998	-	-	-	1	-
Lutheran Church-Missouri	1946	5	-	2	-	-
Medical Ambassadors Intl.	1975	2	-	-	38	-
Medical Missions Philippines	1970	-	-	-	60	-
Mission Ministries, Inc.	1980	-	-	-	2	1
Mission Soc. for United Meth.	1988	2	-	-	-	-
Mission to the World	1991	15	2	-	-	-
Mission To Unreached Peoples	1987	2	-	-	1	-
Missions To Japan, Inc.		1	-	-	-	-
Mutual Faith Ministries Intl.	1994	-	-	-	-	2
Navigators, The	1961	2	6	1	-	-
New Tribes Mission	1951	104	-	4	2	2
North American Baptist Conf.	1986	6	-	-	-	-
OC International, Inc.	1952	17	-	-	-	-
Omega World Missions	1979	5	-	-	-	-
OMF International	1952	15	-	-	-	-
OMS Intl., Inc.	1982	8	-	-	-	-
Open Bible Standard Churches	1979	2	2	-	-	-
Oriental Missionary Crusade	1958	2	-	-	-	-
Partners International	1968	-	-	-	351	-
Pass the Torch Ministries	1991	-	1	-	3	-
Pentecostal Church of God	1958	6	-	-	-	-
Pilgrim Fellowship, Inc.	1998	2	-	-	-	-
Pocket Testament League	1978	-	-	-	8	-
Presbyterian Church (USA)	1899	4	14	-	-	-
Reach Ministries International	1975	6	-	-	-	-
Salvation Army, U.S.A.	1933	2	-	-	-	-
SEND International	1947	29	-	2	-	-
Seventh-day Adventists	1906	44	2	-	12	-
SIM USA	1984	3	-	-	-	-
Source of Light Ministries	1980	-	-	-	5	-
Sowers International, The	1992	-	-	-	4	-
TEAM	1987	14	4	-	-	-
Things To Come Mission, Inc.	1958	-	-	-	20	-
Third World Baptist Missions	1991	2	-	-	53	-
UFM International	1985	10	-	-	-	1
United Church Board World Mins		-	4	-	-	-
United Evangelical Churches		2	-	-	-	2
United Pentecostal Church Intl	1957	8	-	-	-	-
Walk Thru The Bible Ministries	1982	-	-	-	2	-
Wesleyan World Missions	1932	4	-	-	-	-
World Mission Prayer League	1985	4	-	-	-	-
World Missions Far Corners	1976	-	-	-	20	-
World Team	1981	18	-	-	-	9
World-Wide Missions	1971	-	-	-	4	-
Wycliffe Bible Translators	1953	196	-	-	-	-
Youth With A Mission		16	-	-	-	-
	Totals:	1228	65	47	5262	92

COUNTRY Agency	Year Began	Personnel from U. S.			Other Countries	
		4+yrs	2-4 yrs	1-2 yrs	Citizens	Not Citiz.
Poland						
Assemblies of God	1925	4	-	-	-	-
Back to the Bible Intl.	1993	-	-	-	5	-
Baptist International Missions	1991	1	-	-	-	-
Baptist Mid-Missions	1986	2	-	-	-	-
Baptist World Mission	1996	1	-	-	-	-
Brethren Assemblies		-	4	-	-	-
Campus Crusade for Christ	1977	3	-	11	92	-
CBInternational	1991	13	2	-	-	-
Child Evangelism Fellowship	1989	-	-	-	2	-
Christian Aid Mission		-	-	-	6	-
Christian and Msny. Alliance	1993	4	-	-	-	-
Church of The Brethren		-	2	-	-	-
Church Resource Ministries	1994	2	-	-	-	-
Evangelical Free Church Msn.	1993	8	-	-	-	-
Every Home for Christ	1981	-	-	-	2	-
Fellowship International Msn.	1995	1	-	-	-	-
Friendship Mins.	1996	2	-	-	-	-
Global Outreach, Ltd.	1997	2	-	-	-	-
Greater Grace World Outreach	1985	-	-	-	-	1
Habitat for Humanity Intl.	1995	1	-	-	1	-
International Messengers	1985	3	2	2	6	-
International Teams, U.S.A.	1973	5	-	-	-	6
Ministry to Eastern Europe	1990	2	-	-	4	-
Mission To Unreached Peoples	1989	-	1	-	-	-
Perimeter Ch., Global Outreach	1995	-	-	-	2	-
Pocket Testament League	1989	-	-	-	2	-
Presbyterian Church (USA)		2	-	-	-	-
Project Care	1991	-	-	-	3	-
SAND Institutes International	1997	-	1	-	-	-
SEND International	1991	11	-	-	-	-
TEAM		3	-	1	-	-
Walk Thru The Bible Ministries	1992	-	-	-	1	-
Young Life	1990	1	-	-	-	-
Youth With A Mission		4	-	-	-	-
	Totals:	75	12	14	126	7
Portugal						
ABWE	1978	28	-	-	-	-
Assemblies of God	1967	9	-	-	-	-
Assoc of Free Lutheran Congs	1998	-	-	-	1	-
Baptist Bible Fellowship Intl.	1987	6	-	-	-	-
Baptist World Mission	1990	2	-	-	-	-
BCM International		-	-	-	-	1
Brethren Assemblies		4	-	-	-	1
CBInternational	1945	4	-	2	-	-
Child Evangelism Fellowship	1949	-	-	-	2	-
Christian Associates Intl.	1997	4	-	-	-	2
Christian Chs./Chs. of Christ		5	-	-	-	-
Christian Literature Crusade		-	-	2	-	-
Church of God of Prophecy	1976	-	-	-	1	-

COUNTRY Agency	Year Began	Personnel from U. S.			Other Countries	
		4+yrs	2-4 yrs	1-2 yrs	Citizens	Not Citiz.
Church of God World Missions	1965	-	-	2	-	-
Church of the Nazarene	1973	3	-	-	-	-
Church Planting International		-	-	-	1	-
Evangelical Free Church Msn.	1994	2	-	-	-	-
Grace Brethren Intl. Missions	1990	7	-	-	-	-
MBMS International	1986	-	2	-	-	-
Mission to the World	1977	8	1	-	-	-
Pocket Testament League	1985	-	-	-	-	2
Presbyterian Church (USA)	1972	2	-	-	-	-
Salvation Army, U.S.A.	1971	1	-	-	-	-
SIM USA	1979	4	-	-	-	-
TEAM	1936	7	2	-	-	-
United Pentecostal Church Intl	1972	2	-	-	-	-
World Partners USA	1991	4	-	-	-	-
Youth for Christ / USA	1996	2	1	-	-	-
	Totals:	104	6	6	5	6
Puerto Rico						
Apostolic Christian Church	1996	2	-	-	-	4
Baptist Bible Fellowship Intl.	1955	5	-	-	-	-
Baptist Mid-Missions	1959	6	-	-	-	-
Baptist World Mission	1991	3	-	-	-	-
Biblical Ministries Worldwide	1986	2	-	-	-	-
Brethren Assemblies		1	-	-	-	1
Christian Chs. /Chs. of Christ	1976	14	-	16	-	-
Church of God of Prophecy	1940	-	-	-	1	-
Gospel Fellowship Association	1963	4	-	-	-	4
Grace Ministries International	1961	8	-	-	-	-
Lutheran Church-Missouri	1993	2	-	2	-	-
Macedonia World Baptist Msns.	1981	14	-	-	-	-
Maranatha Baptist Mission	1983	2	-	-	-	-
Mennonite Board of Missions	1945	2	-	-	-	-
Open Door Baptist Missions	1995	2	-	-	-	-
Seventh-day Adventists	1901	12	-	-	4	-
UFM International	1986	-	-	2	-	-
United Pentecostal Church Intl	1964	2	-	-	-	-
Wesleyan World Missions	1952	4	-	-	-	-
Wisconsin Evang. Lutheran Syn.	1963	2	2	1	-	-
Youth With A Mission		1	-	-	-	-
	Totals:	88	2	21	5	9
Romania						
ABWE	1990	10	-	-	-	-
All God's Children Intl.	1991	-	-	-	2	-
AMG International	1992	-	-	-	2	-
Assemblies of God	1989	16	-	12	-	-
Baptist Bible Fellowship Intl.	1990	16	-	-	-	-
Baptist International Missions	1990	7	1	-	-	-
Baptist Mid-Missions	1986	2	-	-	-	-
Baptist Missions to Forgotten		2	-	-	-	-
Baptist World Mission	1993	8	-	-	-	-

COUNTRY Agency	Year Began	Personnel from U. S.			Other Countries	
		4+yrs	2-4 yrs	1-2 yrs	Citizens	Not Citiz.
Bible League, The	1993	-	-	-	8	-
Brethren Assemblies		5	1	-	-	-
Calvary Commission, Inc.	1990	7	-	5	4	-
Campus Crusade for Christ	1980	17	-	-	63	-
CBInternational	1991	12	-	-	-	-
Christian Aid Ministries	1992	-	36	-	100	-
Christian Aid Mission		-	-	-	12	-
Christian Reformed Relief	1997	1	2	-	2	-
Christian Reformed World	1993	-	-	3	-	-
Church of God of Prophecy	1996	-	-	-	1	-
Church of the Nazarene	1992	4	-	-	-	14
Church Resource Ministries	1989	8	-	-	-	-
Eastern European Outreach	1992	1	-	-	-	-
Evangelical Baptist Missions	1990	4	-	-	-	-
Evangelical Free Church Msn.	1991	18	-	3	-	-
Final Frontiers Foundation	1996	-	-	-	8	-
Food for the Hungry, Inc.	1991	2	4	-	-	1
Friends in the West	1990	-	1	-	-	-
Global Outreach, Ltd.	1994	2	-	-	-	-
Globe Missionary Evangelism	1995	2	-	-	-	-
Gospel Missionary Union		1	-	-	-	-
Greater Grace World Outreach	1992	-	-	-	2	-
Habitat for Humanity Intl.	1995	1	-	1	1	1
Heart to Heart Intl. Mins.	1994	-	-	3	2	-
Holt Intl. Children's Services	1991	-	2	-	30	-
International Children's Care	1991	-	1	-	-	-
International Messengers	1989	-	-	2	5	-
International Teams, U.S.A.	1973	2	2	3	-	8
InterVarsity Mission	1993	2	1	-	-	-
Intl. Pentecostal Holiness Ch.	1996	-	1	-	-	-
Kids Alive International	1999	-	-	1	3	-
Larry Jones International Mins	1989	-	-	-	5	-
Lifewater International	1992	-	-	-	1	-
Macedonia World Baptist Msns.	1994	2	-	-	-	-
Medical Ambassadors Intl.	1992	-	-	-	3	-
Ministry to Eastern Europe	1988	-	-	-	5	-
Navigators, The		-	2	-	-	-
New Hope International	1990	-	-	-	13	-
OC International, Inc.	1994	4	-	1	-	-
Open Bible Standard Churches	1993	1	-	-	-	-
Presbyterian Church (USA)		5	-	-	-	-
Project Care	1991	-	-	-	1	-
Romanian Missionary Society	1968	4	-	-	3	1
SEND International	1993	2	-	-	-	1
Shield of Faith Mission Intl.	1995	2	-	-	-	-
UFM International	1991	2	-	-	-	2
United World Mission	1991	1	-	-	-	-
Walk Thru The Bible Ministries	1991	-	-	-	5	-
WEC International		-	-	1	-	-
World Bible Translation Center	1993	-	-	-	3	-
World Mission Prayer League	1994	2	-	-	-	-

COUNTRY Agency	Year Began	Personnel from U. S.			Other Countries	
		4+yrs	2-4 yrs	1-2 yrs	Citizens	Not Citiz.
World Reach, Inc.	1998	-	1	-	-	-
Worldwide Discipleship Assoc.	1995	1	-	-	-	-
Youth With A Mission		10	-	-	-	-
	Totals:	186	55	35	284	28
Russian Federation						
American Baptist Churches USA	1864	4	-	-	-	-
Armenian Missionary Assoc.	1998	-	-	-	-	1
Assemblies of God		100	-	10	-	-
Back to the Bible Intl.	1995	-	-	-	8	-
Baptist Bible Fellowship Intl.	1993	18	-	-	-	-
Baptist International Missions	1991	10	1	-	-	-
Baptist Mid-Missions	1992	7	-	-	-	-
Baptist Missions to Forgotten		3	-	-	-	-
Baptist World Mission	1995	13	-	-	-	-
BCM International	1993	1	-	-	2	-
Bible League, The	1995	-	-	-	20	-
Bible Missionary Church	1992	4	-	-	-	-
Brethren Assemblies		7	4	-	-	-
Cadence International	1997	-	-	-	14	-
Calvary International	1990	15	-	-	-	-
Campus Crusade for Christ	1991	38	-	28	72	21
CBInternational	1991	9	2	2	-	-
Child Evangelism Fellowship	1989	2	-	-	2	-
Christ for the Lost World	1994	-	-	-	12	-
Christ to the Nations Missions	1996	4	-	-	4	-
Christian Aid Mission		-	-	-	48	-
Christian and Msny. Alliance	1993	20	5	-	-	-
Christian Associates Intl.	1993	1	-	-	-	-
Christian Chs./Chs. of Christ		2	-	-	-	-
Christian Ministries Intl.	1996	-	-	2	-	-
Christian Reformed World	1994	1	-	-	-	2
Church of God of Prophecy	1994	-	-	-	1	-
Church of God World Missions	1992	3	-	-	-	6
Church of the Nazarene	1992	11	-	-	-	7
Church Resource Ministries	1990	11	-	-	-	-
East-West Ministries Intl.	1993	1	-	-	-	-
Eastern European Outreach	1994	1	-	-	12	-
Equip, Inc.	1996	2	-	-	-	-
Evangelical Baptist Missions	1994	2	-	2	-	-
Evangelical Free Church Msn.	1993	18	-	2	-	-
Evangelical Lutheran Church	1994	2	-	-	-	-
Evangelical Presbyterian Ch.	1993	4	-	-	-	-
Every Home for Christ	1991	-	-	-	10	-
Far East Broadcasting Company	1992	-	-	-	40	-
Final Frontiers Foundation	1993	-	-	-	4	-
General Conf. Mennonite	1993	-	-	-	-	3
Global Outreach Mission	1994	4	-	-	-	-
Global Strategy Mission Assoc.	1991	2	28	5	1	-
Globe Missionary Evangelism	1995	1	-	-	-	-
Gospel Missionary Union		-	-	3	-	1

COUNTRY Agency	Year Began	Personnel from U. S.			Other Countries	
		4+yrs	2-4 yrs	1-2 yrs	Citizens	Not Citiz.
Greater Grace World Outreach	1991	-	-	-	1	4
Help for Christian Nationals	1997	-	-	-	2	-
InterAct Ministries	1994	8	-	-	-	-
International Gospel Outreach	1993	2	-	-	-	-
International Teams, U.S.A.	1979	-	-	2	-	1
InterVarsity Mission	1991	8	1	1	-	-
Intl. Inst. Christian Studies	1991	2	-	-	-	-
Jews for Jesus	1993	-	-	-	10	-
Larry Jones International Mins	1992	-	-	-	17	1
Lutheran Bible Translators	1996	-	-	-	-	-
Lutheran Church-Missouri	1992	12	-	21	-	-
Mission Aviation Fellowship	1993	4	-	1	-	-
Mission Possible Foundation		-	-	-	24	-
Mission Soc. for United Meth.	1994	14	-	4	-	-
Mission to the World	1992	3	-	-	-	-
Mission To Unreached Peoples	1993	4	-	-	-	-
Navigators, The		10	38	6	-	-
New Tribes Mission	1992	18	-	-	-	2
OMS Intl., Inc.	1993	13	2	8	-	7
Operation Mobilization		4	-	3	-	-
Pentecostal Church of God	1993	2	-	-	-	-
Perimeter Ch., Global Outreach	1990	-	-	-	20	-
Peter Deyneka Russian Mins.	1992	-	2	1	205	-
Presb. Evangelistic Fellowship		2	-	-	-	-
Presbyterian Church (USA)		7	-	-	-	-
Ripe for Harvest, Inc.	1995	-	4	-	-	-
Salvation Army, U.S.A.	1991	8	-	-	-	-
SEND International	1990	16	-	-	-	4
Seventh-day Adventists	1886	16	2	-	8	-
Shield of Faith Mission Intl.		2	-	-	-	-
Slavic Gospel Association	1945	-	-	-	36	-
TEAM	1904	9	4	-	-	-
Touch the World Ministries	1995	1	-	-	9	-
United Pentecostal Church Intl	1991	2	-	-	-	-
Walk Thru The Bible Ministries	1993	-	-	-	297	-
WEC International		-	-	3	-	-
Wesleyan World Missions	1992	9	-	-	-	-
Wisconsin Evang. Lutheran Syn.	1991	6	-	-	-	-
Word To Russia		-	-	-	2	-
World Bible Translation Center	1981	-	-	-	2	-
World Harvest Mission	1996	3	-	-	-	-
World Harvest Now		-	3	1	3	-
World Indigenous Missions	1994	6	-	-	-	-
World Partners USA	1994	6	-	-	-	-
World Reach, Inc.	1991	2	-	-	2	-
World Team	1993	14	-	-	-	2
World Witness	1993	4	-	-	-	-
Young Life	1990	4	-	-	-	-
Youth With A Mission		8	-	-	-	-
	Totals:	550	96	105	888	62

COUNTRY Agency	Year Began	Personnel from U. S.			Other Countries	
		4+yrs	2-4 yrs	1-2 yrs	Citizens	Not Citiz.
Rwanda						
African Enterprise, Inc.	1988	-	-	-	7	-
Assemblies of God		4	-	-	-	-
Campus Crusade for Christ	1980	-	-	-	17	-
CBInternational	1967	6	-	-	-	-
Christian Aid Mission		-	-	-	212	-
Christian Reformed Relief	1994	-	1	-	-	-
Church of God of Prophecy	1982	-	-	-	1	-
Church of the Nazarene	1990	4	-	-	-	-
Compassion International, Inc.	1979	-	-	-	18	-
Evangelical Friends Mission	1983	4	-	-	-	-
Food for the Hungry, Inc.	1994	1	1	-	60	2
Free Methodist World Missions	1942	5	-	-	-	1
Harvest	1998	-	-	-	1	-
Seventh-day Adventists	1920	-	2	-	12	-
World Concern	1995	-	-	-	5	-
World Relief Corporation	1994	-	1	-	-	-
	Totals:	24	5	-	333	3
S Africa						
ABWE	1980	32	-	-	-	-
ACM International	1996	2	-	-	-	-
Africa Inland Mission Intl.	1994	1	-	-	-	-
Africa Inter-Mennonite Mission	1982	2	-	-	-	-
African Enterprise, Inc.	1962	-	-	-	70	-
American Baptist Churches USA	1990	5	-	-	-	-
Assemblies of God	1917	22	-	13	-	-
Baptist Bible Fellowship Intl.	1980	17	-	-	-	-
Baptist International Missions	1968	7	-	-	-	-
Baptist International Outreach	1995	8	-	-	-	-
Baptist Missions to Forgotten		2	-	-	-	-
Baptist World Mission	1996	7	-	-	-	-
Bible League, The	1995	-	-	-	4	-
Biblical Ministries Worldwide	1976	9	-	-	-	1
Brethren Assemblies		9	1	-	-	1
Campus Crusade for Christ	1971	6	-	-	100	5
Child Evangelism Fellowship	1947	2	-	-	4	2
Christ Community Church	1907	4	-	-	-	-
Christian Aid Mission		-	-	-	46	-
Christian Chs./Chs. of Christ	1920	24	-	-	-	-
Christian Church of North Am.	1980	4	-	-	20	-
Christian Reformed Relief	1996	1	-	-	-	-
Church of God of Prophecy	1967	-	-	-	3	-
Church of the Nazarene	1919	37	-	-	-	10
Cornerstone Intl.	1994	2	-	-	-	-
Elim Fellowship World Missions	1975	1	-	-	-	-
Evangelical Baptist Missions	1981	14	-	-	-	-
Evangelical Lutheran Church	1844	2	-	-	-	-
Faith Christian Fellowship	1994	-	3	-	-	-
Final Frontiers Foundation	1993	-	-	-	1	-
Free Methodist World Missions	1895	2	-	-	-	2

COUNTRY Agency	Year Began	Personnel from U. S.			Other Countries	
		4+yrs	2-4 yrs	1-2 yrs	Citizens	Not Citiz.
General Conf. Mennonite	1982	2	-	-	-	-
Gospel Fellowship Association	1988	6	-	-	-	6
Gospel Recordings	1959	-	-	-	4	-
Habitat for Humanity Intl.	1987	-	2	-	5	-
Hope for the Hungry	1991	2	-	-	-	-
Independent Faith Mission	1975	9	-	-	-	-
Intl. Pentecostal Holiness Ch.	1911	20	2	-	-	3
Jews for Jesus	1989	1	-	-	5	-
Lott Carey Baptist Mission	1995	-	-	-	15	-
Lutheran Church-Missouri	1982	-	-	2	-	-
Maranatha Baptist Mission	1991	2	-	-	-	-
Mission to the World	1997	26	4	-	-	-
Mutual Faith Ministries Intl.	1985	-	-	-	-	1
National Baptist Conv. USA	1897	-	2	-	51	-
Navigators, The		2	-	-	-	-
OC International, Inc.	1996	7	2	-	-	-
Open Bible Ministries	1969	2	-	-	-	-
Operation Mobilization		2	-	1	-	-
Orthodox Presbyterian Church	1998	-	-	2	-	-
Presbyterian Church (USA)		6	-	-	-	-
Salvation Army, U.S.A.	1883	2	-	-	-	-
Seventh-day Adventists	1887	8	-	-	11	-
SIM USA	1906	12	-	5	37	-
TEAM	1892	22	-	-	2	4
Teen Missions International		3	-	-	-	-
Things To Come Mission, Inc.	1989	2	-	-	-	-
UFM International	1979	3	-	2	-	1
United Church Board World Mins	1835	-	7	-	-	-
United Pentecostal Church Intl	1948	2	-	-	-	-
Walk Thru The Bible Ministries	1990	-	-	-	31	-
WEC International		-	-	1	-	-
Wesleyan World Missions	1901	8	-	-	-	-
World Missions Far Corners	1958	1	-	-	-	-
Wycliffe Bible Translators		2	-	-	-	-
Young Life	1985	2	2	-	-	-
Youth for Christ / USA	1977	5	6	-	-	-
Youth With A Mission		3	-	-	-	-
	Totals:	384	31	26	409	36
Sao Tome & Principe						
Church of the Nazarene	1997	2	-	-	-	-
	Totals:	2	-	-	-	-
Senegal						
Africa Inter-Mennonite Mission	1996	2	2	-	-	-
Assemblies of God	1956	8	-	1	-	-
Brethren Assemblies		3	-	-	-	-
Campus Crusade for Christ	1985	1	-	-	26	1
CBInternational	1962	10	-	-	-	-
Child Evangelism Fellowship	1994	-	-	-	-	1
Christian Aid Mission		-	-	-	34	-

COUNTRY Agency	Year Began	Personnel from U. S.			Other Countries	
		4+yrs	2-4 yrs	1-2 yrs	Citizens	Not Citiz.
Christian Reformed Relief	1992	1	-	-	-	1
Evangelical Lutheran Church	1976	11	-	-	-	-
Gospel Recordings	1998	-	-	-	-	2
Mission to the World	1992	7	-	-	-	-
Mission: Moving Mountains	1995	6	-	-	-	-
New Tribes Mission	1954	63	-	8	-	20
Open Door Baptist Missions	1998	2	-	-	-	-
Pioneers	1991	4	-	-	9	-
Seventh-day Adventists	1952	-	-	-	2	-
SIM USA	1984	9	-	-	3	-
Things To Come Mission, Inc.	1993	-	1	-	-	-
United World Mission	1948	7	3	5	3	-
Walk Thru The Bible Ministries	1994	-	-	-	1	-
WEC International	1936	2	-	-	-	-
World Vision Inc.	1996	-	1	-	-	-
Wycliffe Associates USA	1999	-	-	2	-	-
Wycliffe Bible Translators		28	-	-	-	-
Youth With A Mission		4	-	-	-	-
	Totals:	168	7	16	78	25
Serbia						
Christian Aid Mission		-	-	-	2	-
	Totals:	-	-	-	2	-
Seychelles						
Seventh-day Adventists	1930	-	-	-	2	-
	Totals:	-	-	-	2	-
Sierra Leone						
Assemblies of God	1920	2	-	-	-	-
Campus Crusade for Christ	1981	-	-	-	20	-
Child Evangelism Fellowship	1987	-	-	-	1	-
Christian Aid Mission		-	-	-	8	-
Christian Mission for the Deaf	1987	-	-	-	-	1
Christian Reformed Relief	1979	1	-	-	-	-
Christian Reformed World	1980	2	-	-	-	-
Christians In Action, Inc.	1969	2	-	-	2	-
Church of God of Prophecy	1934	-	-	-	1	-
Every Home for Christ	1993	-	-	-	10	-
Free Gospel Church Msns. Dept.	1927	-	-	-	6	-
Globe Missionary Evangelism	1999	2	-	-	-	-
Gospel Recordings	1990	-	-	-	12	-
Lutheran Bible Translators	1974	-	-	-	20	-
Mutual Faith Ministries Intl.	1986	-	-	-	-	1
National Baptist Conv. USA	1950	2	-	-	52	-
United Pentecostal Church Intl	1975	2	-	-	-	-
Wesleyan World Missions	1889	-	-	-	8	-
World Vision Inc.	1978	1	-	-	-	-
	Totals:	14	-	-	140	2
Singapore						
ABWE	1991	6	-	-	-	-

COUNTRY Agency	Year Began	Personnel from U. S.			Other Countries	
		4+yrs	2-4 yrs	1-2 yrs	Citizens	Not Citiz.
Assemblies of God	1926	14	-	1	-	-
Baptist Bible Fellowship Intl.	1967	6	-	-	-	-
Baptist International Missions	1982	4	-	-	-	-
Baptist World Mission	1989	2	-	-	-	-
Campus Crusade for Christ	1969	16	-	-	-	7
CBInternational	1985	2	-	-	-	-
Child Evangelism Fellowship	1970	-	-	-	2	-
Christian Chs./Chs. of Christ		6	-	-	-	-
Church of God World Missions	1989	-	-	-	-	2
Church Resource Ministries	1997	2	-	-	-	-
CMF International	1990	2	-	-	-	2
East West Ministries		-	-	-	1	-
Evangelical Free Church Msn.	1957	6	-	-	-	-
Evangelical Lutheran Church	1966	4	-	-	-	-
Evangelize China Fellowship	1956	-	-	-	1	-
Foursquare Missions Intl.	1982	2	-	-	-	-
Global Strategy Mission Assoc.	1984	2	-	-	-	-
Gospel Recordings	1980	-	-	-	3	-
International Students, Inc		-	-	-	1	1
Intl. Pentecostal Holiness Ch.	1987	2	-	-	-	-
Mutual Faith Ministries Intl.	1986	-	-	-	-	3
Network of Intl Christian Schs	1995	-	6	4	-	4
New Tribes Mission	1994	4	-	-	-	-
OC International, Inc.	1987	4	-	-	-	2
OMF International	1952	11	-	-	-	-
Overseas Radio & Television		-	-	-	5	-
Partners International	1952	-	-	-	5	-
SIM USA		-	-	-	4	-
Source of Light Ministries	1998	-	-	-	1	-
United Pentecostal Church Intl	1981	2	-	-	-	-
Walk Thru The Bible Ministries	1982	-	-	-	6	-
World Baptist Fellowship Msn.	1987	2	-	-	-	-
Youth for Christ / USA	1982	3	-	-	-	-
Youth With A Mission		8	-	-	-	-
	Totals:	110	6	5	29	21
Slovakia						
ABWE	1990	6	-	-	-	-
Assemblies of God	1981	2	-	2	-	-
Baptist International Missions		1	-	-	-	-
Baptist Mid-Missions	1986	4	-	-	-	-
Campus Crusade for Christ	1993	6	-	8	-	-
Christian Aid Mission		-	-	-	24	-
Evangelical Free Church Msn.	1993	2	-	1	-	-
Evangelical Lutheran Church	1991	2	4	4	-	-
Every Home for Christ		-	-	-	7	-
Global Outreach, Ltd.	1996	1	-	-	-	-
Greater Grace World Outreach	1991	-	-	-	-	2
International Messengers	1989	4	-	-	1	-
International Teams, U.S.A.	1994	2	-	2	-	4
InterVarsity Mission	1994	2	-	-	-	-

COUNTRY Agency	Year Began	Personnel from U. S.			Other Countries	
		4+yrs	2-4 yrs	1-2 yrs	Citizens	Not Citiz.
Lutheran Church-Missouri	1991	-	-	7	-	-
Ministry to Eastern Europe	1992	-	-	-	3	-
Mission to the World	1997	2	-	-	-	-
Navigators, The		-	2	-	-	-
New Hope International	1993	-	-	-	6	-
Presbyterian Church (USA)		4	-	-	-	-
UFM International	1991	3	-	-	-	-
Youth With A Mission		3	-	-	-	-
	Totals:	44	6	24	41	6
Slovenia						
Assemblies of God		4	-	-	-	-
Bethany Fellowship Missions	1992	4	-	-	-	1
Campus Crusade for Christ	1994	4	-	7	-	-
CBInternational	1991	4	-	1	-	-
Child Evangelism Fellowship	1997	-	-	-	-	2
Christian Aid Mission		-	-	-	2	-
Every Home for Christ		-	-	-	1	-
Habitat for Humanity Intl.	1995	1	-	-	-	1
Navigators, The		2	-	-	-	-
	Totals:	19	-	8	3	4
Solomon Isls						
American Baptist Association	1969	1	-	-	-	-
Assemblies of God	1977	2	-	-	-	-
Campus Crusade for Christ	1975	-	-	-	3	1
Child Evangelism Fellowship	1975	-	-	-	3	-
Episcopal World Mission	1984	2	-	-	3	-
Every Home for Christ	1986	-	-	-	7	-
Gospel Recordings	1997	-	-	-	2	-
Maranatha Baptist Mission	1983	2	-	-	-	-
Wycliffe Bible Translators	1977	29	-	-	-	-
Youth With A Mission		2	-	-	-	-
	Totals:	38	-	-	18	1
Somalia						
Eastern Mennonite Missions	1981	1	-	-	-	-
World Concern	1980	-	-	-	-	-
	Totals:	1	-	-	-	-
Spain						
ABWE	1968	18	-	-	-	-
AMG International	1989	10	-	-	1	-
Arab World Ministries	1984	6	-	-	-	-
Assemblies of God	1923	36	-	9	-	-
Baptist Bible Fellowship Intl.	1970	16	-	-	-	-
Baptist Mid-Missions	1979	6	-	-	-	-
Baptist World Mission	1986	9	-	-	-	-
BCM International	1962	2	-	-	-	-
Biblical Ministries Worldwide	1958	5	-	-	-	-
Brethren Assemblies		9	-	-	-	-
Brethren in Christ World Msns.	1988	2	-	-	-	-

COUNTRY Agency	Year Began	Personnel from U. S.			Other Countries	
		4+yrs	2-4 yrs	1-2 yrs	Citizens	Not Citiz.
Cadence International	1974	-	-	1	-	-
CAM International	1972	14	2	-	-	4
Campus Crusade for Christ	1970	10	-	26	-	-
CBInternational	1984	10	-	1	-	-
Christ for the City Intl.	1994	-	-	-	-	4
Christian Aid Mission		-	-	-	7	-
Christian and Msny. Alliance	1978	9	-	-	-	-
Christian Associates Intl.	1992	6	-	-	-	-
Christian Chs. /Chs. of Christ		1	-	-	-	-
Church of God of Prophecy	1981	-	-	-	1	-
Church of God World Missions	1937	1	-	2	-	3
Church of the Nazarene	1981	2	-	-	-	7
East-West Ministries Intl.		1	1	1	-	-
Elim Fellowship World Missions	1966	4	-	-	-	-
European Christian Mission	1983	8	-	-	-	-
Evangelical Covenant Church	1996	4	-	-	-	-
Evangelical Free Church Msn.	1994	5	-	1	-	-
Every Home for Christ	1977	-	-	-	2	-
Faith Christian Fellowship	1994	-	2	-	-	-
Fellowship International Msn.	1991	3	-	-	-	-
Free Will Baptist, Inc.	1974	9	-	-	-	-
Global Outreach Mission		-	-	-	5	-
Gospel Fellowship Association	1978	6	-	-	3	3
Gospel Furthering Fellowship	1992	2	-	-	-	-
Gospel Missionary Union	1976	17	-	-	-	6
Grace Brethren Intl. Missions	1984	2	-	-	-	-
Great Commission Center Intl.	1995	-	-	2	-	-
Help for Christian Nationals	1990	2	-	-	-	-
International Partnership Mins		2	-	-	-	-
International Teams, U.S.A.	1972	2	-	3	-	-
Intl. Pentecostal Holiness Ch.	1988	4	-	-	-	-
Latin America Mission	1989	4	-	-	-	2
Liebenzell Mission USA	1995	2	-	-	-	-
Maranatha Baptist Mission	1987	2	-	-	-	-
Marriage Ministries Intl.	1995	-	-	-	-	2
Mennonite Board of Missions	1976	2	-	-	-	-
Mission to the World	1983	7	-	-	-	-
Missionary Revival Crusade	1969	-	-	-	-	6
Navigators, The	1970	6	2	-	-	-
OC International, Inc.	1996	4	-	-	-	-
OMS Intl., Inc.	1972	8	-	-	-	7
Open Door Baptist Missions	1999	2	-	-	-	-
Pilgrim Fellowship, Inc.	1976	2	-	-	-	-
Pocket Testament League	1978	-	-	-	2	-
Presbyterian Church (USA)		4	-	-	-	-
Salvation Army, U.S.A.	1971	2	-	-	-	-
SEND International	1987	7	-	-	-	2
South American Missionary Soc.	1991	2	-	-	-	-
Spanish World Gospel Mission	1960	-	-	-	3	-
TEAM	1934	25	2	-	-	-
UFM International	1985	8	-	-	-	2
United Pentecostal Church Intl	1979	2	-	-	-	-

COUNTRY Agency	Year Began	Personnel from U. S.			Other Countries	
		4+yrs	2-4 yrs	1-2 yrs	Citizens	Not Citiz.
United World Mission	1948	2	-	-	-	-
Walk Thru The Bible Ministries	1984	-	-	-	2	-
WEC International	1968	5	-	-	-	-
World Baptist Fellowship Msn.	1955	4	-	-	-	-
World Harvest Mission	1998	2	-	-	-	-
World Indigenous Missions	1988	2	-	-	-	-
World Partners USA	1985	9	-	-	-	-
World Team	1972	15	-	-	-	-
Youth for Christ / USA	1982	-	2	-	-	-
Youth With A Mission		9	-	-	-	-
	Totals:	380	11	46	26	48
Sri Lanka						
Back to the Bible Intl.	1955	-	-	-	36	-
Baptist Bible Fellowship Intl.	1989	4	-	-	-	-
BCM International	1985	2	-	-	5	-
Campus Crusade for Christ	1967	-	-	-	49	-
Christian Aid Mission		-	-	-	12	-
Every Home for Christ	1970	-	-	-	8	-
FARMS International, Inc.	1971	-	-	-	-	-
Global Fellowship		-	-	-	25	-
Gospel for Asia	1983	-	-	-	342	-
Habitat for Humanity Intl.	1994	-	2	-	2	2
Hope for the Hungry	1989	-	-	-	2	-
Lutheran Church-Missouri	1927	-	-	2	-	-
Presbyterian Church (USA)		2	-	-	-	-
Seventh-day Adventists	1922	6	-	-	-	-
Shelter Now International	1998	-	-	-	-	2
TEAM	1955	1	-	-	-	1
United Church Board World Mins	1816	-	3	-	-	-
United Pentecostal Church Intl	1949	4	-	-	-	-
Village Ministries Intl.	1997	-	-	-	6	-
Wesleyan World Missions	1993	-	-	-	2	-
	Totals:	19	5	2	489	5
St Chris-Nevis						
Seventh-day Adventists	1900	4	-	-	-	-
	Totals:	4	-	-	-	-
St Lucia						
BCM International		-	-	-	1	-
Grace Baptist Missions Intl.		-	-	-	2	-
Macedonia World Baptist Msns.	1994	2	-	-	-	-
	Totals:	2	-	-	3	-
St Vincent						
Baptist Mid-Missions	1946	5	-	4	-	-
BCM International		-	-	-	1	-
Christian Chs./Chs. of Christ		6	-	-	-	-
Final Frontiers Foundation	1996	-	-	-	2	-
Ministries In Action	1974	-	1	-	1	-

COUNTRY Agency	Year Began	Personnel from U. S.			Other Countries	
		4+yrs	2-4 yrs	1-2 yrs	Citizens	Not Citiz.
Seventh-day Adventists	1900	2	-	-	-	-
World Team	1951	2	-	-	-	-
	Totals:	15	1	4	4	-
Sudan						
Africa Inland Mission Intl.	1949	1	-	-	-	-
Bible League, The	1998	-	-	-	1	1
Christian Aid Mission		-	-	-	31	-
Church of The Brethren	1983	2	2	-	-	-
Gospel Revival Ministries	1997	-	-	-	2	-
Partners International	1973	-	-	-	25	-
Presbyterian Church (USA)	1900	10	5	-	-	-
Project Mercy, Inc.	1977	-	-	-	-	11
Reformed Church In America	1950	3	-	-	-	-
Seventh-day Adventists	1978	6	1	-	7	-
SIM USA	1938	6	-	-	6	-
World Vision Inc.	1997	-	-	1	-	-
Wycliffe Bible Translators		38	-	-	-	-
	Totals:	66	8	1	72	12
Suriname						
Assemblies of God	1959	2	-	-	-	-
BCM International		1	-	-	2	-
Biblical Ministries Worldwide	1979	-	-	-	-	2
Campus Crusade for Christ	1979	-	-	-	1	2
Child Evangelism Fellowship	1973	-	-	-	-	1
Christar	1961	-	3	-	-	-
Church of God of Prophecy	1992	-	-	-	1	-
Church of the Nazarene	1984	-	-	-	-	-
Fellowship International Msn.	1972	2	-	-	-	-
Full Gospel Grace Fellowship		2	-	-	-	-
Independent Faith Mission	1967	17	-	-	-	-
Mennonite Board of Missions	1985	2	-	-	-	-
Mission Aviation Fellowship	1964	6	-	2	-	-
Network of Intl Christian Schs	1999	-	-	2	-	-
Orthodox Presbyterian Church	1987	2	-	-	-	-
Wesleyan World Missions	1945	4	-	-	-	-
World Team	1957	9	-	-	-	-
Wycliffe Bible Translators	1967	27	-	-	-	-
	Totals:	74	3	4	4	5
Swaziland						
Assemblies of God	1985	4	-	2	-	-
BCM International		-	-	-	1	-
Campus Crusade for Christ	1973	-	-	-	10	-
Church of God of Prophecy	1977	-	-	-	1	-
Church of the Nazarene	1910	14	-	-	-	10
Eastern Mennonite Missions	1971	2	-	-	-	-
Greater Grace World Outreach	1998	-	-	-	-	1
National Baptist Conv. USA	1971	-	2	-	19	-
Seventh-day Adventists	1894	-	-	-	2	-

COUNTRY Agency	Year Began	Personnel from U. S.			Other Countries	
		4+yrs	2-4 yrs	1-2 yrs	Citizens	Not Citiz.
United Church Board World Mins		-	2	-	-	-
United Pentecostal Church Intl	1982	6	-	-	-	-
	Totals:	26	4	2	33	11
Sweden						
Evangelical Baptist Missions	1974	4	-	-	-	-
Fellowship International Msn.	1972	3	-	-	-	-
Global Outreach Mission		-	-	-	2	-
Greater Grace World Outreach	1976	-	-	-	1	4
Mission to the World	1999	2	3	-	-	-
Operation Mobilization		2	-	-	-	-
UFM International	1984	-	-	2	-	-
Walk Thru The Bible Ministries	1989	-	-	-	1	-
Wisconsin Evang. Lutheran Syn.	1999	2	-	-	-	-
Youth for Christ / USA	1982	1	-	-	-	-
Youth With A Mission		8	-	-	-	-
	Totals:	22	3	2	4	4
Switzerland						
Baptist International Missions		1	-	-	-	-
Child Evangelism Fellowship	1950	5	-	-	-	5
Christ for the City Intl.	1991	-	-	-	-	4
Church of The Brethren		-	2	-	-	-
Church of the Nazarene	1978	27	-	-	-	4
Development Associates Intl.	1996	-	-	-	-	1
Every Home for Christ		-	-	-	8	-
Food for the Hungry, Inc.	1981	-	-	-	-	1
Gospel Recordings	1966	-	-	-	3	-
InterVarsity Mission	1985	-	-	2	-	-
Latin America Mission	1998	2	-	-	-	-
Seventh-day Adventists	1870	-	-	-	2	-
SIM USA		-	-	-	7	-
Youth for Christ / USA	1964	3	5	-	-	-
Youth With A Mission		26	-	-	-	-
	Totals:	64	7	2	20	15
Syria						
Christian Aid Mission		-	-	-	4	-
World-Wide Missions	1963	-	-	-	1	-
	Totals:	-	-	-	5	-
Taiwan (Republic of China)						
Assemblies of God	1948	12	-	-	-	-
Baptist Bible Fellowship Intl.	1950	14	-	-	-	-
Baptist International Missions		1	-	-	-	-
Baptist Mid-Missions	1972	2	-	-	-	-
Baptist Missionary Assoc.	1953	1	-	-	-	-
Bible League, The	1995	-	-	-	1	-
Brethren Assemblies		2	-	-	-	-
Campus Crusade for Christ	1964	-	-	-	50	1
CBInternational	1952	14	-	-	-	-

COUNTRY Agency	Year Began	Personnel from U. S.			Other Countries	
		4+yrs	2-4 yrs	1-2 yrs	Citizens	Not Citiz.
Child Evangelism Fellowship	1951	2	-	-	-	-
Christian and Msny. Alliance	1952	15	-	-	-	-
Christian Chs./Chs. of Christ		10	-	-	-	-
Christian Reformed World	1953	4	-	-	-	-
Church of the Nazarene	1956	2	-	-	-	-
Evangelical Covenant Church	1954	2	-	-	-	-
Evangelical Free Church Msn.	1994	2	-	-	-	-
Evangelical Lutheran Church	1951	2	-	-	-	-
Evangelize China Fellowship	1949	-	-	-	15	-
Every Home for Christ		-	-	-	5	-
Foursquare Missions Intl.	1988	2	-	-	-	-
Free Methodist World Missions	1952	6	-	-	-	-
General Conf. Mennonite	1954	5	-	-	1	4
Globe Missionary Evangelism	1999	-	2	-	-	-
Hope for the Hungry	1991	1	-	-	-	-
International Students, Inc		-	-	-	-	1
Kids Alive International	1970	2	-	-	-	-
Liberty Corner Mission	1952	2	-	-	-	-
Lutheran Brethren World Msns.	1951	6	-	-	-	-
Lutheran Church-Missouri	1951	6	14	-	-	-
Macedonia World Baptist Msns.	1981	2	-	-	-	-
Mission to the World	1977	8	-	-	-	-
Mission To Unreached Peoples	1989	-	1	-	-	-
Mustard Seed, Inc.	1948	-	-	-	30	-
Navigators, The	1984	2	4	-	-	-
OC International, Inc.	1950	4	-	-	-	-
OMF International	1952	13	-	-	-	-
OMS Intl., Inc.	1917	9	-	2	-	-
Open Door Baptist Missions	1999	1	-	-	-	-
Overseas Radio & Television	1960	6	6	8	150	5
Partners International	1959	-	-	-	50	-
Presbyterian Church (USA)	1952	9	-	-	-	-
Reformed Church In America	1953	5	-	-	-	-
SEND International	1967	20	-	-	-	6
Seventh-day Adventists	1902	8	1	-	-	-
Sowers International, The	1995	-	-	-	1	-
TEAM	1951	20	-	-	-	1
Team Expansion, Inc.	1995	8	-	-	-	-
United Church Board World Mins	1960	-	5	-	-	-
Walk Thru The Bible Ministries	1995	-	-	-	1	-
Wisconsin Evang. Lutheran Syn.	1968	3	-	-	-	-
World Gospel Mission	1953	2	-	-	-	-
World-Wide Missions	1965	-	-	-	8	-
Youth With A Mission		5	-	-	-	-
	Totals:	240	33	10	312	18
Tajikistan						
Bible League, The	1995	-	-	-	1	-
Christian Aid Mission		-	-	-	6	-
Shelter Now International	1994	-	11	-	-	-
Walk Thru The Bible Ministries	1994	-	-	-	2	-
	Totals:	-	11	-	9	-

COUNTRY Agency	Year Began	Personnel from U. S.			Other Countries	
		4+yrs	2-4 yrs	1-2 yrs	Citizens	Not Citiz.
Tanzania						
ACM International	1995	2	-	-	-	-
Africa Inland Mission Intl.	1909	73	-	8	-	-
African Enterprise, Inc.	1970	-	-	-	9	-
Assemblies of God	1940	4	-	-	-	-
Baptist Bible Fellowship Intl.	1988	15	-	-	-	-
Baptist International Missions		1	-	-	-	-
BCM International		1	-	-	-	-
Brethren Assemblies		2	-	-	-	-
Campus Crusade for Christ	1977	-	-	-	22	-
Christian Aid Mission		-	-	-	66	-
Christian Blind Mission Intl.	1971	1	1	-	-	-
Christian Reformed Relief	1989	-	-	-	1	3
Church of God (Anderson, IN)	1968	7	-	-	-	-
Church of God of Prophecy	1978	-	-	-	1	-
Church of the Nazarene	1990	4	-	-	-	-
Eastern Mennonite Missions	1934	3	-	-	-	-
Elim Fellowship World Missions	1955	12	-	-	-	-
Evangelical Free Church Msn.	1993	9	-	-	-	-
Evangelical Lutheran Church	1924	22	-	-	-	-
Free Methodist World Missions	1994	2	-	-	-	1
Globe Missionary Evangelism	1998	1	1	-	-	-
Gospel Furthering Fellowship	1949	2	-	-	-	-
Grace Ministries International	1952	14	-	-	-	-
Habitat for Humanity Intl.	1986	-	4	-	47	-
Heifer Project International	1974	2	-	-	-	-
Interchurch Medical Assistance	1994	-	1	-	-	-
Intl. Pentecostal Holiness Ch.	1996	3	-	-	-	-
Medical Ambassadors Intl.	1987	-	-	-	4	-
Mission to the World	1990	4	-	-	-	-
Mission: Moving Mountains	1993	16	-	-	-	-
Partners International	1986	-	-	-	23	-
Pioneer Bible Translators	1996	7	-	-	5	1
Seventh-day Adventists	1903	-	-	-	7	-
SIM USA	1990	4	-	-	-	-
Team Expansion, Inc.	1995	3	-	-	-	-
United Pentecostal Church Intl	1980	6	-	-	-	-
Walk Thru The Bible Ministries	1994	-	-	-	14	-
World Concern	1995	-	1	-	-	-
World Gospel Mission	1985	12	-	-	-	-
Youth With A Mission		1	-	-	-	-
	Totals:	233	8	8	199	5
Thailand						
ABWE	1993	4	-	-	-	-
American Baptist Churches USA	1833	16	1	-	-	1
AMG International	1976	2	-	-	3	-
Assemblies of God	1968	18	-	2	-	-
Baptist Bible Fellowship Intl.	1983	8	-	-	-	-
Baptist General Conference	1990	4	-	2	-	-
Baptist International Missions	1979	4	-	-	-	-

COUNTRY Agency	Year Began	Personnel from U. S.			Other Countries	
		4+yrs	2-4 yrs	1-2 yrs	Citizens	Not Citiz.
Baptist Mid-Missions	1995	2	-	1	-	-
Baptist World Mission	1984	2	-	-	-	-
Bethany Fellowship Missions	1997	2	-	-	-	-
Bible League, The	1982	-	-	-	5	-
Campus Crusade for Christ	1971	4	-	2	36	-
Central Missionary Fellowship	1991	1	-	-	-	-
Child Evangelism Fellowship	1957	-	-	-	1	-
Christian Aid Mission		-	-	-	782	-
Christian and Msny. Alliance	1929	26	3	-	-	-
Christian Blind Mission Intl.	1982	-	-	1	-	-
Christian Chs. /Chs. of Christ	1949	47	-	-	-	-
Church of God of Prophecy	1968	-	-	-	1	-
Church of the Nazarene	1989	8	-	-	-	2
Church World Service &	1950	-	1	-	4	-
CMF International	1994	-	6	-	-	6
Compassion International, Inc.	1970	-	-	-	17	-
David Livingstone Kure Fndtn		-	-	-	14	-
Eastern Mennonite Missions	1997	6	1	3	-	-
Evangelical Covenant Church	1971	8	3	-	-	-
Evangelical Free Church Msn.	1996	4	-	-	-	-
Evangelize China Fellowship	1959	-	-	-	10	-
Every Home for Christ	1971	-	-	-	2	-
FARMS International, Inc.		-	-	-	-	-
Final Frontiers Foundation	1987	-	-	-	31	-
Food for the Hungry, Inc.	1976	-	-	-	2	2
Foursquare Missions Intl.	1987	2	2	-	-	-
Global Fellowship		-	-	-	-	5
Globe Missionary Evangelism	1985	8	-	-	-	-
Gospel Recordings	1998	1	-	-	-	-
Greater Grace World Outreach	1989	-	-	-	-	2
Holt Intl. Children's Services	1976	-	-	-	60	-
International Teams, U.S.A.	1979	-	-	2	-	-
Larry Jones International Mins	1986	-	-	-	8	-
Liebenzell Mission USA	1998	1	-	-	-	-
Lutheran Church-Missouri	1986	8	-	4	2	-
MBMS International	1992	-	2	-	21	-
Mission To Unreached Peoples	1988	4	-	-	-	-
Mutual Faith Ministries Intl.	1988	-	-	-	-	1
Navigators, The		1	2	1	-	-
Network of Intl Christian Schs	1993	12	12	30	-	2
New Tribes Mission	1951	66	-	1	-	4
OMF International	1952	15	-	1	-	-
Partners International	1955	-	-	-	25	-
Pass the Torch Ministries	1986	-	1	-	-	-
Pioneers	1985	11	-	1	-	1
Pocket Testament League	1976	-	-	-	2	-
Presbyterian Church (USA)	1840	10	20	-	-	-
Seventh-day Adventists	1919	16	-	-	14	-
Sowers International, The	1997	-	-	-	-	1
Teen Missions International		1	-	-	-	-
United Church Board World Mins	1832	-	6	-	-	-

COUNTRY Agency	Year Began	Personnel from U. S.			Other Countries	
		4+yrs	2-4 yrs	1-2 yrs	Citizens	Not Citiz.
Walk Thru The Bible Ministries	1988	-	-	-	5	-
WEC International	1947	8	-	-	-	-
Wisconsin Evang. Lutheran Syn.	1993	1	2	-	-	-
World Baptist Fellowship Msn.		1	-	-	-	-
World Bible Translation Center	1997	-	-	-	7	-
World Concern	1979	1	3	1	20	-
World Missions Far Corners	1996	-	-	-	-	1
World Partners USA	1992	3	-	-	-	-
Youth With A Mission		18	-	-	-	-
	Totals:	354	65	52	1072	28
Tibet						
Anglican Frontier Missions	1996	1	-	-	-	-
Shield of Faith Ministries	1996	-	-	-	-	1
	Totals:	1	-	-	-	1
Togo						
ABWE	1973	37	-	-	-	-
Assemblies of God	1937	11	-	-	-	-
Baptist International Missions		1	-	-	-	-
Campus Crusade for Christ	1979	-	-	-	13	-
Child Evangelism Fellowship	1983	-	-	-	1	-
Christian Aid Mission		-	-	-	4	-
Christian Blind Mission Intl.	1980	-	1	-	-	-
Final Frontiers Foundation	1994	-	-	-	3	-
Gospel Recordings	1996	-	-	-	8	-
Greater Grace World Outreach	1992	-	-	-	-	3
International Partnership Mins	1991	2	-	-	9	-
Lifewater International	1997	-	-	-	1	-
Lutheran Bible Translators	1992	-	-	-	2	-
Lutheran Church-Missouri	1980	9	-	-	-	-
Ministry of Jesus, Inc.	1995	2	-	-	-	-
Seventh-day Adventists	1964	-	-	-	1	-
SIM USA	1994	2	-	-	2	-
Wycliffe Bible Translators	1967	30	-	-	-	-
	Totals:	94	1	-	44	3
Tonga						
Assemblies of God	1975	6	-	-	-	-
Campus Crusade for Christ	1974	-	-	-	4	-
Child Evangelism Fellowship	1988	-	-	-	-	1
Faith Christian Fellowship	1995	-	2	-	-	-
Youth With A Mission		2	-	-	-	-
	Totals:	8	2	-	4	1
Trinidad & Tobago						
Baptist Bible Fellowship Intl.		2	-	-	-	-
Baptist Missions to Forgotten		2	-	-	-	-
BCM International		-	-	-	1	-
Campus Crusade for Christ	1977	-	-	-	7	4
Church of God of Prophecy	1954	-	-	-	1	-
Church of the Nazarene	1926	4	-	-	-	2

COUNTRY Agency	Year Began	Personnel from U. S.			Other Countries	
		4+yrs	2-4 yrs	1-2 yrs	Citizens	Not Citiz.
Fundamental Bapt. Msn	1921	5	-	-	6	-
Habitat for Humanity Intl.	1996	-	2	-	-	-
Intl. Pentecostal Holiness Ch.	1993	2	-	-	-	-
Pentecostal Church of God	1969	2	-	-	-	-
Seventh-day Adventists	1893	6	-	-	3	-
STEM Ministries	1986	-	-	-	-	-
TEAM	1964	4	-	-	-	-
United Pentecostal Church Intl	1980	2	-	-	-	-
Virginia Mennonite Bd. of Msns	1971	2	-	2	-	-
World Team	1953	7	-	-	-	2
	Totals:	38	2	2	18	8
Tunisia						
Arab World Ministries		11	-	-	-	7
Christian Aid Mission		-	-	-	2	-
	Totals:	11	-	-	2	7
Turkey						
AMG International	1977	-	-	-	1	-
Christian Aid Mission		-	-	-	8	-
Church of God World Missions		-	-	2	-	-
Evangelical Free Church Msn.	1994	4	-	-	-	-
InterServe/USA	1985	16	-	-	-	-
Middle East Christian Outreach	1990	-	-	-	-	5
Middle East Media - USA	1991	2	-	-	7	-
New Life League International		2	-	-	-	-
Operation Mobilization	1961	9	3	-	-	-
Presbyterian Church (USA)		2	-	-	-	-
Rosedale Mennonite Missions	1987	8	-	1	-	-
Shield of Faith Mission Intl.		1	-	-	-	-
TEAM	1960	2	-	-	-	-
Turkish World Outreach	1989	5	-	-	1	-
United Church Board World Mins	1819	-	6	-	-	-
World Horizons	1989	1	-	-	-	-
World Missions Far Corners	1996	-	-	-	2	-
World Witness	1993	2	-	-	-	-
World-Wide Missions	1963	-	-	-	1	-
	Totals:	54	9	3	20	5
Turkmenistan						
Greater Grace World Outreach	1996	-	-	-	-	2
	Totals:	-	-	-	-	2
Uganda						
Advancing Renewal Ministries	1990	-	-	-	1	-
Africa Inland Mission Intl.	1918	10	-	1	-	-
African Enterprise, Inc.	1970	-	-	-	14	-
AMG International	1994	2	-	-	1	-
Baptist Bible Fellowship Intl.	1986	2	-	-	-	-
Baptist International Missions	1994	7	-	-	-	-
Baptist International Outreach	1996	-	-	-	2	-
Brethren Assemblies		2	-	-	-	-

COUNTRY Agency	Year Began	Personnel from U. S.			Other Countries	
		4+yrs	2-4 yrs	1-2 yrs	Citizens	Not Citiz.
Campus Crusade for Christ	1971	-	-	-	65	2
CBInternational	1961	13	-	1	-	-
Child Evangelism Fellowship	1965	-	-	-	2	-
Christian Aid Mission		-	-	-	35	-
Christian Blind Mission Intl.	1978	-	2	-	-	-
Christian Reformed Relief	1983	-	1	-	-	1
Church of God (Anderson, IN)	1983	5	-	-	-	-
Church of God of Prophecy	1981	-	-	-	1	-
Church of God World Missions	1982	2	-	-	-	-
Church of the Nazarene	1988	2	-	-	-	-
Church Planting International	1990	-	-	-	12	-
Compassion International, Inc.	1980	-	-	-	20	-
Congregational Methodist Ch.	1999	2	-	-	-	-
Elim Fellowship World Missions	1962	3	-	-	-	-
Evangel Bible Translators	1997	-	-	-	1	1
Faith Christian Fellowship	1998	-	2	-	-	-
Final Frontiers Foundation	1994	-	-	-	3	-
Food for the Hungry, Inc.	1987	4	-	-	42	6
Foursquare Missions Intl.	1997	4	-	-	-	-
Friends in the West	1978	-	4	-	-	-
Global Fellowship		-	-	-	20	-
Global Outreach, Ltd.	1979	14	4	-	-	-
Habitat for Humanity Intl.	1984	-	3	-	43	-
International Gospel League	1979	5	-	-	-	-
Larry Jones International Mins	1990	-	-	-	7	-
Lifewater International	1995	-	-	-	1	-
Medical Ambassadors Intl.	1990	-	-	-	6	-
Mission Aviation Fellowship		4	-	-	-	-
Mission Ministries, Inc.	1993	2	-	-	-	-
Mission to the World	1983	6	-	-	-	-
Mission: Moving Mountains	1982	-	-	-	5	-
Navigators, The	1972	4	-	-	-	-
Orthodox Presbyterian Church	1995	8	-	1	-	-
Presb. Evangelistic Fellowship	1986	2	-	-	-	-
Reformed Episcopal Bd	1958	2	-	-	-	-
Seventh-day Adventists	1926	2	1	-	10	-
Source of Light Ministries	1998	-	-	-	1	-
Teen Missions International		-	-	-	-	2
Walk Thru The Bible Ministries	1990	-	-	-	8	-
World Concern	1985	-	-	1	214	3
World Gospel Mission	1992	4	-	-	-	-
World Harvest Mission	1984	12	-	2	-	-
Youth for Christ / USA		1	-	-	-	-
	Totals:	124	17	6	514	15
UK (United Kingdom)						
ABWE	1984	17	-	-	-	-
ACM International	1997	2	-	-	-	-
Advancing Renewal Ministries	1979	-	-	-	-	3
Apostolic Team Ministries Intl	1987	2	-	-	-	-
Arab World Ministries	1986	13	-	-	-	3

COUNTRY Agency	Year Began	Personnel from U. S.			Other Countries	
		4+yrs	2-4 yrs	1-2 yrs	Citizens	Not Citiz.
Back to the Bible Intl.	1954	-	-	-	7	-
Baptist Bible Fellowship Intl.	1971	50	-	-	-	-
Baptist International Missions	1965	18	-	-	-	-
Baptist Mid-Missions	1972	18	-	4	-	-
Baptist Missions to Forgotten		2	-	-	-	-
Baptist World Mission	1975	10	-	-	-	-
BCM International	1947	5	-	-	-	-
Berean Mission, Inc.	1978	4	-	-	-	2
Biblical Ministries Worldwide	1968	19	-	-	-	2
Brethren in Christ World Msns.	1980	2	-	-	-	-
Calvary International	1988	2	-	-	-	-
Campus Crusade for Christ	1967	18	-	-	-	-
CBInternational	1994	4	-	-	-	-
Child Evangelism Fellowship	1947	2	-	-	-	-
Christar	1966	7	-	-	-	-
Christian and Msny. Alliance	1975	8	1	-	-	-
Christian Chs./Chs. of Christ	1958	55	2	-	-	-
Christian Literature Crusade	1941	2	-	2	-	-
Christians In Action, Inc.	1965	6	-	-	-	6
Church of God of Prophecy	1952	-	-	-	1	-
Church of The Brethren		-	6	-	-	-
Church of the Nazarene	1909	-	-	-	-	1
CMF International	1989	14	-	-	-	14
Covenant Celebration Church		-	-	-	1	-
Eastern Mennonite Missions	1997	2	-	-	-	-
Elim Fellowship World Missions	1979	2	-	-	-	-
European Christian Mission	1987	2	-	-	-	-
Evangelical Baptist Missions	1976	6	-	-	-	-
Evangelical Free Church Msn.	1993	3	-	-	-	-
Every Home for Christ		-	-	-	3	-
Faith Christian Fellowship	1990	4	-	-	-	-
Far East Broadcasting Company	1998	2	-	-	-	-
Fellowship International Msn.	1986	4	-	-	-	-
Global Outreach Mission	1978	14	-	-	10	-
Globe Missionary Evangelism	1979	8	-	-	-	-
Gospel Fellowship Association	1980	18	-	3	-	21
Gospel Missionary Union	1984	5	-	-	1	-
Gospel Recordings	1955	-	-	-	9	-
Grace Brethren Intl. Missions	1982	6	-	1	-	-
Greater Grace World Outreach	1975	-	-	-	4	1
Habitat for Humanity Intl.	1994	3	1	-	3	1
HCJB World Radio	1990	-	-	-	-	2
Helps International Ministries	1989	2	-	-	2	-
Independent Faith Mission	1984	2	-	-	-	-
International Teams, U.S.A.	1986	6	6	1	-	16
InterVarsity Mission	1996	4	-	2	-	-
Intl. Pentecostal Holiness Ch.	1978	6	2	-	-	2
Jews for Jesus	1992	1	-	-	3	1
Maranatha Baptist Mission	1983	11	-	-	-	-
Mennonite Board of Missions	1974	5	-	-	-	-
Mission to the World	1990	13	-	-	-	-

COUNTRY Agency	Year Began	Personnel from U. S.			Other Countries	
		4+yrs	2-4 yrs	1-2 yrs	Citizens	Not Citiz.
Missionary Athletes Intl.	1990	7	-	-	-	-
Operation Mobilization		28	4	11	-	-
Overseas Radio & Television		-	-	-	-	2
Pillar of Fire Missions Intl.	1960	-	5	-	-	-
Presb. Evangelistic Fellowship		4	-	-	-	-
Presbyterian Church (USA)		11	68	-	-	-
Ravi Zacharias Int. Mins.	1984	2	-	-	2	-
Reformed Baptist Mission Svcs.	1985	2	-	-	-	1
Salvation Army, U.S.A.	1865	17	-	-	-	-
SAT-7 North America	1996	-	-	-	2	-
Seventh-day Adventists	1898	2	1	-	28	-
SIM USA		-	-	-	34	-
TEAM		2	-	-	-	-
TMA Ministries	1985	-	-	-	2	-
United Pentecostal Church Intl	1965	4	-	-	-	-
United World Mission	1967	6	-	-	-	-
Walk Thru The Bible Ministries	1984	-	-	-	12	-
WEC International	1913	7	-	-	-	-
Wesleyan World Missions	1995	2	-	-	-	-
World Harvest Mission	1994	8	-	-	-	-
World Missions Far Corners	1976	2	-	-	-	-
World Team	1986	4	-	-	-	2
Wycliffe Bible Translators		14	-	-	-	-
Youth for Christ / USA	1983	4	-	-	-	-
Youth With A Mission		103	-	-	-	-
	Totals:	638	96	24	124	80
Ukraine						
ABWE	1990	14	-	-	-	-
Action International Mins.	1994	2	-	-	-	-
Allegheny Wesleyan Meth. Msns.	1993	3	-	-	-	-
Assemblies of God		12	-	-	-	-
Baptist Bible Fellowship Intl.		2	-	-	-	-
Baptist International Missions	1996	9	-	-	-	-
Baptist Missions to Forgotten		2	-	-	-	-
BCM International	1993	2	-	-	2	-
Bible League, The	1993	-	-	-	11	-
Cadence International	1997	-	-	-	6	-
Calvary International		2	-	-	-	-
Campus Crusade for Christ	1991	17	-	9	28	1
CBInternational	1991	12	-	-	-	-
Chosen People Ministries	1995	-	-	-	3	-
Christian Aid Mission		-	-	-	362	-
Christian Chs. /Chs. of Christ	1991	-	-	4	-	-
Christian Ministries Intl.	1993	-	-	2	-	-
Christian Outreach Intl.	1990	-	9	-	5	-
Church of God (Holiness) Msn.	1996	-	-	2	-	2
Church of God of Prophecy	1973	3	-	-	1	-
Church of God World Missions	1992	2	-	-	-	-
Church of the Nazarene	1992	2	-	-	-	-
CMF International	1994	4	-	1	-	5

COUNTRY Agency	Year Began	Personnel from U. S.			Other Countries	
		4+yrs	2-4 yrs	1-2 yrs	Citizens	Not Citiz.
David Livingstone Kure Fndtn		-	-	-	25	-
Donetsk Christian University		-	6	-	10	10
Eastern European Outreach	1994	4	-	-	10	-
Evangelical Free Church Msn.	1993	6	-	-	-	-
Evangelical Lutheran Synod		-	2	-	-	-
Every Home for Christ	1991	-	-	-	6	-
Fellowship International Msn.	1995	2	-	-	-	-
Foursquare Missions Intl.	1998	-	2	-	-	-
Free Methodist World Missions	1999	1	-	-	-	-
Global Outreach Mission		-	-	-	10	-
Gospel Revival Ministries	1997	-	-	-	1	-
Great Commission Ministries		5	1	2	-	-
Greater Grace World Outreach	1992	-	-	-	-	2
International Teams, U.S.A.	1995	-	3	2	-	2
InterVarsity Mission	1989	-	2	2	-	-
Intl. Inst. Christian Studies	1991	2	1	-	-	-
Jews for Jesus	1991	-	-	-	18	-
Medical Ambassadors Intl.	1992	-	-	-	9	-
Ministry to Eastern Europe	1996	2	2	-	5	-
Mission Ministries, Inc.	1995	-	-	-	-	-
Mission Possible Foundation		-	-	-	4	-
Mission to the World	1993	13	31	-	-	-
Missions to Military	1998	-	-	2	-	-
Muslim Hope	1993	2	-	-	-	2
Navigators, The		3	4	1	-	-
New Hope International	1994	-	-	-	68	-
Peter Deyneka Russian Mins.	1992	-	-	-	80	-
Pioneer Bible Translators	1999	1	-	-	-	1
Reformed Church In America	1997	1	-	-	-	-
SEND International	1990	7	-	1	-	-
Slavic Gospel Association	1945	-	-	-	16	-
Team Expansion, Inc.	1991	14	-	-	-	-
Walk Thru The Bible Ministries	1993	-	-	-	698	-
World Bible Translation Center	1981	-	-	-	1	-
World Concern	1990	-	-	-	55	-
World Gospel Mission	1997	6	-	-	-	-
World Reach, Inc.	1991	-	-	-	-	1
Youth With A Mission		12	-	-	-	-
	Totals:	169	63	28	1434	26
United Arab Emirates						
Arab World Ministries		4	-	-	-	5
Church of God World Missions	1992	-	-	-	-	2
Macedonia World Baptist Msns.	1991	2	-	-	-	-
TEAM	1960	32	-	2	-	-
	Totals:	38	-	2	-	7
Uruguay						
Assemblies of God	1946	10	-	-	-	-
Baptist Bible Fellowship Intl.	1958	2	-	-	-	-
Baptist General Conference	1991	2	-	-	-	-
Baptist International Missions		2	-	-	-	-

COUNTRY Agency	Year Began	Personnel from U. S.			Other Countries	
		4+yrs	2-4 yrs	1-2 yrs	Citizens	Not Citiz.
Baptist Missionary Assoc.		1	-	-	-	-
Baptist World Mission	1968	9	-	-	-	-
Biblical Ministries Worldwide	1967	12	-	-	-	2
Brethren Assemblies		1	-	-	-	-
Campus Crusade for Christ	1966	-	-	-	3	-
CBInternational	1995	2	-	-	-	-
Christian Aid Mission		-	-	-	4	-
Christian Chs./Chs. of Christ		8	-	-	-	-
Church of God of Prophecy	1957	-	-	-	-	1
Church of God World Missions	1945	2	-	-	-	-
Free Will Baptist, Inc.	1961	7	-	-	-	-
Gospel Mission of S. America	1970	6	-	-	2	4
SIM USA	1995	4	-	-	-	-
South American Missionary Soc.	1994	2	-	-	-	-
United Pentecostal Church Intl	1930	2	-	-	-	-
Walk Thru The Bible Ministries	1993	-	-	-	2	-
	Totals:	72	-	-	11	7
Uzbekistan						
Central Missionary Fellowship	1992	-	3	-	-	-
Christian Aid Mission		-	-	-	32	-
Church of God World Missions		-	-	-	-	2
Evangelical Free Church Msn.	1995	2	-	1	-	-
Food for the Hungry, Inc.	1997	-	-	-	-	2
International Teams, U.S.A.	1996	-	2	2	-	-
Macedonia World Baptist Msns.	1996	2	-	-	-	-
Presbyterian Church (USA)		-	-	3	-	-
Walk Thru The Bible Ministries	1994	-	-	-	31	-
World Concern	1993	-	1	-	24	-
	Totals:	4	6	6	87	4
Vanuatu						
Assemblies of God	1967	4	-	-	-	-
Baptist Bible Fellowship Intl.		2	-	-	-	-
Faith Christian Fellowship	1998	-	-	-	-	6
Wycliffe Bible Translators	1981	8	-	-	-	-
	Totals:	14	-	-	-	6
Venezuela						
Assemblies of God	1920	13	-	8	-	-
Baptist Bible Fellowship Intl.	1958	6	-	-	-	-
Baptist International Missions	1980	17	-	-	-	-
Baptist Mid-Missions	1924	7	-	-	-	-
Bible League, The	1997	-	-	-	5	-
Bible Missionary Church	1984	2	-	-	-	-
Brethren Assemblies		1	-	-	-	-
Brethren in Christ World Msns.	1982	4	4	-	5	-
Calvary International		1	-	-	-	-
Campus Crusade for Christ	1971	-	-	7	7	-
CBInternational	1986	12	-	1	-	-
Christian and Msny. Alliance	1972	17	-	-	-	-

COUNTRY Agency	Year Began	Personnel from U. S.			Other Countries	
		4+yrs	2-4 yrs	1-2 yrs	Citizens	Not Citiz.
Christian Chs./Chs. of Christ		10	-	-	-	-
Christian Outreach Intl.	1994	-	6	4	2	-
Church of God (Anderson, IN)	1980	2	-	-	-	-
Church of God of Prophecy	1968	1	-	-	-	-
Church of God World Missions	1966	3	-	-	-	2
Church of the Nazarene	1982	8	-	-	-	4
Church Resource Ministries	1993	6	-	-	-	-
Evangelical Free Church Msn.	1920	26	-	8	-	-
Fellowship International Msn.	1968	4	-	-	-	-
Harvest	1997	-	-	-	1	-
Impact International	1989	-	-	-	2	-
Intl. Pentecostal Holiness Ch.	1978	2	-	-	-	-
Latin America Mission	1989	3	-	-	-	1
Lutheran Church-Missouri	1951	24	-	3	-	-
Maranatha Baptist Mission	1983	7	-	-	-	-
Medical Ambassadors Intl.	1995	-	-	-	3	-
Mission Aviation Fellowship	1965	8	-	2	-	-
Mission Ministries, Inc.	1990	2	-	-	-	-
Navigators, The	1975	4	-	-	-	-
New Tribes Mission	1946	111	-	6	-	6
Pentecostal Free Will Bapt.Ch.	1979	2	-	-	-	-
Presbyterian Church (USA)	1897	2	8	-	-	-
Seventh-day Adventists	1910	-	-	-	3	-
Spanish World Gospel Mission	1988	-	-	-	2	-
TEAM	1906	61	10	15	-	-
Team Expansion, Inc.	1986	11	-	-	-	-
United Pentecostal Church Intl	1956	4	-	-	-	-
United World Mission	1947	4	-	-	-	-
WEC International	1954	3	-	-	-	-
Youth With A Mission		3	-	-	-	-
	Totals:	391	28	54	30	13

Vietnam						
Bible League, The	1989	-	-	-	-	1
Christian Aid Mission		-	-	-	353	-
Christian and Msny. Alliance	1911	1	2	-	-	-
Church of the Nazarene	1994	2	-	-	-	-
Church World Service &	1950	-	-	-	-	1
Evangelize China Fellowship	1998	-	-	-	1	-
Final Frontiers Foundation	1989	-	-	-	103	-
Globe Missionary Evangelism	1999	3	-	-	-	-
Holt Intl. Children's Services	1972	-	3	-	15	1
International Teams, U.S.A.	1995	2	3	3	-	4
Lutheran Church-Missouri	1995	2	-	-	-	-
Mission To Unreached Peoples	1997	2	-	-	-	-
Partners International	1991	-	-	-	472	-
Presbyterian Church (USA)		4	-	-	-	-
Seventh-day Adventists	1929	4	-	-	2	-
United Church Board World Mins		-	1	-	-	-
World Concern	1985	-	-	2	5	-
World Missions Far Corners	1993	3	-	-	-	-

COUNTRY Agency	Year Began	Personnel from U. S.			Other Countries	
		4+yrs	2-4 yrs	1-2 yrs	Citizens	Not Citiz.
World Partners USA	1997	2	-	-	-	-
World Vision Inc.	1992	2	-	-	-	-
	Totals:	27	9	5	951	7
Virgin Islands USA						
Christian Chs./Chs. of Christ	1986	2	-	-	-	-
Church of God of Prophecy	1926	-	-	-	1	-
Mission to the World	1991	2	-	-	-	-
National Baptist Conv. of Am.	1978	-	-	-	6	-
World Gospel Mission	1996	2	-	-	-	-
	Totals:	6	-	-	7	-
W Samoa						
Baptist Bible Fellowship Intl.		2	-	-	-	-
Church of the Nazarene	1964	2	-	-	-	-
	Totals:	4	-	-	-	-
West Bank						
Helps International Ministries	1992	2	-	-	-	-
	Totals:	2	-	-	-	-
Yemen						
Anglican Frontier Missions	1998	2	-	-	-	-
Arab World Ministries		6	-	-	-	-
InterServe/USA	1991	2	-	-	-	-
	Totals:	10	-	-	-	-
Yugoslavia						
Campus Crusade for Christ	1979	2	-	-	12	-
Child Evangelism Fellowship	1989	2	-	-	4	-
Christian Aid Mission		-	-	-	12	-
Every Home for Christ		-	-	-	2	-
Global Outreach Mission		-	-	-	2	-
Pocket Testament League	1980	-	-	-	6	-
World Bible Translation Center	1991	-	-	-	5	-
World Vision Inc.	1997	-	-	1	-	-
	Totals:	4	-	1	43	-
Zambia						
Baptist Bible Fellowship Intl.	1989	16	-	-	-	-
Baptist International Missions		3	-	-	-	-
Baptist International Outreach	1987	4	-	-	-	-
Baptist Mid-Missions	1990	9	-	11	-	-
Brethren Assemblies		19	1	-	-	-
Brethren in Christ World Msns.	1906	3	2	-	-	4
Campus Crusade for Christ	1975	-	-	-	27	-
CBInternational	1981	2	-	-	-	-
Child Evangelism Fellowship	1970	-	-	-	4	-
Christian Aid Mission		-	-	-	11	-
Christian Chs. /Chs. of Christ	1962	16	-	-	-	-
Christian Reformed Relief	1990	1	-	-	-	-

COUNTRY Agency	Year Began	Personnel from U. S.			Other Countries	
		4+yrs	2-4 yrs	1-2 yrs	Citizens	Not Citiz.
Church of God (Anderson, IN)	1990	2	-	-	-	-
Church of God of Prophecy	1977	-	-	-	1	-
Church of God World Missions	1965	2	-	1	-	-
Church of the Nazarene	1961	6	-	-	-	-
Every Home for Christ	1967	-	-	-	5	-
Grace Ministries International	1998	2	-	-	-	2
Habitat for Humanity Intl.	1982	-	2	-	17	-
Hope for the Hungry	1994	-	-	-	2	-
Independent Faith Mission		12	-	-	-	-
Intl. Pentecostal Holiness Ch.	1950	2	-	-	-	-
Lifewater International		-	-	-	-	1
National Baptist Conv. USA	1993	2	-	-	16	-
Navigators, The	1985	2	-	-	-	-
Presbyterian Church (USA)		5	-	-	-	-
Salvation Army, U.S.A.	1922	7	-	-	-	-
Seventh-day Adventists	1905	-	-	-	7	-
SIM USA	1910	31	-	3	16	-
United Pentecostal Church Intl	1980	4	-	-	-	-
Walk Thru The Bible Ministries	1994	-	-	-	1	-
Wesleyan World Missions	1930	7	-	-	-	1
Wisconsin Evang. Lutheran Syn.	1953	11	-	-	-	-
Youth With A Mission		2	-	-	-	-
	Totals:	170	5	15	107	8
Zimbabwe						
African Enterprise, Inc.	1980	-	-	-	10	-
BCM International		1	-	-	-	-
Bible League, The	1995	-	-	-	3	-
Brethren Assemblies		1	-	-	-	2
Brethren in Christ World Msns.	1898	6	7	-	-	-
Campus Crusade for Christ	1978	12	-	-	46	2
Child Evangelism Fellowship	1951	-	-	-	2	-
Christian Aid Mission		-	-	-	164	-
Christian Chs. /Chs. of Christ	1956	59	-	-	-	-
Church of God of Prophecy	1976	-	-	-	1	-
Church of the Nazarene	1963	2	-	-	-	-
Elim Fellowship World Missions	1995	1	-	-	-	-
Every Home for Christ	1995	-	-	-	53	-
Faith Christian Fellowship	1987	-	2	-	-	-
Free Methodist World Missions	1938	2	-	-	-	-
Habitat for Humanity Intl.	1996	-	4	-	-	-
Hope for the Hungry	1994	-	-	-	1	-
Independent Faith Mission		4	-	-	-	-
Intl. Pentecostal Holiness Ch.	1950	5	-	-	-	-
Marriage Ministries Intl.	1988	-	-	-	2	-
Mission Aviation Fellowship	1964	4	-	-	-	-
Partners International	1973	-	-	-	10	-
Presbyterian Church (USA)		2	-	-	-	-
Salvation Army, U.S.A.	1922	2	-	-	-	-
Seventh-day Adventists	1894	7	3	-	17	-
SIM USA	1906	3	-	-	6	-

COUNTRY Agency	Year Began	Personnel from U. S.			Other Countries	
		4+yrs	2-4 yrs	1-2 yrs	Citizens	Not Citiz.
TEAM	1942	14	4	-	-	-
Teen Missions International		2	-	-	-	-
United Church Board World Mins	1893	-	4	-	-	-
Youth for Christ / USA		2	-	-	-	-
Youth With A Mission		2	-	-	-	-
	Totals:	131	24	-	315	4

CHAPTER 8

Canadian Protestant Agencies

This chapter contains the basic information for Canadian Protestant agencies engaged in mission ministries outside Canada and the U.S. The comprehensive coverage includes agencies that directly support the work of such ministries or the work of overseas national churches/workers. The agencies supplied the information. The Survey Questionnaire used to gather the information is reproduced in the Appendix.

The *Handbook* covers an agency's overseas ministry and support activities but not its mission work in Canada. Much cross-cultural mission work takes place in Canada, but due to the additional complexities of reporting such activities we have not undertaken the task for this publication. Agencies with both overseas and Canadian mission ministries, however, were asked to include Canada-based ministry personnel in the total that appears in the "home ministry and office staff" line of the "Other Personnel" section.

Each agency will have at least seven of the basic categories of information listed below, with others included as applicable.

Agency Name

Agencies are listed alphabetically. If the article "the" is in an agency's name, it will appear at the end of the name so the agency is in the most commonly referenced alphabetical order. Rare exceptions occur where the Christian public commonly uses the article "the" as the first word in the agency's name.

Agencies that have changed their name since the previous *Handbook* have their prior name listed, with a cross-reference to the current or new name. A subdivision of a larger organization may be listed separately if it is organized to also serve the larger mission community rather than just its parent organization.

Telephone and Fax Numbers

The common format of showing the area code in parentheses is used throughout. Area codes have changed rapidly in the last few years, so some may even have been changed since publication.

E-mail Address

The Internet format and emerging standards for capitalization are used. For example, upper case letters may be used to the left of the @ sign when meaningful, but all characters to the right are lower case.

In some cases, agencies have a general e-mail address, such as Info@xxxx.org. Others have supplied an individual person's address within the organization. In cases where only a Web address is given, it generally means a Web page provides access to several e-mail addresses so an inquiry can be immediately directed to the relevant department or person.

Instead of providing a general e-mail address, an agency may indicate the format to be used to contact individuals within the agency. This may take the format of something like Firstname.Lastname@xxxx.org and would be used by the sender when the individual is known.

Mission agencies began to use e-mail on a fairly broad scale by 1995, and now a large percentage of the agencies use e-mail on a regular basis.

Web Address

A request for a Web address was first included in the survey for the 1998-2000 edition. This new edition reports a considerably larger number of Web addresses, now including most agencies.

Postal Mailing Address

A post office box number appears whenever the agency has one, since it is more unlikely to change over time.

Chief Executive Officer

In some cases where there are multiple primary contacts, two officers are listed.

Short Descriptive Paragraph

A brief description appears based on the denominational orientation and primary activities information supplied by the agency. It keeps the same general order so the reader is presented with a consistent format across agencies. Additional specific information, such as name changes, mergers, or other unique aspects may also be included.

Purpose Statement

Some of the purpose statements are concise and shown in their entirety, straight from promotional material of the agency. For most, however, because of space considerations, common or similar phrases such as "exists for the purpose of" are replaced by ellipses to present a more concise statement.

Year Founded in Canada

This date is the year the agency or overseas mission component of a larger organization was founded in Canada. In some cases the denomination or organization may have existed earlier in another country. For some organizations, the founding date of the missionary-sending component may be later than the founding of the larger organization. For organizations that have experienced mergers, the founding date is generally that of the oldest component involved in the merger.

Income for Overseas Ministries

This is the part of an agency's overall income used for ministry activities outside Canada and the USA or in activities that directly facilitate overseas ministries. "NA" indicates that income in this sense is not applicable, and usually applies to specialized service agencies or agencies whose income is reported under a sister or parent organization. "NR" indicates that the agency did not report income for overseas ministries for the survey, but may make this information available on request.

Amount of Gifts-in-kind

If applicable, this is the portion of the income received in the form of donated gifts-in-kind commodities and/or services used for overseas ministries. Please note that some agencies do not include gifts-in-kind as part of their financial audit process, so the value of such gifts is not included in their income for overseas ministries. Gifts-in-kind amounts that were an insignificant percentage (usually 1 percent or less) are not shown as a separate item.

Fully Supported Canadian Personnel Overseas

Not all agencies have overseas personnel in the following categories, so the above heading will not always appear. If applicable, the following lines will appear with the appropriate numbers:

- "Expecting to serve more than 4 years" for persons from Canada who are fully supported by the agency
- "Expecting to serve 1 up to 4 years" for persons from Canada who are fully supported by the agency
- "Nonresidential mission personnel" for fully supported Canadian mission personnel not residing in the country or countries of their ministry, but assigned to work and travel overseas at least 12 weeks per year on operational aspects of the overseas ministry

Other Personnel

If applicable for the agency, the following lines will appear:

- "Non-Canadian serving in own/other country" for persons with either citizenship in their country of service or another non-Canadian country, who are fully or partially supported from Canada
- "Bivocational/Tentmaker from Canada" for persons sponsored or supervised by the agency, but who support themselves partially or fully through non-church/non-mission vocations and live overseas for the purpose of Christian witness, evangelism and/or encouraging believers
- "Short-Term less than 1 year from Canada" for persons who went on overseas projects or mission trips that lasted at least two weeks but less than one year through the agency, either fully or partially supported, including those raising their own support
- "Home ministry and office staff in Canada" for persons assigned to ministry and/or office duties in Canada either as full-time or part-time paid staff/associates

Countries

These are the countries where the agency sends Canadian personnel or regularly supports national or other non-Canadian personnel. Following the name of the country is the number of Canadian personnel with terms of service of one year or more. In some cases a continent or other general region is shown instead of a country. This may be due to several reasons, such as mission personnel whose ministry covers several countries.

Where an agency's work is maintained by nationals of countries other than Canada or the U.S., or by personnel serving less than one year, the country of activity may be listed without a number. Please refer to chapter 10 for more detailed country personnel totals.

ABWE (Assoc. of Baptists for World Evangelism) - Canada

(519)690-1009
E-Mail: abwecanada@compuserve.com
160 Adelaide St. S., Suite 205, London, ON N5Z 3L1
Mr. Frank Bale, Director

A denominational sending agency of Baptist and independent tradition engaged in church planting, theological education, TEE, evangelism and medical work. Personnel and financial information from 1996.

Year Founded in CAN 1940
Income for Overseas Mins $630,984
Gifts-in-Kind $77,839
Fully Supported CAN Personnel Overseas:
Expecting to serve more than 4 years 15
Expecting to serve 1 to 4 years 8
Nonresidential mission personnel 4
Other Personnel:
Short-Term less than 1 year from CAN 5
Home ministry & office staff in CAN 7
Countries: Argentina 2, Asia 2, Bangladesh 3, Brazil 5, Chile 1, Peru 2, Portugal 4, S Africa 2, Ukraine 2

Action International Ministries

(403)443-2221 **Fax: (403)443-7455**
E-Mail: 75342.663@compuserve.com
Web: www.actionintl.org
P.O. Box 280, Three Hills, AB T0M 2A0
Mr. Arnold Olver, Canadian Director

An interdenominational sending agency of evangelical tradition engaged in evangelism, camping programs, childrens programs and training.

Year Founded in CAN 1980
Income for Overseas Mins $1,075,458
Fully Supported CAN Personnel Overseas:
Expecting to serve more than 4 years 8
Expecting to serve 1 to 4 years 11
Other Personnel:
Home ministry & office staff in CAN 5
Countries: Brazil 4, Colombia 4, Mexico 2, Philippines 9

Africa Community Technical Service

(250)339-1212 **Fax: (250)339-1300**
E-Mail: Moore@nicad3.nic.bc.ca
2064 Comox Ave., Comox, BC V9M 3S5
Mr. David Moore, Director

An interdenominational service agency of evangelical tradition engaged in technical assistance and development. Income from 1992 report.

Year Founded in CAN 1972
Income for Overseas Mins $117,355
Personnel:
Short-Term less than 1 year from CAN 3

Africa Evangelical Fellowship SEE: SIM Canada

Africa Inland Mission (Canada)

(416)751-6077 **Fax: (416)751-3467**
E-Mail: AIM-CAN@aimint.org
Web: www.aimcanada.org
1641 Victoria Park Ave., Scarborough, ON M1R 1P8
Dr. John Brown, Director

An interdenominational sending agency of evangelical tradition engaged in church planting, development, theological education, evangelism, leadership development and medical work. Financial and personnel information from 1996.

Purpose: "...to plant maturing churches...through the evangelization of unreached people groups and the effective preparation of church leaders."

Year Founded in CAN 1953
Income for Overseas Mins $1,815,000
Fully Supported CAN Personnel Overseas:
Expecting to serve more than 4 years 57
Expecting to serve 1 to 4 years 38
Nonresidential mission personnel 1
Other Personnel:
Short-Term less than 1 year from CAN 31
Home ministry & office staff in CAN 11
Countries: Cen Africa Rep 2, Chad 1, Congo/Zaire 17, Kenya 66, Lesotho 4, Sudan 1, Tanzania 4

African Enterprise Association of Canada

(604)228-0930 **Fax: (604)228-0936**
E-Mail: aecanada@compuserve.com
Web: www.africanenterprise.org
4509 W. 11th Ave., Vancouver, BC V6R 2M5

Mr. David Richardson, Exec. Director

An interdenominational support agency of evangelical tradition engaged in funds transmission, evangelism, missions information service and mobilization for mission in more than 30 countries of Africa.

Purpose: "To service and expand an active partnership among Canadian Christians to raise prayer, financial, material and human resources to enable African Enterprise to achieve its mission to: Evangelise the Cities of Africa, through Word and Deed, in Partnership with the Church."

Year Founded in CAN 1964
Income for Overseas Mins $16,804
Personnel:
Short-Term less than 1 year from CAN 2
Home ministry & office staff in CAN 2

Anglican Church of Canada, Partners in Mission

(416)924-9192 **Fax: (416)924-3483**
Web: www.anglican.ca
600 Jarvis St., Toronto, ON M4Y 2J6
Dr. Eleanor Johnson, Director

A denominational sending agency of Anglican tradition engaged in support of national churches, development, theological education, evangelism and relief and/or rehabilitation. Statistical information from 1992.

Year Founded in CAN 1885
Income for Overseas Mins $6,000,000
Personnel:
Home ministry & office staff in CAN 31

Apostolic Church In Canada, The

(416)489-0453 **Fax: (416)489-6479**
E-Mail: castlefield@apostolic.ca
Web: www.apostolic.ca
27 Castlefield Ave., Toronto, ON M4R 1G3
Rev. J. Karl Thomas, Gen. Secretary

An interdenominational support agency of Pentecostal and evangelical tradition engaged in church planting, Bible distribution, evangelism, funds transmission and providing medical supplies.

Year Founded in CAN 1930
Income for Overseas Mins $250,000
Gifts-in-Kind $15,000
Fully Supported CAN Personnel Overseas:
Nonresidential mission personnel 2
Other Personnel:
Non-CAN serving in own/other country 22
Bivocational/Tentmaker from CAN 3
Short-Term less than 1 year from CAN 4
Home ministry & office staff in CAN 11

Apostolic Church of Pentecost of Canada, Missionary Dept.

(403)273-5777 **Fax: (403)273-8102**
E-Mail: acop@compuserve.com
Web: www.acop.ca
#5 - 2340 Pegasus Way NE, Calgary, AB T2E 8M5
Rev. Rick Parkyn, Missions Director

A sending agency of Pentecostal and charismatic tradition engaged in church planting, evangelism, funds transmission, leadership development and support of national churches.

Year Founded in CAN 1945
Income for Overseas Mins $1,149,906
Fully Supported CAN Personnel Overseas:
Expecting to serve more than 4 years 30
Expecting to serve 1 to 4 years 1
Nonresidential mission personnel 4
Other Personnel:
Non-CAN serving in own/other country 2
Home ministry & office staff in CAN 6
Countries: Brazil 2, Burkina Faso 4, El Salvador 2, Estonia 3, Guatemala 2, India 2, Malawi 3, Mexico 4, S Africa 2, Spain 1, Taiwan (ROC) 2, Thailand 2, Zimbabwe 2

Arab World Ministries (Canada)

(519)653-3170 **Fax: (519)653-3002**
E-Mail: awmcan@awm.org
Web: www.awm.org
P.O. Box 3398, Cambridge, ON N3H 4T3
Mr. Don Little, Canadian Director

An interdenominational sending agency of evangelical tradition engaged in church planting, broadcasting, correspondence courses, evangelism, and video/film production/distribution in the Arab World and among Arabs in N. America and Europe.

Year Founded in CAN 1967
Income for Overseas Mins $400,000

Fully Supported CAN Personnel Overseas:
Expecting to serve more than 4 years 16
Other Personnel:
Bivocational/Tentmaker from CAN 10
Home ministry & office staff in CAN 15
Countries: Africa 3, Asia 6, France 6, UK 1

Associated Gospel Churches

(905)634-8184 **Fax: (905)634-6283**
E-Mail: admin@agcofcanada.com
Web: www.agcofcanada.com
3228 S. Service Rd., Burlington, ON L7N 3H8
Rev. A. F. (Bud) Penner, President
An association of churches of evangelical and Baptist tradition encouraging mission mobilization for evangelism and church planting.
Purpose: "...to assist member churches in their obedience to the Great Commission of Jesus Christ."
Year Founded in CAN 1922
Income for Overseas Mins .... NA
Personnel:
Home ministry & office staff in CAN 6

Association of Baptists for World Evangelism – Canada See: ABWE – Canada

Barry Moore Ministries

(519)661-0205 **Fax: (519)661-0206**
E-Mail: bmoore@odyssey.on.ca
Web: www.bmoore.on.ca
Box 9100, London, ON N6E 1V0
Rev. John Laari, Exec. Director
An interdenominational service agency of evangelical and fundamental tradition engaged in evangelism, leadership development, support of national churches and training.
Year Founded in CAN 1960
Income for Overseas Mins $79,000
Personnel:
Short-Term less than 1 year from CAN 2
Home ministry & office staff in CAN 3

BCM International (Canada), Inc.

(905)549-9810 **Fax: (905)549-7664**
E-Mail: mission@bcmintl.ca
Web: www.bcmintl.ca
798 Main St., E., Hamilton, ON L8M 1L4
Miss Chloe Chamberlain, Exec. Secretary
A nondenominational support agency of evangelical and fundamental tradition engaged in Christian education, childrens programs, correspondence courses, literature distribution and training.
Year Founded in CAN 1942
Income for Overseas Mins $58,171
Personnel:
Home ministry & office staff in CAN 9

BGCC Global Ministries

(604)448-1242 **Fax: (604)448-1241**
E-Mail: BGCC@datanet.ab.ca
313 - 3851 Francis Rd., Richmond, BC V7C 1J6
Dann Pantoja, Director of Global Ministries
A denominational sending agency of Baptist tradition engaged in church planting, development, evangelism, leadership development and support of national churches. The mission agency of the Baptist General Conference of Canada. Statistical information from 1996.
Year Founded in CAN 1995
Income for Overseas Mins $275,000
Gifts-in-Kind $50,000
Fully Supported CAN Personnel Overseas:
Expecting to serve more than 4 years 2
Expecting to serve 1 to 4 years 6
Other Personnel:
Bivocational/Tentmaker from CAN 3
Short-Term less than 1 year from CAN 32
Home ministry & office staff in CAN 2
Countries: Asia 3, Hungary 2, Ireland 1, Macedonia 1, Portugal 1

Bible Holiness Movement

(250)492-3376
P.O. Box 223, Postal Station A, Vancouver, BC V6C 2M3
Evangelist Wesley H. Wakefield, Bishop-General
A denominational support agency of Wesleyan and Holiness tradition engaged in evangelism, Bible distribution, church planting, literature distribution, literature production and support of national churches. Financial data from 1996.

Purpose: "...to establish, conduct and maintain worldwide missionary work; to spread Scriptural holiness, vital Christianity and practical Godliness through a proper qualified ministry."

Year Founded in CAN 1949

Income for Overseas Mins $28,966

Gifts-in-Kind $2,026

Personnel:

Non-CAN serving in own/other country 47

Home ministry & office staff in CAN 1

Countries: Ghana, India, Malawi, Nigeria, Philippines, Korea-S, Tanzania, Zambia

Bible League of Canada, The

(905)319-9500 **Fax: (905)319-0484**

E-Mail: bibleag@worldchat.com

Web: www.thebibleleague.ca

P.O. Box 5037, Burlington, ON L7R 3Y8

Rev. David J. Tigchelaar, Exec. Director

A nondenominational specialized agency of evangelical tradition engaged in Bible distribution, correspondence courses, evangelism, literacy work and missionary training.

Purpose: "To provide Scriptures that bring people into the fellowship of Christ and His Church."

Year Founded in CAN 1949

Income for Overseas Mins $3,500,000

Personnel:

Short-Term less than 1 year from CAN 18

Home ministry & office staff in CAN 17

Brethren Assemblies (Canada)

(No central office)

The Brethren Assemblies are also known as "Christian Brethren" or "Plymouth Brethren". Missionaries are sent from each local assembly (church) and not through a central agency. Personnel totals were reported by MSC Canada.

Year Founded in CAN 0

Income for Overseas Mins .... NA

Fully Supported CAN Personnel Overseas:

Expecting to serve more than 4 years 192

Other Personnel:

Home ministry & office staff in CAN 4

Countries: Angola 1, Argentina 4, Austria 4, Belgium 6, Bolivia 10, Botswana 2, Brazil 3, Chile 14, Colombia 1, Congo/Zaire 3, Costa Rica 2, Dominican Rep 2, Ecuador 5, El Salvador 3, Finland 2, France 19, Guatemala 2, Hong Kong 2, India 2, Ireland 12, Italy 4, Japan 7, Kenya 4, Madagascar 2, Mexico 6, Nigeria 4, Peru 4, Philippines 4, Poland 2, Portugal 6, Puerto Rico 1, Russia 3, S Africa 1, Spain 4, St Vincent 1, Uruguay 5, Venezuela 6, Zambia 29

Calcutta Mission of Mercy

(780)424-7157 **Fax: (780)424-8510**

E-Mail: aspire@connect.ab.ca

P.O. Box 65599, Vancouver, BC V5N 5K5

Rev. Mohan Maharaj, Exec. Director

A service agency of Pentecostal tradition engaged in childcare/orphanage programs, Christian education, medical work and youth programs. Affiliated with the Pentecostal Assemblies of Canada and the Assemblies of God USA.

Year Founded in CAN 1978

Income for Overseas Mins $928,000

Gifts-in-Kind $816,640

Fully Supported CAN Personnel Overseas:

Expecting to serve more than 4 years 1

Nonresidential mission personnel 2

Other Personnel:

Bivocational/Tentmaker from CAN 5

Home ministry & office staff in CAN 3

Countries: India 1

Campus Crusade for Christ of Canada

(604)514-2000 **Fax: (604)514-2093**

Web: http://www.crusade.org

P.O. Box 300, Vancouver, BC V6C 2X3

Mr. Marvin Kehler, President

An interdenominational sending agency of evangelical tradition engaged in evangelism, leadership development, literature distribution and support of national churches.

Purpose: "...helping to fulfill the Great Commission in Canada and around the world, by developing a movement of evangelism and discipleship."

Year Founded in CAN 1967

Income for Overseas Mins $7,329,055

Fully Supported CAN Personnel Overseas:

Expecting to serve 1 to 4 years 10

Nonresidential mission personnel 15

Other Personnel:
Short-Term less than 1 year from CAN 398
Home ministry & office staff in CAN 253
Countries: Japan 1, Nigeria 1, Philippines 2, S Africa 2, Ukraine 4

Canadian Baptist Ministries

(905)821-3533 **Fax: (905)826-3441**
E-Mail: communications@cbmin.org
Web: www.cbmin.org
7185 Millcreek Dr., Mississauga, ON L5N 5R4
Rev. David Phillips, Gen. Secretary

A national partnership of four regional Baptist communities engaged in leadership development, church planting, development, theological education and relief and/or rehabilitation. Overseas personnel from 1996 report.
Year Founded in CAN 1874
Income for Overseas Mins $5,400,000
Fully Supported CAN Personnel Overseas:
Expecting to serve more than 4 years 51
Expecting to serve 1 to 4 years 26
Other Personnel:
Short-Term less than 1 year from CAN 700
Home ministry & office staff in CAN 27
Countries: Albania 2, Angola 2, Asia 5, Belgium 11, Bolivia 5, China (PRC) 2, Congo/Zaire 8, Croatia 2, France 2, Guyana 6, Hong Kong 2, India 4, Indonesia 4, Kenya 12, Latvia 2, Slovakia 2, Ukraine 4, Venezuela 2

Canadian Bible Society / La Societe Biblique Canadienne

(416)757-4171 **Fax: (416)757-3376**
E-Mail: natdir@canbible.ca
Web: www.canbible.ca
10 Carnforth Rd., Toronto, ON M4A 2S4
The Rev. Greg Bailey, National Director

A transdenominational support agency serving churches of all confessions and engaged in Bible distribution, linguistics and Bible translation.
Purpose: "...to promote and encourage the wider circulation and use, without doctrinal note or comment, of the Scriptures throughout Canada, and to cooperate with the United Bible Societies in its worldwide work."
Year Founded in CAN 1904
Income for Overseas Mins $3,909,000
Personnel:
Home ministry & office staff in CAN 110

Canadian Churches' Forum for Global Ministries

(416)924-9351 **Fax: (416)924-5356**
E-Mail: ccforum@web.net
230 St. Clair Ave., West, Toronto, ON M4V 1R5
Mr. Robert Faris, Coord. Outreach/Comm.

An affiliated interdenominational service institution of the Canadian Council of Churches engaged in missionary orientation, furloughed missionary support and literature production.
Purpose: "...an agency through which the Canadian churches reflect and work together on global mission issues through programs of education, dialogue and training."
Year Founded in CAN 1921
Income for Overseas Mins .... NA
Personnel:
Home ministry & office staff in CAN 5

Canadian Convention of Southern Baptists

(403)932-5688 **Fax: (403)932-4937**
E-Mail: office@ccsb.ca
P.O. Box 300, Cochrane, AB T0L 0W0
Rev. Gerald Taillon, Exec. Director

A denominational sending agency of Baptist tradition engaged in church planting, agricultural programs, Christian education, evangelism and relief and/or rehabilitation.
Year Founded in CAN 1985
Income for Overseas Mins $112,271
Fully Supported CAN Personnel Overseas:
Expecting to serve more than 4 years 4
Other Personnel:
Short-Term less than 1 year from CAN 25
Home ministry & office staff in CAN 14
Countries: Chile 2, Nigeria 2

Canadian Food for the Hungry

(604)853-4262 **Fax: (604)853-4332**
E-Mail: info@cfh.ca
Web: www.cfh.ca
005-2580 Cedar Park Place, Abbotsford, BC V2T 3S5

Rev. David Collins, Exec. Director

A service agency of evangelical tradition engaged in development, agricultural programs, leadership development, support of national churches and relief and/or rehabilitation.

Year Founded in CAN 1988
Income for Overseas Mins $20,934,835
Gifts-in-Kind $19,668,436
Fully Supported CAN Personnel Overseas:
Nonresidential mission personnel 7
Other Personnel:
Non-CAN serving in own/other country 11
Short-Term less than 1 year from CAN 1
Home ministry & office staff in CAN 20
Countries: Rwanda, Bolivia, Myanmar, Guatemala, Peru, Brazil

Canadian South America Mission

(403)443-2250 **Fax: (403)443-2099**
E-Mail: 75457.2247@compuserve.com
Web: www.samlink.org
Box 716, Three Hills, AB T0M 2A0
Dan C. Wiebe, Exec. Director

An interdenominational sending agency of fundamental and evangelical tradition engaged in leadership development, church planting, Christian education and support of national churches.

Purpose: "...to establish the church of Jesus Christ in South America by planting and nurturing churches, training church leaders, [and] developing church associations."

Year Founded in CAN 1983
Income for Overseas Mins $132,123
Fully Supported CAN Personnel Overseas:
Expecting to serve more than 4 years 5
Other Personnel:
Home ministry & office staff in CAN 1
Countries: Colombia 2, Peru 3

Centre for World Mission - British Columbia

(604)854-3818 **Fax: (604)854-3818**
E-Mail: CWMBC@telus.net
Web: www3.telus.net/cwmbc
P.O. Box 2436, Clearbook, BC V2T 4X3
Mr. John Burman, Director

An interdenominational support agency of evangelical tradition engaged in missions information service, mobilization for mission, mission-related research and training services for other agencies.

Purpose: "...to promote information on people groups of Canada and the world isolated by social and/or language barriers from mainstream society where a viable indigenous church is not yet existing."

Year Founded in CAN 1981
Income for Overseas Mins .... NA
Personnel:
Home ministry & office staff in CAN 1

Child Evangelism Fellowship of Canada

(204)943-2774 **Fax: (204)943-9967**
E-Mail: cefofcanada@compuserve.com
P.O. Box 165 - Stn. Main, Winnipeg, MB R3C 2G9
Rev. Don Collins, Natl. Director

An interdenominational sending agency of evangelical tradition engaged in evangelism, childrens programs, literature distribution, literature production and training.

Purpose: "...to assist and promote the evangelizing and discipling of children through leadership, coordination and administrative support to CEF ministries across Canada and overseas."

Year Founded in CAN 1963
Income for Overseas Mins $555,000
Fully Supported CAN Personnel Overseas:
Expecting to serve more than 4 years 15
Other Personnel:
Non-CAN serving in own/other country 12
Short-Term less than 1 year from CAN 4
Home ministry & office staff in CAN 7
Countries: Albania 1, Argentina 1, Brazil 2, France 1, Hungary 2, Italy 2, Japan 2, S Africa 2, Sweden 2

Christian Aid Mission

(800)871-0882 **Fax: (905)871-5165**
E-Mail: friends@christianaid.ca
Web: www.christianaid.ca
201 Stanton St., Fort Erie, ON L2A 3N8
Mr. James S. Eagles, President

A nondenominational support agency of evangelical tradition engaged in support of national workers, funds transmission, missions information service, support of

national churches and mission-related research.
Purpose: "To aid, encourage and strengthen indigenous New Testament Christianity, particularly where Christians are impoverished, few or persecuted..."
Year Founded in CAN 1953
Income for Overseas Mins $512,092
Personnel:
Non-CAN serving in own/other country 500
Home ministry & office staff in CAN 18

Christian and Missionary Alliance in Canada, The

(905)771-6747 Fax: (905)771-9874
E-Mail: nationaloffice@cmacan.org
Web: www.cmacan.org
P.O. Box 7900, Station B, Willowdale, ON M2K 2R6
Rev. Wallace C.E. Albrecht, Vice President

A denominational sending agency of evangelical tradition engaged in church planting, TEE and evangelism.
Purpose: "...committed to world evangelization, stressing the Fullness of Christ in personal experience, building the Church and preaching the Gospel to the ends of the earth."
Year Founded in CAN 1981
Income for Overseas Mins $12,430,005
Fully Supported CAN Personnel Overseas:
Expecting to serve more than 4 years 187
Expecting to serve 1 to 4 years 23
Nonresidential mission personnel 6
Other Personnel:
Bivocational/Tentmaker from CAN 17
Short-Term less than 1 year from CAN 8
Home ministry & office staff in CAN 21
Countries: Argentina 2, Benin 3, Brazil 3, Burkina Faso 2, Cambodia 6, Chile 2, Colombia 3, Congo 4, Costa Rica 1, Cote d'Ivoire 14, Ecuador 9, France 4, Gabon 9, Germany 18, Guatemala 4, Guinea Bissau 9, Hong Kong 4, Hungary 6, Indonesia 19, Israel 2, Japan 4, Laos 2, Lebanon 2, Malaysia 3, Mali 5, Mexico 16, Peru 5, Philippines 15, Poland 4, Russia 8, Spain 2, Taiwan (ROC) 4, Thailand 5, Venezuela 9, Yugoslavia 2

Christian Blind Mission International (Canada)

(905)640-6464 Fax: (905)640-4332
E-Mail: cbmican@compuserve.com
Web: www.cbmi-can.org
P.O. Box 800, Stouffville, ON L4A 7Z9
Mr. David McComiskey, Natl. Director

An interdenominational specialized agency of evangelical tradition engaged in disability assistance programs, development and medical work.
Purpose: "...serving the blind and handicapped in the developing world, irrespective of nationality, race, sex, or religion...[with] the ultimate aim...to show the love of Christ..."
Year Founded in CAN 1978
Income for Overseas Mins $6,527,419
Gifts-in-Kind $2,205,500
Fully Supported CAN Personnel Overseas:
Expecting to serve more than 4 years 6
Expecting to serve 1 to 4 years 2
Nonresidential mission personnel 5
Other Personnel:
Short-Term less than 1 year from CAN 1
Home ministry & office staff in CAN 30
Countries: Bangladesh 2, Congo/Zaire 1, Kenya 2, Tanzania 1, Uganda 2

Christian Indigenous Development Overseas

(403)286-0611 Fax: (403)247-4686
E-Mail: 74401.3712@compuserve.com
142 Dalhousie Rd., NW, Calgary, AB T3A 2H1
Mr. H.A. McLean, President

A transdenominational service agency of evangelical tradition engaged in microenterprise development and technical assistance with previously-selected nationals.
Year Founded in CAN 1977
Income for Overseas Mins $173,000

Christian Literature Crusade

See: Croisade du Livre Chretien

Christian Reformed World Relief Committee of Canada

(905)336-2920 Fax: (905)336-8344
E-Mail: Dejongwa@crcna.org

P.O. Box 5070, Burlington, ON L7R 3Y8
Mr. Wayne DeJong, Director

A denominational service agency of Reformed tradition engaged in development, agricultural programs, leadership development, literacy work, management consulting/training and relief and/or rehabilitation.

Year Founded in CAN 1969
Income for Overseas Mins $5,684,175
Fully Supported CAN Personnel Overseas:
Expecting to serve more than 4 years 20
Other Personnel:
Short-Term less than 1 year from CAN 8
Home ministry & office staff in CAN 7
Countries: Cambodia 1, Haiti 2, Honduras 3, Indonesia 1, Kenya 2, Mali 1, Niger 2, Senegal 2, Tanzania 3, Uganda 1, Zambia 2

Christian Studies International of Canada

(416)690-4774
E-Mail: vennen@ibm.net
One Massey Square, Suite 1910, Toronto, ON M4C 5L4
Dr. Robert Vander Vennen, Exec. Secretary

A nondenominational service agency of evangelical tradition engaged in extension education, theological education and leadership development. An affiliate of International Institute for Christian Studies.

Purpose: "To develop leaders who think and live Christianly, by establishing Departments of Christian Studies in secular universities overseas and by providing evangelical academicians, business leaders and professionals teaching with a Christian worldview in the full range of disciplines overseas."

Year Founded in CAN 1997
Income for Overseas Mins $60,000
Fully Supported CAN Personnel Overseas:
Expecting to serve more than 4 years 2
Other Personnel:
Home ministry & office staff in CAN 1
Countries: Russia 2

Church of God (Anderson, IN), Canadian Board of Missions

(780)672-0772 **Fax: (780)672-6888**
E-Mail: wcdncog@cable-lynx.net
Web: www.cable-lynx.net/wcdncog
4717-56th St., Camrose, AB T4V 2C4
Rev. John D. Campbell, Chr. Serv./Msn. Coordinator

A denominational support agency of Holiness tradition engaged in funds transmission, church construction, Christian education and support of national churches.

Year Founded in CAN 1946
Income for Overseas Mins $240,857
Gifts-in-Kind $294
Personnel:
Non-CAN serving in own/other country 6
Short-Term less than 1 year from CAN 30
Home ministry & office staff in CAN 4
Countries: Guam, Uganda, Zambia

Compassion Canada

(519)668-0224 **Fax: (519)685-1107**
E-Mail: compcanada@capc.ci.org
Web: www.compassioncanada.ca
P.O. Box 5591, London, ON N6A 5G8
Rev. Barry Slauenwhite, President

A transdenominational service agency of evangelical tradition engaged in childcare/orphanage programs, childrens programs, development, funds transmission and support of national churches.

Year Founded in CAN 1964
Income for Overseas Mins $6,500,000
Personnel:
Home ministry & office staff in CAN 20

Croisade du Livre Chretien / Christian Literature Crusade

(514)933-9466 **Fax: (514)933-7629**
E-Mail: clccanada@netcom.ca
4257 ouest Ste-Catherine, Montreal, PQ H3Z 1P7
Mr. Rod Fowler, Director

An interdenominational service agency of evangelical tradition engaged in literature distribution and Bible distribution.

Year Founded in CAN 1977
Income for Overseas Mins $5,000
Personnel:
Home ministry & office staff in CAN 9

Czechoslovak Evangelical Mission

(905)822-8808
1601 Bramsey Dr., Mississauga, ON L5J 2H8
Rev. Joseph R. Novak, President

An interdenominational support agency of Baptist tradition engaged in literature production and literature distribution in the Czech and Slovakia Republics.

Year Founded in CAN 1984
Income for Overseas Mins $30,000
Personnel:
Short-Term less than 1 year from CAN 1
Home ministry & office staff in CAN 1

Door of Hope International (Canada)

(604)430-1747
P.O. Box 65959, Vancouver, BC V5N 5L3
Rev. E. Culley, Chairman

An interdenominational service agency of evangelical tradition engaged in Bible distribution, literature distribution/production, support of national churches and relief aid. Statistical information from 1996.

Year Founded in CAN 1972
Income for Overseas Mins $36,458
Fully Supported CAN Personnel Overseas:
Expecting to serve more than 4 years 2
Other Personnel:
Short-Term less than 1 year from CAN 1
Home ministry & office staff in CAN 1
Countries: Albania 1, Russia 1

Emmanuel International

(905)640-2111 Fax: (905)640-2186
E-Mail: info@e-i.org
Web: www.e-i.org
P.O. Box 4050, Stouffville, ON L4A 8B6
Mr. Andrew Atkins, Gen. Director

An interdenominational sending agency of evangelical tradition engaged in development, TEE, evangelism, medical work, support of national churches and relief and/ or rehabilitation.

Purpose: "...to encourage, strengthen and assist churches worldwide to meet the spiritual and physical needs of the poor in accordance with Holy Scriptures..."

Year Founded in CAN 1975
Income for Overseas Mins $1,100,000
Fully Supported CAN Personnel Overseas:
Expecting to serve more than 4 years 7
Expecting to serve 1 to 4 years 8
Other Personnel:
Non-CAN serving in own/other country 10
Short-Term less than 1 year from CAN 20
Home ministry & office staff in CAN 12
Countries: Haiti 2, Malawi 6, Philippines 2, Sudan 4, Uganda 1

Equip, Canada

(250)743-7171 Fax: (250)743-7171
P.O. Box 683, Duncan, BC V9L 3Y1
Rev. Barrie G. Flitcroft, Gen. Director

An interdenominational sending agency of evangelical tradition engaged in development, agricultural programs, evangelism, medical work, technical assistance and missionary training.

Purpose: "...to prepare, send and support evangelical missionaries to assist the church around the world to be responsive to the poor, sensitive to the Holy Spirit, focused on personal evangelism, and practically engaged in strengthening the Body of Christ."

Year Founded in CAN 1997
Income for Overseas Mins $100,211
Gifts-in-Kind $5,600
Fully Supported CAN Personnel Overseas:
Expecting to serve more than 4 years 2
Expecting to serve 1 to 4 years 4
Other Personnel:
Short-Term less than 1 year from CAN 3
Countries: Argentina 2, Cote d'Ivoire 2, Uganda 2

European Christian Mission

(604)943-0211 Fax: (604)943-0212
E-Mail: 74663.3176@compuserve.com
1077 56th St., Ste 226, Delta, BC V4L 2A2
Rev. Vincent Price, Dir. for N. America

An interdenominational sending agency of evangelical tradition engaged in evangelism, broadcasting, literature distribution and support of national churches, working with, through, and under national churches.

Year Founded in CAN 1960
Income for Overseas Mins $802,540

Eurovangelism

(905)821-6301 **Fax: (905)821-6311**
207-2476 Argentia Rd., Missisauga, ON L5N 6M1
Mr. John Murray, Exec. Director

A nondenominational support agency of evangelical tradition engaged in support of national workers, TEE, evangelism and relief and/or rehabilitation.

Purpose: "...to serve the Church across Europe by envisioning, encouraging, and equipping national Christian workers."

Year Founded in CAN 1976
Income for Overseas Mins $145,000
Personnel:
Non-CAN serving in own/other country 39
Home ministry & office staff in CAN 2
Countries: Austria, Bulgaria, Poland, Romania, Russia, Serbia

Evangelical Covenant Church of Canada

(403)934-5845 **Fax: (403)934-5847**
E-Mail: ccc@escape.ca
2791 Pembina Hwy., Winnipeg, MB R3T 2H5
Mr. Jeffrey Anderson, Superintendent

A denominational conference of covenantal and evangelical tradition engaged in denominational funds transmission and mission mobilization for evangelism and church planting. Statistics from 1996.

Year Founded in CAN 1904
Income for Overseas Mins $52,280
Personnel:
Short-Term less than 1 year from CAN 1
Home ministry & office staff in CAN 3

Evangelical Lutheran Church in Canada, ELCIC Mission

(204)984-9150 **Fax: (204)984-9185**
E-Mail: rhgranke@elcic.ca
Web: www.elcic.ca
302-393 Portage Ave., Winnipeg, MB R3B 3H6
Mr. Robert Granke, ELCIC Secretary

The national mission office of a Lutheran denomination engaged in support of overseas partner churches, mission in Canada, and campus ministry.

Purpose: "...to share the Gospel of Jesus Christ with people in Canada and around the world through the proclamation of the Word, the celebration of the Sacraments and through service in Christ's name."

Year Founded in CAN 1967
Income for Overseas Mins $500,000
Fully Supported CAN Personnel Overseas:
Expecting to serve more than 4 years 4
Expecting to serve 1 to 4 years 5
Other Personnel:
Short-Term less than 1 year from CAN 9
Home ministry & office staff in CAN 4
Countries: Argentina 2, Cameroon 1, El Salvador 1, Guatemala 1, Papua New Guin 1, Peru 1, Slovakia 1, Thailand 1

Evangelical Mennonite Conference Board of Missions

(204)326-6401 **Fax: (204)326-1613**
E-Mail: emconf@mts.net
P.O. Box 1268, Steinbach, MB R0A 2A0
Rev. Henry Klassen, Exec. Secretary

A denominational sending agency of Mennonite and evangelical tradition engaged in church planting, broadcasting, TEE, evangelism, leadership development and medical work.

Year Founded in CAN 1953
Income for Overseas Mins $1,325,000
Fully Supported CAN Personnel Overseas:
Expecting to serve more than 4 years 28
Other Personnel:
Short-Term less than 1 year from CAN 15
Home ministry & office staff in CAN 2
Countries: Burkina Faso 3, Mexico 12, Paraguay 13

Evangelical Mennonite Mission Conference Board of Missions & Service

(204)253-7929 **Fax: (204)256-7384**
E-Mail: emmc@mb.sympatico.ca
Web: www.sbcollege.mb.ca/EMMC/
Box 52059 Niakwa P.O., Winnipeg, MB R2M 5P9
Mr. Len Sawatzky, Director

A denominational sending agency of Mennonite and evangelical tradition engaged in church planting, broadcasting, leadership development, support of national churches, short-term programs and support of national workers. Financial information from 1996.

Year Founded in CAN 1959
Income for Overseas Mins $301,171
Fully Supported CAN Personnel Overseas:
Expecting to serve more than 4 years 8
Expecting to serve 1 to 4 years 2
Nonresidential mission personnel 2
Other Personnel:
Non-CAN serving in own/other country 4
Short-Term less than 1 year from CAN 7
Home ministry & office staff in CAN 4
Countries: Belize 2, Bolivia 4, Mexico 4

Evangelical Missionary Church of Canada Missions

(403)250-2759 **Fax: (403)291-4720**
E-Mail: evanmiss@emcc.ca
Web: www.emcc.ca
4031 Brentwood Road NW, Calgary, AB T2L1L1
Rev. G. Keith Elliott, Exec. Dir., Missions & Adm.
Rev. Mark Bolender, President

A denominational sending agency of evangelical tradition engaged in church planting, church construction, theological education, TEE and support of national churches.

Purpose: "...to win the lost, to build up believers and equip them to establish indigenous churches which participate in worldwide outreach until Christ comes."

Year Founded in CAN 1993
Income for Overseas Mins $819,175
Fully Supported CAN Personnel Overseas:
Expecting to serve more than 4 years 18
Other Personnel:
Home ministry & office staff in CAN 5
Countries: Brazil 6, Mexico 3, Nigeria 5, Portugal 2, Spain 2

Evangelical Tract Distributors

(780)477-1538 **Fax: (780)477-3795**
E-Mail: support@evangelicaltract.com
Web: www.evangelicaltract.com
P.O. Box 146, Edmonton, AB T5J 2G9
Mr. John Harder, Managing Dir.

A specialized agency of evangelical tradition engaged in literature distribution, evangelism and literature production.

Year Founded in CAN 1935
Income for Overseas Mins $550,000
Personnel:
Home ministry & office staff in CAN 8

FAIR (Fellowship Agency for International Relief)

(519)821-4830 **Fax: (519)821-9829**
E-Mail: international@fellowship.ca
Web: www.fellowship.ca
679 Southgate Dr., Guelph, ON N1G 4S2
Mr. Norman Nielsen, Coordinator

A denominational support agency of Baptist tradition engaged in funds transmission, medical work and relief and/or rehabilitation. The relief arm of FEBInternational.

Year Founded in CAN 1974
Income for Overseas Mins $121,800

Far East Broadcasting Associates of Canada

(604)430-8439 **Fax: (604)430-5272**
E-Mail: kenreeve@telus.ca
Web: www.febc.org/febchome.html
6850 Antrim Ave., Burnaby, BC V5J 4M4
Mr. Don Patterson, Dir./Intl. Broadcast Support
Mr. Ken Reeve, Dir. /Administration/Controller

An interdenominational specialized agency of evangelical tradition engaged in broadcasting, audio recording/distribution, evangelism and literature distribution.

Purpose: "...to promote missions...to encourage evangelical Christians to participate in FEBCanada's ministries through prayer, financial support and personal involvement...to participate directly in FEB Radio International's broadcast ministry through the provision of staff, production of programs and the funding of missionaries and special projects."

Year Founded in CAN 1964
Income for Overseas Mins $1,142,719
Fully Supported CAN Personnel Overseas:
Expecting to serve more than 4 years 7
Expecting to serve 1 to 4 years 2
Other Personnel:
Short-Term less than 1 year from CAN 3
Home ministry & office staff in CAN 25
Countries: Cambodia 1, Hong Kong 2, N Mariana Isls 2, Philippines 2, Thailand 2

FEBInternational

(519)821-4830 **Fax: (519)821-9829**
E-Mail: international@fellowship.ca
Web: www.fellowship.ca
679 Southgate Dr., Guelph, ON N1G 4S2
Rev. Paul S. Kerr, Director

A denominational sending agency of Baptist and evangelical tradition engaged in church planting, correspondence courses, TEE, evangelism, medical work and relief and/or rehabilitation.

Year Founded in CAN 1964
Income for Overseas Mins $3,000,000
Fully Supported CAN Personnel Overseas:
Expecting to serve more than 4 years 66
Expecting to serve 1 to 4 years 6
Nonresidential mission personnel 2
Other Personnel:
Non-CAN serving in own/other country 7
Short-Term less than 1 year from CAN 4
Home ministry & office staff in CAN 6
Countries: Asia 4, Belgium 6, Colombia 10, France 8, Italy 2, Japan 12, Kenya 2, Latin America 2, Lebanon 2, Pakistan 16, Spain 2, Venezuela 6

Frontiers Canada

(780)421-9090 **Fax: (780)421-9292**
P.O. Box 9090, Edmonton, AB T5P 4K1
Nelson Wolf, National Director

An interdenominational sending agency of evangelical tradition engaged in church planting, evangelism, support of national workers and missionary training. Statistical information from 1996.

Purpose: "...working in close cooperation with local churches to see vital, worshipping witnessing churches established..."

Year Founded in CAN 1984
Income for Overseas Mins $450,000
Fully Supported CAN Personnel Overseas:
Expecting to serve more than 4 years 22
Nonresidential mission personnel 3
Other Personnel:
Non-CAN serving in own/other country 3
Bivocational/Tentmaker from CAN 2
Home ministry & office staff in CAN 8
Countries: Africa 2, Asia 3, Central Asia 10, Europe 3, Indonesia 4

Fundamental Baptist Mission of Trinidad and Tobago (Canada)

(905)839-4621
E-Mail: ropel@hotmail.com
817 Kingston Rd., P. O. Box 37, Pickering, ON L1V 2R2
Rev. Garry Francis, Secretary-Treasurer
Rev. Thomas D. Murray, Board Chairman

A support agency of Baptist and fundamental tradition engaged in funds transmission for support of national workers. Financial data included in USA sister agency.

Year Founded in CAN 1990
Income for Overseas Mins .... NA
Personnel:
Non-CAN serving in own/other country 1

Galcom International

(905)574-4626 **Fax: (905)574-4633**
E-Mail: galcom@galcom.org
Web: www.galcom.org
65 Nebo Rd., Hamilton, ON L8W 2C9
Rev. Allan T. McGuirl, Intl. Director

An interdenominational support agency of evangelical tradition engaged in designing, building, and distributing high-tech communications equipment for other agencies used in evangelism and other ministries in many countries.

Purpose: "To provide durable technical equipment for communicating the Gospel worldwide...at the lowest possible price."

Year Founded in CAN 1989
Income for Overseas Mins $51,154

Glad Tidings Missionary Society

(604)873-3621 **Fax: (604)876-1558**
3456 Fraser St., Vancouver, BC V5V 4C4
Pastor Ernest C. Culley, President

A nondenominational sending agency of independent tradition engaged in evangelism and church planting.

Year Founded in CAN 1948
Income for Overseas Mins $500,000
Fully Supported CAN Personnel Overseas:
Expecting to serve more than 4 years 6
Expecting to serve 1 to 4 years 6

Other Personnel:

Short-Term less than 1 year from CAN 24

Countries: Mexico 2, Philippines 1, Taiwan (ROC) 2, Uganda 7

Global Outreach Mission

(905)684-1401
E-Mail: glmissl@aol.com
P.O. Box 1210, St. Catharines, ON L2R 7A7
Dr. James O. Blackwood, President

A transdenominational sending agency of evangelical and independent tradition engaged in church planting, broadcasting, evangelism, medical work and supplying equipment.

Purpose: "...sharing the Gospel...planting and encouraging His church, helping the hurting physically and serving in every area of Christian development."

Year Founded in CAN 1943

Income for Overseas Mins $1,049,825

Fully Supported CAN Personnel Overseas:

Expecting to serve more than 4 years 29

Other Personnel:

Non-CAN serving in own/other country 38

Short-Term less than 1 year from CAN 3

Home ministry & office staff in CAN 34

Countries: Antigua 2, Belgium 1, Brazil 1, Colombia 2, Congo/Zaire 1, France 7, Guatemala 2, Haiti 2, India 3, Ireland 4, Kazakhstan 2, S Africa 2

Gospel for Asia

(905)574-8800 **Fax: (905)574-1849**
E-Mail: 104017.2011@compuserve.com
Web: www.gfa.org
120 Lancing Dr. #6, Hamilton, ON L8W 3A1
Pastor Wendell Leytham, Canadian Director

An interdenominational support agency of evangelical tradition engaged in support of national workers, Bible distribution, evangelism and support of national churches. Financial information from 1996 report.

Year Founded in CAN 1985

Income for Overseas Mins $755,000

Personnel:

Home ministry & office staff in CAN 8

Gospel Missionary Union of Canada

(204)338-7831 **Fax: (204)339-3321**
E-Mail: 76756.2126@compuserve.com
Web: www.gmu.org
2121 Henderson Hwy., Winnipeg, MB R2G 1P8
Mr. Grant Morrison, Canadian Director

An interdenominational sending agency of evangelical tradition engaged in church planting, broadcasting, theological education, TEE, evangelism and support of national churches.

Year Founded in CAN 1949

Income for Overseas Mins $2,725,019

Fully Supported CAN Personnel Overseas:

Expecting to serve more than 4 years 66

Expecting to serve 1 to 4 years 12

Other Personnel:

Non-CAN serving in own/other country 5

Short-Term less than 1 year from CAN 15

Home ministry & office staff in CAN 19

Countries: Argentina 2, Austria 7, Bahamas 2, Belgium 1, Belize 6, Bolivia 24, Brazil 4, Colombia 2, Ecuador 8, Germany 1, Mali 14, Panama 1, Spain 6

Greater Europe Mission (Canada)

(905)728-8222 **Fax: (905)728-8958**
E-Mail: gemcanada@gemission.com
Web: www.gemission.org
100 Ontario St., Oshawa, ON L1G 4Z1
Rev. Neil Rempel, Canadian Director

An interdenominational sending agency of evangelical tradition engaged in theological education, camping programs, church planting and evangelism.

Purpose: "...to assist the peoples of Europe in building up the Body of Christ so every person in Europe is within reach of a witnessing fellowship."

Year Founded in CAN 1959

Income for Overseas Mins $877,300

Fully Supported CAN Personnel Overseas:

Expecting to serve more than 4 years 22

Expecting to serve 1 to 4 years 1

Other Personnel:

Short-Term less than 1 year from CAN 8

Home ministry & office staff in CAN 4

Countries: Austria 2, Croatia 2, France 3, Germany 2, Hungary 1, Italy 2, Latvia 5, Luxembourg 2, Portugal 2, Romania 1, Ukraine 1

HCJB World Radio Missionary Fellowship in Canada

(905)821-6313 **Fax: (905)821-6314**
E-Mail: hcjbcan@hcjb.org
Web: www.hcjb.org
2476 Argentia Rd., Suite 201, Mississauga, ON L5N 6M1
Mr. Craig Cook, Director for Canada

An interdenominational support agency of evangelical tradition engaged in broadcasting, evangelism and medical work.

Year Founded in CAN 1967
Income for Overseas Mins .... NA
Personnel:
Home ministry & office staff in CAN 1

High Adventure Gospel Communication Ministries

(905)898-5447 **Fax: (905)898-5447**
E-Mail: hiadvcan@home.com
Web: www.highadventure.org
P.O. Box 425, Station E, Toronto, ON M6H 4E3
Mrs. Jackie Yockey, COO

An interdenominational support agency of Pentecostal and evangelical tradition engaged in broadcasting and evangelism.

Year Founded in CAN 1975
Income for Overseas Mins .... NA
Personnel:
Home ministry & office staff in CAN 2

HOPE International Development Agency

(604)525-5481 **Fax: (604)525-3471**
E-Mail: Hope@web.apc.org
Web: web.idirect.com/~hope/index.html
P.O. Box 608, New Westminster, BC V3L 9Z9
Mr. David McKenzie, Exec. Director

A nondenominational service agency of independent and Baptist tradition engaged in development, agricultural programs, funds transmission, supplying equipment and technical assistance.

Purpose: "...founded on Christian principles [to] provide alternate technological and educational support to people in developing countries where environmental, economic and/or social circumstances have interfered with the ability of local communities to sustain themselves..."

Year Founded in CAN 1975
Income for Overseas Mins $9,060,000
Gifts-in-Kind $6,000,000
Fully Supported CAN Personnel Overseas:
Expecting to serve 1 to 4 years 2
Nonresidential mission personnel 2
Other Personnel:
Short-Term less than 1 year from CAN 16
Home ministry & office staff in CAN 6
Countries: S Africa 2, Dominican Republic

Inter-Varsity Christian Fellowship of Canada

(416)443-1170 **Fax: (416)443-1499**
E-Mail: National@ivcf.ca
Web: www.ivcf.ca
64 Prince Andrew Place, Toronto, ON M3C 2H4
Mr. James E. Berney, Gen. Director

An interdenominational support agency of evangelical tradition engaged in evangelism, short-term programs and missionary training.

Purpose: "...mobilizing a diverse community of Christians through its camps, student and alumni movements to proclaim Jesus Christ as Saviour and Lord."

Year Founded in CAN 1928
Income for Overseas Mins $500,000
Fully Supported CAN Personnel Overseas:
Nonresidential mission personnel 2
Other Personnel:
Short-Term less than 1 year from CAN 50
Home ministry & office staff in CAN 180

International Child Care (Canada)

(905)821-6318 **Fax: (905)821-6319**
E-Mail: ICC.Canada@sympatico.ca
Web: www.intlchildcare.org
2476 Argentia Rd., #113, Mississauga, ON L5N 6M1
Mr. Dana Osburn, Natl. Director

An interdenominational sending agency of evangelical tradition engaged in childcare programs and providing medical supplies. Statistical information from 1996.

Year Founded in CAN 1972
Income for Overseas Mins $998,040
Gifts-in-Kind $144,756
Fully Supported CAN Personnel Overseas:
Expecting to serve more than 4 years 2
Expecting to serve 1 to 4 years 4

Other Personnel:
Short-Term less than 1 year from CAN 4
Home ministry & office staff in CAN 1
Countries: Haiti 6

International Children's Haven (Canada)

(604)795-9853
47982 Yale Rd. E., Chilliwack, BC V2P 6H4
Mr. Victor Epp, President

An interdenominational support agency of evangelical tradition engaged in childcare/orphanage programs.
Year Founded in CAN 1984
Income for Overseas Mins $49,215

International Christian Aid Canada

(905)331-7799 **Fax: (905)331-7699**
P.O. Box 5090, Burlington, ON L7R 4G5
Mr. Kenneth D. Roe, Exec. Director

A support agency of evangelical tradition engaged in childcare/orphanage programs, development, medical work and relief and/or rehabilitation.
Year Founded in CAN 1979
Income for Overseas Mins $2,582,000
Gifts-in-Kind $867,000
Fully Supported CAN Personnel Overseas:
Nonresidential mission personnel 2
Other Personnel:
Non-CAN serving in own/other country 99
Short-Term less than 1 year from CAN 2
Home ministry & office staff in CAN 7
Countries: Honduras, Kenya, Philippines, Uganda

International Missions in Ontario

(905)646-0228 **Fax: (905)646-8707**
E-Mail: imont@npiec.on.ca
Web: www.intermissions.org
P.O. Box 20164, St. Catharines, ON L2M 7W7
Marty Frisk, Director

An interdenominational sending agency of evangelical tradition engaged in church planting and evangelism.
Purpose: "...proclaiming the gospel and establishing local indigenous churches, primarily among least-reached Asian communities world-wide."
Year Founded in CAN 1953
Income for Overseas Mins $293,000
Fully Supported CAN Personnel Overseas:
Expecting to serve more than 4 years 14
Expecting to serve 1 to 4 years 1
Other Personnel:
Short-Term less than 1 year from CAN 4
Home ministry & office staff in CAN 3
Countries: Asia 1, Bangladesh 2, India 2, Pakistan 3, Philippines 4, Tajikistan 1, UK 2

International Needs - Canada

(604)607-0850 **Fax: (604)607-0852**
E-Mail: inc@international-needs.org
Web: www.international-needs.org
P.O. Box 1288, Aldergrove, BC V4W 2V1
Rev. Glenn Fretz, Exec. Director

A transdenominational service agency of evangelical tradition engaged in support of national workers, literature distribution and youth programs.
Purpose: "...to link Canadian Christians and churches with overseas ministries of INC that seek to integrate evangelism, discipleship, and fulfillment of human needs through effective development."
Year Founded in CAN 1976
Income for Overseas Mins $549,150
Personnel:
Non-CAN serving in own/other country 220
Short-Term less than 1 year from CAN 2
Home ministry & office staff in CAN 2

International Teams of Canada

(519)669-8844 **Fax: (519)669-5644**
E-Mail: ITCAN@iteams.org
Web: www.iteams.org
1 Union St., Elmira, ON N3B 3J9
Mr. Neil Ostrander, President

An interdenominational sending agency of evangelical tradition engaged in evangelism, church planting, development, leadership development, short-term programs and youth programs.
Purpose: "...engages in authentic partnerships with local churches and other missions to mobilize teams of people around the world to compassionate evangelism and training next generation leaders."

Year Founded in CAN 1966
Income for Overseas Mins $1,328,000
Fully Supported CAN Personnel Overseas:
Expecting to serve more than 4 years 15
Expecting to serve 1 to 4 years 3
Other Personnel:
Short-Term less than 1 year from CAN 501
Home ministry & office staff in CAN 26
Countries: Australia 1, Austria 2, France 2, Germany 5, Italy 2, Poland 4, UK 2

INTERSERVE (Canada)

(416)499-7511 **Fax: (416)499-4472**
E-Mail: iscan@idirect.com
Web: www.interserve.org
10 Huntingdale Blvd., Scarborough, ON M1W 2S5
Mr. Craig Shugart, Exec. Director

An interdenominational sending agency of evangelical tradition engaged in evangelism, development, medical work, support of national churches and technical assistance.
Purpose: "...recruiting, resourcing and deployment of Christian professionals and entrepreneurs for the establishment of the church among the Muslim, Hindu and Buddhist peoples of North Africa, the Middle East, Central and Southwest Asia."
Year Founded in CAN 1908
Income for Overseas Mins $800,000
Fully Supported CAN Personnel Overseas:
Expecting to serve more than 4 years 27
Other Personnel:
Bivocational/Tentmaker from CAN 6
Short-Term less than 1 year from CAN 17
Home ministry & office staff in CAN 10
Countries: Asia 7, Bangladesh 1, Cyprus 4, India 2, Nepal 10, Pakistan 3

Italian Pentecostal Church of Canada, The

(514)279-1100 **Fax: (514)279-1131**
E-Mail: IPCC@novalink.ca
6724 Fabre St., Montreal, PQ H2G 2Z6
Mr. Daniel Ippolito, Gen. Superintendent

A denominational support agency of Pentecostal tradition engaged in evangelism, literature production and youth programs.
Year Founded in CAN 1926
Income for Overseas Mins $67,814
Personnel:
Bivocational/Tentmaker from CAN 1
Short-Term less than 1 year from CAN 1

Janz Team Ministries

(204)334-0055 **Fax: (204)339-3321**
E-Mail: jtmwpg@aol.com
Web: www.janzteam.com
2121 Henderson Hwy., Winnipeg, MB R2G 1R7
Mr. Jack Stenekes, North American Director

An interdenominational sending agency of evangelical tradition engaged in evangelism, audio recording/distribution, camping programs, Christian education, support of national churches and mobilization for mission.
Year Founded in CAN 1954
Income for Overseas Mins $1,154,000
Fully Supported CAN Personnel Overseas:
Expecting to serve more than 4 years 48
Expecting to serve 1 to 4 years 3
Other Personnel:
Non-CAN serving in own/other country 20
Short-Term less than 1 year from CAN 6
Home ministry & office staff in CAN 9
Countries: Austria 2, Brazil 2, Germany 42, Hungary 2, Portugal 1, Russia 2

Language Recordings International

(905)574-8220 **Fax: (905)574-6843**
E-Mail: LRICDN@inforamp.net
Web: www.home.inforamp.net/~lricdn
#210-1059 Upper James Street, Hamilton, ON L9C 3A6
Rev. Roy Grant, Exec. Director

An interdenominational specialized agency of evangelical tradition engaged in audio recording/distribution, evangelism and support of national workers.
Purpose: "...committed to the preparation and distribution of audio-visual materials and related equipment for evangelism and discipleship purposes."
Year Founded in CAN 1967
Income for Overseas Mins $88,470
Fully Supported CAN Personnel Overseas:
Expecting to serve more than 4 years 3

Other Personnel:
Home ministry & office staff in CAN 4
Countries: Kenya 1, UK 2

Latin America Mission (Canada)

(905)569-0001
E-Mail: lam@idirect.com
Web: www.lam.org (for U.S. office)
3075 Ridgeway Dr. Unit #14, Mississauga, ON L5L 5M6
Dr. Garth Wilson, Director

An interdenominational sending agency of evangelical tradition engaged in evangelism, theological education, funds transmission and support of national workers. Personnel and financial totals from 1996 report.

Year Founded in CAN 1961
Income for Overseas Mins $513,142
Fully Supported CAN Personnel Overseas:
Expecting to serve more than 4 years 23
Other Personnel:
Non-CAN serving in own/other country 4
Short-Term less than 1 year from CAN 12
Home ministry & office staff in CAN 3
Countries: Colombia 8, Costa Rica 10, Guatemala 2, Mexico 3

Leprosy Mission Canada, The

(416)441-3618 **Fax: (416)441-0203**
E-Mail: tlm@tlmcanada.org
Web: www.tlmcanada.org
75 The Donway West, Suite 1410, North York, ON M3C 2E9
Rev. Peter Derrick, Exec. Director

An interdenominational service agency of evangelical tradition engaged in medical work, disability assistance programs and specialized missionary training.

Year Founded in CAN 1892
Income for Overseas Mins .... NR
Fully Supported CAN Personnel Overseas:
Nonresidential mission personnel 4
Other Personnel:
Non-CAN serving in own/other country 100
Short-Term less than 1 year from CAN 1
Home ministry & office staff in CAN 11

Liebenzell Mission of Canada

(519)822-9748 **Fax: (519)767-1069**
E-Mail: LMCANADA@sentex.net
Web: www.sentex.net/~lmcanada
R.R. 1, Moffat, ON L0P 1J0
Rev. Jakob Koch, Exec. Director

An interdenominational sending agency of evangelical and Lutheran tradition engaged in evangelism, church planting, TEE, medical work, support of national churches and youth programs.

Year Founded in CAN 1966
Income for Overseas Mins $170,000
Fully Supported CAN Personnel Overseas:
Expecting to serve more than 4 years 2
Other Personnel:
Short-Term less than 1 year from CAN 1
Home ministry & office staff in CAN 2
Countries: Ecuador 2

Lutheran Bible Translators of Canada, Inc.

(519)742-3361 **Fax: (519)742-5989**
E-Mail:
Canada_LBT@lbt.ccmail.compuserve.com
Box 934, Kitchener, ON N2G 4E3
Mr. Robert Schmitt, Exec. Director

A denominational specialized agency of Lutheran tradition engaged in Bible translation, linguistics, literacy work, literature distribution, literature production and training.

Year Founded in CAN 1974
Income for Overseas Mins $225,000
Fully Supported CAN Personnel Overseas:
Expecting to serve more than 4 years 3
Other Personnel:
Non-CAN serving in own/other country 8
Home ministry & office staff in CAN 5
Countries: Cameroon 2, Papua New Guin 1

MBMS International

(204)669-6575 **Fax: (204)654-1865**
E-Mail: mbmsi@mbconf.ca
Web: www.mbmsinternational.org
2 - 169 Riverton Ave., Winnipeg, MB R2L 2E5
Rev. Harold W. Ens, Gen. Director

A denominational sending agency of Mennonite and evangelical tradition engaged in church planting, theological education, furloughed missionary support, leadership

development, support of national churches and support of national workers.
Purpose: "...to participate in making disciples of all people groups, sharing the gospel of Jesus Christ cross-culturally and globally, in Spirit-empowered obedience to Christ's Commission and in partnership with local Mennonite Brethren churches."
Year Founded in CAN 1878
Income for Overseas Mins $4,097,862
Fully Supported CAN Personnel Overseas:
Expecting to serve 1 to 4 years 25
Nonresidential mission personnel 2
Other Personnel:
Non-CAN serving in own/other country 627
Short-Term less than 1 year from CAN 167
Home ministry & office staff in CAN 6
Countries: Austria 2, Botswana 2, Brazil 2, Colombia 2, Germany 6, India, Japan 2, Lithuania 2, Mexico 3, Panama, Paraguay, Peru 2, Russia, Uruguay 2

Mennonite Brethren Missions/ Services
See: MBMS International

Mennonite Central Committee Canada
(204)261-6381 **Fax: (204)269-9875**
E-Mail: canada@mennonitecc.ca
Web: www.mcc.org
134 Plaza Dr., Winnipeg, MB R3T 5K9
Mr. Marvin Frey, Exec. Director
A denominational service agency of Mennonite tradition engaged in development, agricultural programs, relief and/or rehabilitation and technical assistance. Overseas personnel totals are consolidated in the Mennonite Central Committee International (USA) report.
Year Founded in CAN 1963
Income for Overseas Mins $17,645,500
Gifts-in-Kind $340,000

Mennonite Economic Development Associates
(204)956-6430 **Fax: (204)942-4001**
E-Mail: MEDA@meda.org
Web: www.meda.org
#302 - 280 Smith St., Winnipeg, MB R3C 1K2
Dr. Ben Sprunger, President
An interdenominational service agency of Mennonite tradition engaged in development, agricultural programs, microcredit, management consulting/training and technical assistance.
Purpose: "...to address the needs of the disadvantaged through programs of economic development."
Year Founded in CAN 1953
Income for Overseas Mins $300,000
Fully Supported CAN Personnel Overseas:
Expecting to serve more than 4 years 1
Expecting to serve 1 to 4 years 1
Nonresidential mission personnel 2
Other Personnel:
Non-CAN serving in own/other country 8
Short-Term less than 1 year from CAN 4
Home ministry & office staff in CAN 12
Countries: Bolivia, Haiti, Mozambique 1, Nicaragua, Romania, Tanzania 1

Middle East Christian Outreach - Canada
(905)453-5790 **Fax: (905)453-5790**
P.O. Box 23555, Brampton, ON L6V 4J4
Mr. Don Joshua, Canadian Director
An interdenominational service agency of evangelical tradition engaged in evangelism, theological education, literature distribution and support of national churches. Statistical information from 1996.
Year Founded in CAN 1976
Income for Overseas Mins $28,000
Fully Supported CAN Personnel Overseas:
Expecting to serve more than 4 years 1
Other Personnel:
Short-Term less than 1 year from CAN 1
Home ministry & office staff in CAN 1
Countries: Asia 1

Mission Aviation Fellowship of Canada
(519)821-3914 **Fax: (519)823-1650**
E-Mail: mafc@mafc.org
P.O. Box 368, Guelph, ON N1H 6K5
Mr. Ron Epp, President
A nondenominational specialized agency of

evangelical tradition engaged in aviation services, development and technical assistance.

Year Founded in CAN 1972
Income for Overseas Mins $2,500,000
Fully Supported CAN Personnel Overseas:
Expecting to serve more than 4 years 36
Expecting to serve 1 to 4 years 4
Other Personnel:
Home ministry & office staff in CAN 12
Countries: Angola 7, Botswana 2, Brazil 3, Indonesia 8, Kenya 4, Papua New Guin 14, Tanzania 2

Mission Possible Canada

(519)285-2644
E-Mail: MissionPossible@odyssey.on.ca
Web: www.odyssey.on.ca/~missionpossible
P.O. Box 46047, London, ON N5W 3A1
Mr. James McKeegan, Board Vice-Chair

An interdenominational support agency of charismatic and evangelical tradition engaged in childrens programs, Bible distribution, Christian education, extension education and evangelism.

Year Founded in CAN 1994
Income for Overseas Mins $33,619

Missionary Ventures Canada

(519)824-9380 Fax: (519)824-9452
E-Mail: Javco@in.on.ca
Web: www.mvcanada.org
336 Speedvale Ave. W., Guelph, ON N1H 7M7
Mr. John Verdone, President

An interdenominational service agency of evangelical tradition engaged in short-term mission trips for church and school construction, evangelism, and medical teams.
Financial information from 1996.

Purpose: "To encourage and support indigenous missions...through personal involvement, financial sponsorship, and ministry development."

Year Founded in CAN 1991
Income for Overseas Mins $250,000
Personnel:
Non-CAN serving in own/other country 16
Bivocational/Tentmaker from CAN 2
Short-Term less than 1 year from CAN 150
Home ministry & office staff in CAN 1

MSC Canada

(905)947-0468 Fax: (905)947-0352
E-Mail: msc@msc.on.ca
Web: www.msc.on.ca
509-3950 14th Ave., Markham, ON L3R 0A9
Mr. William Yuille, President

A service agency for Brethren assemblies missionaries sent by their local assemblies. Personnel totals are reported under Brethren Assemblies (Canada).

Purpose: "...to encourage and support service for the Lord by assembly-commended workers, in compliance with scriptural guidelines, government legislation and agreements with other organizations with which MSC is associated."

Year Founded in CAN 1940
Income for Overseas Mins $4,573,211

Navigators of Canada, The

(519)666-0301 Fax: (519)666-2004
E-Mail:
navigatorsofcanada@ldn.mediaglobe.net
Web: www.navigators.ca
Box 27070, London, ON N5X 3X5
Mr. Ross Rains, Canadian Director

An interdenominational sending agency of evangelical tradition engaged in literature distribution, evangelism, literature production and youth programs.

Purpose: "...to reach the university campus and the community and to disciple believers intent on reproducing Christian values in following generations."

Year Founded in CAN 1960
Income for Overseas Mins $1,677,730
Fully Supported CAN Personnel Overseas:
Expecting to serve more than 4 years 27
Expecting to serve 1 to 4 years 1
Nonresidential mission personnel 2
Other Personnel:
Bivocational/Tentmaker from CAN 5
Home ministry & office staff in CAN 105
Countries: Bulgaria 1, Chile 4, China (PRC) 2, Hungary 3, Lithuania 2, Mongolia 2, Russia 1, Slovakia 4, St Vincent 2, Thailand 2, Turkey 2, Vietnam 3

New Tribes Mission of Canada

(519)369-2622 Fax: (519)369-5828
E-Mail: ntmc@ntmc.ca

Web: www.ntmc.ca
P.O. Box 707, Durham, ON N0G 1R0
Mr. Raymond Jones, Chairman
A nondenominational sending agency of fundamental and independent tradition engaged in church planting, linguistics, literacy work, missionary training and Bible translation.
Purpose: "...to assist the ministry of the local church through the mobilizing, equipping, and coordinating of missionaries to evangelize unreached people groups, translate the Scriptures and see indigenous New Testament churches established among unreached people groups..."
Year Founded in CAN 1950
Income for Overseas Mins $3,943,909
Fully Supported CAN Personnel Overseas:
Expecting to serve more than 4 years 187
Other Personnel:
Short-Term less than 1 year from CAN 5
Home ministry & office staff in CAN 44
Countries: Bolivia 12, Brazil 9, Colombia 4, Cote d'Ivoire 9, Guinea Bissau 9, Indonesia 9, Mexico 14, Mongolia 2, Panama 1, Papua New Guin 57, Paraguay 7, Philippines 6, Russia 3, Senegal 13, Thailand 4, Venezuela 28

OMF International - Canada

(905)568-9971 **Fax: (905)568-9974**
E-Mail: omfcanada@omf.ca
Web: www.omf.ca
5759 Coopers Ave., Mississauga, ON L4Z 1R9
Rev. William Fietje, National Director
A nondenominational sending agency of evangelical tradition engaged in church planting, development, theological education, evangelism, support of national churches and relief and/or rehabilitation in East Asia.
Purpose: "...to see an indigenous biblical church movement in each people group of East Asia, evangelizing their own people and reaching out in mission to other peoples."
Year Founded in CAN 1888
Income for Overseas Mins $1,426,495
Fully Supported CAN Personnel Overseas:
Expecting to serve more than 4 years 70
Expecting to serve 1 to 4 years 6
Other Personnel:
Bivocational/Tentmaker from CAN 9
Short-Term less than 1 year from CAN 41
Home ministry & office staff in CAN 29
Countries: Asia 9, Indonesia 1, Japan 9, Korea-S 1, Malaysia 4, Philippines 20, Singapore 2, Taiwan (ROC) 5, Thailand 25

OMS International - Canada

(905)639-3000 **Fax: (905)639-3433**
E-Mail: inform@omscanada.org
P.O. Box 10, Burlington, ON L7R 3Y3
Mr. Gordon Morley, Exec. Director
A nondenominational sending agency of Wesleyan and evangelical tradition engaged in theological education, church planting, evangelism, and support of national churches. Statistical information from 1996.
Year Founded in CAN 1944
Income for Overseas Mins .... NR
Fully Supported CAN Personnel Overseas:
Expecting to serve more than 4 years 3
Expecting to serve 1 to 4 years 14
Other Personnel:
Short-Term less than 1 year from CAN 70
Home ministry & office staff in CAN 6
Countries: Ecuador 2, Estonia 3, Haiti 3, Hong Kong 1, Indonesia 2, Japan 2, Korea-S 1, Mexico 1, Russia 2

Open Doors With Brother Andrew Canada

(905)567-1303 **Fax: (905)567-9398**
E-Mail: opendoorsca@compuserve.com
Web: www.opendoorsca.org
P.O. Box 597, Streetsville, ON L5M 2C1
Rev. Paul W. Johnson, Director for Canada
A nondenominational support agency of evangelical tradition engaged in Bible distribution, correspondence courses, missions information service, leadership development, literature distribution and support of national workers.
Year Founded in CAN 1977
Income for Overseas Mins $450,000
Personnel:
Short-Term less than 1 year from CAN 68
Home ministry & office staff in CAN 4

Operation Mobilization Canada

(905)835-2546 **Fax: (905)835-2533**

E-Mail: info@cdn.om.org
Web: www.omcanada.org
212 West St., Port Colborne, ON L3K 4E3
Mr. Gordon Abraham, Exec. Director
An interdenominational sending agency of evangelical tradition engaged in evangelism, church planting, literature distribution, literature production and support of national workers.
Purpose: "...to motivate, develop and equip people for world evangelization, and to strengthen and help plant churches, especially among the unreached in the Middle East, South and Central Asia and Europe."
Year Founded in CAN 1966
Income for Overseas Mins $2,365,036
Fully Supported CAN Personnel Overseas:
Expecting to serve more than 4 years 51
Expecting to serve 1 to 4 years 25
Other Personnel:
Non-CAN serving in own/other country 241
Short-Term less than 1 year from CAN 75
Home ministry & office staff in CAN 28
Countries: Africa 4, Asia 7, Austria 2, Belgium 1, Central Asia 6, Czech Rep 2, Germany 2, India 4, Mexico 1, Pakistan 3, Philippines 2, Russia 5, S Africa 6, Spain 2, Sudan 2, Turkey 7, UK 6, Unspecified 12, Uruguay 2

Outreach Canada

(604)952-0050 **Fax: (604)502-1667**
E-Mail: gkraft@outreach.ca
Web: www.outreach.ca
2 - 7201 72nd Street, Delta, BC V4G 1M5
Dr. Gerald Kraft, Exec. Director
An interdenominational support agency of evangelical tradition engaged in missions information service, leadership development, support of national churches and mission-related research. A sister agency of OCInternational.
Purpose: "...to assist the Body of Christ to make disciples of all peoples."
Year Founded in CAN 1977
Income for Overseas Mins $70,000
Personnel:
Bivocational/Tentmaker from CAN 4
Short-Term less than 1 year from CAN 21
Home ministry & office staff in CAN 16

Overseas Council for Theological Education and Missions

(604)241-0487 **Fax: (604)241-0491**
E-Mail: 74563.1113@compuserve.com
Web: www.overseascouncil.org
12071 Hayashi Court, Richmond, BC V7E 5W2
Mr. William H. Amerding, Chairman
An interdenominational support agency of evangelical tradition engaged in theological education, leadership development, management consulting/training, support of national churches and technical assistance.
Year Founded in CAN 1979
Income for Overseas Mins $89,250
Gifts-in-Kind $60,000
Personnel:
Non-CAN serving in own/other country 16
Short-Term less than 1 year from CAN 6

Partners International Canada

(905)458-1202 **Fax: (905)458-4339**
8500 Torbram Rd. #48, Brampton, ON L6T 5C6
Rev. Grover Crosby, President
A nondenominational support agency of evangelical tradition engaged in support of national workers and churches, and funds transmission. Statistical information from 1996.
Year Founded in CAN 1959
Income for Overseas Mins $830,000
Personnel:
Home ministry & office staff in CAN 6

Pentecostal Assemblies of Canada/Les Assemblees de la Pentecote du Canada, Intl. Office/ Bureau Intl.

(905)542-7400 **Fax: (905)542-0377**
E-Mail: wmd@paoc.org
Web: www.paoc.org
6745 Century Ave., Mississauga, ON L5N 6P7
Mr. Randy Sohnchen, Director World Missions
A denominational sending agency of Pentecostal tradition engaged in church planting, childcare/orphanage programs, theological education, TEE, leadership development and relief and/or rehabilitation.

Purpose: "To make disciples everywhere by the proclamation and practice of the gospel of Jesus Christ in the power of the Holy Spirit; to establish local congregations and train spiritual leaders."
Year Founded in CAN 1919
Income for Overseas Mins $12,057,000
Fully Supported CAN Personnel Overseas:
Expecting to serve more than 4 years 140
Expecting to serve 1 to 4 years 25
Nonresidential mission personnel 59
Other Personnel:
Non-CAN serving in own/other country 2
Home ministry & office staff in CAN 13
Countries: Brazil 6, Bulgaria 1, Colombia 1, Estonia 2, Ethiopia 7, Greece 2, Guatemala 6, Guinea Bissau 4, Haiti 2, Hong Kong 18, India 5, Indonesia 7, Israel 4, Kenya 17, Latin America 2, Liberia 4, Macao 3, Malawi 11, Mozambique 4, Philippines 1, Poland 2, Russia 2, Rwanda 4, Senegal 4, S Africa 4, Sri Lanka 2, Tanzania 6, Thailand 7, Uganda 6, Ukraine 4, Yugoslavia 3, Zambia 8, Zimbabwe 6

Persecuted Church Fellowship

(604)278-0692 **Fax: (604)279-9080**
15620 Westminster Hwy, Richmond, BC V6V 1A6
Mr. Michael S. Lapka, President
An interdenominational service agency of evangelical tradition engaged in support of national workers, Bible distribution, evangelism and literature distribution.
Year Founded in CAN 1976
Income for Overseas Mins $150,000
Personnel:
Non-CAN serving in own/other country 28
Short-Term less than 1 year from CAN 2
Countries: Ukraine

Pioneers

(519)268-8778 **Fax: (519)268-2787**
E-Mail: picanada@wwdc.com
Web: www.pioneers.org
P.O. Box 220, Dorchester, ON N0L 1G0
Mr. Ted Esler, Canadian Director
A nondenominational sending agency of evangelical tradition engaged in church planting, evangelism and mobilization for mission.
Purpose: "...mobilizes teams to glorify God among unreached peoples by initiating church planting movements in partnership with local churches."
Year Founded in CAN 1981
Income for Overseas Mins $686,589
Fully Supported CAN Personnel Overseas:
Expecting to serve more than 4 years 13
Other Personnel:
Short-Term less than 1 year from CAN 30
Home ministry & office staff in CAN 3
Countries: Asia 5, Belize 2, Bolivia 3, Bosnia 1, Brazil 2

Presbyterian Church in Canada, Life and Mission Agency

(416)441-1111 **Fax: (416)441-2825**
E-Mail: intmin@presbyterian.ca
Web: www.presbyterian.ca/international
50 Wynford Dr., North York, ON M3C 1J7
Rev. Ian Morrison, Gen. Secretary
A denominational sending agency of Presbyterian and Reformed tradition engaged in support of national churches, development, theological education, leadership development and medical work.
Year Founded in CAN 1875
Income for Overseas Mins $1,400,000
Fully Supported CAN Personnel Overseas:
Expecting to serve more than 4 years 23
Expecting to serve 1 to 4 years 8
Other Personnel:
Non-CAN serving in own/other country 3
Bivocational/Tentmaker from CAN 1
Short-Term less than 1 year from CAN 20
Home ministry & office staff in CAN 4
Countries: Cyprus 4, El Salvador 2, Guatemala 4, Guyana 1, India 1, Japan 4, Kenya 1, Malawi 3, Mozambique 1, Nicaragua 2, Nigeria 3, Romania 1, Taiwan (ROC) 4

Salvation Army, The

(416)425-2111 **Fax: (416)422-6102**
E-Mail: communications@sallynet.org
Web: www.salvationarmy.ca
2 Overlea Blvd., Toronto, ON M4H 1P4
Norman Howe, Commissioner
A denominational sending agency of Methodist and Wesleyan tradition engaged in evangelism, development, Christian education, social services and relief and/or rehabilitation.

Year Founded in CAN 1882
Income for Overseas Mins $4,000,000
Fully Supported CAN Personnel Overseas:
Expecting to serve more than 4 years 35
Expecting to serve 1 to 4 years 57
Nonresidential mission personnel 2
Other Personnel:
Short-Term less than 1 year from CAN 6
Home ministry & office staff in CAN 3
Countries: Australia 4, Bahamas 4, Bangladesh 2, Belgium 2, Brazil 5, Czech Rep 2, Finland 1, France 2, Germany 8, Ghana 2, Hong Kong 2, Hungary 2, Jamaica 5, Mexico 1, Mozambique 1, New Zealand 2, Pakistan 1, Papua New Guin 2, Russia 6, Singapore 4, S Africa 10, Spain 2, Sri Lanka 3, Suriname 2, Tanzania 2, UK 8, Zambia 2, Zimbabwe 5

Samaritan's Purse - Canada

(403)250-6565 Fax: (403)250-6567
E-Mail: canada@samaritan.org
Web: www.samaritan.org
Box 20100, Calgary Pl., Calgary, AB T2P 4J2
Rev. Sean P. Campbell, Exec. Director
Mr. Franklin Graham, Chairman & President

A nondenominational service agency of evangelical tradition engaged in relief and/or rehabilitation, childrens programs, evangelism, and medical work.

Purpose: "...providing spiritual and physical aid to hurting people around the world...meeting the needs of people who are victims of war, poverty, natural disasters, disease and famine...serving the church worldwide to promote the Gospel..."

Year Founded in CAN 1973
Income for Overseas Mins $18,721,623
Gifts-in-Kind $13,657,696
Fully Supported CAN Personnel Overseas:
Expecting to serve more than 4 years 6
Other Personnel:
Bivocational/Tentmaker from CAN 6
Short-Term less than 1 year from CAN 8
Home ministry & office staff in CAN 26
Countries: China (PRC) 2, Laos 2, Pakistan 1, Vietnam 1

Scripture Gift Mission (Canada)

(905)475-0521 Fax: (905)475-8643
E-Mail: Can@sgm.org
300 Steelcase Rd. W. #32, Markham, ON L3R 2W2
Mr. Ted Bartlett, Exec. Director

A nondenominational support agency of evangelical tradition engaged in literature distribution and literature production.

Year Founded in CAN 1973
Income for Overseas Mins .... NA
Personnel:
Home ministry & office staff in CAN 2

SEND International of Canada

(519)657-6775 Fax: (519)657-7027
E-Mail: SENDCanada@compuserve.com
Web: www.send.org
22423 Jefferies Rd., Unit 1, R.R.#3, Komoka, ON N0L 1R0
Rev. Leander Rempel, Director

An interdenominational sending agency of evangelical and Baptist tradition engaged in church planting, theological education, evangelism, leadership development and support of national churches.

Purpose: "...to start churches...evangelize the unreached...nurture disciples...develop leaders..."

Year Founded in CAN 1963
Income for Overseas Mins $1,591,000
Fully Supported CAN Personnel Overseas:
Expecting to serve more than 4 years 35
Nonresidential mission personnel 2
Other Personnel:
Bivocational/Tentmaker from CAN 2
Short-Term less than 1 year from CAN 28
Home ministry & office staff in CAN 12
Countries: Asia 4, Czech Rep 2, Hong Kong 1, Japan 3, Philippines 10, Russia 8, Spain 2, Ukraine 5

SIM Canada

(416)497-2424 Fax: (416)497-2444
E-Mail: postmast@sim.ca
Web: www.sim.org/canada
10 Huntingdale Blvd., Scarborough, ON M1W 2S5
Mr. Pep Philpott, Director

An interdenominational sending agency of evangelical and Baptist tradition engaged in church planting, broadcasting, theological education, medical work, relief and/or rehabilitation and Bible translation. Financial and personnel information from 1996.

Includes merger of Africa Evangelical Fellowship in 1999.

Purpose: "...evangelizing the unreached and ministering to human need, discipling believers into churches equipped to fulfill Christ's Commission."

Year Founded in CAN 1893

Income for Overseas Mins $8,257,568

Fully Supported CAN Personnel Overseas:

Expecting to serve more than 4 years 110

Expecting to serve 1 to 4 years 20

Nonresidential mission personnel 2

Other Personnel:

Non-CAN serving in own/other country 17

Short-Term less than 1 year from CAN 70

Home ministry & office staff in CAN 62

Countries: Angola 5, Benin 15, Bolivia 4, Botswana 3, Burkina Faso 10, Chile 1, Cote d'Ivoire 3, Ecuador 1, Ethiopia 13, Ghana 6, India 3, Kenya 1, Malawi 1, Mozambique 2, Niger 12, Nigeria 6, Pakistan 3, Paraguay 1, Peru 3, S Africa 13, Zambia 18, Zimbabwe 6

Slavic Gospel Assoc. of Canada

(905)821-6321 **Fax: (905)821-6322**

E-Mail: canada@sga.org

Web: www.sga.org

205-2476 Argentia Rd., Mississauga, ON L5N 6M1

Mr. Allan W. Vincent, Canadian Director

An interdenominational support agency of evangelical tradition engaged in church planting, Bible distribution, theological education, literature distribution, literature production and support of national workers.

Year Founded in CAN 1947

Income for Overseas Mins $313,715

Personnel:

Home ministry & office staff in CAN 2

South American Missionary Society in Canada

(705)728-7151 **Fax: (705)728-6703**

E-Mail: dstock@barint.on.ca

Web: www.episcopalian.org/SAMS-canada

Box 21082, Barrie, ON L4M 6JI

A denominational sending agency of Anglican and evangelical tradition engaged in mobilization for mission, evangelism, leadership development and support of national workers.

Purpose: "...to find and send those whom God is calling to the mission field, and to widen and deepen the missionary vision of Canadian Anglicans."

Year Founded in CAN 1979

Income for Overseas Mins $293,925

Fully Supported CAN Personnel Overseas:

Expecting to serve more than 4 years 2

Expecting to serve 1 to 4 years 6

Other Personnel:

Non-CAN serving in own/other country 2

Short-Term less than 1 year from CAN 22

Home ministry & office staff in CAN 3

Countries: Chile 2, Honduras 4, Peru 2

TEAM - The Evangelical Alliance Mission of Canada

(403)248-2344 **Fax: (403)207-6025**

E-Mail: TEAM@teamcanada.org

Web: www.teamcanada.org

Airways P.O. Box 56030, Calgary, AB T2E 8K5

Mr. Lorne Strom, Director

An interdenominational sending agency of evangelical tradition engaged in church planting, theological education, TEE, leadership development, medical work and support of national churches.

Purpose: "...to help [local] churches send missionaries to establish reproducing churches among the nations."

Year Founded in CAN 1890

Income for Overseas Mins $2,516,033

Fully Supported CAN Personnel Overseas:

Expecting to serve more than 4 years 61

Expecting to serve 1 to 4 years 5

Other Personnel:

Non-CAN serving in own/other country 15

Bivocational/Tentmaker from CAN 10

Short-Term less than 1 year from CAN 16

Home ministry & office staff in CAN 10

Countries: Chad 9, China (PRC) 1, Czech Rep 2, France 3, Germany 2, India 2, Indonesia 2, Italy 5, Japan 12, Mexico 2, Nepal 4, Pakistan 5, Peru 2, S Africa 2, Spain 2, Taiwan (ROC) 2, United Arab Emr 3, Venezuela 3, Zimbabwe 3

Trinitarian Bible Society (Canada)

(905)454-4688 **Fax: (905)454-1788**
E-Mail: tbsc@ica.net
Web: www.trinitarian.com
39 Caldwell Crescent, Brampton, ON L6W 1A2
Dr. Robert A. Baker, Gen. Director

A nondenominational service agency of fundamental and independent tradition engaged in Bible distribution and translation. Financial information from 1992.

Year Founded in CAN 1968
Income for Overseas Mins $169,969
Personnel:
Home ministry & office staff in CAN 2

UFM International in Canada

(905)238-0904 **Fax: (905)629-8439**
E-Mail: ufmcan@ican.net
Web: www.ufm.org
1020 Matheson Blvd. E. #11, Mississauga, ON L4W 4J9
Mr. Dale Losch, Managing Director

An interdenominational sending agency of evangelical and Baptist tradition engaged in church planting, missionary education, TEE, evangelism and medical work.

Year Founded in CAN 1931
Income for Overseas Mins $708,262
Fully Supported CAN Personnel Overseas:
Expecting to serve more than 4 years 11
Expecting to serve 1 to 4 years 5
Other Personnel:
Non-CAN serving in own/other country 1
Short-Term less than 1 year from CAN 5
Home ministry & office staff in CAN 5
Countries: Brazil 8, Germany 2, Haiti 2, Ireland 1, Italy 1, Spain 2

United Church of Canada, Division of World Outreach

(416)231-5931 **Fax: (416)231-3103**
E-Mail: UCCDWO@uccan.org
Web: www.uccan.org
3250 Bloor St. West, Etobicoke, ON M8X 2Y4
Mr. Chris Ferguson, Gen. Secretary

A denominational sending agency of ecumenical tradition engaged in development, agricultural programs, extension education, funds transmission, and missionary training. Financial and personnel information from 1992.

Year Founded in CAN 1925
Income for Overseas Mins $9,000,000
Fully Supported CAN Personnel Overseas:
Expecting to serve more than 4 years 96
Countries: Unspecified 96

Venture Teams International

(403)777-2970 **Fax: (403)777-2973**
E-Mail: vti@spots.ab.ca
Web: www.spots.ab.ca/~vti
#3A, 3023 - 21st St. NE, Calgary, AB T2E 7T1
Mr. Len Lane, Exec. Director

An interdenominational service agency of evangelical tradition engaged in missionary training, childrens programs, evangelism, leadership development, mobilization for mission and short-term programs.

Purpose: "Training young adults for ministry in order to bridge the gap between classroom learning and life experience."

Year Founded in CAN 1978
Income for Overseas Mins $400,000
Personnel:
Short-Term less than 1 year from CAN 78
Home ministry & office staff in CAN 4

Voice of the Martyrs, The

(905)602-4832 **Fax: (905)602-4833**
E-Mail: vom@planeteer.com
Web: www.persecution.net
Box 117, Port Credit, Mississauga, ON L5G 4L5
Mr. Klaas Brobbel, Exec. Director

A nondenominational support agency of evangelical tradition engaged in literature distribution, Bible distribution, missions information service, literature production, medical work and relief and/or rehabilitation.

Purpose: "...to be an effective source of information and support of persecuted Christians around the world."

Year Founded in CAN 1971
Income for Overseas Mins $200,344
Personnel:
Non-CAN serving in own/other country 2
Short-Term less than 1 year from CAN 4
Home ministry & office staff in CAN 4

WEC International (Canada)

(905)529-0166 Fax: (905)529-0630
E-Mail: 76604.1246@compuserve.com
Web: www.hwcn.org/link/wec
37 Aberdeen Ave., Hamilton, ON L8P 2N6
Drs. Philip & Nancy Wood, Canadian Directors

An interdenominational sending agency of evangelical tradition engaged in church planting, childrens programs, evangelism, support of national churches, mobilization for mission and missionary training.

Purpose: "...to evangelize the unreached peoples...to establish fully discipled, self-governing, self-supporting and reproducing churches able to fulfill their part in the Great Commission."

Year Founded in CAN 1936
Income for Overseas Mins $1,327,740
Fully Supported CAN Personnel Overseas:
Expecting to serve more than 4 years 83
Expecting to serve 1 to 4 years 6
Nonresidential mission personnel 2
Other Personnel:
Bivocational/Tentmaker from CAN 51
Short-Term less than 1 year from CAN 14
Home ministry & office staff in CAN 27
Countries: Brazil 4, Cambodia 1, Chad 1, Congo 1, Cote d'Ivoire 5, Gambia 3, Germany 1, Ghana 2, Guinea Bissau 4, India 1, Indonesia 2, Mexico 2, New Zealand 2, Senegal 2, S Africa 1, Thailand 2, UK 3, Unspecified 51, Zambia 1

Western Tract Mission, Inc.

(306)244-0446 Fax: (306)242-6115
401 - 33rd St., West, Saskatoon, SK S7L 0V5
Mr. David Wolfrom, Chairman of the Board

An interdenominational service agency of evangelical tradition engaged in literature distribution, correspondence courses, evangelism and literature production.

Year Founded in CAN 1941
Income for Overseas Mins .... NA
Personnel:
Home ministry & office staff in CAN 10

World Gospel Mission (Canada)

(506)375-8262 Fax: (506)375-8220
26 Clark Street, Hartland, NB E7P 1L1
Rev. Brian Murray, Director Canada

An interdenominational support agency of Wesleyan tradition engaged in evangelism, church planting and theological education. Statistical data consolidated in U. S. report.

Year Founded in CAN 1982
Income for Overseas Mins .... NR

World Mission Prayer League

(403)672-0464 Fax: (403)672-0464
E-Mail: wmplcdn@cable-lynx.net
Web: www.wmpl.org
5408 49th Ave., Camrose, AB T4V 0N7
Rev. Rob Lewis, Exec. Director

A denominational sending agency of Lutheran tradition engaged in church planting, development, TEE, evangelism, medical work and Bible translation.

Year Founded in CAN 1969
Income for Overseas Mins $83,433
Fully Supported CAN Personnel Overseas:
Expecting to serve more than 4 years 4
Expecting to serve 1 to 4 years 2
Other Personnel:
Short-Term less than 1 year from CAN 3
Home ministry & office staff in CAN 3
Countries: Central Asia 4, Mexico 2

World Relief Canada

(905)415-8181 Fax: (905)415-0287
E-Mail: wrcanada@compuserve.com
600 Alden Rd., Suite 310, Markham, ON L3R 0E7
Rev. Doug Stiller, President

A nondenominational specialized agency of evangelical tradition engaged in relief and/or rehabilitation, agricultural programs and development in 17 countries in 1998.

Purpose: "...partners with the evangelical church in Canada and overseas to respond to the basic needs of the world's most oppressed, poor and suffering people, empowering them to meet their own needs in the name of Jesus Christ."

Year Founded in CAN 1970
Income for Overseas Mins $3,689,000
Personnel:
Home ministry & office staff in CAN 11

World Team

(905)821-6300 **Fax: (905)821-6325**
E-Mail: infocanada@worldteam.org
Web: www.worldteam.org
2476 Argentia Road, Suite 203, Mississauga, ON
L5N 6M1
Rev. Kenneth Bennett, Canadian Director

A nondenominational sending agency of evangelical tradition engaged in church planting, theological education and Bible translation.

Purpose: "...to establish reproducing churches among the least-evangelized peoples of the world."

Year Founded in CAN 1948
Income for Overseas Mins $2,217,265
Fully Supported CAN Personnel Overseas:
Expecting to serve more than 4 years 38
Expecting to serve 1 to 4 years 6
Nonresidential mission personnel 4
Other Personnel:
Bivocational/Tentmaker from CAN 2
Short-Term less than 1 year from CAN 20
Home ministry & office staff in CAN 24
Countries: Cameroon 8, Haiti 4, Indonesia 7, Italy 1, Mexico 2, Peru 8, Philippines 10, Singapore 2, Spain 2

World Vision Canada

(905)821-3030 **Fax: (905)821-1825**
E-Mail: Info@worldvision.ca
Web: www.worldvision.ca
6630 Turner Valley Road, Mississauga, ON
L5N 2S4
Mr. Dave Toycen, President

A transdenominational service agency of evangelical tradition engaged in relief and/or rehabilitation, childcare/orphanage programs, development, evangelism, leadership development and training.

Purpose: "...a Christian humanitarian relief and development organization inviting Canadians to share their resources to empower people living in poverty."

Year Founded in CAN 1954
Income for Overseas Mins $94,167,000
Gifts-in-Kind $7,695,000
Fully Supported CAN Personnel Overseas:
Expecting to serve more than 4 years 14
Expecting to serve 1 to 4 years 2
Nonresidential mission personnel 5
Other Personnel:
Non-CAN serving in own/other country 5
Short-Term less than 1 year from CAN 42
Home ministry & office staff in CAN 318
Countries: Angola 1, Burundi 1, Chad 2, India 1, Indonesia 1, Malawi 2, Palestine 1, Romania 2, Rwanda 1, Sudan 2, Tanzania 2

Wycliffe Bible Translators of Canada

(403)250-5411 **Fax: (403)250-2623**
E-Mail: info@wycliffe.ca
Web: www.wycliffe.ca
4316 - 10 St. NE, Calgary, AB T2E 6K3
Mr. Jack Popjes, Exec. Director

A nondenominational sending agency of evangelical tradition engaged in Bible translation, agricultural programs, linguistics, literacy work, support of national workers and training. Overseas personnel totals from 1996 report.

Purpose: "[To] challenge, train and assist Canadians to serve indigenous peoples through Bible translation and literacy-based development."

Year Founded in CAN 1968
Income for Overseas Mins $11,000,000
Fully Supported CAN Personnel Overseas:
Expecting to serve more than 4 years 395
Expecting to serve 1 to 4 years 20
Nonresidential mission personnel 6
Other Personnel:
Home ministry & office staff in CAN 2
Countries: Africa 7, Asia 16, Australia 4, Benin 2, Bolivia 1, Brazil 13, Burkina Faso 7, Cameroon 24, Cen Africa Rep 2, Colombia 15, Congo 4, Congo/Zaire 5, Cote d'Ivoire 3, Ecuador 2, Europe-W 10, Ghana 6, Guatemala 10, Guyana 2, India 3, Indonesia 9, Kenya 6, Malaysia 3, Mexico 14, Mozambique 5, New Zealand 4, Panama 2, Papua New Guin 40, Peru 11, Philippines 29, Suriname 5, Thailand 6, Togo 1, Unspecified 144

Young Life of Canada

(604)688-7622 **Fax: (604)688-3125**
E-Mail: YLife@younglife.ca
Web: www.younglife.ca
1155 W. Pender, #610, Vancouver, BC V6E 2P4

Mr. Harold J. Merwald, Natl. Director
A transdenominational support agency of evangelical tradition engaged in evangelism, camping programs, leadership development and youth programs.
Purpose: "...loving teenagers in their world encouraging them to know Jesus Christ."
Year Founded in CAN 1954
Income for Overseas Mins $50,000
Personnel:
Home ministry & office staff in CAN 65

Youth for Christ - Canada

(403)291-1195 **Fax: (403)291-1197**
E-Mail: yfccan@cadvision.com
Web: www.yfccanada.com
1212 - 31 Ave. N.E., #540, Calgary, AB T2E 7S8
Mr. Randy Steinwand, National Director
A transdenominational support agency of evangelical tradition engaged in youth programs, camping programs, evangelism and mobilization for mission.
Purpose: "To participate in the body of Christ in responsible evangelism of youth, presenting them with the person, work and teachings of Christ and discipling them into the Church."
Year Founded in CAN 1944
Income for Overseas Mins $500,000
Personnel:
Bivocational/Tentmaker from CAN 5
Short-Term less than 1 year from CAN 7
Home ministry & office staff in CAN 251

Youth With A Mission (Canada)

(250)766-3838 **Fax: (250)766-2387**
E-Mail: ywam@disciples.com
Web: www.ywam.ca
2718 Robinson Rd., Winfield, BC V4V 1G6
Mr. Paul Martinson, Canada Representative
Mr. Peter Iliyn, N. American Regional Director
A sending agency of evangelical tradition engaged in evangelism, missionary education, mobilization for mission, short-term programs and youth programs.
Purpose: "...presenting Jesus Christ personally to this generation, to mobilize as many as possible to help in this task and to the training and equipping of believers for their part in fulfilling the Great Commission."
Year Founded in CAN 1966
Income for Overseas Mins $1,400,000
Fully Supported CAN Personnel Overseas:
Expecting to serve more than 4 years 134
Nonresidential mission personnel 146
Other Personnel:
Short-Term less than 1 year from CAN 200
Home ministry & office staff in CAN 104
Countries: Argentina 1, Australia 16, Barbados 4, Belize 4, Chile 1, Denmark 1, Dominican Rep 2, Fiji 2, Greenland 2, Guyana 2, India 8, Indonesia 1, Jamaica 2, Japan 2, Jordan 2, Kenya 1, Lithuania 3, Mexico 4, Mozambique 2, Netherlands 8, New Zealand 2, N Mariana Isls 1, Norway 2, Oceania 1, Philippines 8, Russia 10, Switzerland 1, Taiwan (ROC) 2, Thailand 2, Ukraine 7, UK 24, Unspecified 4, Venezuela 1, Zimbabwe 1

Chapter 9

Indices to Canadian Protestant Agencies

Many *Handbook* users find it valuable to locate agencies by particular categories of church tradition or ministry activity. This chapter provides the user with those indices. Agency responses on the *Mission Handbook* survey questionnaire helped define the listed categories. The organizations in each category appear in alphabetical order by organization name.

Index by Church Tradition

If an agency needed more than one generic or denominational category to describe its traditional doctrinal and/or ecclesiastical stance, the agency may appear under as many as two of the given categories. We have arranged the list alphabetically by category and within each category by agency name. See question #7 of the survey questionnaire reproduced in the Appendix for the actual wording of the question and the check-off list of choices.

Index by Ministry Activity

Almost all agencies are involved in several types of ministry activities. Each agency may be listed under as many as six primary categories of activity. We asked those with more than six primary activities to indicate the six activities toward which they had committed the largest amount of resources.

We have divided the broad activities of education and evangelism into subcategories. For example, the evangelism category appears as "evangelism, mass" and "evangelism, student," and so on. See question #8 of the survey questionnaire in the appendix for the actual wording of the question and the check-off list of activities.

Agencies sometimes have written in new categories under the "other" choice in previous surveys. Some of these may be included in the check-off list of the next survey questionnaire. Sometimes categories are dropped because of lack of use. The most used categories, however, have remained the same over the years. Three new categories added during this edition (which will appear as options on the next survey) are Association of Missions, Member Care, and Partnership Development.

Anglican

Anglican Church of Canada
South American Missionary Soc.

Baptist

ABWE - Canada
Associated Gospel Churches
BGCC Global Ministries
Canadian Baptist Ministries
Canadian Conv. of So. Baptists
Czechoslovak Evangelical Msn.
FAIR
FEBInternational
Fundamental Baptist Mission
HOPE Intl. Development Agency
SEND Intl. of Canada
SIM Canada
UFM Intl. in Canada

Charismatic

Apostolic Church of Pentecost
Mission Possible Canada
Youth With A Mission (Canada)

Christian/Plymouth

Brethren Assemblies (Canada)

Ecumenical

Canadian Churches' Forum
United Church of Canada

Evangelical

Action International Mins.
Africa Community Technical Svc
Africa Inland Mission (Canada)
African Enterprise Association
Apostolic Church In Canada
Arab World Ministries (Canada)
Associated Gospel Churches
Barry Moore Ministries
BCM International (Canada)
Bible League of Canada, The
Campus Crusade for Christ
Canadian Food for the Hungry
Canadian S. American Mission
Centre for World Mission B.C.
Child Evangelism Fellowship
Christian Aid Mission
Christian and Msny. Alliance
Christian Blind Mission Intl.
Christian Indigenous Dev.
Christian Studies Int. Canada
Compassion Canada
Croisade du Livre Chretien
Door of Hope Intl. (Canada)
Emmanuel International
Equip, Canada
European Christian Mission
Eurovangelism
Evangelical Covenant Ch Canada
Evangelical Mennonite Conf.
Evangelical Mennonite Msn Conf
Evangelical Missionary Church
Evangelical Tract Distributors
Far East Broadcasting Assocs.
FEBInternational
Frontiers Canada
Galcom International
Global Outreach Mission
Gospel for Asia
Gospel Missionary Union Canada
Greater Europe Mission
HCJB World Radio Msnry. Flwshp
High Adventure Ministries
Inter-Varsity Christian Flwshp
International Child Care
International Children's Haven
International Christian Aid
International Missions Ontario
International Needs - Canada
International Teams of Canada
INTERSERVE (Canada)
Janz Team Ministries
Language Recordings Intl.
Latin America Mission (Canada)
Leprosy Mission Canada
Liebenzell Mission of Canada
MBMS International
Middle East Christian Outreach
Mission Aviation Flwshp Canada
Mission Possible Canada
Missionary Ventures of Canada
Navigators of Canada, The
OMF International
OMS International - Canada
Open Doors W. Brother Andrew
Operation Mobilization Canada
Outreach Canada
Overseas Council Theol.Ed.
Partners International Canada

Fundamental

Holiness

Independent

Lutheran

Mennonite

Methodist

Pentecostal

Presbyterian

Reformed

Wesleyan

Agricultural Programs

Canadian Conv. of So. Baptists
Canadian Food for the Hungry
Christian Reformed Wld. Relief
Equip, Canada
HOPE Intl. Development Agency
Mennonite Central Committee
Mennonite Economic Development
United Church of Canada
World Relief Canada
Wycliffe Bible Translators

Audio Recording/Distribution

Far East Broadcasting Assocs.
Janz Team Ministries
Language Recordings Intl.

Aviation Services

Mission Aviation Flwshp Canada

Bible Distribution

Apostolic Church In Canada
Bible Holiness Movement
Bible League of Canada, The
Canadian Bible Society
Croisade du Livre Chretien
Door of Hope Intl. (Canada)
Gospel for Asia
Mission Possible Canada
Open Doors W. Brother Andrew
Persecuted Church Fellowship
Slavic Gospel Assoc.
Trinitarian Bible Society
Voice of the Martyrs, The

Broadcasting, Radio and/or TV

Arab World Ministries (Canada)
European Christian Mission
Evangelical Mennonite Conf.
Evangelical Mennonite Msn Conf
Far East Broadcasting Assocs.
Global Outreach Mission
Gospel Missionary Union Canada
HCJB World Radio Msnry. Flwshp
High Adventure Ministries
SIM Canada

Camping Programs

Action International Mins.
Associated Gospel Churches
Greater Europe Mission
Janz Team Ministries
Young Life of Canada
Youth for Christ - Canada

Childcare/Orphanage

Calcutta Mission of Mercy
Compassion Canada
International Child Care
International Children's Haven
International Christian Aid
Pentecostal Assemblies Canada
World Vision Canada

Children's Programs

Action International Mins.
BCM International (Canada)
Child Evangelism Fellowship
Compassion Canada
Galcom International
International Children's Haven
Mission Possible Canada
Samaritan's Purse - Canada
Venture Teams International
WEC Intl. (Canada)

Church Construction

Church of God (Anderson, IN)
Evangelical Missionary Church
Missionary Ventures of Canada

Church Establishing/Planting

ABWE - Canada
Africa Inland Mission (Canada)
Apostolic Church in Canada
Apostolic Church of Pentecost
Arab World Ministries (Canada)
Associated Gospel Churches
BGCC Global Ministries
Bible Holiness Movement
Brethren Assemblies (Canada)
Canadian Baptist Ministries
Canadian Conv. of So. Baptists
Canadian S. American Mission
Christian and Msny. Alliance
Evangelical Covenant Ch Canada
Evangelical Mennonite Conf.
Evangelical Mennonite Msn Conf
Evangelical Missionary Church
FEBInternational
Frontiers Canada

Correspondence Courses

Development, Community/Other

Disability Assistance Programs

Education, Church/School General Christian

Education, Extension (other)

Education, Missionary (Certificate/ Degree)

Education, Theological

Overseas Council Theol.Ed.
Pentecostal Assemblies Canada
Presbyterian Church in Canada
SEND Intl. of Canada
SIM Canada
Slavic Gospel Assoc.
TEAM of Canada
World Gospel Mission (Canada)
World Team
Youth With A Mission (Canada)

Education, Theological by Extension (TEE)

ABWE - Canada
Christian and Msny. Alliance
Emmanuel International
Eurovangelism
Evangelical Mennonite Conf.
Evangelical Missionary Church
FEBInternational
Gospel Missionary Union Canada
Liebenzell Mission of Canada
Pentecostal Assemblies Canada
TEAM of Canada
UFM Intl. in Canada
World Mission Prayer League

Evangelism, Mass

African Enterprise Association
Apostolic Church of Pentecost
Associated Gospel Churches
Barry Moore Ministries
Eurovangelism
Evangelical Tract Distributors
Far East Broadcasting Assocs.
Gospel for Asia
High Adventure Ministries
International Teams of Canada
Italian Pentecostal Church
Janz Team Ministries
OMS International - Canada
Operation Mobilization Canada
Salvation Army, The
SEND Intl. of Canada
Youth for Christ - Canada

Evangelism, Personal and Small Group

ABWE - Canada
Action International Mins.
Africa Inland Mission (Canada)
African Enterprise Association
Anglican Church of Canada
Apostolic Church In Canada
Apostolic Church of Pentecost
Arab World Ministries (Canada)
Barry Moore Ministries
BGCC Global Ministries
Bible Holiness Movement
Bible League of Canada, The
Campus Crusade for Christ
Canadian Conv. of So. Baptists
Child Evangelism Fellowship
Christian and Msny. Alliance
Emmanuel International
Equip, Canada
European Christian Mission
Evangelical Covenant Ch Canada
Evangelical Mennonite Conf.
FEBInternational
Frontiers Canada
Glad Tidings Missionary Soc.
Global Outreach Mission
Gospel Missionary Union Canada
Greater Europe Mission
HCJB World Radio Msnry. Flwshp
International Missions Ontario
International Teams of Canada
INTERSERVE (Canada)
Italian Pentecostal Church
Language Recordings Intl.
Latin America Mission (Canada)
Liebenzell Mission of Canada
Middle East Christian Outreach
Mission Possible Canada
Missionary Ventures of Canada
Navigators of Canada, The
OMF International
OMS International - Canada
Operation Mobilization Canada
Persecuted Church Fellowship
Pioneers
Samaritan's Purse - Canada
SEND Intl. of Canada
South American Missionary Soc.
UFM Intl. In Canada
Venture Teams International
WEC Intl. (Canada)
Western Tract Mission, Inc.
World Gospel Mission (Canada)
World Mission Prayer League

World Vision Canada
Youth for Christ - Canada
Youth With A Mission (Canada)

Evangelism, Student

Inter-Varsity Christian Flwshp
Navigators of Canada, The
Young Life of Canada
Youth for Christ - Canada

Funds Transmission

African Enterprise Association
Apostolic Church In Canada
Apostolic Church of Pentecost
Christian Aid Mission
Church of God (Anderson, IN)
Compassion Canada
FAIR
Fundamental Baptist Mission
HOPE Intl. Development Agency
Latin America Mission (Canada)
Partners International Canada
Samaritan's Purse - Canada
United Church of Canada

Furloughed Missionary Support

Canadian Churches' Forum
MBMS International

Information Services

African Enterprise Association
Centre for World Mission B.C.
Christian Aid Mission
Open Doors W. Brother Andrew
Outreach Canada
Voice of the Martyrs, The

Leadership Development

Africa Inland Mission (Canada)
Apostolic Church of Pentecost
Barry Moore Ministries
BGCC Global Ministries
Campus Crusade for Christ
Canadian Baptist Ministries
Canadian Food for the Hungry
Canadian S. American Mission
Christian Reformed Wld. Relief
Christian Studies Int. Canada
Evangelical Mennonite Conf.
Evangelical Mennonite Msn Conf
International Teams of Canada
MBMS International
Open Doors W. Brother Andrew
Outreach Canada
Overseas Council Theol.Ed.
Pentecostal Assemblies Canada
Presbyterian Church in Canada
SEND Intl. of Canada
South American Missionary Soc.
TEAM of Canada
Venture Teams International
World Vision Canada
Young Life of Canada

Linguistics

Canadian Bible Society
Lutheran Bible Translators
New Tribes Mission
Wycliffe Bible Translators

Literacy

Bible League of Canada, The
Christian Reformed Wld. Relief
Lutheran Bible Translators
New Tribes Mission
Wycliffe Bible Translators

Literature Distribution

BCM International (Canada)
Bible Holiness Movement
Campus Crusade for Christ
Child Evangelism Fellowship
Croisade du Livre Chretien
Czechoslovak Evangelical Msn.
Door of Hope Intl. (Canada)
European Christian Mission
Evangelical Lutheran Church
Evangelical Tract Distributors
Far East Broadcasting Assocs.
International Needs - Canada
Lutheran Bible Translators
Middle East Christian Outreach
Navigators of Canada, The
Open Doors W. Brother Andrew
Operation Mobilization Canada
Persecuted Church Fellowship
Scripture Gift Mission
Slavic Gospel Assoc.
Voice of the Martyrs, The
Western Tract Mission, Inc.

Literature Production

Bible Holiness Movement
Canadian Churches' Forum
Child Evangelism Fellowship
Czechoslovak Evangelical Msn.
Door of Hope Intl. (Canada)
Evangelical Lutheran Church
Evangelical Tract Distributors
Italian Pentecostal Church
Lutheran Bible Translators
Navigators of Canada, The
Operation Mobilization Canada
Scripture Gift Mission
Slavic Gospel Assoc.
Voice of the Martyrs, The
Western Tract Mission, Inc.

Management Consulting/Training

Christian Reformed Wld. Relief
Mennonite Economic Development
Overseas Council Theol.Ed.

Medical Supplies

Apostolic Church In Canada
International Child Care
Missionary Ventures of Canada
Samaritan's Purse - Canada

Medicine, incl. Dental and Public Health

ABWE - Canada
Africa Inland Mission (Canada)
Calcutta Mission of Mercy
Christian Blind Mission Intl.
Emmanuel International
Equip, Canada
Evangelical Mennonite Conf.
FAIR
FEBInternational
Global Outreach Mission
HCJB World Radio Msnry. Flwshp
International Christian Aid
INTERSERVE (Canada)
Leprosy Mission Canada
Liebenzell Mission of Canada
Missionary Ventures of Canada
Presbyterian Church in Canada
SIM Canada
TEAM of Canada
UFM Intl. In Canada
Voice of the Martyrs, The
World Mission Prayer League

National Church Nurture/Support

Anglican Church of Canada
Apostolic Church of Pentecost
Arab World Ministries (Canada)
Barry Moore Ministries
BGCC Global Ministries
Bible Holiness Movement
Campus Crusade for Christ
Canadian Food for the Hungry
Canadian S. American Mission
Christian Aid Mission
Church of God (Anderson, IN)
Compassion Canada
Door of Hope Intl. (Canada)
Emmanuel International
European Christian Mission
Evangelical Lutheran Church
Evangelical Mennonite Msn Conf
Evangelical Missionary Church
Gospel for Asia
Gospel Missionary Union Canada
INTERSERVE (Canada)
Janz Team Ministries
Liebenzell Mission of Canada
MBMS International
Middle East Christian Outreach
OMF International
OMS International - Canada
Outreach Canada
Overseas Council Theol.Ed.
Partners International Canada
Presbyterian Church in Canada
SEND Intl. of Canada
TEAM of Canada
WEC Intl. (Canada)

Recruiting/Mobilizing

African Enterprise Association
Centre for World Mission B.C.
Evangelical Covenant Ch Canada
Evangelical Lutheran Church
Janz Team Ministries
Pioneers
South American Missionary Soc.
Venture Teams International
WEC Intl. (Canada)
Youth for Christ - Canada
Youth With A Mission (Canada)

Translation, Bible

Canadian Bible Society
Lutheran Bible Translators
New Tribes Mission
SIM Canada
Trinitarian Bible Society
World Mission Prayer League
World Team
Wycliffe Bible Translators

Video/Film

Arab World Ministries (Canada)

Youth Programs

Calcutta Mission of Mercy
International Needs - Canada
International Teams of Canada
Italian Pentecostal Church
Liebenzell Mission of Canada
Navigators of Canada, The
Young Life of Canada
Youth for Christ - Canada
Youth With A Mission (Canada)

CHAPTER 10

Countries of Activity for Canadian Protestant Agencies

In this chapter you will find the countries where agencies reported field personnel in answer to question #12 of the Survey Questionnaire (see the Appendix for details). The few exceptions to this are agencies whose whole program supports (with funds raised in Canada, but which may not be designated to specific personnel on a regular basis) churches or other initiatives in a country.

All countries are listed in alphabetical order according to the name most commonly recognized in North America. Countries that are part of the Commonwealth of Independent States (most of the former Soviet Union) have been listed separately. Examples of this include Armenia, Kyrgyzstan and Belarus. In a few cases we have listed a territory or other administrative district of a country because it is commonly viewed as a separate entity and mission agencies report it that way. An example would be the Azores, located in the Atlantic Ocean 900 miles west of mainland Portugal.

We have separated the personnel totals for all agencies into five categories. Under the "personnel from Canada" heading, the term of expected service has been divided into three categories: 4+ years, 2-4 years and 1-2 years for fully supported personnel. For non-Canadian personnel in the "other countries" heading, the categories are those who are citizens of that ministry country and those who are not citizens, and are fully or partially supported by funds raised in Canada by the associated agency. For example, a Kenyan with specific mission/ministry duties serving in Kenya would be included in an agency's "citizens" column of the Kenya section. A Kenyan serving in Russia would be listed in the "not citizen" column of the Russian Federation section.

At the end of each country section, totals of each category for that country are given. Please note that the totals for the "other countries" heading do not necessarily reflect all non-Canadian mission personnel who draw support from Canadian agencies. Some agencies give grants for ongoing institutions and other programs without specifying individual recipients. This may be in addition to Canadian mission personnel based in that country or the agency may not have Canadian personnel living in that country.

Please note also that the totals will be minimum numbers only because of the bigger number of large agencies in this edition that reported their personnel only by general regions and not by specific countries. Therefore, their numbers are not included in this "countries of activity" chapter.

COUNTRY Agency	Year Began	Personnel from CAN			Other Countries	
		4+yrs	2-4 yrs	1-2 yrs	Citizens	Not Citiz.
Albania						
Canadian Baptist Ministries	1993	2	-	-	-	-
Child Evangelism Fellowship	1995	1	-	-	-	-
Door of Hope Intl. (Canada)	1993	1	-	-	-	-
	Totals:	4	-	-	-	-
Angola						
Brethren Assemblies (Canada)	1958	1	-	-	-	-
Canadian Baptist Ministries	1956	2	-	-	-	-
Mission Aviation Flwshp	1989	6	1	-	-	-
SIM Canada	1917	5	-	-	-	-
World Vision Canada		1	-	-	-	-
	Totals:	15	1	-	-	-
Antigua						
Global Outreach Mission		2	-	-	-	-
	Totals:	2	-	-	-	-
Argentina						
ABWE - Canada	1950	2	-	-	-	-
Brethren Assemblies (Canada)	1987	4	-	-	-	-
Child Evangelism Fellowship	1956	1	-	-	-	-
Christian and Msny. Alliance		2	-	-	-	-
Equip, Canada	1997	-	2	-	-	-
Evangelical Lutheran Church	1990	1	-	1	-	-
Gospel Missionary Union	1955	2	-	-	-	-
Youth With A Mission		1	-	-	-	-
	Totals:	13	2	1	-	-
Australia						
International Teams of Canada	1996	1	-	-	-	-
Operation Mobilization		-	-	-	2	-
Salvation Army, The	1996	-	4	-	-	-
Wycliffe Bible Translators	1950	4	-	-	-	-
Youth With A Mission		16	-	-	-	-
	Totals:	21	4	-	2	-
Austria						
Brethren Assemblies (Canada)	1983	4	-	-	-	-
Eurovangelism	1987	-	-	-	2	-
Gospel Missionary Union	1966	7	-	-	-	1
Greater Europe Mission	1963	2	-	-	-	-
International Teams of Canada	1970	2	-	-	-	-
Janz Team Ministries		2	-	-	-	-
MBMS International	1953	-	2	-	-	-
Operation Mobilization		2	-	-	-	12
	Totals:	19	2	-	2	13

COUNTRY Agency	Year Began	Personnel from CAN			Other Countries	
		4+yrs	2-4 yrs	1-2 yrs	Citizens	Not Citiz.
Bahamas						
Gospel Missionary Union	1956	2	-	-	-	-
Salvation Army, The	1997	-	4	-	-	-
	Totals:	2	4	-	-	-
Bangladesh						
ABWE - Canada	1968	2	1	-	-	-
Christian Blind Mission Intl.	1995	-	2	-	-	-
International Missions Ontario	1989	2	-	-	-	-
INTERSERVE (Canada)	1952	1	-	-	-	-
Operation Mobilization		-	-	-	-	-
Salvation Army, The	1994	2	-	-	-	-
SIM Canada	1957	-	-	-	-	11
	Totals:	7	3	-	-	11
Barbados						
Youth With A Mission		4	-	-	-	-
	Totals:	4	-	-	-	-
Belgium						
Brethren Assemblies (Canada)	1970	6	-	-	-	-
Canadian Baptist Ministries	1985	6	-	5	-	-
FEBInternational	1977	6	-	-	-	-
Global Outreach Mission		1	-	-	-	-
Gospel Missionary Union	1966	1	-	-	1	-
Operation Mobilization		-	-	1	-	9
Salvation Army, The	1997	-	2	-	-	-
	Totals:	20	2	6	1	9
Belize						
Evangelical Mennonite Msn	1965	-	-	2	-	-
Gospel Missionary Union	1955	2	-	4	-	-
Pioneers	1986	2	-	-	-	-
Youth With A Mission		4	-	-	-	-
	Totals:	8	-	6	-	-
Benin						
Christian and Msny. Alliance		3	-	-	-	-
SIM Canada	1946	10	1	4	-	1
Wycliffe Bible Translators	1993	2	-	-	-	-
	Totals:	15	1	4	-	1
Bolivia						
Brethren Assemblies (Canada)	1976	10	-	-	-	-
Canadian Baptist Ministries	1898	5	-	-	-	-
Canadian Food for the	1999	-	-	-	1	-
Evangelical Mennonite Msn	1969	4	-	-	-	-
Global Outreach Mission		-	-	-	4	-
Gospel Missionary Union	1949	20	-	4	-	-

COUNTRY Agency	Year Began	Personnel from CAN 4+yrs	2-4 yrs	1-2 yrs	Other Countries Citizens	Not Citiz.
Mennonite Economic	1992	-	-	-	1	1
New Tribes Mission	1942	12	-	-	-	-
Pioneers	1984	3	-	-	-	-
SIM Canada	1907	3	-	1	-	-
Wycliffe Bible Translators	1955	1	-	-	-	-
	Totals:	58	-	5	6	1
Bosnia						
Pioneers	1998	1	-	-	-	-
	Totals:	1	-	-	-	-
Botswana						
Brethren Assemblies (Canada)	1991	2	-	-	-	-
MBMS International	1985	-	2	-	-	-
Mission Aviation Flwshp	1990	2	-	-	-	-
SIM Canada	1973	3	-	-	-	-
	Totals:	7	2	-	-	-
Brazil						
ABWE - Canada	1936	5	-	-	-	-
Action International Mins.		-	4	-	-	-
Apostolic Church In Canada	1980	-	-	-	6	-
Apostolic Church of Pentecost	1998	2	-	-	-	-
Brethren Assemblies (Canada)	1948	3	-	-	-	-
Canadian Food for the Hungry		-	-	-	1	-
Child Evangelism Fellowship	1995	2	-	-	-	-
Christian and Msny. Alliance		3	-	-	-	-
Emmanuel International	1981	-	-	-	4	-
Evangelical Missionary		6	-	-	-	-
Global Outreach Mission		1	-	-	-	-
Gospel Missionary Union	1949	4	-	-	-	-
Janz Team Ministries	1975	2	-	-	2	-
MBMS International	1946	-	2	-	18	-
Mission Aviation Flwshp	1972	3	-	-	-	-
New Tribes Mission	1946	9	-	-	-	-
Pentecostal Assemblies Canada	1965	6	-	-	-	-
Pioneers	1990	2	-	-	-	-
Salvation Army, The	1991	2	3	-	-	-
UFM Intl. in Canada	1931	8	-	-	-	-
WEC Intl. (Canada)	1957	4	-	-	-	-
Wycliffe Bible Translators	1956	13	-	-	-	-
	Totals:	75	9	-	31	-
Bulgaria						
Eurovangelism	1996	-	-	-	3	-
Navigators of Canada, The	1990	1	-	-	-	-
Pentecostal Assemblies Canada	1998	-	-	1	-	-
	Totals:	1	-	1	3	-

COUNTRY Agency	Year Began	Personnel from CAN 4+yrs	 2-4 yrs	 1-2 yrs	Other Countries Citizens	 Not Citiz.
Burkina Faso						
Apostolic Church of Pentecost	1989	4	-	-	-	-
Christian and Msny. Alliance		2	-	-	-	-
Evangelical Mennonite Conf.	1991	3	-	-	-	-
SIM Canada	1930	7	3	-	-	-
Wycliffe Bible Translators	1983	7	-	-	-	-
	Totals:	23	3	-	-	-
Burundi						
World Vision Canada		1	-	-	-	1
	Totals:	1	-	-	-	1
Cambodia						
Christian and Msny. Alliance		6	-	-	-	-
Christian Reformed Wld. Relief		1	-	-	-	-
Far East Broadcasting Assocs.	1993	1	-	-	-	-
WEC Intl. (Canada)	1993	1	-	-	-	-
	Totals:	9	-	-	-	-
Cameroon						
Evangelical Lutheran Church	1999	-	-	1	-	-
Lutheran Bible Translators	1981	2	-	-	-	6
World Team	1985	6	-	2	-	-
Wycliffe Bible Translators	1968	20	-	4	-	-
	Totals:	28	-	7	-	6
Cen Africa Rep						
Africa Inland Mission	1924	-	2	-	-	-
Wycliffe Bible Translators	1989	2	-	-	-	-
	Totals:	2	2	-	-	-
Chad						
Africa Inland Mission	1986	1	-	-	-	-
TEAM of Canada	1969	9	-	-	6	-
WEC Intl. (Canada)	1962	1	-	-	-	-
World Vision Canada		2	-	-	-	-
	Totals:	13	-	-	6	-
Chile						
ABWE - Canada	1950	1	-	-	-	-
Brethren Assemblies (Canada)	1952	14	-	-	-	-
Canadian Conv. of So. Baptists	1993	2	-	-	-	-
Christian and Msny. Alliance		2	-	-	-	-
Navigators of Canada, The	1987	4	-	-	-	-
SIM Canada	1986	1	-	-	-	1
South American Missionary	1996	-	2	-	-	-
Youth With A Mission		1	-	-	-	-
	Totals:	25	2	-	-	1

COUNTRY Agency	Year Began	Personnel from CAN			Other Countries	
		4+yrs	2-4 yrs	1-2 yrs	Citizens	Not Citiz.
China (PRC)						
Canadian Baptist Ministries	1990	-	2	-	-	-
Christian and Msny. Alliance		-	-	-	-	-
Navigators of Canada, The	1990	2	-	-	-	-
Samaritan's Purse - Canada	1993	2	-	-	-	-
TEAM of Canada	1997	1	-	-	-	-
World Vision Canada		-	-	-	2	-
	Totals:	5	2	-	2	-
Colombia						
Action International Mins.		-	4	-	-	-
Brethren Assemblies (Canada)	1972	1	-	-	-	-
Canadian S. American Mission	1934	2	-	-	-	-
Christian and Msny. Alliance		3	-	-	-	-
FEBInternational	1969	8	2	-	2	-
Global Outreach Mission		2	-	-	-	-
Gospel Missionary Union	1949	2	-	-	-	-
Latin America Mission		8	-	-	-	-
MBMS International	1945	-	2	-	16	-
New Tribes Mission	1944	4	-	-	-	-
Pentecostal Assemblies Canada	1996	-	1	-	-	-
Wycliffe Bible Translators	1962	15	-	-	-	-
	Totals:	45	9	-	18	-
Congo						
Christian and Msny. Alliance		4	-	-	-	-
WEC Intl. (Canada)	1913	1	-	-	-	-
Wycliffe Bible Translators	1985	4	-	-	-	-
	Totals:	9	-	-	-	-
Congo/Zaire						
Africa Inland Mission	1912	10	-	7	-	-
Brethren Assemblies (Canada)	1952	3	-	-	-	-
Canadian Baptist Ministries	1961	8	-	-	-	-
Christian Blind Mission Intl.	1983	1	-	-	-	-
Global Outreach Mission		1	-	-	-	-
Wycliffe Bible Translators	1985	3	-	2	-	-
	Totals:	26	-	9	-	-
Costa Rica						
Brethren Assemblies (Canada)	1956	2	-	-	-	-
Christian and Msny. Alliance		1	-	-	-	-
Latin America Mission		10	-	-	-	-
Presbyterian Church		-	-	-	1	-
Voice of the Martyrs, The	1988	-	-	-	2	-
	Totals:	13	-	-	3	-
Cote d'Ivoire						
Christian and Msny. Alliance		13	1	-	-	-
Equip, Canada	1997	2	-	-	-	-

COUNTRY Agency	Year Began	Personnel from CAN			Other Countries	
		4+yrs	2-4 yrs	1-2 yrs	Citizens	Not Citiz.
New Tribes Mission	1982	9	-	-	-	-
Pentecostal Assemblies Canada	1986	-	-	-	-	-
SIM Canada	1968	3	-	-	-	-
WEC Intl. (Canada)	1934	3	-	2	-	-
Wycliffe Bible Translators	1970	3	-	-	-	-
	Totals:	33	1	2	-	-
Croatia						
Canadian Baptist Ministries	1991	-	2	-	-	-
Greater Europe Mission	1998	2	-	-	-	-
Overseas Council Theol. Ed.	1990	-	-	-	3	-
	Totals:	2	2	-	3	-
Cyprus						
INTERSERVE (Canada)	1965	4	-	-	-	-
Presbyterian Church	1990	4	-	-	-	-
	Totals:	8	-	-	-	-
Czech Rep						
Operation Mobilization		-	2	-	-	-
Salvation Army, The	1998	-	2	-	-	-
SEND Intl. of Canada	1992	2	-	-	-	-
TEAM of Canada	1994	2	-	-	-	-
	Totals:	4	4	-	-	-
Denmark						
Operation Mobilization	-	-	-	-	-	
Youth With A Mission		1	-	-	-	-
	Totals:	1	-	-	-	-
Dominican Rep						
Brethren Assemblies (Canada)	1947	2	-	-	-	-
HOPE Intl. Development		-	-	-	-	-
Italian Pentecostal Church	1989	-	-	-	-	-
Youth With A Mission		2	-	-	-	-
	Totals:	4	-	-	-	-
Ecuador						
Brethren Assemblies (Canada)	1983	5	-	-	-	-
Christian and Msny. Alliance		8	1	-	-	-
Gospel Missionary Union	1949	7	-	1	-	1
Liebenzell Mission of Canada	1989	2	-	-	-	-
OMS International - Canada	1946	2	-	-	-	-
SIM Canada	1989	-	-	1	-	-
Wycliffe Bible Translators	1953	2	-	-	-	-
	Totals:	26	1	2	-	1
El Salvador						
Apostolic Church of Pentecost	1977	2	-	-	-	-
Brethren Assemblies (Canada)	1991	3	-	-	-	-

COUNTRY Agency	Year Began	Personnel from CAN			Other Countries	
		4+yrs	2-4 yrs	1-2 yrs	Citizens	Not Citiz.
Evangelical Lutheran Church	1988	1	-	-	-	-
Presbyterian Church	1999	2	-	-	-	-
	Totals:	8	-	-	-	-
Estonia						
Apostolic Church of Pentecost	1991	3	-	-	-	-
OMS International - Canada	1995	-	3	-	-	-
Pentecostal Assemblies Canada	1991	2	-	-	-	-
	Totals:	5	3	-	-	-
Ethiopia						
Pentecostal Assemblies Canada	1958	7	-	-	-	-
SIM Canada	1927	11	2	-	-	2
	Totals:	18	2	-	-	2
Fiji						
Youth With A Mission		2	-	-	-	-
	Totals:	2	-	-	-	-
Finland						
Brethren Assemblies (Canada)	1982	2	-	-	-	-
Salvation Army, The	1997	-	-	1	-	-
	Totals:	2	-	1	-	-
France						
Arab World Ministries	1960	6	-	-	-	-
Brethren Assemblies (Canada)	1949	19	-	-	-	-
Canadian Baptist Ministries	1992	2	-	-	-	-
Child Evangelism Fellowship	1955	1	-	-	-	-
Christian and Msny. Alliance		4	-	-	-	-
FEBInternational	1985	8	-	-	-	-
Global Outreach Mission		7	-	-	6	-
Greater Europe Mission	1959	3	-	-	-	-
International Teams of Canada	1989	1	1	-	-	-
Operation Mobilization		-	-	-	8	2
Salvation Army, The	1994	2	-	-	-	-
TEAM of Canada	1952	3	-	-	2	-
	Totals:	56	1	-	16	2
Gabon						
Christian and Msny. Alliance		9	-	-	-	-
	Totals:	9	-	-	-	-
Gambia						
WEC Intl. (Canada)	1957	3	-	-	-	-
	Totals:	3	-	-	-	-
Germany						
Christian and Msny. Alliance		10	8	-	-	-
FEBInternational	1996	-	-	-	-	-
Gospel Missionary Union	1997	-	-	1	-	-

COUNTRY Agency	Year Began	Personnel from CAN 4+yrs	2-4 yrs	1-2 yrs	Other Countries Citizens	Not Citiz.
Greater Europe Mission	1959	2	-	-	-	-
International Teams of Canada	1991	5	-	-	-	-
Janz Team Ministries	1955	39	1	2	-	18
MBMS International	1953	-	6	-	16	-
Operation Mobilization	1962	1	-	1	1	10
Salvation Army, The	1991	6	2	-	-	-
TEAM of Canada	1994	2	-	-	-	-
UFM Intl. in Canada		2	-	-	-	-
WEC Intl. (Canada)	1948	-	-	1	-	-
	Totals:	67	17	5	17	28
Ghana						
Bible Holiness Movement	1961	-	-	-	12	-
Global Outreach Mission		-	-	-	2	-
Presbyterian Church		-	-	-	1	-
Salvation Army, The	1995	2	-	-	-	-
SIM Canada	1956	4	2	-	-	-
WEC Intl. (Canada)	1940	2	-	-	-	-
Wycliffe Bible Translators	1962	6	-	-	-	-
	Totals:	14	2	-	15	-
Greece						
Pentecostal Assemblies Canada	1965	2	-	-	-	-
	Totals:	2	-	-	-	-
Greenland						
Youth With A Mission		2	-	-	-	-
	Totals:	2	-	-	-	-
Guam						
Church of God (Anderson, IN)		-	-	-	-	2
	Totals:	-	-	-	-	2
Guatemala						
Apostolic Church of Pentecost	1991	2	-	-	-	-
Brethren Assemblies (Canada)	1998	2	-	-	-	-
Canadian Food for the Hungry	1999	-	-	-	4	-
Christian and Msny. Alliance		4	-	-	-	-
Evangelical Lutheran Church	1999	-	-	1	-	-
Global Outreach Mission		2	-	-	11	-
Latin America Mission		2	-	-	-	-
Missionary Ventures of Canada	1992	-	-	-	-	6
Pentecostal Assemblies Canada	1990	2	4	-	-	-
Presbyterian Church	1992	4	-	-	-	-
Wycliffe Bible Translators	1991	9	-	1	-	-
	Totals:	27	4	2	15	6
Guinea Bissau						
Christian and Msny. Alliance		9	-	-	-	-
New Tribes Mission	1986	9	-	-	-	-

COUNTRY Agency	Year Began	Personnel from CAN			Other Countries	
		4+yrs	2-4 yrs	1-2 yrs	Citizens	Not Citiz.
Pentecostal Assemblies Canada	1988	4	-	-	-	-
WEC Intl. (Canada)	1933	2	-	2	-	-
	Totals:	24	-	2	-	-
Guyana						
Canadian Baptist Ministries	1992	-	-	6	-	-
Presbyterian Church	1997	1	-	-	-	-
Wycliffe Bible Translators	1991	2	-	-	-	-
Youth With A Mission		2	-	-	-	-
	Totals:	5	-	6	-	-
Haiti						
Christian Reformed Wld. Relief	1986	2	-	-	-	-
Emmanuel International	1978	-	-	2	2	-
Global Outreach Mission		2	-	-	2	-
International Child Care	1986	2	4	-	-	-
Mennonite Economic	1972	-	-	-	1	-
OMS International - Canada	1964	1	2	-	-	-
Pentecostal Assemblies Canada	1996	2	-	-	-	-
UFM Intl. in Canada	1943	1	1	-	-	-
World Team	1936	4	-	-	-	-
	Totals:	14	7	2	5	-
Honduras						
Christian Reformed Wld. Relief		3	-	-	-	-
International Christian Aid	1994	-	-	-	44	-
Missionary Ventures of Canada	1992	-	-	-	-	4
South American Missionary	1991	2	1	1	2	-
	Totals:	5	1	1	46	4
Hong Kong						
Brethren Assemblies (Canada)	1994	2	-	-	-	-
Canadian Baptist Ministries	1992	-	2	-	-	-
Child Evangelism Fellowship	1991	-	-	-	-	2
Christian and Msny. Alliance		4	-	-	-	-
Far East Broadcasting Assocs.	1986	2	-	-	-	-
OMS International - Canada	1950	-	1	-	-	-
Operation Mobilization		-	-	-	-	-
Pentecostal Assemblies Canada	1908	14	-	4	-	-
Salvation Army, The	1996	2	-	-	-	-
SEND Intl. of Canada	1989	1	-	-	-	-
	Totals:	25	3	4	-	2
Hungary						
BGCC Global Ministries	1996	-	2	-	-	-
Child Evangelism Fellowship	1995	2	-	-	-	-
Christian and Msny. Alliance		6	-	-	-	-
Greater Europe Mission	1998	-	-	1	-	-
Janz Team Ministries	1991	2	-	-	-	-
Navigators of Canada, The	1992	3	-	-	-	-

COUNTRY Agency	Year Began	Personnel from CAN			Other Countries	
		4+yrs	2-4 yrs	1-2 yrs	Citizens	Not Citiz.
Operation Mobilization		-	-	-	-	-
Salvation Army, The	1997	-	2	-	-	-
	Totals:	13	4	1	-	-
India						
Apostolic Church In Canada	1994	-	-	-	1	1
Apostolic Church of Pentecost	1998	2	-	-	-	-
Bible Holiness Movement	1991	-	-	-	3	-
Brethren Assemblies (Canada)	1982	2	-	-	-	-
Calcutta Mission of Mercy	1954	1	-	-	-	-
Canadian Baptist Ministries	1870	4	-	-	-	-
FEBInternational	1967	-	-	-	4	-
Global Outreach Mission	1972	3	-	-	12	-
International Missions Ontario	1930	1	-	1	-	-
INTERSERVE (Canada)	1952	2	-	-	-	-
MBMS International	1898	-	-	-	409	-
Operation Mobilization	1963	4	-	-	35	4
Pentecostal Assemblies Canada	1911	4	1	-	-	-
Presbyterian Church	1959	-	1	-	-	-
SIM Canada	1893	1	2	-	-	-
TEAM of Canada	1894	2	-	-	-	-
WEC Intl. (Canada)	1926	1	-	-	-	-
World Vision Canada		1	-	-	-	-
Wycliffe Bible Translators	1966	3	-	-	-	-
Youth With A Mission		8	-	-	-	-
	Totals:	39	4	1	464	5
Indonesia						
Canadian Baptist Ministries	1973	3	-	1	-	-
Christian and Msny. Alliance		18	1	-	-	-
Christian Reformed Wld. Relief		1	-	-	-	-
Frontiers Canada	1990	4	-	-	-	-
MBMS International	1975	-	-	-	57	-
Mission Aviation Flwshp	1972	7	1	-	-	-
New Tribes Mission	1970	9	-	-	-	-
OMF International	1954	1	-	-	-	-
OMS International - Canada	1978	-	2	-	-	-
Operation Mobilization		-	-	-	2	-
Pentecostal Assemblies Canada	1982	7	-	-	-	-
TEAM of Canada	1950	2	-	-	-	-
WEC Intl. (Canada)	1950	2	-	-	-	-
World Team	1954	7	-	-	-	-
World Vision Canada		-	-	1	-	-
Wycliffe Bible Translators	1971	9	-	-	-	-
Youth With A Mission		1	-	-	-	-
	Totals:	71	4	2	59	-
Ireland						
BGCC Global Ministries		-	1	-	-	-
Brethren Assemblies (Canada)	1968	12	-	-	-	-

COUNTRY Agency	Year Began	Personnel from CAN			Other Countries	
		4+yrs	2-4 yrs	1-2 yrs	Citizens	Not Citiz.
Child Evangelism Fellowship	1995	-	-	-	2	-
Global Outreach Mission	1972	4	-	-	1	-
UFM Intl. in Canada	1980	-	1	-	1	-
	Totals:	16	2	-	4	-
Israel						
Christian and Msny. Alliance		-	2	-	-	-
Pentecostal Assemblies Canada	1989	4	-	-	-	-
Presbyterian Church		-	-	-	1	-
	Totals:	4	2	-	1	-
Italy						
Brethren Assemblies (Canada)	1987	4	-	-	-	-
Child Evangelism Fellowship	1990	2	-	-	-	-
FEBInternational	1985	2	-	-	-	1
Greater Europe Mission	1959	2	-	-	-	-
International Teams of Canada	1993	-	2	-	-	-
Operation Mobilization		-	-	-	1	-
TEAM of Canada	1981	5	-	-	-	-
UFM Intl. in Canada		-	1	-	-	-
World Team	1970	1	-	-	-	-
	Totals:	16	3	-	1	1
Jamaica						
Apostolic Church in Canada	1949	-	-	-	14	-
Overseas Council Theol.Ed.	1990	-	-	-	2	-
Salvation Army, The	1994	1	4	-	-	-
Youth With A Mission		2	-	-	-	-
	Totals:	3	4	-	16	-
Japan						
Brethren Assemblies (Canada)	1949	7	-	-	-	-
Campus Crusade for Christ		-	-	1	-	-
Child Evangelism Fellowship	1962	2	-	-	-	-
Christian and Msny. Alliance		4	-	-	-	-
FEBInternational	1965	12	-	-	-	-
MBMS International	1950	-	2	-	-	-
OMF International	1951	8	-	1	-	-
OMS International - Canada	1901	-	2	-	-	-
Operation Mobilization		-	-	-	1	1
Presbyterian Church	1962	2	-	2	-	-
SEND Intl. of Canada	1947	3	-	-	-	-
TEAM of Canada	1891	9	2	1	-	-
Youth With A Mission		2	-	-	-	-
	Totals:	49	6	5	1	1
Jordan						
Youth With A Mission		2	-	-	-	-
	Totals:	2	-	-	-	-

COUNTRY Agency	Year Began	Personnel from CAN			Other Countries	
		4+yrs	2-4 yrs	1-2 yrs	Citizens	Not Citiz.
Kazakhstan						
Global Outreach Mission		2	-	-	-	-
	Totals:	2	-	-	-	-
Kenya						
Africa Inland Mission	1895	42	2	22	-	-
Bible Holiness Movement	1980	-	-	-	1	-
Brethren Assemblies (Canada)	1963	4	-	-	-	-
Canadian Baptist Ministries	1970	6	4	2	-	-
Christian Blind Mission Intl.	1985	2	-	-	-	-
Christian Reformed Wld. Relief		2	-	-	-	-
FEBInternational	1999	2	-	-	-	-
International Christian Aid	1982	-	-	-	2	-
Language Recordings Intl.	1976	1	-	-	-	-
Mission Aviation Flwshp	1972	4	-	-	-	-
Pentecostal Assemblies Canada	1939	15	-	2	-	-
Presbyterian Church	1979	1	-	-	-	-
SIM Canada	1977	1	-	-	-	-
Wycliffe Bible Translators	1978	6	-	-	-	-
Youth With A Mission		1	-	-	-	-
	Totals:	87	6	26	3	-
Korea-S						
OMF International	1968	1	-	-	-	-
OMS International - Canada	1907	-	1	-	-	-
Operation Mobilization		-	-	-	-	-
	Totals:	1	1	-	-	-
Laos						
Christian and Msny. Alliance		2	-	-	-	-
Samaritan's Purse - Canada	1997	2	-	-	-	-
	Totals:	4	-	-	-	-
Latvia						
Canadian Baptist Ministries	1995	2	-	-	-	-
Greater Europe Mission	1992	5	-	-	-	-
	Totals:	7	-	-	-	-
Lebanon						
Christian and Msny. Alliance		2	-	-	-	-
FEBInternational	1999	-	2	-	-	-
	Totals:	2	2	-	-	-
Lesotho						
Africa Inland Mission	1986	-	2	2	-	-
	Totals:	-	2	2	-	-
Liberia						
Pentecostal Assemblies Canada	1915	3	-	1	-	-
	Totals:	3	-	1	-	-

COUNTRY Agency	Year Began	Personnel from CAN			Other Countries	
		4+yrs	2-4 yrs	1-2 yrs	Citizens	Not Citiz.
Lithuania						
MBMS International	1994	-	2	-	6	-
Navigators of Canada, The	1990	2	-	-	-	-
Youth With A Mission		3	-	-	-	-
	Totals:	5	2	-	6	-
Luxembourg						
Greater Europe Mission	1994	2	-	-	-	-
	Totals:	2	-	-	-	-
Macao						
Pentecostal Assemblies Canada	1953	3	-	-	-	-
	Totals:	3	-	-	-	-
Macedonia						
BGCC Global Ministries	1996	-	1	-	-	-
	Totals:	-	1	-	-	-
Madagascar						
Brethren Assemblies (Canada)	1997	2	-	-	-	-
	Totals:	2	-	-	-	-
Malawi						
Apostolic Church of Pentecost	1994	2	1	-	-	-
Bible Holiness Movement	1992	-	-	-	1	-
Emmanuel International	1986	2	4	-	-	-
Pentecostal Assemblies Canada	1980	10	1	-	-	-
Presbyterian Church	1995	3	-	-	-	-
SIM Canada	1900	1	-	-	-	-
World Vision Canada	1975	2	-	-	-	-
	Totals:	20	6	-	1	-
Malaysia						
Christian and Msny. Alliance		-	2	1	-	-
OMF International	1928	4	-	-	-	-
Operation Mobilization		-	-	-	2	2
Wycliffe Bible Translators	1978	3	-	-	-	-
	Totals:	7	2	1	2	2
Mali						
Christian and Msny. Alliance		5	-	-	-	-
Christian Reformed Wld. Relief		1	-	-	-	-
Gospel Missionary Union	1949	12	-	2	-	1
	Totals:	18	-	2	-	1
Mexico						
Action International Mins.		-	2	-	-	-
Apostolic Church of Pentecost	1975	4	-	-	1	-
Brethren Assemblies (Canada)	1988	6	-	-	-	-
Christian and Msny. Alliance		14	2	-	-	-

COUNTRY Agency	Year Began	Personnel from CAN			Other Countries	
		4+yrs	2-4 yrs	1-2 yrs	Citizens	Not Citiz.
Evangelical Mennonite Conf.	1954	12	-	-	-	-
Evangelical Mennonite Msn	1982	4	-	-	4	-
Evangelical Missionary Church		3	-	-	-	-
Glad Tidings Missionary Soc.		2	-	-	-	-
Latin America Mission		3	-	-	4	-
MBMS International	1905	-	3	-	27	-
New Tribes Mission	1975	14	-	-	-	-
OMS International - Canada	1985	-	1	-	-	-
Operation Mobilization	1957	1	-	-	-	-
Salvation Army, The	1997	-	-	1	-	-
TEAM of Canada	1988	2	-	-	-	-
WEC Intl. (Canada)	1990	2	-	-	-	-
World Mission Prayer League	1950	-	2	-	-	-
World Team	1994	-	2	-	-	-
Wycliffe Bible Translators	1936	12	-	2	-	-
Youth With A Mission		4	-	-	-	-
	Totals:	83	12	3	36	-
Mongolia						
Navigators of Canada, The	1993	2	-	-	-	-
New Tribes Mission		2	-	-	-	-
	Totals:	4	-	-	-	-
Mozambique						
Mennonite Economic	1997	-	1	-	-	-
Pentecostal Assemblies Canada	1927	4	-	-	-	2
Presbyterian Church	1997	-	1	-	-	-
Salvation Army, The	1997	-	1	-	-	-
SIM Canada	1937	2	-	-	-	-
Wycliffe Bible Translators	1994	5	-	-	-	-
Youth With A Mission		2	-	-	-	-
	Totals:	13	3	-	-	2
Myanmar/Burma						
Canadian Food for the Hungry	1997	-	-	-	2	-
Christian and Msny. Alliance		-	-	-	-	-
	Totals:	-	-	-	2	-
N Mariana Isls						
Far East Broadcasting Assocs.	1995	2	-	-	-	-
Youth With A Mission		1	-	-	-	-
	Totals:	3	-	-	-	-
Nepal						
Christian and Msny. Alliance		-	-	-	-	-
INTERSERVE (Canada)	1952	10	-	-	-	-
Operation Mobilization		-	-	-	-	-
TEAM of Canada	1968	2	2	-	2	-
	Totals:	12	2	-	2	-

COUNTRY Agency	Year Began	Personnel from CAN			Other Countries	
		4+yrs	2-4 yrs	1-2 yrs	Citizens	Not Citiz.
Netherlands						
Operation Mobilization		-	-	-	-	-
Youth With A Mission		8	-	-	-	-
	Totals:	8	-	-	-	-
New Zealand						
Salvation Army, The	1998	-	2	-	-	-
WEC Intl. (Canada)	1922	2	-	-	-	-
Wycliffe Bible Translators	1991	4	-	-	-	-
Youth With A Mission		2	-	-	-	-
	Totals:	8	2	-	-	-
Nicaragua						
Mennonite Economic	1989	-	-	-	1	-
Missionary Ventures of Canada	1992	-	-	-	-	4
Presbyterian Church	1985	2	-	-	-	-
	Totals:	2	-	-	1	4
Niger						
Christian Reformed Wld. Relief		2	-	-	-	-
SIM Canada	1924	12	-	-	-	1
	Totals:	14	-	-	-	1
Nigeria						
Bible Holiness Movement	1959	-	-	-	20	-
Brethren Assemblies (Canada)	1954	4	-	-	-	-
Campus Crusade for Christ	1987	-	-	1	-	-
Canadian Conv. of So. Baptists	1990	2	-	-	-	-
Evangelical Missionary Church		5	-	-	-	-
FEBInternational	1979	-	-	-	-	-
Presbyterian Church	1980	2	-	1	-	-
SIM Canada	1893	5	-	1	-	1
	Totals:	18	-	3	20	1
Norway						
Youth With A Mission		2	-	-	-	-
	Totals:	2	-	-	-	-
Pakistan						
FEBInternational	1969	14	2	-	-	-
International Missions Ontario	1950	3	-	-	-	-
INTERSERVE (Canada)	1952	3	-	-	-	-
Operation Mobilization	1978	3	-	-	-	3
Salvation Army, The	1997	-	-	1	-	-
Samaritan's Purse - Canada	1994	1	-	-	-	-
SIM Canada	1957	3	-	-	-	-
TEAM of Canada	1946	5	-	-	2	-
	Totals:	32	2	1	2	3

COUNTRY Agency	Year Began	Personnel from CAN			Other Countries	
		4+yrs	2-4 yrs	1-2 yrs	Citizens	Not Citiz.
Panama						
Gospel Missionary Union	1953	1	-	-	-	-
MBMS International	1965	-	-	-	26	-
New Tribes Mission	1953	1	-	-	-	-
Wycliffe Bible Translators	1970	2	-	-	-	-
	Totals:	4	-	-	26	-
Papua New Guin						
Evangelical Lutheran Church	1999	-	-	1	-	-
Lutheran Bible Translators	1970	1	-	-	-	2
Mission Aviation Flwshp	1987	12	2	-	-	-
New Tribes Mission	1950	57	-	-	-	-
Operation Mobilization		-	-	-	-	2
Salvation Army, The	1998	-	2	-	-	-
Wycliffe Bible Translators	1956	32	1	7	-	-
	Totals:	102	5	8	-	4
Paraguay						
Evangelical Mennonite Conf.	1957	13	-	-	-	-
MBMS International	1948	-	-	-	18	-
New Tribes Mission	1946	7	-	-	-	-
SIM Canada	1987	1	-	-	-	-
	Totals:	21	-	-	18	-
Peru						
ABWE - Canada	1945	2	-	-	-	-
Brethren Assemblies (Canada)	1977	4	-	-	-	-
Canadian Food for the Hungry	2000	-	-	-	2	-
Canadian S. American Mission	1926	3	-	-	-	-
Christian and Msny. Alliance		5	-	-	-	-
Evangelical Lutheran Church	1994	1	-	-	-	-
MBMS International	1954	-	2	-	22	-
SIM Canada	1965	3	-	-	-	-
South American Missionary	1997	-	2	-	-	-
TEAM of Canada	1961	2	-	-	-	-
World Team	1906	8	-	-	-	-
Wycliffe Bible Translators	1946	11	-	-	-	-
	Totals:	39	4	-	24	-
Philippines						
Action International Mins.	1980	8	-	1	-	-
Bible Holiness Movement	1961	-	-	-	4	-
Brethren Assemblies (Canada)		4	-	-	-	-
Campus Crusade for Christ	1991	-	2	-	-	-
Christian and Msny. Alliance		12	3	-	-	-
Emmanuel International	1979	2	-	-	4	-
Far East Broadcasting Assocs.	1996	-	2	-	-	-
Glad Tidings Missionary Soc.		-	1	-	-	-
International Christian Aid	1987	-	-	-	36	-
International Missions Ontario	1955	4	-	-	-	-

COUNTRY Agency	Year Began	Personnel from CAN			Other Countries	
		4+yrs	2-4 yrs	1-2 yrs	Citizens	Not Citiz.
New Tribes Mission	1951	6	-	-	-	-
OMF International	1951	20	-	-	-	-
Operation Mobilization		-	2	-	3	-
Pentecostal Assemblies Canada	1992	1	-	-	-	-
SEND Intl. of Canada	1947	10	-	-	-	-
World Team	1981	10	-	-	-	-
Wycliffe Bible Translators	1953	29	-	-	-	-
Youth With A Mission		8	-	-	-	-
	Totals:	114	10	1	47	-
Poland						
Brethren Assemblies (Canada)	1996	2	-	-	-	-
Christian and Msny. Alliance		4	-	-	-	-
Eurovangelism	1980	-	-	-	7	-
International Teams of Canada	1993	4	-	-	-	-
Overseas Council Theol. Ed.	1990	-	-	-	4	-
Pentecostal Assemblies Canada	1999	2	-	-	-	-
	Totals:	12	-	-	11	-
Portugal						
ABWE - Canada	1976	-	2	2	-	-
BGCC Global Ministries	1996	-	1	-	-	-
Brethren Assemblies (Canada)	1959	6	-	-	-	-
Evangelical Missionary Church		2	-	-	-	-
Greater Europe Mission	1998	2	-	-	-	-
Janz Team Ministries	1988	1	-	-	-	-
	Totals:	11	3	2	-	-
Puerto Rico						
Brethren Assemblies (Canada)	1967	1	-	-	-	-
	Totals:	1	-	-	-	-
Romania						
Eurovangelism	1974	-	-	-	11	-
Greater Europe Mission	1998	1	-	-	-	-
Mennonite Economic	1998	-	-	-	-	1
Missionary Ventures of Canada	1992	-	-	-	-	2
Presbyterian Church in	1994	1	-	-	-	-
World Vision Canada		2	-	-	-	-
	Totals:	4	-	-	11	3
Russia						
Brethren Assemblies (Canada)	1998	3	-	-	-	-
Christian and Msny. Alliance		8	-	-	-	-
Christian Studies Int. Canada	1995	2	-	-	-	-
Door of Hope Intl. (Canada)	1978	1	-	-	-	-
Eurovangelism	1987	-	-	-	12	-
Janz Team Ministries	1992	2	-	-	-	-
MBMS International	1994	-	-	-	12	-
Navigators of Canada, The	1990	-	-	1	-	-

COUNTRY Agency	Year Began	Personnel from CAN			Other Countries	
		4+yrs	2-4 yrs	1-2 yrs	Citizens	Not Citiz.
New Tribes Mission	1992	3	-	-	-	-
OMS International - Canada	1991	-	2	-	-	-
Operation Mobilization		4	-	1	-	3
Overseas Council Theol. Ed.	1993	-	-	-	2	-
Pentecostal Assemblies Canada	1993	2	-	-	-	-
Salvation Army, The	1990	5	1	-	-	-
SEND Intl. of Canada	1991	8	-	-	-	-
Youth With A Mission		10	-	-	-	-
	Totals:	48	3	2	26	3
Rwanda						
Canadian Food for the Hungry	1999	-	-	-	1	-
Pentecostal Assemblies Canada	1998	2	2	-	-	-
World Vision Canada		-	1	-	-	-
	Totals:	2	3	-	1	-
S Africa						
ABWE - Canada	1978	1	-	1	-	-
Apostolic Church of Pentecost	1993	2	-	-	-	-
Brethren Assemblies (Canada)	1957	1	-	-	-	-
Campus Crusade for Christ	1987	-	2	-	-	-
Child Evangelism Fellowship	1995	2	-	-	-	-
Global Outreach Mission	1976	2	-	-	-	-
HOPE Intl. Development	1982	-	2	-	-	-
Operation Mobilization		4	-	2	5	-
Pentecostal Assemblies Canada	1908	4	-	-	-	-
Salvation Army, The	1991	6	4	-	-	-
SIM Canada	1889	11	2	-	-	-
TEAM of Canada	1892	2	-	-	-	-
WEC Intl. (Canada)	1955	1	-	-	-	-
	Totals:	36	10	3	5	-
Senegal						
Christian Reformed Wld. Relief		2	-	-	-	-
New Tribes Mission	1954	13	-	-	-	-
Pentecostal Assemblies Canada	1989	4	-	-	-	-
WEC Intl. (Canada)	1936	2	-	-	-	-
	Totals:	21	-	-	-	-
Serbia						
Eurovangelism	1991	-	-	-	4	-
	Totals:	-	-	-	4	-
Singapore						
OMF International	1951	2	-	-	-	-
Salvation Army, The	1997	-	4	-	-	-
World Team	1997	-	2	-	-	-
	Totals:	2	6	-	-	-

COUNTRY Agency	Year Began	Personnel from CAN			Other Countries	
		4+yrs	2-4 yrs	1-2 yrs	Citizens	Not Citiz.
Slovakia						
Canadian Baptist Ministries	1989	2	-	-	-	-
Evangelical Lutheran Church	1999	-	-	1	-	-
Navigators of Canada, The	1985	4	-	-	-	-
	Totals:	6	-	1	-	-
Spain						
Apostolic Church of Pentecost	1972	1	-	-	-	-
Brethren Assemblies (Canada)	1975	4	-	-	-	-
Christian and Msny. Alliance		2	-	-	-	-
Evangelical Missionary Church		2	-	-	-	-
FEBInternational	1985	2	-	-	-	-
Gospel Missionary Union	1967	6	-	-	-	1
Operation Mobilization		2	-	-	2	2
Salvation Army, The	1998	-	2	-	-	-
SEND Intl. of Canada	1988	2	-	-	-	-
TEAM of Canada	1952	2	-	-	-	-
UFM Intl. in Canada		-	2	-	-	-
World Team	1972	2	-	-	-	-
	Totals:	25	4	-	2	3
Sri Lanka						
Overseas Council Theol. Ed.	1997	-	-	-	1	-
Pentecostal Assemblies Canada	1982	2	-	-	-	-
Salvation Army, The	1994	1	2	-	-	-
	Totals:	3	2	-	1	-
St Vincent						
Brethren Assemblies (Canada)	1990	1	-	-	-	-
Child Evangelism Fellowship	1991	-	-	-	2	-
Navigators of Canada, The	1990	2	-	-	-	-
	Totals:	3	-	-	2	-
Sudan						
Africa Inland Mission	1949	-	1	-	-	-
Emmanuel International	1985	2	2	-	-	-
Operation Mobilization	1978	2	-	-	2	2
World Vision Canada	1972	2	-	-	-	-
	Totals:	6	3	-	2	2
Suriname						
Salvation Army, The	1996	-	2	-	-	-
Wycliffe Bible Translators	1967	5	-	-	-	-
	Totals:	5	2	-	-	-
Sweden						
Child Evangelism Fellowship	1985	2	-	-	-	-
Operation Mobilization		-	-	-	-	-
	Totals:	2	-	-	-	-

COUNTRY Agency	Year Began	Personnel from CAN			Other Countries	
		4+yrs	2-4 yrs	1-2 yrs	Citizens	Not Citiz.
Switzerland						
Child Evangelism Fellowship	1950	-	-	-	-	4
Youth With A Mission		1	-	-	-	-
	Totals:	1	-	-	-	4
Taiwan (ROC)						
Apostolic Church of Pentecost	1963	2	-	-	-	-
Christian and Msny. Alliance		4	-	-	-	-
Glad Tidings Missionary Soc.	1963	2	-	-	-	-
OMF International	1952	5	-	-	-	-
Presbyterian Church	1958	1	-	3	-	-
SEND Intl. of Canada	1968	-	-	-	-	-
TEAM of Canada	1951	2	-	-	1	-
Youth With A Mission		2	-	-	-	-
	Totals:	18	-	3	1	-
Tajikistan						
International Missions Ontario	1996	1	-	-	-	-
	Totals:	1	-	-	-	-
Tanzania						
Africa Inland Mission	1909	4	-	-	-	-
Bible Holiness Movement	1995	-	-	-	1	-
Christian Blind Mission Intl.	1976	1	-	-	-	-
Christian Reformed Wld. Relief	1978	3	-	-	-	-
Mennonite Economic	1997	1	-	-	1	2
Mission Aviation Flwshp	1987	2	-	-	-	-
Pentecostal Assemblies Canada	1914	6	-	-	-	-
Salvation Army, The	1998	-	2	-	-	-
World Vision Canada	1970	2	-	-	-	-
	Totals:	19	2	-	2	2
Thailand						
Apostolic Church of Pentecost	1992	2	-	-	1	-
Christian and Msny. Alliance		3	2	-	-	-
Evangelical Lutheran Church	1999	1	-	-	-	-
Far East Broadcasting Assocs.	1994	2	-	-	-	-
Navigators of Canada, The	1993	2	-	-	-	-
New Tribes Mission	1951	4	-	-	-	-
OMF International	1952	23	-	2	-	-
Pentecostal Assemblies Canada	1961	7	-	-	-	-
WEC Intl. (Canada)	1947	2	-	-	-	-
Wycliffe Bible Translators	1987	6	-	-	-	-
Youth With A Mission		2	-	-	-	-
	Totals:	54	2	2	1	-
Togo						
Wycliffe Bible Translators	1967	1	-	-	-	-
	Totals:	1	-	-	-	-

COUNTRY Agency	Year Began	Personnel from CAN			Other Countries	
		4+yrs	2-4 yrs	1-2 yrs	Citizens	Not Citiz.
Trinidad & Tobg						
Fundamental Baptist Mission	1990	-	-	-	1	-
	Totals:	-	-	-	1	-
Turkey						
Christian and Msny. Alliance		-	-	-	-	-
Navigators of Canada, The	1992	2	-	-	-	-
Operation Mobilization		7	-	-	-	4
	Totals:	9	-	-	-	4
Uganda						
Bible Holiness Movement	1980	-	-	-	3	-
Christian Blind Mission Intl.	1996	2	-	-	-	-
Christian Reformed Wld. Relief	1986	1	-	-	-	-
Church of God (Anderson, IN)	1983	-	-	-	-	2
Emmanuel International	1983	1	-	-	-	-
Equip, Canada	1997	-	2	-	-	-
Glad Tidings Missionary Soc.		2	5	-	-	-
International Christian Aid	1992	-	-	-	17	-
Pentecostal Assemblies Canada	1955	6	-	-	-	-
	Totals:	12	7	-	20	2
UK						
Arab World Ministries	1984	1	-	-	-	-
Child Evangelism Fellowship	1986	-	-	-	-	2
International Missions Ontario	1965	2	-	-	-	-
International Teams of Canada	1992	2	-	-	-	-
Language Recordings Intl.	1998	2	-	-	-	-
Operation Mobilization	1962	4	-	2	19	16
Salvation Army, The	1985	4	4	-	-	-
WEC Intl. (Canada)	1913	3	-	-	-	-
Youth With A Mission		24	-	-	-	-
	Totals:	42	4	2	19	18
Ukraine						
ABWE - Canada	1986	-	2	-	-	-
Campus Crusade for Christ	1991	-	4	-	-	-
Canadian Baptist Ministries	1987	4	-	-	-	-
Greater Europe Mission	1994	1	-	-	-	-
Overseas Council Theol. Ed.	1997	-	-	-	4	-
Pentecostal Assemblies Canada	1993	1	3	-	-	-
Persecuted Church Fellowship	1976	-	-	-	28	-
SEND Intl. of Canada	1991	5	-	-	-	-
Youth With A Mission		7	-	-	-	-
	Totals:	18	9	-	32	-
United Arab Emirates						
TEAM of Canada	1960	3	-	-	-	-
Totals:		3	-	-	-	-

COUNTRY Agency	Year Began	Personnel from CAN 4+yrs	2-4 yrs	1-2 yrs	Other Countries Citizens	Not Citiz.
Uruguay						
Brethren Assemblies (Canada)	1974	5	-	-	-	-
MBMS International	1950	-	2	-	-	-
Operation Mobilization	1990	2	-	-	-	-
	Totals:	7	2	-	-	-
Venezuela						
Brethren Assemblies (Canada)	1947	6	-	-	-	-
Canadian Baptist Ministries	1992	2	-	-	-	-
Christian and Msny. Alliance		9	-	-	-	-
FEBInternational	1990	6	-	-	-	-
New Tribes Mission	1946	28	-	-	-	-
TEAM of Canada	1906	3	-	-	-	-
Youth With A Mission		1	-	-	-	-
	Totals:	55	-	-	-	-
Vietnam						
Navigators of Canada, The	1994	3	-	-	-	-
Samaritan's Purse - Canada	1998	1	-	-	-	-
World Vision Canada		-	-	-	-	2
	Totals:	4	-	-	-	2
Yugoslavia						
Christian and Msny. Alliance		2	-	-	-	-
Pentecostal Assemblies Canada	1995	-	-	3	-	-
	Totals:	2	-	3	-	-
Zambia						
Bible Holiness Movement	1992	-	-	-	2	-
Brethren Assemblies (Canada)		29	-	-	-	-
Christian Reformed Wld. Relief		2	-	-	-	-
Church of God (Anderson, IN)		-	-	-	-	2
Pentecostal Assemblies Canada	1955	6	-	2	-	-
Salvation Army, The	1998	-	2	-	-	-
SIM Canada	1910	17	1	-	-	-
WEC Intl. (Canada)	1998	-	-	1	-	-
	Totals:	54	3	3	2	2
Zimbabwe						
Apostolic Church of Pentecost	1978	2	-	-	-	-
Pentecostal Assemblies Canada	1947	6	-	-	-	-
Salvation Army, The	1988	2	3	-	-	-
SIM Canada	1897	6	-	-	-	-
TEAM of Canada	1939	3	-	-	2	-
Youth With A Mission		1	-	-	-	-
	Totals:	20	3	-	2	-

CHAPTER 11

United States Catholic Mission Association

3029 Fourth Street, NE
Washington DC 20017
Ph: 202-832-3112
Fax: 202-832-3688
Email: uscma@uscatholicmission.org
Web site: www.uscatholicmission.org
Sr. Christine Beckett, GHMS, President
Sr. Rosanne Rustemeyer, Executive Director

We are happy to share with you the compilation of the missionary survey results received by the U.S. Catholic Mission Association in response to a questionnaire and updated 1997 statistics originally mailed to 672 institutes in April, 1999. A fax reminder and follow-up mailing was done in August, 1999. Acknowledging that our mission outreach is to the global community, for the first time this tabulation is inclusive of U.S. citizens serving in mission both in the United States and outside the borders of this country. While USCMA has been compiling these statistics on U.S. citizens working outside the country for many years, this is the first time results are shared on missioners working in the U.S. A trial survey was conducted in 1996-97 to assure accuracy. Also included is a section on charts and analysis of the new data received in relation to previous data.

Guidelines to the Presentation

The following 1998-1999 tabulation of United States Catholic missioners serving abroad has been compiled by the U.S. Catholic Mission Association from data gathered from many sources. USCMA has compiled the lists of missioners from data forms received from mission-sending groups and home dioceses (with additional reference to *The Official Catholic Directory*). They are, therefore, as reliable as the most diligent effort can make them and as the constant changes in personnel will allow. Some comment, however, on several terms is necessary.

The lists of data include only U.S. missioners, which means those who are or have been United States citizens by birth or naturalization. Those who have taken out citizenship in their country of mission service are still listed here as missioners from the United States. On the other hand, citizens of other countries serving as members of mission-sending groups headquartered in the U.S., are not listed. As an example, there are numerous Maryknoll sisters serving abroad, often in countries other than their homeland who are not U.S. citizens and therefore are not listed here among the Maryknoll sisters serving as U.S. Catholic missioners abroad. This policy helps to prevent overlapping when the various national mission councils publish their tabulations. It must be remembered, however, that mission-sending groups which appear to have only very few members in a given mission field may have many more who are not of U.S. citizenship.

The lists bear the heading U.S. Catholic Missioners. This includes all those Catholics who are sponsored by Catholic mission-sending agencies, even if they work for projects not sponsored by the Catholic Church.

The term missioner is used in its generally accepted sense. It includes not only those engaged in the primary and subsequent stages of evangelization but also those in closely related areas of community service and development.

The term serving ordinarily stands for service over a period of years. While some groups provide opportunities for short-term service, only those individuals are included in these statistics who serve for a minimum of one year.

The term abroad means "outside" of the 50 United States. Those working in Alaska and Hawaii are not included in this data as missioners in foreign areas as they were in previous surveys. While Puerto Rico and the Virgin Islands are U.S. territories, they are not states and so their data falls in the "abroad" category for the statistical purposes of this inventory.

The 1998-1999 tabulation includes, for the first time, the many "home missioners/ volunteers" working in cross-cultural situations in the U.S. Also, recent political shifts have enabled a renewed mission effort in Eastern Europe.

U.S. Catholic Missioners: 1998-1999 By Country, Gender, and Sending Organization

ALBANIA
WOMEN: Missionaries of Charity (NE Region) 1...TOTAL 1

ALGERIA
WOMEN: Little Sisters of the Poor (NY) 1...TOTAL 1

AMERICAN SAMOA
MEN: Lay Mission-Helpers Association 1; Maryknoll Fathers & Brothers 1...TOTAL 2

WOMEN: Lay Mission-Helpers Association 2; Maryknoll Sisters 1...TOTAL 3

ANTIGUA
WOMEN: Providence, Sisters (IN) 2...TOTAL 2

ARGENTINA
MEN: Cabrini Mission Corps 1; Jesuits (WI) 1; LaSalette Fathers (No. American Prov.) 6; Marian Fathers (IL) 1; Maryknoll Mission Assoc of the Faithful 1...TOTAL 10

WOMEN: Cabrini Mission Corps 1; Christian Charity, Sisters (IL) 1; Christian Charity, Sisters (NJ) 1; Maryknoll Mission Assoc of the Faithful 1; Missionary Srs of Sacred Heart 1; St. Casimir, Sisters (IL) 3...TOTAL 8

ARMENIA

WOMEN: Charity, Sisters (OH) 1...TOTAL 1

AUSTRALIA

MEN: Divine Word, Society (IL) 8; Franciscan OFM Cap (MI) 1...TOTAL 9

WOMEN: Franciscan Missionaries of Mary 1; Holy Family of Nazareth, Srs (IL) 4; Holy Family of Nazareth, Srs (Phil, PA) 1; Little Sisters of Jesus 1; Missionary Sr Servs of Holy Spirit 2...TOTAL 9

AUSTRIA

MEN: Legionaries of Christ 1...TOTAL 1

BAHAMAS

MEN: Benedictine - Am Cassinese Cong (MN) 6; Cong. of the Sacred Hearts (MA) 3; Passionists (NJ) 2; Providence Diocese 1...TOTAL 12

WOMEN: Charity, Sisters (NY) 4; Dominican Sisters (Caldwell, NJ) 2; Mercy, Sisters (ME) 2...TOTAL 8

BANGLADESH

MEN: Franciscan Third Order Regular (FL) 1; Holy Cross Brothers (IN) 3; Holy Cross Brothers (TX) 1; Holy Cross Fathers (CT) 1; Holy Cross Fathers (IN) 8; Marianists (MO) 1; Maryknoll Fathers & Brothers 3; Pontifical Institute for Foreign Missions 1...TOTAL 19

WOMEN: Holy Cross, Cong. Of Sisters (IN) 7; Maryknoll Sisters 3...TOTAL 10

BELGIUM

MEN: Lansing Diocese 1; New York Archdiocese 1...TOTAL 2

WOMEN: Franciscan Sisters of Atonement 1...TOTAL 1

BELIZE

MEN: Benedictine - Swiss Am Fed (AR) 4; Jesuit Volunteers: International 4; Jesuits (LA) 1; Jesuits (MO) 13; Jesuits (WI) 2; O.L. Most Holy Trinity, Society 3; St. Louis Archdiocese 3; Viatorians (IL) 2...TOTAL 32

WOMEN: Charity of Nazareth, Sisters (KY) 4; Holy Family, Sisters (LA) 4; Jesuit Volunteers: International 6; Mercy, Sisters (CT) 1; Mercy, Sisters (MD) 1; O.L. Most Holy Trinity, Society 3; Pallottine Sisters (MO) 4...TOTAL 23

BENIN

WOMEN: Daughters of Charity/Sac. Hrt. of Jesus 1...TOTAL **1**

BERMUDA

WOMEN: Charity of SVP, Sisters (Halifax) 4...TOTAL 4

BOLIVIA

MEN: Bridgeport Diocese 1; Christian Brothers, De La Salle (MD) 1; Dominican Friars (IL) 6; Fort Worth Diocese 1; Franciscan Mission Service 1; Kansas City-St Joseph (MO) Diocese 1; LaCrosse Diocese 2; LaSalette Fathers (No. American Prov.) 2; Maryknoll Fathers & Brothers 16; Maryknoll Mission Assoc of the Faithful 5; Oblates of Mary Immaculate 2; Order of Friars Minor (Holy Name Prov) 5; Salesian Lay Missioners (NY) 5; St James Society 8; St. Louis Archdiocese 10; Washington Archdiocese 1; Worcester Diocese 1; Xaverian Brothers 2...TOTAL 70

WOMEN: Adorers of the Blood of Christ (IL) 3; Bernardine Franciscan Sisters 1; Daughters of Charity (MD) 1; Daughters of Charity (MO) 1; Daughters of Charity (NY) 1; Dominican Sisters (Sinsinawa) 4; Franciscan Mission Service 1; Franciscan Sisters of Allegany 1; Maryknoll Mission Assoc of the Faithful 2; Maryknoll Sisters 24; Mercy, Sisters (Merion, PA) 1; Most Precious Blood, Sisters (MO) 6; Our Lady of Victory Missionary Sisters 3; Presentation, Sisters (Dubuque, IA) 3; Presentation, Sisters (NY) 1; Presentation, Sisters (Sioux Falls, SD) 1; Salesian Lay Missioners (NY) 6; School Sisters of Notre Dame (MD) 1...TOTAL 61

BOSNIA

MEN: Franciscan Mission Service 1...TOTAL 1

BOTSWANA

WOMEN: Ursulines (NY) 1...TOTAL 1

BRAZIL

MEN: Benedictine - Am Cassinese Cong (KS) 3; Benedictine - Am Cassinese Cong (PA) 2; Bridgeport Diocese 1; Camden Diocese 2; Columbans 3; Davenport Diocesan Volunteer Prog 4; Detroit Archdiocese 1; Franciscan Mission Service 2; Franciscan OFM Conv (NY) 2; Holy Cross Brothers (TX) 13; Jesuits (CA) 1; Jesuits (LA) 7; Jesuits (New England) 2; Kansas City (KS) Archdiocese 1; Legionaries of Christ 1; Maryknoll Fathers & Brothers 5; Maryknoll Mission Assoc of the Faithful 3; Missionhurst 2; Oblates of Mary Immaculate 9; Oblates of the Virgin Mary 1; Order of Friars Minor (Holy Name Prov) 11; Order of Friars Minor (S Heart Prov) 18; Pontifical Institute for Foreign Missions 2; Redemptorists (Brazil) 21; Redemptorists (CO) 17; Saginaw Diocese 1; St. Francis de Sales, Oblates (DE) 3; St. Francis de Sales, Oblates (OH) 2; Stigmatine Fathers 2; Xaverian Missionaries 3...TOTAL 145

WOMEN: Benedictine Sisters (Atchison, KS) 1; Benedictine Sisters (St. Joseph, MN) 3; Bernardine Franciscan Sisters 1; Columbus Diocese 1; Comboni Lay Missionary Program 3; Davenport Diocesan Volunteer Prog 4; Divine Savior, Sisters (WI) 1; Felician Sisters (IL) 1; Felician Sisters (MI) 1; Felician Sisters (NY) 1; Franciscan Mission Service 1; Franciscan Sisters (Wheaton) 3; Franciscan Sisters of Allegany 3; Franciscan Sisters of Atonement 1; Franciscan Sisters of Joliet, IL 5; Franciscan Sisters of Mary 3; Franciscan Sisters of Providence of God 4; Franciscan Sisters of Sacred Heart 3; Franciscan Sisters of St Joseph 1; Franciscan Sisters of St. George 2; Franciscan Sisters of the Poor 1; Holy Cross, Cong. of Sisters (IN) 9; IHM Sisters of Monroe 1; Imm Heart of Mary, Servs (ME) 2; Kansas City (KS) Archdiocese 1; Maryknoll Mission Assoc of the Faithful 5; Maryknoll Sisters 1; Mission Srs Imm Concept (NJ) 2; Missionary Srs of Sacred Heart 1; Notre Dame de Namur, Srs (CA) 1; Notre Dame de Namur, Srs (CT) 1; Notre Dame de Namur, Srs (MA) 1; Notre Dame de Namur, Srs (MD) 3; Notre Dame de Namur, Srs (OH) 3; Order of St. Clare (OH) 2; Poor Handmaids of Jesus Christ 1; St Joseph, Sisters, TOSF 1; St. Joseph, Cong of Srs (Concordia) 2; St. Joseph, Cong of Srs (Rockville Ctr) 1; St. Joseph, Sisters (Rochester) 10; St. Mary of Namur, Sisters (NY) 2; St. Mary of Namur, Sisters (TX) 1; Ursuline Sisters (MO) 1...TOTAL 96

BURKINA FASO

MEN: Redemptorists (PR) 1...TOTAL 1

WOMEN: Daughters of the Holy Spirit 1...TOTAL 1

CAMBODIA

MEN: Maryknoll Fathers & Brothers 3; Maryknoll Mission Assoc of the Faithful 2...TOTAL 5

WOMEN: Maryknoll Mission Assoc of the Faithful 2; Maryknoll Sisters 3...TOTAL 5

CAMEROON

MEN: Claretian Missionaries (IL) 1; Xaverian Missionaries 1...TOTAL 2

WOMEN: Daughters of Mary and Joseph 1; Daughters of the Holy Spirit 1; Holy Union Sisters

(MA) 2; Lay Mission-Helpers Association 5; Notre Dame, Cong of Srs (CT) 1; Presentation of Mary, Srs (MA) 1; Presentation of Mary, Srs (NH) 1; Servants of Mary, Srs 2; Shared Horizons 1; Ursuline Sisters (MO) 1...TOTAL 16

CANADA

MEN: Augustinians of the Assumption 1; Buffalo Diocese 1; Camden Diocese 2; El Paso Diocese 1; Fort Wayne-South Bend Diocese 1; Franciscan Friars of Atonement 9; Holy Family, Missionaries of 1; Jesuits (MD) 1; Lansing Diocese 1; LaSalette Fathers (No. American Prov.) 1; Legionaries of Christ 1; Oblates of Mary Immaculate 3; Providence Diocese 1; Salesians (NY) 4; San Bernardino Diocese 1; Springfield (IL) Diocese 1...TOTAL 30

WOMEN: Franciscan Mission Srs O.L. Sorrows 1; Franciscan Sisters of Atonement 4; Franciscan Sisters of Providence of God 1; Little Sisters of the Poor (NY) 4; Mission de N D des Anges, Srs (Quebec) 3; Mission Srs Imm Concept (Quebec) 13; Missionaries of Charity (NE Region) 1; Missionary Srs of Our Lady of Africa 2; Sacred Heart, Society 1; Scalabrini Sisters (IL) 2; Sisters of St Chretienne 1; St. Joseph of Peace, Sisters 5; St. Mary of Namur, Sisters (NY) 1...TOTAL 39

CENTRAL AFRICAN REPUBLIC

MEN: Franciscan OFM (ME) 1...TOTAL 1

WOMEN: Missionaries of Charity (NE Region) 1...TOTAL 1

CHAD

MEN: Missionaries of Africa 1...TOTAL 1

CHILE

MEN: Columban Lay Mission Program 1; Columbans 4; Holy Cross Associates 2; Holy Cross Brothers (IN) 1; Holy Cross Brothers (NY) 1; Holy Cross Fathers (IN) 11; Jesuits (MD) 6; Maryknoll Fathers & Brothers 17; Maryknoll Mission Assoc of the Faithful 4; Precious Blood, Society (OH) 3; Salesians (NY) 1...TOTAL 51

WOMEN: Columban Lay Mission Program 2; Columbans 1; Daughters of the Holy Spirit 2; Holy Child Jesus, Society (PA) 4; Holy Cross Associates 3; Holy Cross, Sisters (NH) 1; Jesuit Volunteers: International 4; Maryknoll Mission Assoc of the Faithful 3; Maryknoll Sisters 11; Mercy, Sisters (MI) 1; Mercy, Sisters (Rochester) 5; Precious Blood, Sisters (OH) 5; Response-Ability Program 4; School Sisters of Notre Dame (CT) 3; School Sisters of St. Francis of Bethlehem, PA 1; School Sisters of St. Francis of Pgh, PA 1; St. Anne, Sisters (MA) 1; St. Columban, Sisters 3; St. Joseph Carondelet, Srs (CA) 2; St. Joseph Carondelet, Srs (NY) 1; Ursuline Sisters (KY) 1...TOTAL 59

CHINA PRC - Hong Kong SAR

[Missioners serve in Hong Kong. In China, U.S. personnel are present through professional service.]

MEN: Columbans 2; Jesuits (CA) 1; Jesuits (MD) 1; Maryknoll Fathers & Brothers 36; Maryknoll Mission Assoc of the Faithful 1; New York Archdiocese 1; Order of Friars Minor (S Heart Prov) 2; Salesians (NY) 1...TOTAL 45

WOMEN: Columban Lay Mission Program 1; Daughters of Charity (MO) 2; Franciscan Mission Srs O.L. Sorrows 5; Good Shepherd Sisters (MO) 2; Little Sisters of the Poor (NY) 2; Maryknoll Sisters 21; Missionary Benedicitine Sisters 1; Providence, Sisters (IN) 1; Scarboro Lay Mission Office 4; St. Columban, Sisters 1...TOTAL 40

COLOMBIA

MEN: Basilian Fathers (Toronto) 2; Consolata Missionary Fathers 1; Denver Archdiocese 1; Missionary Servants/Most Holy Trinity 1; Sacred Heart Missionaries (IL) 2; Scalabrini Fathers (IL) 1; Viatorians (IL) 2...TOTAL 10

WOMEN: Dominican Sisters (NY) 2; Franciscan Sisters (Rochester, MN) 5; Grey Nuns (MA) 2; Little Sisters of the Poor (NY) 1; Manchester Diocese 1; Marist Missionary Sisters (MA) 2; Portland (ME) Diocese 1...TOTAL 14

CONGO

MEN: Adorno Fathers 1; Divine Word, Society (IL) 1...TOTAL 2

WOMEN: Little Sisters of the Poor (NY) 1; Mission Srs Imm Heart of Mary 1; St. Ursula, Society 1; Ursuline Sisters (Tildonk) 1...TOTAL 4

COOK ISLANDS

MEN: Cong. of the Sacred Hearts (CA) 1...TOTAL 1

COSTA RICA

MEN: Franciscan OFM Cap (MI) 2; Franciscan OFM Cap (St Mary Prov) 1; Franciscan OFM Conv (NY) 2; Missionary Servants/Most Holy Trinity 3; New Orleans Archdiocese 1...TOTAL 9

WOMEN: Christian Foundation for Children & Aging 1; Missionary Cenacle Volunteers 1...TOTAL 2

COTE D'IVOIRE

MEN: African Missions, Society of 1...TOTAL 1

WOMEN: St. Joseph of Lyons, Srs 1...TOTAL 1

CUBA

MEN: Christian Brothers, De La Salle (MD) 1...TOTAL 1

CYPRUS

MEN: Franciscan OFM (DC) 1; Milwaukee Archdiocese 1...TOTAL 2

CZECH REP

MEN: Marianists (OH) 1; New York Archdiocese 1...TOTAL 2

WOMEN: Good Shepherd Sisters (DC) 1...TOTAL 1

DENMARK

MEN: Oblates of Mary Immaculate 4...TOTAL 4

DOMINICA

MEN: Redemptorists (MD) 4...TOTAL 4

WOMEN: Mission Srs Imm Heart of Mary 1...TOTAL 1

DOMINICAN REPUBLIC

MEN: Arlington Diocese 1; Green Bay Diocese 2; Milwaukee Archdiocese 1; Missionhurst 3; Montfort Missionaries (NY) 1; Redemptorists (PR) 7...TOTAL 15

WOMEN: Divine Providence, Sisters (PA) 1; Dominican Sisters (Adrian, MI) 5; Franciscan Sisters of Millvale, PA 1; Franciscan Sisters of Philadelphia 2; Holy Child Jesus, Society (PA) 2; Inter. Mission Program of the Diocese of Orlando 1; Oblate Sisters of Providence 1; Our Lady Christian Doctrine, Sisters 1; Rel Hospitalieres de St Joseph 2; Response-Ability Program 2; Schoenstatt Sisters of Mary (WI) 2; Sisters of Notre Dame (Chardon, OH) 1; St. Joseph, Cong of Srs (Rockville Ctr) 2...TOTAL 23

EAST TIMOR

WOMEN: Maryknoll Sisters 2...TOTAL 2

ECUADOR

MEN: Comboni Missionaries 1; Family Unity International, Inc. 2; Indianapolis Archdiocese 1; Jesuits (CA) 1; Jesuits (NY) 1; Metuchen Diocese 1; Rostro de Cristo Mission Vol Program 4; Salesian Lay Missioners (NY) 2; Scarboro Lay Mission Office 1; St James Society 7...TOTAL 21

WOMEN: Charity of Leavenworth, Sisters 2; Charity, Sisters (OH) 1; Divine Providence, Congregation (KY) 1; Dominican Sisters (Kenosha, WI) 1; Family Unity International, Inc. 1; Franciscan Sisters of Little Falls 3; Handmaids of Sacred Heart of Jesus 1; Rostro de Cristo Mission Vol Program 3; Salesian Lay Missioners (NY) 2; Scarboro Lay Mission Office 1; Sisters of Charity, BVM (IA) 4...TOTAL 20

EGYPT

MEN: Franciscan OFM (DC) 1; Jesuits (New England) 1; Maryknoll Fathers & Brothers 2...TOTAL 4

WOMEN: Little Sisters of the Assumption 1...TOTAL 1

EL SALVADOR

MEN: Cleveland Diocese 4; Davenport Diocese 1; Gary Diocese 1; Jesuits (LA) 1; Jesuits (NY) 1; Maryknoll Fathers & Brothers 4; Maryknoll Mission Assoc of the Faithful 1; Missionaries of Pastoral Charity Society 1; Order of Friars Minor (Imm Conc Prov) 2...TOTAL 16

WOMEN: Cleveland Diocese 4; Dominican Sisters (Sinsinawa) 1; Franciscan Sisters of Holy Family (IA) 1; Franciscan Srs Perpetual Adoration 1; Maryknoll Mission Assoc of the Faithful 5; Maryknoll Sisters 7; Notre Dame, Cong of Srs (CT) 1; Providence, Sisters (WA) 1; School Sisters of Notre Dame (MD) 1; St. Joseph, Cong of Srs (Orange) 1; Ursuline Nuns of the Cong. of Paris 1; Volunteer Missionary Movement 3...TOTAL 27

ENGLAND

MEN: Christian Brothers, De La Salle (CA) 1; Columbans 1; Divine Word, Society (IL) 2; Franciscan Friars of Atonement 3; O.L. Most Holy Trinity, Society 1; Sacred Heart, Brothers (RI) 1; Wilmington Diocese 1...TOTAL 10

WOMEN: Franciscan Sisters of Philadelphia 1; Missionaries of Charity (NE Region) 2; Missionary Sr Servs of Holy Spirit 1; Religious of the Assumption (N Am Prov) 2...TOTAL 6

ESTONIA

WOMEN: Most Precious Blood, Sisters (MO) 1...TOTAL 1

ETHIOPIA

MEN: Christian Brothers, De La Salle (CA) 1; Christian Brothers, De La Salle (NY) 2; Christian Brothers, De La Salle (RI) 2; Consolata Missionary Fathers 1; Jesuits (New England) 1; Maryknoll Fathers & Brothers 2; Spiritans (PA) 1; Vincentians (PA) 2...TOTAL 12

WOMEN: Comboni Missionary Sisters 1; Daughters of Charity (MD) 1; Daughters of Charity (MO) 1; Franciscan Missionaries of Mary 1; Franciscan Sisters of Philadelphia 1; Medical Mission Sisters 2; Medical Missionaries of Mary 2; Religious Teachers Filippini 1;St. Joseph, Sisters (Springfield) 1...TOTAL 11

FIJI

MEN: Columbans 2; Jesuits (CA) 1...TOTAL 3

WOMEN: Marist Missionary Sisters (MA) 2...TOTAL 2

FINLAND

WOMEN: Most Precious Blood, Sisters (MO) 3...TOTAL 3

FRANCE

MEN: Associate Missionaries 1; Society of St. Edmund 1...TOTAL 2

WOMEN: Associate Missionaries 3; Daughters of Charity (MO) 1; Daughters of the Holy Spirit 2; Jesus and Mary, Rel (MD) 1; Religious of the Assumption (N Am Prov) 2...TOTAL 9

GAMBIA

WOMEN: Presentation of Mary, Srs (MA) 1; School Sisters of Notre Dame (MO) 1...TOTAL 2

GERMANY

MEN: Lansing Diocese 1; Legionaries of Christ 2; Saginaw Diocese 1; Savannah Diocese 1; Servite Friars (IL) 1; Sioux City Diocese 1...TOTAL 7

WOMEN: Dominican Sisters (Mission San Jose) 1; Religious of the Assumption (N Am Prov) 1; School Sisters of Notre Dame (WI) 1...TOTAL 3

GHANA

MEN: Comboni Lay Missionary Program 1; Divine Word, Society (IL) 10; Franciscan OFM Conv (MD) 6; Holy Cross Brothers (IN) 5; Holy Cross Fathers (IN) 1; Jesuits (NY) 1; Mission Doctors Association 1; Missionaries of Africa 3; SMA Lay Missionaries 1...TOTAL 29

WOMEN: Comboni Lay Missionary Program 3; Divine Providence, Congregation (KY) 4; Divine Providence, Congregation (TX) 2; Franciscan Missionaries of Mary 1; Holy Cross, Cong. of Sisters (IN) 4; IHM Sisters of Monroe 1; Loretto, Sisters (CO) 2; Medical Mission Sisters 3; Mission Doctors Association 1; Missionary Sr Servs of Holy Spirit 4; Missionary Srs of Our Lady of Africa 1; Presentation, Sisters (NY) 1; San Bernardino Diocese 1; School Sisters of Notre Dame (CT) 2; School Sisters of Notre Dame (MO) 5; School Sisters of Notre Dame (TX) 5; Sisters of Charity, BVM (IA) 1; SMA Lay Missionaries 2...TOTAL 43

GREECE

MEN: Order of Friars Minor (St John Bapt Prov) 1...TOTAL 1

GUAM

MEN: Franciscan OFM Cap (St Mary Prov) 7; Great Falls-Billings Diocese 1; Jesuit Volunteers: International 1; Jesuits (NY) 2...TOTAL 11

WOMEN: Franciscan Sisters of Joliet, IL 1; Mercedarian Missionaries of Berriz 2...TOTAL 3

GUATEMALA

MEN: Augustinians (PA) 1; Benedictine - Swiss Am Fed (IL) 2; Benedictine - Swiss Am Fed (LA) 1; Benedictine - Swiss Am Fed (SD) 3; Christian Foundation for Children & Aging 2; Claretian Missionaries (IL) 3; Claretian Vol & Lay Missionaries 2; Dominican Friars (CA) 1; Galveston-Houston Diocese 1; God's Child Project 1; Greensburg Diocese 1; Helena Diocese 1; Jesuits (NY) 2; Kansas City-St Joseph (MO) Diocese 1; Maryknoll Fathers & Brothers 13; Missionhurst 1; New Ulm Diocese 3; Oblates of Mary Immaculate 2; Oklahoma City Archdiocese 1; Order of Friars Minor (Imm Conc Prov) 3; Order of Friars Minor (OL Guadalupe Prov) 1; Order of Friars Minor (St Barbara Prov) 2; Precious Blood, Society (OH) 1; Spokane Diocese 1; Volunteer Missionary Movement 2...TOTAL 52

WOMEN: Adorers of the Blood of Christ (IL) 1; Adorers of the Blood of Christ (PA) 1; Benedictine Sisters (Ferdinand, IN) 3; Benedictine Sisters (Watertown, SD) 1; Charity, Sisters (NY) 6; Charity, Sisters (OH) 1; Christian Foundation for Children & Aging 4; Claretian Vol & Lay Missionaries 1; Dominican Sisters (Akron, OH) 1; Dominican Sisters (Houston, TX) 2; Dominican Sisters (Sinsinawa) 2; Franciscan Mission Service 1; Franciscan Sisters of Little Falls 1; Franciscan Sisters of Peace 2; Franciscan Sisters of Philadelphia 3; Helena Diocese 2; IHM Sisters of Scranton 1; Maryknoll Sisters 26; Mercy, Sisters (CT) 2; Mercy, Sisters (Dallas, PA) 1; Mercy, Sisters (Pgh, PA) 1; Mission Srs Imm Heart of Mary 1; Notre Dame, Cong of Srs

(CT) 2; Order of St. Clare (TN) 2; Precious Blood, Sisters (OH) 3; Presentation, Sisters (CA) 2; Presentation, Sisters (Dubuque, IA) 2; Presentation, Sisters (Sioux Falls, SD) 1; San Bernardino Diocese 1; School Sisters of Notre Dame (MN) 3; School Sisters of Notre Dame (TX) 2; School Sisters of Notre Dame (WI) 1; School Sisters of St. Francis (Milwaukee, WI) 2; Sisters of Charity Incarnate Word 2; Sisters of Charity, BVM (IA) 1; Spokane Diocese 1; SSSF Volunteers of Tau 1; Volunteer Missionary Movement 4...TOTAL 94

GUYANA

MEN: Catholic Medical Mission Board 1; Scarboro Lay Mission Office 2...TOTAL 3

WOMEN: Mercy, Sisters (NE) 1; Scarboro Lay Mission Office 3; Ursuline Nuns of the Roman Union (MA) 1...TOTAL 5

HAITI

MEN: Christian Foundation for Children & Aging 1; Christian Instruction, Brothers (ME) 2; Hands Together, Inc. 1; Missionhurst 1; O.L. Most Holy Trinity, Society 1; Oblates of Mary Immaculate 14; Our Little Brothers & Sisters 1; Passionists (NJ) 1; St. Francis de Sales, Oblates (DE) 1; Xaverian Brothers 2...TOTAL 25

WOMEN: Blessed Sacrament Sisters 2; Daughters of Charity (CA) 1; Daughters of Charity (IN) 1; Daughters of Charity (NY) 1; Dominican Sisters (Edmonds, WA) 1; Franciscan Missionaries of O. L. (N Am Prov) 1; Hands Together, Inc. 1; Holy Cross, Sisters (NH) 3; Hospital Sisters of St. Francis (Am Prov) 2; Imm Heart of Mary, Servs (ME) 1; Jesus and Mary, Rel (MD) 3; Little Sisters of Jesus 1; Mercy, Sisters (CT) 1; Missionaries of Charity (NE Region) 1; O.L. Most Holy Trinity, Society 1; Sisters of St Joseph (IN) 1; Spiritan Associates 1; St. Anne, Sisters (MA) 1...TOTAL 24

HONDURAS

MEN: Dominican Friars (LA) 1; Franciscan Mission Service 1; Franciscan OFM Cap (MI) 1; Franciscan OFM Cap (St Mary Prov) 2; Franciscan OFM Conv (MD) 1; Hartford Archdiocese 1; Jesuits (CA) 4; Jesuits (MO) 8; Jesuits (New England) 1; Jesuits (WI) 2; Maryknoll Fathers & Brothers 6; Order of Friars Minor (Imm Conc Prov) 2...TOTAL 30

WOMEN: Dominican Sisters (Columbus, OH) 1; Dominican Sisters (Grand Rapids, MI) 1; IHM Sisters of Monroe 1; Mercy, Sisters (CA) 1; Mercy, Sisters (Dallas, PA) 1; Mercy, Sisters (IL) 2; School Sisters of Notre Dame (MO) 3; School Sisters of Notre Dame (TX) 2; School Sisters of Notre Dame (WI) 2; School Sisters of St. Francis (Milwaukee, WI) 2; St. Agnes, Cong. of Sisters (WI) 2...TOTAL 18

HONG KONG - See China

HUNGARY

WOMEN: Sacred Heart, Society Devoted (CA) 4; School Sisters of Notre Dame (TX) 1; St. Joseph, Cong of Srs (Orange) 1...TOTAL 6

INDIA

MEN: Adorno Fathers 1; Cong. of the Sacred Hearts (MA) 3; Davenport Diocesan Volunteer Prog 1; Divine Word, Society (IL) 1; Duluth Diocese 1; Jesuits (IL) 10; Jesuits (MD) 9; Jesuits (MI) 11; Marianists (MD) 1; Marianists (MO) 6; Passionists (IL) 1; Philadelphia Archdiocese 1; Pontifical Institute for Foreign Missions 1; Sacred Heart, Priests of the (WI) 1; St. Francis de Sales, Oblates (DE) 1; St. Francis de Sales, Oblates (OH) 1...TOTAL 50

WOMEN: Charity of Nazareth, Sisters (KY) 2; Christian Foundation for Children & Aging 1; Holy Cross, Cong. of Sisters (IN) 1; Little Sisters of the Poor (NY) 3; Mary Immaculate, Sisters (PA) 1; Missionaries of Charity (NE Region) 4; Sisters of Notre Dame (Chardon, OH) 3; Sisters of the Sacred Hearts (HI) 3...TOTAL 18

INDONESIA

MEN: Crosier Fathers & Brothers 5; Divine Word, Society (IL) 7; Jesuits (New England) 1; Maryknoll Fathers & Brothers 2; Oblates of Mary Immaculate 1; Sacred Heart, Priests of the (WI) 2; Xaverian Missionaries 1...TOTAL 19

WOMEN: Franciscan Sisters 1; Sacred Heart, Society 1...TOTAL 2

IRELAND

MEN: Associate Missionaries 1; Marianists (OH) 5; Religious of the Assumption (N Am Prov) 1; San Antonio Archdiocese 1...TOTAL 8

WOMEN: Associate Missionaries 2; Dominican Sisters (Blauvelt, NY) 1; Franciscan Sisters of Philadelphia 5; Religious of the Assumption (N Am Prov) 3...TOTAL 11

ISRAEL

MEN: Augustinians of the Assumption 1; Christian Brothers, De La Salle (CA) 1; Christian Brothers, De La Salle (Midwest) 4; Christian Brothers, De La Salle (NY) 1; Christian Brothers, De La Salle (RI) 1; Franciscan OFM (DC) 11; Jesuits (New England) 1; Order of Friars Minor (Assumption Prov) 1; Sioux Falls Diocese 1...TOTAL 22

WOMEN: Daughters of Charity (IN) 1; Holy Cross, Cong. of Sisters (IN) 1; Ursulines (NY) 1...TOTAL 3

ITALY

MEN: Christian Brothers, De La Salle (Midwest) 1; Divine Word, Society (IL) 5; Franciscan Friars of Atonement 3; Jesuits (NY) 1; Legionaries of Christ 2; Marianists (OH) 1; Metuchen Diocese 1; O.L. Most Holy Trinity, Society 1; Order of Friars Minor (S Heart Prov) 3; Redemptorists (PR) 1; Salesians (NY) 2...TOTAL 21

WOMEN: Christian Charity, Sisters (IL) 1; Daughters of St Mary of Providence 1; Daughters of Wisdom 1; Divine Savior, Sisters (WI) 2; Holy Family of Nazareth, Srs (Pgh, PA) 1; Holy Family of Nazareth, Srs (Phil, PA) 2; Holy Union Sisters (MA) 2; Jesus and Mary, Rel (MD) 1; Marist Missionary Sisters (MA) 1; Mission Srs Imm Heart of Mary 1; Missionaries of Charity (NE Region) 1; Missionary Benedictine Sisters 1; Missionary Srs of Our Lady of Africa 2; Notre Dame de Namur, Srs (CT) 1; O.L. Most Holy Trinity, Society 1; School Sisters of Notre Dame (WI) 2; Side by Side Lay Volunteer Program 1...TOTAL 22

JAMAICA

MEN: Franciscan Friars of Atonement 1; Jesuits (New England) 18; Passionists (NJ) 3...TOTAL 22

WOMEN: Dominican Sisters (Blauvelt, NY) 1; Franciscan Sisters 1; Franciscan Sisters of Allegany 3; LAMP Ministries 1; Marist Missionary Sisters (MA) 5; Mercy, Sisters (OH) 6; Mission Srs Imm Heart of Mary 1; Missionaries of Charity (NE Region) 1; Servants of Mary (NE) 2; St. Joseph, Cong of Srs (Pittsburgh) 4...TOTAL 25

JAPAN

MEN: Augustinians (IL) 1; Augustinians (PA) 6; Benedictine - Am Cassinese Cong (MN) 7; Columban Lay Mission Program 1; Columbans 5; Cong. of the Sacred Hearts (MA) 7; Divine Word, Society (IL) 10; Franciscan Friars of Atonement 4; Franciscan OFM Cap (MI) 1; Franciscan OFM Cap (St Mary Prov) 2; Franciscan OFM Conv (MD) 3; Jesuits (CA) 5; Jesuits (IL) 1; Jesuits (MD) 4; Jesuits (MI) 2; Jesuits (New England) 1; Jesuits (NY) 4; Marianists (MO) 1; Marianists (OH) 1; Marist Brothers (NY) 4; Maryknoll Fathers & Brothers 27; Maryknoll Mission Assoc of the Faithful 1; Missionhurst 1; Oblates of Mary Immaculate 9; Order of Friars Minor (Assumption Prov) 1; Order of Friars Minor (Holy Name Prov) 7; Order of Friars Minor (St John Bapt Prov) 1; Passionists (IL) 7; Pontifical Institute for Foreign Missions 2; Salesian Lay Missioners (NY) 1; Salesians (NY) 1; Xaverian Missionaries 2...TOTAL 130

WOMEN: Daughters of Charity (IN) 1; Daughters of Charity (MO) 4; Dominican Sisters of the Roman Congregation 1; Franciscan Missionaries of Mary 2; Hospital Sisters of St. Francis (Am Prov) 1; Maryknoll Mission Assoc of the Faithful 1; Maryknoll Sisters 13; Notre Dame de Namur, Srs (MA) 1; Notre Dame de Namur, Srs (MD) 1; Order of St. Clare (MA) 1; Passionist Nuns (PA) 2; Presentation of Mary, Srs (MA) 1; Salesian Lay Missioners (NY) 1; School Sisters of Notre Dame (IL) 1; School Sisters of Notre Dame (MO) 4; St. Joseph Carondelet, Srs (CA) 1; St. Joseph Carondelet, Srs (NY) 1; St. Joseph, Cong of Srs (Wichita) 2...TOTAL 39

JORDAN

MEN: Franciscan OFM (DC) 1; Jesuits (New England) 2...TOTAL 3

WOMEN: Comboni Missionary Sisters 1...TOTAL 1

KAZAKHSTAN

MEN: Order of Friars Minor (Assumption Prov) 1...TOTAL 1

KENYA

MEN: African Missions, Society of 1; Augustinians of the Assumption 2; Carmelites, Discalced (WI) 3; Catholic Medical Mission Board 2; Christian Brothers, Cong. (NY) 1; Christian Brothers, De La Salle (CA) 1; Christian Brothers, De La Salle (MD) 3; Christian Brothers, De La Salle (Midwest) 4; Christian Brothers, De La Salle (NY) 4; Christian Brothers, De La Salle (RI) 3; Consolata Missionary Fathers 4; Divine Word, Society (IL) 1; Dominican Friars (CA) 1; Dominican Friars (IL) 1; Dominican Friars (NY) 3; Franciscan Mission Service 1; Holy Cross Brothers (NY) 1; Holy Cross Fathers (IN) 3; Jesuits (IL) 1; Jesuits (MD) 1; Jesuits (NY) 1; Jesuits (OR) 1; Jesuits (WI) 3; Lalmba Association 1; Marianists (CA) 2; Marianists (MD) 1; Marianists (OH) 6; Maryknoll Fathers & Brothers 15; Maryknoll Mission Assoc of the Faithful 3; Mill Hill Missionaries 2; O.L. Most Holy Trinity, Society 1; Order of Friars Minor (Holy Name Prov) 2; Order of Friars Minor (St John Bapt Prov) 1; Passionists (NJ) 1; Sacred Heart, Brothers (NY) 2; SMA Lay Missionaries 1; Vincentians (MO) 6; Xaverian Brothers 1...TOTAL 91

WOMEN: Catholic Medical Mission Board 2; Comboni Missionary Sisters 2; Consolata Missionary Sisters 7; Felician Sisters 1; Felician Sisters (NJ) 1; Franciscan Mission Srs for Africa 1; Franciscan Missionaries of Mary 3; Franciscan Sisters (Buffalo, NY) 2; Franciscan Sisters of Philadelphia 4; Lalmba Association 3; Lasallian Volunteers 2; Lay Mission-Helpers Association 1; Maryknoll Mission Assoc of the Faithful 4; Maryknoll Sisters 7; Medical Mission Sisters 2; Missionaries of Charity (NE Region) 1; Missionary Srs of Our Lady of Africa 2; Notre Dame de Namur, Srs (CA) 3; Notre Dame de Namur, Srs (MA) 5; Notre Dame de Namur, Srs (MD) 1; Sacred Heart of Jesus & Poor, Serv 3; Sacred Heart, Society 3; Salesian Lay Missioners (NY) 1; School Sisters of Notre Dame (MN) 3; School Sisters of Notre Dame (MO) 1; School Sisters of Notre Dame (WI) 2; Sisters of Charity Incarnate Word 9; SMA Lay Missionaries 2; St. Joseph, Sisters (Springfield) 3...TOTAL 81

KOREA

MEN: Augustinians of the Assumption 1; Columbans 4; Divine Word, Society (IL) 2; Maryknoll Fathers & Brothers 20; Salesians (NY) 2...TOTAL 29

WOMEN: Adorers of the Blood of Christ (KS) 2; Charity of Seton Hill, Sisters (PA) 4; Franciscan Missionaries of Mary 2; Good Shepherd Sisters (MO) 2; Little Sisters of the Poor (NY) 1; Maryknoll Sisters 12; Mission Sisters, Sacred Heart (PA) 1; Missionary Benedictine Sisters 1; Order of St. Clare (MN) 2; St. Columban, Sisters 2...TOTAL 29

LATVIA

MEN: Marianists (OH) 1...TOTAL 1

LEBANON

MEN: Jesuits (New England) 3...TOTAL 3

WOMEN: Daughters of Charity (IN) 1; Jesus and Mary, Rel (MD) 1...TOTAL 2

LESOTHO

MEN: Sacred Heart, Brothers (RI) 3...TOTAL 3

LIBERIA

MEN: African Missions, Society of 3; Salesians (NY) 2; SMA Lay Missionaries 3...TOTAL 8

WOMEN: Bernardine Franciscan Sisters 1; Franciscan Missionaries of Mary 2; SMA Lay Missionaries 1...TOTAL 4

LITHUANIA

MEN: Dominican Friars (NY) 1; Glenmary Home Missioners 1; Jesuits (LA) 1...TOTAL 3

WOMEN: Franciscan Sisters of Providence of God 1...TOTAL 1

MADAGASCAR

MEN: LaSalette Fathers (No. American Prov.) 3...TOTAL 3

WOMEN: Christian Foundation for Children & Aging 1; Daughters of Charity (NY) 1...TOTAL 2

MALAWI

MEN: Comboni Missionaries 1; Marianists (OH) 4; Missionaries of Africa 2; Order of Friars Minor (Holy Name Prov) 1; Order of Friars Minor (St John Bapt Prov) 1...TOTAL 9

WOMEN: Missionary Srs of Our Lady of Africa 1...TOTAL 1

MALI

WOMEN: Holy Cross, Sisters (NH) 2...TOTAL 2

MALTA

WOMEN: Little Sisters of the Poor (NY) 1...TOTAL 1

MARSHALL ISLANDS

MEN: Jesuit Volunteers: International 4; Jesuits (NY) 5; Lay Mission-Helpers Association 1...TOTAL 10

WOMEN: Jesuit Volunteers: International 2; Lay Mission-Helpers Association 2...TOTAL 4

MEXICO

MEN: Augustinians of the Assumption 2; Austin Diocese 1; Basilian Fathers (Toronto) 5; Carmelite Friars (IL) 4; Christian Brothers, De La Salle (CA) 1; Christian Brothers, De La Salle (NY) 3; Comboni Lay Missionary Program 1; Comboni Missionaries 2; Davenport Diocesan Volunteer Prog 1; Divine Word, Society (IL) 7; Dominican Friars (CA) 4; Erie Diocese 1; Franciscan OFM Cap (MI) 1; Franciscan OFM Conv (CA) 1; Franciscan OFM Conv (IL) 3; Green Bay Diocese 1; Holy Cross Fathers (IN) 5; Holy Family, Missionaries of 2; Jackson Diocese 1; Jesuits (CA) 2; Jesuits (MD) 1; Jesuits (MO) 1; Lay Mission Oblates of Mary Imm 1; Legionaries of Christ 7; Marianists (MO) 7; Maryknoll Fathers & Brothers 13; Maryknoll Mission Assoc of the Faithful 3; Missionaries of Africa 1; Missionary Servants/Most Holy Trinity 3; New York Archdiocese 1; O.L. Most Holy Trinity, Society 1; Oblates of Mary Immaculate 10; Order of Friars Minor (Assumption Prov) 1; Order of Friars Minor (OL Guadalupe Prov) 2; Order of Friars Minor (St Barbara Prov) 6; Order of Friars Minor (St John Bapt Prov) 1; Our Little Brothers & Sisters 2; Pontifical Institute for Foreign Missions 1; Redemptorists (PR) 1; Resurrection Congregation 3; Saginaw Diocese 1; San Francisco Archdiocese 1; Savannah Diocese 1; Sin Fronteras Mission 1; Spiritans (TX) 1; St. Francis de Sales, Oblates (DE) 2; St.

Francis de Sales, Oblates (OH) 1; St. Joseph, Congregation of 1; Xaverian Missionaries 1...TOTAL 124

WOMEN: Cleveland Diocese 1; Comboni Lay Missionary Program 1; Daughters of Mary and Joseph 2; Daughters of St Mary of Providence 1; Davenport Diocesan Volunteer Prog 3; Divine Providence, Congregation (TX) 1; Dominican Sisters (Mission San Jose) 4; Dominican Sisters (San Rafael, CA) 1; Erie Diocese 4; Felician Franciscan Sisters (Assumpt Prov) 4; Franciscan Sisters of Penance 1; Franciscan Sisters of Providence of God 2; Franciscan Sisters of Tiffin, OH 2; Franciscan Srs Perpetual Adoration 1; Holy Cross, Cong. of Sisters (IN) 3; Holy Spirit/ Mary Imm, Srs (TX) 7; Humility of Mary, Cong (IA) 3; IHM Sisters of Monroe 1; Marianites of Holy Cross, Cong. 1; Marist Sisters 1; Maryknoll Mission Assoc of the Faithful 3; Maryknoll Sisters 9; Mercedarian Missionaries of Berriz 2; Mercy, Sisters (IL) 1; Mercy, Sisters (NE) 1; Missionaries of Charity (NE Region) 1; Missionary Cenacle Volunteers 1; Missionary Servants/ Most Blessed Trinity 3; Missionary Sr Servs of Holy Spirit 1; Missionary Srs, Most Sacred Heart (PA) 2; Our Little Brothers & Sisters 2; Poor Handmaids of Jesus Christ 6; Quest 4; Sacred Heart of Jesus, Sisters (TX) 3; Sacred Heart, Society 1; Scalabrini Sisters (IL) 1; Sin Fronteras Mission 3; Social Service, Sisters (CA) 2; St Francis Mission Community (TX) 1; St. Joseph of Lyons, Srs 1; St. Joseph, Cong of Srs (Orange) 2; Ursuline Sisters (MO) 3; Ursulines (NY) 1; Xaverian Mission Soc of Mary (MA) 2...TOTAL 100

MICRONESIA

MEN: Jesuit Volunteers: International 6; Jesuits (LA) 1; Jesuits (NY) 12; Lay Mission-Helpers Association 1...TOTAL 20

WOMEN: Jesuit Volunteers: International 7; Maryknoll Sisters 8; Mercedarian Missionaries of Berriz 7; Mercy, Sisters (NC) 2...TOTAL 24

MOROCCO

MEN: Order of Friars Minor (Assumption Prov) 1; Order of Friars Minor (S Heart Prov) 1...TOTAL 2

MOZAMBIQUE

MEN: Jesuits (New England) 1; Jesuits (OR) 1; Maryknoll Fathers & Brothers 3...TOTAL 5

MYANMAR

MEN: Jesuits (MI) 1...TOTAL 1

NAMIBIA

MEN: Franciscan Mission Service 1; Maryknoll Fathers & Brothers 1; Sacred Heart Missionaries (IL) 1; St. Francis de Sales, Oblates (OH) 1...TOTAL 4

WOMEN: Maryknoll Sisters 1; Missionary Benedictine Sisters 2; Missionary Srs, Most Sacred Heart (PA) 2...TOTAL 5

NEPAL

MEN: Jesuit Volunteers: International 2; Jesuits (IL) 4; Jesuits (MI) 1; Maryknoll Fathers & Brothers 2...TOTAL 9

WOMEN: Jesuit Volunteers: International 4; Maryknoll Sisters 1; School Sisters of Notre Dame (IL) 1; School Sisters of Notre Dame (MO) 1...TOTAL 7

NETHERLANDS

MEN: Legionaries of Christ 1; Philadelphia Archdiocese 1...TOTAL 2

NEW CALEDONIA

MEN: Marist Fathers & Brothers (MA) 1...TOTAL 1

NICARAGUA

MEN: Blessed Sacrament, Cong. of (OH) 1; Christian Brothers, De La Salle (Midwest) 1; Franciscan OFM Cap (MI) 8; Franciscan OFM Cap (St Mary Prov) 1; Jesuit Volunteers: International 1; Jesuits (MD) 1; Jesuits (MI) 1; Jesuits (MO) 1; Montfort Missionaries (NY) 2...TOTAL 17

WOMEN: Capuchin Franciscan Volunteer Corps 3; Charity of Nazareth, Sisters (KY) 1; Franciscan Sisters of Philadelphia 1; Franciscan Sisters of the Holy Cross 1; Holy Names, Sisters (CA) 2; Intercommunity Ministry Volunteer Program 1; Jesuit Volunteers: International 4; Marianites of Holy Cross, Cong. 1; Maryknoll Sisters 8; Missionaries of Charity (NE Region) 1; Notre Dame de Namur, Srs (CA) 1; Notre Dame de Namur, Srs (OH) 1; St. Agnes, Cong. of Sisters (WI) 9; St. Joseph Carondelet, Srs (CA) 1; St. Joseph of Medaille, Sisters 2; St. Teresa of Jesus, Soc 1...TOTAL 38

NIGERIA

MEN: Christian Brothers, De La Salle (Midwest) 1; Claretian Missionaries (IL) 1; Dominican Friars (IL) 8; Jesuits (LA) 1; Jesuits (MD) 4; Jesuits (NY) 11; Redemptorists (CO) 5...TOTAL 31

WOMEN: Daughters of the Holy Spirit 2; Dominican Sisters (Great Bend, KS) 1; Franciscan Sisters (Wheaton) 1; Franciscan Sisters of Millvale, PA 1; Franciscan Sisters of Tiffin, OH 1; Holy Child Jesus, Society (African Prov) 3; Holy Child Jesus, Society (PA) 1; Medical Missionaries of Mary 1; Notre Dame de Namur, Srs (CA) 1; Notre Dame de Namur, Srs (OH) 1; Parish Visitors of Mary Imm 2; School Sisters of Notre Dame (MD) 6; School Sisters of Notre Dame (MO) 1; School Sisters of Notre Dame (WI) 2; Sisters of Charity Incarnate Word 1...TOTAL25

OKINAWA

MEN: Franciscan OFM Cap (St Mary Prov) 7...TOTAL 7

PAKISTAN

MEN: Christian Brothers, De La Salle (Midwest) 1; Dominican Friars (NY) 5; Mill Hill Missionaries 1...TOTAL 7

WOMEN: Dominican Sisters (Sparkill, NY) 3; Franciscan Missionaries of Mary 1; Jesus and Mary, Rel (MD) 1; Medical Mission Sisters 4...TOTAL 9

PALAU

MEN: Jesuits (NY) 1...TOTAL 1

PANAMA

MEN: Franciscan OFM Cap (MI) 3; Holy Cross Fathers (IN) 1; Jesuits (MO) 1; Lay Mission-Helpers Association 1; Vincentians (PA) 12...TOTAL 18

WOMEN: Lay Mission-Helpers Association 1; Maryknoll Sisters 6...TOTAL 7

PAPUA NEW GUINEA

MEN: Capuchin Franciscan Volunteer Corps 2; Divine Word, Society (IL) 21; Dominican Friars (IL) 1; Franciscan OFM Cap (Mid-America Prov) 6; Franciscan OFM Cap (St Augustine Prov) 14; Lay Mission-Helpers Association 1; Marist Fathers & Brothers (DC) 1; O.L. Most Holy Trinity, Society 1; Order of Friars Minor (Assumption Prov) 1; Pontifical Institute for Foreign Missions 1; Sacred Heart Missionaries (IL) 12; Salesian Lay Missioners (NY) 1...TOTAL 62

WOMEN: Charity Sisters of Ottowa (St Joseph Prov) 1; Marist Missionary Sisters (MA) 2; Missionary Sr Servs of Holy Spirit 1; Missionary Srs, Most Sacred Heart (PA) 2; Sacred Heart of Jesus, Sisters (TX) 3; Sisters of Notre Dame (Toledo, OH) 8...TOTAL 17

PARAGUAY

MEN: Brooklyn Diocese 1; Divine Word, Society (IL) 1; Jesuits (LA) 2; Oblates of Mary Immaculate 1; Redemptorists (MD) 2...TOTAL 7

WOMEN: School Sisters of Notre Dame (CT) 1; School Sisters of Notre Dame (IL) 2...TOTAL 3

PERU

MEN: Augustinians (IL) 5; Augustinians (PA) 4; Bridgeport Diocese 1; Carmelite Friars (IL) 8; Christian Brothers, Cong. 2; Christian Brothers, Cong. (NY) 11; Comboni Missionaries 1; Dominican Friars (NY) 2; Holy Cross Brothers (IN) 1; Holy Cross Fathers (CT) 7; Holy Cross Fathers (IN) 2; Jefferson City Diocese 4; Jesuit Volunteers: International 3; Jesuits (CA) 1; Jesuits (IL) 15; Jesuits (MI) 1; LaCrosse Diocese 1; Louisville Diocese 1; Marianists (MD) 1; Marianists (MO) 2; Marist Fathers & Brothers (DC) 1; Marist Fathers & Brothers (MA) 2; Maryknoll Fathers & Brothers 17; Maryknoll Mission Assoc of the Faithful 5; Norbertines (PA) 1; Norbertines (WI) 6; Ogdensburg Diocese 2; Order of Friars Minor (Holy Name Prov) 4; Order of Friars Minor (OL Guadalupe Prov) 1; Order of Friars Minor (St Barbara Prov) 1; Philadelphia Archdiocese 1; Pittsburgh Diocese 1; Precious Blood, Society (OH) 7; Redemptorists (PR) 1; Springfield (IL) Diocese 1; St James Society 16; Worcester Diocese 2...TOTAL 142

WOMEN: Benedictine Sisters (Ferdinand, IN) 3; Charity of Leavenworth, Sisters 5; Charity of SVP, Sisters (Halifax) 3; Daughters of the Holy Spirit 2; Davenport Diocesan Volunteer Prog 3; Divine Providence, Sisters (MO) 1; Dominican Sisters (Columbus, OH) 2; Dominican Sisters (Grand Rapids, MI) 2; Dominican Sisters (Sparkill, NY) 1; Dominican Sisters (Springfield, IL) 5; Family Unity International, Inc. 1; Franciscan Sisters of Christian Charity 4; Franciscan Sisters of Clinton, IA 1; Franciscan Sisters T.O.R. (Syracuse) 2; Holy Cross, Cong. of Sisters (IN) 5; Holy Cross, Sisters (NH) 4; IHM Sisters of Scranton 2; Jefferson City Diocese 2; Jesuit Volunteers: International 6; Marist Missionary Sisters (MA) 5; Maryknoll Mission Assoc of the Faithful 7; Maryknoll Sisters 10; Medical Mission Sisters 3; Mercy, Sisters (IA) 1; Mercy, Sisters (ME) 1; Mercy, Sisters (Merion, PA) 5; Mercy, Sisters (Pgh, PA) 2; Most Precious Blood, Sisters (MO) 1; Notre Dame de Namur, Srs (CA) 1; Notre Dame de Namur, Srs (CT) 1; Notre Dame de Namur, Srs (MD) 1; Presentation of Mary, Srs (MA) 1; Presentation Sisters (ND) 1; Presentation, Sisters (CA) 1; Sacred Heart of Jesus, Sisters (TX) 2; School Sisters of Notre Dame (MO) 1; School Sisters of St. Francis (Milwaukee, WI) 1; St Joseph, Sisters, TOSF 2; St. Columban, Sisters 2; St. Joseph Carondelet, Srs (CA) 3; St. Joseph Carondelet, Srs (MN) 3; St. Joseph Carondelet, Srs (NY) 5; St. Joseph, Sisters (Nazareth) 2; St. Joseph, Sisters (Philadelphia) 2; Ursuline Sisters (MO) 1; Ursuline Sisters of Louisville KY 4; Ursulines of Toledo 1; Vincentian Sisters of Charity (PA) 1...TOTAL 125

PHILIPPINES

MEN: Alexian Brothers (IL) 2; Blessed Sacrament, Cong. of (OH) 5; Carmelites, Discalced (WI) 4; Christian Brothers, De La Salle (CA) 1; Christian Brothers, De La Salle (MD) 4; Christian Brothers, De La Salle (Midwest) 2; Columbans 14; Comboni Missionaries 1; Cong. of the Sacred Hearts (MA) 1; Divine Word, Society (IL) 17; Dominican Friars (NY) 1; Franciscan OFM Conv (MD) 1; Jesuits (CA) 2; Jesuits (MD) 1; Jesuits (NY) 41; Jesuits (WI) 1; LaSalette Fathers (No. American Prov.) 3; Marist Fathers & Brothers (DC) 1; Maryknoll Fathers & Brothers 20; Missionhurst 1; New Orleans Archdiocese 1; Oblates of Mary Immaculate 5; Oblates of the Virgin Mary 1; Order of Friars Minor (Assumption Prov) 1; Order of Friars Minor (St Barbara Prov) 2; Order of Friars Minor (St John Bapt Prov) 10; Passionists (NJ) 5; Pontifical Institute for Foreign Missions 3; Sons of Mary, Health of the Sick 2; Spiritans (TX) 1; Xaverian Missionaries 2...TOTAL 156

WOMEN: Christian Charity, Sisters (NJ) 1; Daughters of St Mary of Providence 1; Dominican Nuns (Summit, NJ) 1; Franciscan Mission Service 1; Handmaids of Sacred Heart of Jesus 1; Holy Family of Nazareth, Srs (Pgh, PA) 2; Holy Family of Nazareth, Srs (Phil, PA) 2; Maryknoll Sisters 10; Mercy, Sisters (NY) 1; Missionary Benedictine Sisters 1; Missionary Sr Servs of Holy Spirit 1; Missionary Srs of Sacred Heart 1; Presentation of Mary, Srs (NH) 1; Providence,

Sisters (WA) 4; Scalabrini Sisters (IL) 1; Sisters of the Sacred Hearts (HI) 3; Social Service, Sisters (CA) 2; St. Columban, Sisters 3...TOTAL 37

POLAND

MEN: Christian Brothers, De La Salle (NY) 1...TOTAL 1

WOMEN: Bernardine Franciscan Sisters 1; Charity, Sisters (OH) 1...TOTAL 2

PORTUGAL

MEN: San Francisco Archdiocese 1...TOTAL 1

PUERTO RICO

MEN: Franciscan OFM (DC) 1; Franciscan OFM Cap (St Augustine Prov) 5; Franciscan OFM Cap (St Mary Prov) 1; Jesuits (NY) 7; Marianists (MD) 6; Missionary Servants/Most Holy Trinity 3; Oblates of Mary Immaculate 2; Order of Friars Minor (Holy Name Prov) 2; Order of Friars Minor (OL Guadalupe Prov) 1; Redemptorists (PR) 36; Spiritans (PA) 3...TOTAL 67

WOMEN: Benedictine Sisters (St. Joseph, MN) 13; Bernardine Franciscan Sisters 3; Divine Providence, Sisters (PA) 3; Dominican Sisters (Adrian, MI) 2; Franciscan Sisters of Philadelphia 4; IHM Sisters of Monroe 6; Missionary Servants/Most Blessed Trinity 1; Social Service, Sisters (NY) 1; St Joseph, Sisters, TOSF 2; St. Joseph, Cong of Srs (Rockville Ctr) 8...TOTAL 43

ROMANIA

WOMEN: Daughters of Charity (MO) 1; Divine Providence, Sisters (MO) 1; Good Shepherd Sisters (NY) 1...TOTAL 3

RUSSIA

MEN: Anchorage Diocese 2; Augustinians of the Assumption 1; Corpus Christi Diocese 1; Divine Word, Society (IL) 1; Dominican Friars (NY) 1; Jesuits (LA) 1; Jesuits (MD) 1; Maryknoll Fathers & Brothers 2; Order of Friars Minor (Assumption Prov) 1...TOTAL 11

WOMEN: St. Agnes, Cong. Of Sisters (WI) 4...TOTAL 4

RWANDA

WOMEN: St. Mary of Namur, Sisters (NY) 1...TOTAL 1

SAIPAN

MEN: Jesuits (NY) 1...TOTAL 1

WOMEN: Mercedarian Missionaries of Berriz 1; Mercy, Sisters (NY) 1...TOTAL 2

SENEGAL

MEN: Marist Fathers & Brothers (MA) 1...TOTAL 1

WOMEN: Marist Sisters 1...TOTAL 1

SIBERIA

MEN: Order of Friars Minor (Assumption Prov) 1...TOTAL 1

SIERRA LEONE

MEN: Salesians (NY) 4; Xaverian Missionaries 6...TOTAL 10

WOMEN: Xaverian Mission Soc of Mary (MA) 2...TOTAL 2

SINGAPORE

MEN: New York Archdiocese 1...TOTAL 1

WOMEN: Little Sisters of the Poor (NY) 1...TOTAL 1

SLOVENIA

MEN: Blessed Sacrament, Cong. of (OH) 1...TOTAL 1

SOLOMON ISLANDS

MEN: Dominican Friars (NY) 1; Marist Fathers & Brothers (MA) 2...TOTAL 3

WOMEN: Marist Missionary Sisters (MA) 2...TOTAL 2

SOUTH AFRICA

MEN: Charity, Brothers of (PA) 1; Comboni Missionaries 1; Franciscan Mission Service 1; Franciscan Third Order Regular (FL) 1; Jesuits (MD) 1; Jesuits (MO) 2; Marianhill Missionaries 1; Order of Friars Minor (Assumption Prov) 2; Order of Friars Minor (Holy Name Prov) 1; Order of Friars Minor (St John Bapt Prov) 1; Richmond Diocese 1; Sacred Heart, Priests of the (WI) 3; Servite Friars (IL) 5; Spiritans (PA) 2; St. Francis de Sales, Oblates (DE) 8...TOTAL 31

WOMEN: IHM Sisters of Monroe 4; Missionary Benedictine Sisters 1; Missionary Srs of Precious Blood 1; Notre Dame de Namur, Srs (MA) 1; School Sisters of St. Francis of Pgh, PA 2; St Joseph, Sisters, TOSF 1; Ursulines 1...TOTAL 11

SPAIN

MEN: Legionaries of Christ 2; Metuchen Diocese 2; Missionaries of Africa 1...TOTAL 5
WOMEN: Associate Missionaries 3; Religious of the Assumption (N Am Prov) 2; Sacred Heart, Society 1...TOTAL 6

SRI LANKA

MEN: Jesuits (LA) 5...TOTAL 5

WOMEN: Franciscan Missionaries of Mary 1...TOTAL 1

ST. LUCIA

MEN: Redemptorists (MD) 5...TOTAL 5

ST. VINCENT

MEN: Lasallian Volunteers 2...TOTAL 2

WOMEN: Inst. of the Blessed Virgin Mary 1...TOTAL 1

SUDAN

MEN: Comboni Missionaries 3; Jesuits (LA) 1; Jesuits (MI) 1; Mill Hill Missionaries 1...TOTAL 6

WOMEN: Maryknoll Mission Assoc of the Faithful 1; Maryknoll Sisters 4; Medical Missionaries of Mary 1...TOTAL 6

SWAZILAND

WOMEN: Mantellate Sr. Servants of Mary 3...TOTAL 3

SWEDEN

MEN: Oblates of Mary Immaculate 3...TOTAL 3

WOMEN: Missionaries of Charity (NE Region) 1; Sacred Heart, Society 1...TOTAL 2

SYRIA

MEN: Order of Friars Minor (S Heart Prov) 1...TOTAL 1

TAHITI

MEN: Oblates of Mary Immaculate 1...TOTAL 1

TAIWAN

MEN: Benedictine - Am Cassinese Cong (IL) 1; Benedictine - Am Cassinese Cong (MN) 1; Benedictine - Am Cassinese Cong (PA) 1; Columbans 3; Divine Word, Society (IL) 5; Jesuits (CA) 9; Jesuits (MO) 1; Maryknoll Fathers & Brothers 36; Order of Friars Minor (S Heart Prov) 1; Vincentians (PA) 9...TOTAL 67

WOMEN: Apostles of the Sacred Heart of Jesus 2; Columban Lay Mission Program 1; Daughters of Charity (IN) 1; Daughters of Charity (MD) 2; Daughters of Charity (MO) 3; Daughters of Charity (NY) 2; Divine Savior, Sisters (WI) 4; Franciscan Mission Srs O.L. Sorrows 3; Hospital Sisters of St. Francis (Am Prov) 2; Maryknoll Sisters 8; Missionary Sr Servs of Holy Spirit 1; Providence, Sisters (IN) 5; Sacred Heart, Society Devoted (CA) 4; Sisters of St. Francis of Assisi 1; Social Service, Sisters (CA) 1...TOTAL 40

TANZANIA

MEN: Dominican Friars (NY) 2; Jesuit Volunteers: International 7; Jesuits (MI) 2; Jesuits (OR) 1; Maryknoll Fathers & Brothers 25; Maryknoll Mission Assoc of the Faithful 4; Missionaries of Africa 1; Order of Friars Minor (Holy Name Prov) 1; Order of Friars Minor (S Heart Prov) 1; Pontifical Institute for Foreign Missions 1; Precious Blood, Society (MO) 1; Salesians (NY) 1; Society of the Divine Savior 3; Spiritans (PA) 11...TOTAL 61

WOMEN: Franciscan Sisters 1; Franciscan Sisters of Holy Family (IA) 1; Franciscan Sisters of Little Falls 1; Holy Union Sisters (MA) 1; Jesuit Volunteers: International 2; Maryknoll Mission Assoc of the Faithful 4; Maryknoll Sisters 21; Medical Missionaries of Mary 2; Missionary Benedictine Sisters 3; Missionary Srs of Our Lady of Africa 2; Presentation, Sisters (Dubuque, IA) 1; School Sisters of Notre Dame (MN) 1; School Sisters of St. Francis (Milwaukee, WI) 1; Side by Side Lay Volunteer Program 1; Spiritan Associates 1; St. Joseph, Sisters (Springfield) 1...TOTAL 44

THAILAND

MEN: Christian Brothers, De La Salle (Midwest) 1; Jesuits (CA) 2; Jesuits (MD) 1; Maryknoll Fathers & Brothers 9; Maryknoll Mission Assoc of the Faithful 5; O.L. Most Holy Trinity, Society 1; Redemptorists (CO) 11; Stigmatine Fathers 2...TOTAL 32

WOMEN: Maryknoll Mission Assoc of the Faithful 4; Maryknoll Sisters 3; O.L. Most Holy Trinity, Society 1; Ursuline Nuns of the Roman Union (MA) 1; Ursuline Sisters (MO) 1; Ursulines (NY) 4; Ursulines Roman Union (CA) 2...TOTAL 16

TRINIDAD

MEN: Carmelite Friars (NY) 2...TOTAL 2

UGANDA

MEN: Comboni Missionaries 3; Holy Cross Brothers (IN) 1; Holy Cross Brothers (NY) 6; Holy Cross Fathers (CT) 1; Holy Cross Fathers (IN) 8; Jesuits (MI) 3; Jesuits (WI) 2; Missionaries of Africa 1; Redemptorists (PR) 1; Sacred Heart, Brothers (RI) 1; Volunteer Missionary Movement 1...TOTAL 28

WOMEN: Daughters of Mary and Joseph 1; Franciscan Mission Srs for Africa 2; Holy Cross, Cong. of Sisters (IN) 7; IHM Sisters of Monroe 1; Mary of the Presentation, Srs (ND) 1; Medical Mission Sisters 4; Medical Missionaries of Mary 2; Missionary Srs of Our Lady of Africa 1; Sacred Heart, Society 1; Sisters of Notre Dame (Chardon, OH) 1...TOTAL 21

UNITED STATES

MEN: African Missions, Society of 2; Annunciation House 7; Apostolic Volunteers 2; Augustinians (PA) 1; Capuchin Franciscan Volunteer Corps 3; Casa Juan Diego 1; Catholic Volunteers in Florida 2; Christian Brothers, Cong. (NY) 7; Christian Brothers, De La Salle

(Midwest) 10; Christian Brothers, De La Salle (NY) 34; Claretian Vol & Lay Missionaries 2; Columbans 5; Comboni Missionaries 9; Cong. of the Sacred Hearts (MA) 3; Consolata Missionary Fathers 3; Diocese of Tororo, Uganda 1; Divine Word, Society (IL) 23; Franciscan OFM (DC) 2; Franciscan OFM Cap (MI) 1; Franciscan OFM Cap (St Joseph Prov) 5; Franciscan OFM Cap (St Mary Prov) 4; Franciscan Outreach Association 3; Franciscan Third Order Regular (FL) 1; Franciscan Volunteer Ministry 7; Franciscan Volunteer Program 5; Glenmary Home Missioners 66; Great Falls-Billings Diocese 3; Holy Cross Brothers (IN) 1; Holy Cross Brothers (TX) 1; Intercommunity Ministry Volunteer Program 1; Jesuit Volunteer Corps - Midwest 6; Jesuits (IL) 2; Jesuits (New England) 1; Jesuits (OR) 35; Jesuits (WI) 39; Knoxville Diocese 2; LAMP Ministries 5; LaSalette Fathers (No. American Prov.) 5; Legionaries of Christ 1; Lexington Diocese 1; Marist Fathers & Brothers (DC) 3; Marist Volunteer Program 2; Maryknoll Fathers & Brothers 9; Maryknoll Mission Assoc of the Faithful 9; Mercy Corps 8; Milford Spiritual Center 2; Mill Hill Missionaries 2; Missionaries of Africa 2; Missionary Cenacle Volunteers 4; Missionhurst 4; O.L. Most Holy Trinity, Society 2; Oblates of Mary Immaculate 19; Order of Friars Minor (Assumption Prov) 2; Order of Friars Minor (Holy Name Prov) 8; Order of Friars Minor (Imm Conc Prov) 1; Order of Friars Minor (OL Guadalupe Prov) 41; Order of Friars Minor (S Heart Prov) 3; Order of Friars Minor (St John Bapt Prov) 1; Owensboro Diocese 1; Passionists (NJ) 5; Redemptorists (PR) 6; Resurrection Congregation 1; Sacred Heart Lay Missioners 2; Sacred Heart Missionaries (IL) 1; Sacred Heart, Brothers (LA) 1; Salesian Lay Missioners (NY) 1; Society of St. Edmund 11; Society of the Divine Savior 3; St Bonaventure Indian School 9; Urban Catholic Teacher Corps of Boston 1; Vincentian Service Corps (Central) 10; Vincentian Service Corps (East) 1; Vincentians (CA) 2; Vincentians (PA) 6; Volunteer Missionary Movement 1; Volunteers for Educ & Social Services 1...TOTAL 497

WOMEN: Adorers of the Blood of Christ (IL) 8; Annunciation House 2; Apostles of the Sacred Heart of Jesus 6; Apostolic Volunteers 5; Associate Missionaries 2; Benedictine Sisters (Mt. Angel, OR) 4; Benedictine Sisters (St. Joseph, MN) 9; Benedictine Sisters (Watertown, SD) 5; Bernardine Franciscan Sisters 16; Blessed Sacrament Sisters 109; Cabrini Mission Corps 8; Capuchin Franciscan Volunteer Corps 10; Casa Juan Diego 2; Catholic Volunteers in Florida 14; Change A Heart- Millvale Franciscan Volunteer Program 3; Charity of Seton Hill, Sisters (PA) 2; Charity of St. Elizabeth, Sisters 1; Charity of St. Joan Antida, Sisters 1; Charity, Sisters (OH) 14; Christian Charity, Sisters (IL) 5; Claretian Vol & Lay Missionaries 5; Consolata Missionary Sisters 5; Daughters of Charity (CA) 2; Daughters of Charity (IN) 1; Daughters of Charity (MD) 1; Daughters of Charity (NY) 1; Daughters of Mary Help of Christians 3; Daughters of St Mary of Providence 1; Daughters of the Holy Spirit 8; Divine Providence, Congregation (KY) 6; Divine Savior, Sisters (WI) 7; Dominican Sisters (Columbus, OH) 6; Dominican Sisters (Edmonds, WA) 3; Dominican Sisters (Sinsinawa) 5; Dominican Sisters (Sparkill, NY) 17; Dominican Sisters (Springfield, IL) 14; Dominican Sisters (St. Katharine, KY) 1; Dominican Sisters of the Roman Congregation 1; Felician Sisters 1; Franciscan Missionaries of Mary 30; Franciscan Outreach Association 3; Franciscan Sisters of Atonement 22; Franciscan Sisters of Christian Charity 21; Franciscan Sisters of Clinton, IA 1; Franciscan Sisters of Little Falls 12; Franciscan Sisters of Mary 2; Franciscan Sisters of Millvale, PA 5; Franciscan Sisters of Peace 4; Franciscan Sisters of Sylvania, OH 1; Franciscan Sisters of the Holy Cross 1; Franciscan Sisters T.O.R. (Syracuse) 1; Franciscan Volunteer Ministry 9; Franciscan Volunteer Program 3; Glenmary Home Mission Sisters 15; Glenmary Home Missioners 5; Good Shepherd Sisters (DC) 4; Good Shepherd Sisters (MO) 2; Great Falls-Billings Diocese 2; Handmaids of Sacred Heart of Jesus 7; Hands Together, Inc. 1; Holy Child Jesus, Society (PA) 5; Holy Cross, Cong. of Sisters (IN) 1; Holy Cross, Sisters (NH) 3; Holy Family of Nazareth, Srs (Phil, PA) 1; Holy Family, Sisters (LA) 8; Holy Names, Sisters (CA) 4; Holy Spirit/Mary Imm, Srs (TX) 27; Holy Union Sisters (MA) 5; Humility of Mary, Cong (IA) 1; Humility of Mary, Sisters 1; IHM Sisters of Scranton 1; Incarnate Word Bl. Sacrament, Srs. 1; Jesuit Volunteer Corps - Midwest 29; Jesus and Mary, Rel (MD) 1; Knoxville Diocese 7; LAMP Ministries 7; Little Sisters of the Poor (NY) 3; Marist Missionary Sisters (MA) 25; Marist Volunteer Program 2; Mary of the Presentation, Srs (ND) 1; Maryknoll Mission Assoc of the Faithful 18; Maryknoll Sisters 96; Medical Mission Sisters 41; Medical Missionaries of Mary 20; Mercy Corps 30; Mercy, Sisters 1; Mercy, Sisters (ME) 4; Mercy, Sisters (Merion, PA) 4; Mercy, Sisters (MI) 1; Mercy, Sisters (NE) 9; Mercy, Sisters (NY) 1; Mercy, Sisters (OH) 5; Mercy, Sisters (Pgh, PA) 3; Milford Spiritual Center 2; Mission Srs Imm Concept (NJ) 4;

Mission Srs Imm Heart of Mary 18; Missionaries of Charity (NE Region) 57; Missionary Benedictine Sisters 6; Missionary Cenacle Volunteers 8; Missionary Sr Servs of Holy Spirit 3; Missionary Srs of Our Lady of Africa 11; Missionary Srs of Precious Blood 2; Missionary Srs, Most Sacred Heart (PA) 3; Most Precious Blood, Sisters (MO) 7; Notre Dame de Namur, Srs (CA) 1; Notre Dame de Namur, Srs (MA) 27; Notre Dame de Namur, Srs (MD) 1; Notre Dame de Namur, Srs (OH) 1; O.L. Most Holy Trinity, Society 6; Oblate Sisters of Providence 4; Our Lady of Victory Missionary Sisters 5; Passionists (NJ) 1; Poor Clare Missionary Sisters 2; Precious Blood, Sisters (OH) 2; Presentation of Mary, Srs (NH) 5; Presentation Sisters (ND) 11; Presentation, Sisters (CA) 12; Presentation, Sisters (Sioux Falls, SD) 8; Providence Volunteer Ministry 4; Providence, Sisters (IN) 34; Providence, Sisters (WA) 3; Quest 1; Sacred Heart Lay Missioners 2; Sacred Heart of Jesus, Sisters (TX) 19; Sacred Heart, Society 46; Salesian Lay Missioners (NY) 1; Scalabrini Sisters (IL) 1; School Sisters of Notre Dame (CT) 4; School Sisters of Notre Dame (IL) 16; School Sisters of Notre Dame (MD) 5; School Sisters of Notre Dame (MN) 20; School Sisters of Notre Dame (MO) 24; School Sisters of Notre Dame (TX) 1; School Sisters of Notre Dame (WI) 16; School Sisters of St. Francis (Milwaukee, WI) 19; School Sisters of St. Francis of Pgh, PA 4; Shared Horizons 2; Shreveport Diocese 1; Side by Side Lay Volunteer Program 3; Sisters of Charity Incarnate Word 13; Sisters of Charity, BVM (IA) 48; Sisters of Notre Dame (Toledo, OH) 3; Sisters of St Chretienne 2; Sisters of the Living Word 4; Sisters of the Most Holy Sacrament 1; Sisters of the Sacred Hearts (HI) 1; St Bonaventure Indian School 17; St Joseph, Sisters, TOSF 2; St. Agnes, Cong. of Sisters (WI) 47; St. Anne, Sisters (MA) 2; St. Joseph Carondelet, Srs (MN) 12; St. Joseph Carondelet, Srs (NY) 6; St. Joseph of Chambery, Srs 9; St. Joseph of Lyons, Srs 1; St. Joseph, Cong of Srs (Rockville Ctr) 6; St. Joseph, Sisters (Philadelphia) 7; St. Joseph, Sisters (Rochester) 19; St. Mary of Namur, Sisters (NY) 10; St. Ursula, Society 1; Urban Catholic Teacher Corps of Boston 10; Ursuline Nuns of the Cong. of Paris 2; Ursuline Sisters (KY) 7; Ursuline Sisters (MO) 1; Ursuline Sisters of Louisville KY 1; Ursulines (NY) 6; Ursulines Roman Union (CA) 7; Vincentian Service Corps (Central) 11; Vincentian Service Corps (East) 5; Vincentians (CA) 1; Volunteer Missionary Movement 1; Volunteers for Educ & Social Services 12; Volunteers in Mission 4...TOTAL 1543

URUGUAY

MEN: Jesuits (CA) 1...TOTAL 1

VANUATU

MEN: Marist Fathers & Brothers (MA) 1...TOTAL 1

VENEZUELA

MEN: Augustinians of the Assumption 1; Lincoln Diocese 2; Maryknoll Fathers & Brothers 2; Maryknoll Mission Assoc of the Faithful 4; Philadelphia Archdiocese 1; Redemptorists (PR) 2; San Diego Diocese 1; Society of St. Edmund 2; St. Paul-Minneapolis Archdiocese 1...TOTAL 16

WOMEN: Maryknoll Mission Assoc of the Faithful 7; Medical Mission Sisters 2; Mission Helpers of the Sacred Heart 1; Ursulines (NY) 1...TOTAL 11

VIETNAM

MEN: Divine Word, Society (IL) 1; Maryknoll Fathers & Brothers 2; Maryknoll Mission Assoc of the Faithful 1; Washington Archdiocese 1...TOTAL 5

WOMEN: Maryknoll Mission Assoc of the Faithful 1...TOTAL 1

VIRGIN ISLANDS

MEN: Redemptorists (MD) 5...TOTAL 5

WOMEN: Charity of St. Elizabeth, Sisters 2; Good Shepherd Sisters (NY) 1; Good Shepherd Sisters (OH) 1; Missionaries of Charity (NE Region) 1...TOTAL 5

WEST INDIES

MEN: Divine Word, Society (IL) 3...TOTAL 3

WOMEN: Carmelite Sisters (Corpus Christi) 2; Dominican Sisters (Sinsinawa) 1; Franciscan Sisters of Philadelphia 2; Missionaries of Charity (NE Region) 1...TOTAL 6

WESTERN SAMOA

MEN: Marist Fathers & Brothers (DC) 1; Maryknoll Fathers & Brothers 1; Monterey Diocese 1...TOTAL 3

ZAIRE

MEN: Crosier Fathers & Brothers 2; Jesuits (OR) 1; Missionhurst 1; Order of Friars Minor (S Heart Prov) 1; Order of Friars Minor (St John Bapt Prov) 1; Sacred Heart, Priests of the (WI) 2; Xaverian Missionaries 1...TOTAL 9

WOMEN: Daughters of Charity (MO) 2; Notre Dame de Namur, Srs (MD) 3; St. Mary of Namur, Sisters (NY) 1; St. Mary of Namur, Sisters (TX) 3...TOTAL 9

ZAMBIA

MEN: Franciscan Mission Service 1; Franciscan OFM Conv (IL) 1; Franciscan OFM Conv (IN) 8; Jesuits (LA) 2; Jesuits (NY) 2; Jesuits (OR) 7; Lay Mission Oblates of Mary Imm 2; Marianists (MD) 4; Marianists (OH) 1; Missionaries of Africa 1; Oblates of Mary Immaculate 5; Sacred Heart, Brothers (RI) 1; Society of St. Sulpice (MD) 7...TOTAL 42

WOMEN: Comboni Missionary Sisters 2; Franciscan Mission Srs for Africa 1; Holy Spirit/Mary Imm, Srs (TX) 6; Lay Mission Oblates of Mary Imm 1; Missionary Srs of Our Lady of Africa 1...TOTAL 11

ZIMBABWE

MEN: Jesuits (LA) 3; Jesuits (MD) 1; Jesuits (NY) 1; Jesuits (WI) 1; Marianhill Missionaries 2; Sacred Heart, Brothers (RI) 1; Toledo Diocese 1...TOTAL 10

WOMEN: Franciscan Mission Srs for Africa 2; Franciscan Sisters of Providence of God 1; Franciscan Srs Perpetual Adoration 2; Maryknoll Sisters 3; Missionary Srs of Precious Blood 1; Notre Dame de Namur, Srs (CA) 1; Notre Dame de Namur, Srs (OH) 1; Sacred Heart of Mary, Rel 3; Toledo Diocese 1...TOTAL 15

GRAND TOTAL — MEN AND WOMEN FOR ALL COUNTRIES = 5883

U.S. Catholic Missioners: 1998-1999
By Region, Country, and Gender

REGION/COUNTRY	MEN	WOMEN	TOTAL
AFRICA			
BENIN	0	1	1
BOTSWANA	0	1	1
BURKINA FASO	1	1	2
CAMEROON	2	16	18
CENTRAL AFRICAN REPUBLIC	1	1	2
CHAD	1	0	1
CONGO	2	4	6
COTE D'IVOIRE	1	1	2
ETHIOPIA	12	11	23
GAMBIA	0	2	2
GHANA	29	43	72
KENYA	91	81	172
LESOTHO	3	0	3
LIBERIA	8	4	12
MADAGASCAR	3	2	5
MALAWI	9	1	10
MALI	0	2	2
MOZAMBIQUE	5	0	5
NAMIBIA	4	5	9
NIGERIA	31	25	56
RWANDA	0	1	1
SENEGAL	1	1	2
SIERRA LEONE	10	2	12
SOUTH AFRICA	31	11	42
SWAZILAND	0	3	3
TANZANIA	61	44	105
UGANDA	28	21	49
ZAIRE	9	9	18
ZAMBIA	42	11	53
ZIMBABWE	10	15	25
AFRICA TOTALS	**395**	**319**	**714**
ASIA			
BANGLADESH	19	10	29
CAMBODIA	5	5	10
CHINA PRC - HONG KONG SAR	45	40	85
EAST TIMOR	0	2	2
INDIA	50	18	68
INDONESIA	19	2	21
JAPAN	130	39	169
KOREA	29	29	58
MYANMAR	1	0	1
NEPAL	9	7	16
PAKISTAN	7	9	16
PHILIPPINES	156	37	193
SINGAPORE	1	1	2
SRI LANKA	5	1	6
TAIWAN	67	40	107

THAILAND	32	16	48
VIETNAM	5	1	6
ASIA TOTALS	**580**	**257**	**837**
CARIBBEAN			
ANTIGUA	0	2	2
BAHAMAS	12	8	20
BELIZE	32	23	55
BERMUDA	0	4	4
CUBA	1	0	1
DOMINICA	4	1	5
DOMINICAN REPUBLIC	15	23	38
GUYANA	3	5	8
HAITI	25	24	49
JAMAICA	22	25	47
PUERTO RICO	67	43	110
ST. LUCIA	5	0	5
ST. VINCENT	2	1	3
TRINIDAD	2	0	2
VIRGIN ISLANDS	5	5	10
WEST INDIES	3	6	9
CARIBBEAN TOTALS	**198**	**170**	**368**
EURASIA			
KAZAKHSTAN	1	0	1
RUSSIA	11	4	15
SIBERIA	1	0	1
EURASIA TOTALS	**13**	**4**	**17**
EUROPE			
ALBANIA	0	1	1
ARMENIA	0	1	1
AUSTRIA	1	0	1
BELGIUM	2	1	3
BOSNIA	1	0	1
CYPRUS	2	0	2
CZECH REP	2	1	3
DENMARK	4	0	4
ENGLAND	10	6	16
ESTONIA	0	1	1
FINLAND	0	3	3
FRANCE	2	9	11
GERMANY	7	3	10
GREECE	1	0	1
HUNGARY	0	6	6
IRELAND	8	11	19
ITALY	21	22	43
LATVIA	1	0	1
LITHUANIA	3	1	4
MALTA	0	1	1
NETHERLANDS	2	0	2
POLAND	1	2	3
PORTUGAL	1	0	1
ROMANIA	0	3	3
SLOVENIA	1	0	1

SPAIN	5	6	11
SWEDEN	3	2	5
EUROPE TOTALS	**78**	**80**	**158**
LATIN AMERICA			
ARGENTINA	10	8	18
BOLIVIA	70	61	131
BRAZIL	145	96	241
CHILE	51	59	110
COLOMBIA	10	14	24
COSTA RICA	9	2	11
ECUADOR	21	20	41
EL SALVADOR	16	27	43
GUATEMALA	52	94	146
HONDURAS	30	19	49
MEXICO	124	100	224
NICARAGUA	17	38	55
PANAMA	18	7	25
PARAGUAY	7	3	10
PERU	142	125	267
URUGUAY	1	0	1
VENEZUELA	16	11	27
LATIN AMERICA TOTALS	**739**	**684**	**1423**
MIDDLE EAST			
ALGERIA	0	1	1
EGYPT	4	1	5
ISRAEL	22	3	25
JORDAN	3	1	4
LEBANON	3	2	5
MOROCCO	2	0	2
SUDAN	6	6	12
SYRIA	1	0	1
MIDDLE EAST TOTALS	**41**	**14**	**55**
NORTH AMERICA			
CANADA	30	39	69
UNITED STATES	497	1543	2040
NORTH AMERICA TOTALS	**527**	**1582**	**2109**
OCEANIA			
AMERICAN SAMOA	2	3	5
AUSTRALIA	9	9	18
COOK ISLANDS	1	0	1
FIJI	3	2	5
GUAM	11	3	14
MARSHALL ISLANDS	10	4	14
MICRONESIA	20	24	44
NEW CALEDONIA	1	0	1
OKINAWA	7	0	7
PALAU	1	0	1
PAPUA NEW GUINEA	62	17	79
SAIPAN	1	2	3
SOLOMON ISL.	3	2	5

TAHITI	1	0	1
VANUATU	1	0	1
WESTERN SAMOA	3	0	3
OCEANIA TOTALS	**136**	**66**	**202**
GRAND TOTAL — ALL MISSIONERS	**2707**	**3176**	**5883**

U.S. Missioners By Church Role: 1960-1999

Year	Diocesan Priests	Rel. Priests	Rel. Bros.	Rel. Sisters	Semin-arians	Lay Persons	TOTAL
1960	14	3018	575	2827	170	178	6872
1962	31	3172	720	2764	152	307	7146
1964	80	3438	782	3137	157	532	8126
1966	215	3731	901	3706	201	549	9303
1968	282	3727	869	4150	208	419	9655
1970	373	3117	666	3824	90	303	8373
[1]1972	246	3182	634	3121	97	376	7656
1973	237	[2]3913		3012		529	7691
1974	220	3048	639	2916	101	458	7418
1975	197	3023	669	2850	65	344	7148
1976	193	2961	691	2840	68	257	7010
1977	182	2882	630	2781	42	243	6760
1978	166	2830	610	2673	43	279	6601
1979	187	2800	592	2568	50	258	6455
1980	188	2750	592	2592	50	221	6393
1981	187	2702	584	2574	43	234	6324
1982	178	2668	578	2560	44	217	6245
1983	174	2668	569	2450	48	247	6346
1984	187	2603	549	2492	40	263	6134
1985	171	2500	558	2505	30	292	6056
1986	204	2473	532	2481	30	317	6037
1987	200	2394	570	2505	53	351	6073
1988	200	2420	504	2495	50	394	6063
1989	209	2364	494	2473	51	410	6001
1990	200	2257	477	2347	42	421	5744
1991	187	2200	468	2264	30	446	5595
1992	181	2183	449	2222	26	406	5467
1994	177	2007	408	1887	22	374	[3]4875
1996	173	1770	347	1513	18	343	[4]4164
'98-'99	[5]167	[5]1903	370	2693	11	739	[6]5883

1 A corrected total for 1972 should read 7937, indicating losses of 436 from 1970 to 1972, and 246 from 1972 to 1973.

2 Includes Religious Brothers and Seminarians.

3 Totals estimated due to inconclusive survey results.

4 Alaska and Hawaii are no longer included as overseas Missioners.

5 Includes Bishops

6 Includes missioners/volunteers serving outside U.S. borders and within U.S. borders in cross-cultural mission.

Field Distribution of U.S. Catholic Missioners: 1960-1999

Year	Africa	Near East	Far East	Oceania	Europe	North Am	Caribbean	Central Am	South Am	TOTAL
1960	781	111	1959	986	203	337	991	433	981	6782
1962	901	75	2110	992	93	224	967	537	1274	7146
1964	1025	122	2332	846	69	220	1056	660	1796	8126
1966	1184	142	2453	953	38	211	1079	857	2386	9303
1968	1157	128	2470	1027	33	251	1198	936	2455	9655
1970	1141	39	2137	900	38	233	1067	738	2080	8373
1972	1107	59	1955	826	39	234	819	728	1889	7656
1973	1229	54	1962	811	40	253	796	763	1783	7691
1974	1121	60	1845	883	43	241	757	752	1716	7418
1975	1065	71	1814	808	37	252	698	734	1669	7148
1976	1042	68	1757	795	34	313	671	712	1618	7010
1977	1003	62	1659	784	34	296	629	702	1591	6760
1978	966	57	1601	769	34	339	593	705	1537	6601
1979	923	65	1562	743	37	332	562	686	1545	6455
1980	909	65	1576	711	35	294	548	699	1556	6393
1981	946	70	1529	696	36	315	511	686	1535	6324
1982	956	62	1501	673	32	319	522	669	1511	6245
1983	990	68	1468	640	34	346	517	650	1533	6246
1984	967	84	1420	644	29	329	513	650	1498	6134
1985	986	78	1366	650	31	312	500	692	1441	6056
1986	944	73	1356	631	28	306	495	743	1461	6037
1987	971	76	1335	635	27	283	499	762	1485	6073
1988	984	72	1332	584	27	289	466	818	1491	6063
1989	968	65	1299	595	28	267	472	832	1475	6001
1990	945	64	1253	560	—	264	449	796	1413	5744
1991	933	65	1198	546	—	265	453	785	1350	5595
1992	949	59	1163	512	—	[1]105	431	810	1286	5467
1994	Survey results inconclusive for exact distribution by area.									4875
1996	799	965		213	172	[1]82	360	1573		4164
'98-'99	714	909		202	158	[2]2109	368	1423		5883

[1] **Alaska and Hawaii are no longer considered to be foreign mission areas in North America.**

[2] **This number refers to missioners/volunteers in cross-cultural mission within U.S. borders.**

Charts and Tables

The information drawn from the survey is illustrated in charts which permit comparisons to be made with data from earlier surveys and also on missioners working in traditional mission areas versus those now working in mission environments in the U.S.

We have used the field distribution of missioners to illustrate the variations in numbers of U.S. citizens serving in major geographical areas over the past 40 years. You will note that the peak year for numbers of missioners sent was in 1968. This along with the fact that the current survey is for 1998–99 is the basis for the decades chosen. You will note that the usual number of U.S. missioners was around 6,000 individuals. For 1998–99 that number remains nearly 6,000 when including those who recognize themselves as missioners in the U.S. church. A large number of these 2109 individuals have returned from mission areas abroad and now work with immigrant communities and the marginalized in the U.S.

The next pages look at the primary work activity of missioners. There is a comparative chart illustrating the similarities and differences of those working in traditional mission areas and those serving in the U.S.

Field Distribution of U.S. Catholic Missioners: Comparative Chart

YEAR	Africa	Near East	Far East	Oceania	Europe	North Am.	Caribbean	Central Am.	South Am.	TOTAL
1960	781	111	1959	986	203	337	991	433	981	6782
1968	1157	128	2470	1027	33	251	1198	936	2455	9655
1978	966	57	1601	769	34	339	593	705	1537	6601
1988	984	72	1332	584	27	289	466	818	1491	6063
'98-'99	714	909		202	158	[1]2109	368	1423		5883

[1] This number refers to missioners/volunteers in cross-cultural mission within U.S. borders.

Primary Work Activity - All Missioners/Volunteers

Primary Work Activity All Missioners/Volunteers	Number of Responses	Percentage
Administration	479	8.14
Catechetics	239	4.06
Contemplative	49	0.83
Development	79	1.34
Education	1,175	19.98
Formation - Priestly/Religious	222	3.77
Health Care	392	6.66
Immigration/Refugees	118	2.01
Mass Communication	21	0.36
Childcare	33	0.56
Other	868	14.48
Pastoral	1,742	28.58
Relief Services	59	1.00
Social Transformation	407	5.53
TOTAL:	**5,883**	**100.00**

Primary Work Activity
Missioners/Volunteers in U.S. Cross-Cultural Mission

Primary Work Activity— Missioners/Volunteers in U.S. Cross-Cultural Mission	Number of Responses	Percentage
Administration	195	9.56
Catechetics	75	3.68
Contemplative	25	1.23
Development	19	0.93
Education	445	21.81
Formation - Priestly/Religious	16	0.78
Health Care	140	6.86
Immigration/Refugees	96	4.71
Mass Communication	6	0.29
Childcare	6	0.29
Other	192	9.41
Pastoral	499	24.46
Relief Services	43	2.11
Social Transformation	283	16.87
TOTAL:	**2,040**	**100.00**

Primary Work Activity—U.S. Missioners/Volunteers: Outside U.S. Borders // Within U.S. Borders

Primary Work Activity U.S. Missioners/Volunteers	Outside U.S. Borders	Within U.S.Borders
Administration	284	195
Catechetics	164	75
Contemplative	24	25
Development	60	19
Education	730	445
Formation - Priestly/Religious	206	16
Health Care	252	140
Immigration/Refugees	22	96
Mass Communication	15	6
Childcare	27	6
Other	676	192
Pastoral	1243	499
Relief Services	16	43
Social Transformation	124	283
TOTAL:	**3843**	**2040**

(Editorial Note: Our thanks to the United States Catholic Mission Association for providing the contents of this chapter.)

CHAPTER 12

The Orthodox Christian Mission Center

P.O. Box 4319
St. Augustine, FL 32085
Ph: (904) 829-5132
Fax: (904) 829-1635
Email: ocmc@aug.com
Web site: www.ocmc.org
Rev. Fr. Martin Ritsi, Executive Director

The foreign mission program of the Orthodox Churches in the United States is part of a unified program of Orthodox Missions and Evangelism, under the auspices of the Standing Conference of Canonical Orthodox Bishops in the Americas (SCOBA). It seeks to bring our Lord's message of salvation to all who thirst for the water of life. Formulated by a Board of Missions, the program is administrated by the Mission Center in St. Augustine, Florida. The Mission Center is located just a ten-minute walk from the historic Saint Photios Greek Orthodox National Shrine.

The 1999 programs included:

- Monthly support of missionaries Fr. Luke and Pres. Faith Veronis; Nathan and Lynette Hoppe in Albania; Craig and Victoria Goodwin in Romania
- Monthly support of more than 186 local priests in Ghana, Kenya, Uganda, Tanzania, Nigeria, Chad, Cameroon, the Congo, Madagascar, Indonesia, India, and the Philippines
- Sending 47 people on Mission Teams to Galilee, Guatamala, India, and Kenya. The concept of short-term mission teams was first implemented in 1987. The members of these teams have alerted thousands to the critical need for mission and evangelism.
- Scholarships for seven mission students at Holy Cross School of Theology (Brookline, Massachusetts), St. Vladimir's Theological Seminary (Crestwood, New York), and St. Sophia Seminary (Baltimore, Maryland).
- Assistance through the Agape Canisters to philanthropic programs and development projects throughout the world.

Nine full-time staff members serve at the Center including the Rev. Fr. Martin Ritsi, Executive Director. Other staff members are Mr. Athan E. Stephanopoulos, Development Director, Mr. Robert Hund, Finance Director, Mr. Andrew Lekos, Project Coordinator, Ms. Carolyn Crossley, Canister Coordinator, Mr. Alex Cadman, Communications Coordinator, Pres. Renee Ritsi, and Mrs. Jeanne Folsom and Mrs. Lynn Bresan, secretaries.

The officers of the Board of Directors are Fr. Alexander Veronis, President Emeritus; Fr. John Chakos, President; Fr. Peter Gillquist, Vice President; Fr. George Liacopoulos, Secretary, and Mrs. Catherine Lingas, Treasurer

The OCMC is grateful to be engaged cooperatively in the never ending task and responsibility passed on by the Lord and Savior Jesus Christ as he ascended into the heavens, directing his followers to "Go therefore and make disciples of all nations, baptizing them in the name of the Father and of the Son and of the Holy Spirit, teaching them to observe all that I have commanded you; and lo, I am with you always, to the close of the age" (Matt. 28:19-20, RSV).

A Selective Bibliography

Prepared by Ferne Lauraine Weimer, Billy Graham Center Library and John A. Siewert, World Vision

As background to the study of contemporary mission activities, this bibliography seeks to introduce several types of materials to readers of the *Mission Handbook*. Categories include General Reference Works, Directories, Books on Mission in the Twenty-First Century, and Journals. Selections emphasize empirical or reasonably objective data, with most having global or regional coverage. The Directory section adds a sampling of single country sources that were selected because they included multiple denominations.

General Reference Works

The majority of works in this section are recently published dictionaries, encyclopedias, atlases, handbooks, or other reference tools in the field of mission. A few historical works give context and perspective to statistics in the current *Mission Handbook*.

Anderson, Gerald H., ed. *Biographical Dictionary of Christian Missions.* New York: Simon & Schuster Macmillan, 1998; Grand Rapids, MI: Eerdmans, 1999. Web: www.omsc.org

Barrett, David B., ed. *World Christian Encyclopedia: A Comparative Survey of Churches and Religions, AD 30–AD 2000.* 2nd ed. 3 vols. New York: Oxford University Press. Forthcoming March 2001. Web: www.oup-usa.org

Brierley, Peter, and Heather Wraight. *Atlas of World Christianity: 2000 Years.* Nashville, TN: Thomas Nelson, 1998. Web: www.thomasnelsonpublishers.com

Brierley, Peter, ed. *World Churches Handbook.* London, England: Christian Research, 1997. Based on the Operation World database by Patrick Johnstone, WEC International, 1993. Web: www.christian-research.org.uk

Fahlbusch, Erwin, et al., eds. *The Encyclopedia of Christianity.* 5 vols. Grand Rapids, MI: Eerdmans; Leiden, The Netherlands: E.J. Brill, 1999– . Work in progress. Web: www.eerdmans.com

Goddard, Burton L., ed. *The Encyclopedia of Modern Christian Missions: The Agencies.* Camden, NJ: Thomas Nelson & Sons, 1967.

Grimes, Barbara F., ed. *Ethnologue: Languages of the World.* 14th ed. Dallas, TX: Summer Institute of Linguistics, 2000. Web: www.sil.org/acpub/catalog; web version: www.sil.org/ethnologue

Johnstone, Patrick. *Operation World.* 5th ed. Waynesboro, GA: OM Literature, 1995. New edition to be published in 2001. Web: www.wec-int.org

Linder, Eileen W., ed. *Yearbook of American & Canadian Churches.* Nashville, TN: Abingdon Press. Annual. Web: www.abingdon.org

Missionary Research Library. Various predecessor titles to the *Mission Handbook.* Editions 1–7. New York: Missionary Research Library, 1953–1966.

- 1953: Foreign Missionary Agencies in the United States
- 1956: Directory of Foreign Missionary Agencies in North America, Revised ed.
- 1958: Directory of North American Protestant Foreign Missionary Agencies, 3rd ed.
- 1960: Directory of North American Protestant Foreign Missionary Agencies, 4th ed.
- 1962: North American Protestant Foreign Mission Agencies, 5th ed.
- 1964: North American Protestant Foreign Mission Agencies, 6th ed.
- 1966: North American Protestant Foreign Mission Agencies, 7th ed.

Missionary Research Library and MARC. *Mission Handbook.* Editions 8-9. New York: Missionary Research Library; Pasadena, CA: MARC, 1968-1970.

- 1968: North American Protestant Foreign Mission Agencies, 8th ed.
- 1970: North American Protestant Ministries Overseas, 9th ed.

Mission Advanced Research and Communication Center (MARC). *Mission Handbook.* Editions 10–17. Pasadena, CA: MARC, 1973-1997.

- 1973: Mission Handbook: North American Protestant Ministries Overseas, 10th ed.
- 1976: Mission Handbook: North American Protestant Ministries Overseas, 11th ed.
- 1979: Mission Handbook: North American Protestant Ministries Overseas, 12th ed.
- 1986: Mission Handbook: North American Protestant Ministries Overseas, 13th ed.
- 1989: Mission Handbook: USA/Canada Protestant Ministries Overseas, 14th ed.
- 1993: Mission Handbook: USA/Canada Christian Ministries Overseas, 15th ed.
- 1995: Mission Handbook. Directory Edition, 16th ed.
- 1997: Mission Handbook, 1998–2000: U.S. and Canadian Christian Ministries Overseas, 17th ed.

Moreau, A. Scott, ed. *Evangelical Dictionary of World Missions.* Grand Rapids, MI: Baker Book House, 2000. Web: www.bakerbooks.com

Müller, Karl, Theo Sundermeier, Stephen B. Bevans, and Richard H. Bliese, eds. *Dictionary of Mission: Theology, History, Perspectives.* (American Society of Missiology Series, 24). Maryknoll, NY: Orbis Books, 1997. Web: www.orbisbooks.com

National Association of Evangelicals. *National Evangelical Directory.* Carol Stream, IL: National Association of Evangelicals. Biennial. Web: www.nae.net

Siewert, John A., and Dotsey Welliver, eds. *Directory of Schools and Professors of Mission and Evangelism in the USA and Canada, 1999-2001.* Wheaton, IL: Evangelism and Missions Information Service, 1999. Web: www.wheaton.edu/bgc/emis

United States Catholic Mission Association. *U.S. Catholic Mission Handbook 2000.* Jubilee edition. Washington, DC: U.S. Catholic Mission Association, 2000. Web: www.uscatholicmission.org

Mission and Church Directories Beyond the United States and Canada

The entries in this section offer a sampling of printed and electronic directories from around the world. Some directories focus on mission agencies while others cover multiple types of Christian organizations. Specifically excluded are directories limited to specific denominations or traditions.

Bentley, Peter, and Philip J. Hughes. *A Directory of Australian Religious Organizations: 1999.* Kew, Victoria, Australia: Christian Research Association, 1999.

Brierley, Peter, and Boyd Myers. *Irish Christian Handbook = Lámhleabhar Chríostaí na hEireann, 1995/96.* Eltham, London: Christian Research, 1994.

Brierley, Peter, Heather Wraight, and David Longley. *UK Christian Handbook.* [2000/01 Millennium ed.] London: Christian Research; HarperCollins Religious, 1999. Web: www.christian-research.org.uk

Centre for Mission Direction. *New Zealand Mission Agencies.* Web: www.cmd.org.nz/agencies.html

Chao, Jonathan. *The China Mission Handbook: a Portrait of China and its Church.* Hong Kong: Chinese Church Research Center, 1989.

Downes, D. R. *Directory of Kenya's Missionary-Sending Ministries.* Nairobi, Kenya: Daystar University College, 2000.

European Churches Handbook. London: MARC Europe, 1991. Contents: vol. 1.— Denmark, Finland, France, Norway, Switzerland (French), United Kingdom. Vol. 2— Austria, Netherlands, Northern Ireland, Republic of Ireland, Spain.

Froise, Marjorie. *Lesotho Christian Handbook, 1992-93.* Johannesburg: Christian Info, 1992.

Froise, Marjorie. *South African Christian Handbook 1999/2000.* Welkom, South Africa: Christian Info, [1999?]. Web: www.presbyterian.org.za/chr-hb.htm

Froise, Marjorie. *Swaziland Christian Handbook 1994.* Welkom, South Africa: Christian Info, 1994.

Guillermo, Merlyn L., and L. P. Verora. *Protestant Churches and Missions in the Philippines.* [Philippines]: World Vision Philippines, 1982.

InfoBrasil. *Agências e Juntas Missionárias.* Web: www.infobrasil.org

Japan Evangelical Missionary Association. *JEMA Directory for 1997.* Tokyo, Japan: The Association, 1996. 47th ed. Web: www.keikyo.com/jema/directory

Korea Research Institute for Missions and Communication. *Directory of Korean Missionaries & Mission Societies.* [South Korea]: Korea Research Institute for Missions and Communication, 1992. Note: Text in Korean, with some English. [See also: Korean World Missions Association website: www.kwma.org and Korean World Mission Council for Christ: www.kwmc.com]

Lazarus, Sam. *Proclaiming Christ: a Handbook of Indigenous Missions in India.* Madras, Tamil Nadu, India: Church Growth Association of India, 1992.

Limpic, Ted, et al. *Ibero-American Missions Handbook.* Acapulco, Mexico: Comibam & OC International (Sepal), 1997. Web: www.comibam.org/catalogo/index.htm

Linzey, Sharon, and Peter Kuzmic. *Directory of Indigenous Christian Organizations of the Former Soviet Union and East Central Europe; Between Two Worlds: the Challenges of Ministry in Eastern Europe.* Evanston, IL: Berry Publishing Services, 1996.

Linzey, Sharon, M. Holt Ruffin, and Mark R. Elliot. *East-West Christian Organizations: a Directory of Western Christian Organizations Working in East Central Europe and the Newly Independent States Formerly Part of the Soviet Union.* Evanston, IL: Berry Publishing Services, 1993.

Malaysia & Brunei Church Directory 1986–1987. Singapore: Singapore Every Home Crusade, Ltd., 1986.

Pate, Larry D. *From Every People: A Handbook of Two-Thirds World Missions with Directory/ Histories/Analysis.* Monrovia, CA: MARC, 1989.

Shane, John. *The Nairobi Networker: A Christian Worker's Directory.* 2nd ed. Nairobi, Kenya: Urban Ministries Support Group, 1997.

Sydney Centre for World Missions. *Evangelical Missionary Alliance,* NSW [Directory of Australian Mission Agencies] Web: www.pastornet.net.au/scwm/ema_html.htm

Tumusiime, Ephraim N. *Uganda Christian Missions Directory 1995–96.* [Kampala, Uganda]: Published by the Directory of Uganda Christian Mission Agencies, 1995.

Books on Mission in the Twenty-First Century

These monographs and collected essays discuss the future of global evangelization and selected issues in missiology. They focus on the thinking of the church in the 1990s and encourage examination of new approaches to mission in the new millennium.

Barrett, David B., and Todd M. Johnson. *Our Globe and How to Reach It: Seeing the World Evangelized by AD 2000 & Beyond.* Birmingham, AL: New Hope, 1990.

Bible Translation and the Spread of the Church: the Last 200 Years. Leiden; New York: E. J. Brill, 1990.

Bosch, David. *Believing in the Future: Toward a Missiology of Western Culture.* Valley Forge, PA: Trinity Press International; Leominster, England: Gracewing, 1995.

Brierley, Peter. *Future Church: A Global Analysis of the Christian Community to the Year 2010.* London, England: Christian Research, 1998.

Bryant, David. *The Hope at Hand: National and World Revival for the 21st Century.* Grand Rapids, MI: Baker Books, 1995.

Bush, Luis, ed. *AD 2000 & Beyond Handbook: a Church for Every People and the Gospel for Every Person by AD 2000.* [S.l.: s.n.], 1992.

Elmer, Duane H., and Lois McKinney, general eds. *With an Eye on the Future: Development and Mission in the 21st Century: Essays in Honor of Ted W. Ward.* Monrovia, CA: MARC, 1996.

Engel, James F. *A Clouded Future? Advancing North American World Missions.* Milwaukee, WI: Christian Stewardship Association, 1996. Note: "A study of parachurch financing underwritten by the Lilly Endowment Inc."

Engel, James F., and William A. Dyrness. *Changing the Mind of Missions: Where Have We Gone Wrong?* Downers Grove, IL: InterVarsity Press, 2000.

Johnstone, Patrick J. *The Church is Bigger than You Think: Structures and Strategies for the Church in the 21st Century.* Pasadena, CA: William Carey; Fearn, Ross-shire, Great Britain: Christian Focus Publications; Gerrards Cross, Bucks, Great Britain: WEC, 1998.

Martinson, Paul Varo, ed. *Mission at the Dawn of the 21st Century: A Vision for the Church.* Minneapolis, MN: Kirk House Publishers, 1999. Note: Chiefly papers from the Congress on the World Mission of the Church, held at the Luther Theological Seminary in St. Paul in 1998.

McKaughan, Paul, Dellanna O'Brien, and William R. O'Brien. *Choosing a Future for U. S. Missions.* Monrovia, CA: MARC, 1998.

Myers, Bryant. *The Changing Shape of World Mission.* Monrovia, CA: MARC 1993.

Phillips, James M., and Robert T. Coote, eds. *Toward the Twenty-First Century in Christian Mission.* Grand Rapids, MI: Eerdmans, 1993. Festschrift in honor of Gerald H. Anderson.

Pobee, J. S. *A.D. 2000 and After: the Future of God's Mission in Africa.* Accra: Asempa Publishers, Christian Council of Ghana, 1991.

Rainer, Thom S, ed. *Evangelism in the 21st Century.* Wheaton, IL: Harold Shaw Publishers, 1989. Festschrift in honor of Lewis A. Drummond.

Samuel, Vinay, and Chris Sugden, eds. *A.D. 2000 and Beyond: A Mission Agenda.* Oxford, UK: Regnum Books, 1991. Festschrift for John Stott's 70th birthday.

Shenk, Wilbert R. *Changing Frontiers of Mission.* Maryknoll, NY: Orbis Books, 1999.

Telford, Tom, with Lois Shaw. *Missions in the 21st Century: Getting Your Church into the Game.* Wheaton, IL: Harold Shaw Publishers, 1998.

Wuthnow, Robert. *Christianity in the Twenty-First Century: Reflections on the Challenges Ahead.* New York: Oxford University Press, 1993.

Mission Journals and Newsletters

The following are important journals and news sources for mission research. Whenever known, subscription addresses are included.

Section 1 contains English language titles of highest interest to readers of the *Mission Handbook;* annotations note specific reasons for inclusion. Section 2 offers additional titles, emphasizing the international research community.

Section 1: High-Interest English Language Journals and Newsletters

Bibliographia Missionaria. Vatican City: Pontifical Missionary Library, 1987– . Annual. Pontifical Urbaniana University, 00120 Vatican City, Italy.

This annual bibliography covers a wide range of Catholic and Protestant literature from multiple language sources. The topical section, "Present State and Future of Mission," offers both articles and books of interest.

Evangelical Missions Quarterly. Wheaton, IL: Evangelism and Missions Information Service, 1964– . 4 issues per year. $21.95. *Evangelical Missions Quarterly,* Box 794, Wheaton, IL 60189, USA. E-mail: emis@wheaton.edu; Web: www. wheaton.edu/bgc/emis.

Using both academic and missionary authors, EMQ tackles contemporary issues from a conservative perspective. Readers can keep up-to-date in research by reading the book reviews, highlights from periodicals, listings of conferences and seminars, and the internet resource guide, "Missions on the Web."

International Bulletin of Missionary Research. New Haven, CT: Overseas Ministries Study Center, 1981– . Quarterly. $21.00/year. IBMR, Overseas Ministries Study Center, 490 Prospect Street, New Haven, CT 06511, USA. E-mail: ibmr@omsc.org; Web: www.omsc.org.

Beyond its many fine articles, several features are noteworthy. In each January issue, David B. Barrett and Todd M. Johnson publish the "Annual Statistical Table on Global Mission," and the editors issue their "Fifteen Outstanding Books of [the previous year] for Mission Studies." Each issue contains book reviews, and "Dissertation Notices" appear periodically.

International Journal of Frontier Missions. El Paso, TX: International Student Leaders Coalition for Frontier Missions, 1984– . Quarterly. $15.00. IJFM, 7665 Wenda Way, El Paso, TX 79915, USA. E-mail: 103121.2610@compuserve.com.

The editors seek to be "forerunners in missions to the frontiers."

International Review of Mission. Geneva, Switzerland: Commission on World Mission and Evangelism of the World Council of Churches, 1912– . Quarterly. $35.00. IRM, World Council of Churches, 150 route de Ferney, 1211 Geneva 2, Switzerland.

Covering a broad ecumenical spectrum, each issue contains 10–12 scholarly articles on one topic. Of particular interest is the ongoing "Bibliography on Mission Studies." Section 02.00.00 contains citations to "Surveys of the Christian Situation" with Section 02.04.00 specifically featuring "Mission Futures."

Missiology. Scottdale, PA: American Society of Missiology, 1973– . Quarterly. Individual subscription for one year = $21.00. *Missiology,* American Society of Missiology, 616 Walnut Avenue, Scottdale, PA 15683, USA. Web: www.asmweb.org.

As the official publication of the ASM, *Missiology* is a "forum for the exchange of ideas" among scholars in the field of missiology. Besides lengthy book reviews and brief sketches on "books and media resources received," each issue contains a highly selective list of "Essential Books on Missiology" for a $100 budget and a secondary list of "Important Books on Missiology" for an additional $200 budget.

Missionalia. Menlo Park, South Africa: Southern African Missiological Society, 1973– . 3 issues per year. Individual subscription for one year (airmail) = $40.00. The Editor, *Missionalia,* P. O. Box 35704, Menlo Park 0102, South Africa. E-mail: Jansie@CPro.co.za.

Missionalia is of particular interest to missionaries and scholars working in Africa. A significant portion of each issue is devoted to "Missiological Abstracts" with an annual index compiled in the last issue of each volume. The editors also provide a list of journals abstracted in each volume.

World Pulse. Wheaton, IL: Evangelism and Missions Information Service, 1984– . Semi-monthly. $29.95/year. *World Pulse,* P.O. Box 794, Wheaton, IL 60189, USA. E-mail: emis@wheaton.edu; Web: www.wheaton.edu/bgc/emis

World Pulse reports and analyzes mission news, interviews key leaders, and offers an "Info Corner" highlighting, "Newsmakers, Milestones, and Things to Come."

Section 2: International Mission Journals

Bulletin (United Bible Societies). Reading, England: United Bible Societies, 1950– . 4 numbers per year. World Service Center, Reading Bridge House, 7th Floor, Reading, RG1 8PJ, England. Web: www.biblesociety.org

Evangelikale Missiologie. Korntal, Germany: Arbeitskreis für Evangelikale Missiologie, 1985– . 4 issues per year. Arbeitskreis für Evangelikale Missiologie, Engstlatter Weg 19, 70567 Stuttgart, Germany.

Exchange: Journal of Missiological and Ecumenical Research. Leiden, The Netherlands: Brill Academic Publishers in cooperation with the Interuniversity Institute for Missiological and Ecumenical Research, 1972– . 4 issues per year. *Exchange,* Brill Academic Publishers, P.O. Box 9000, 2300 PA, Leiden, The Netherlands.

Mission: Journal of Mission Studies = Revue des Sciences de la Mission. Ottawa, Ontario, Canada: Institut des Sciences de la Mission = Institute of Mission Studies, 1994– . 2 issues per year. *Mission,* Saint Paul University, 223 Main Street, Ottawa, ON, Canada K1S 1C4.

Mission Studies: Journal of the International Association for Mission Studies. Leiden, Netherlands: IAMS, 1984– . 2 issues per year. IAMS Secretariat, Normannenweg 17–21, 20537 Hamburg, Germany. E-mail: iams@emw-d.de; Web: www.missionstudies.org.

Neue Zeitschrift für Missionswissenschaft. Nouvelle Revue de Science Missionaire. Immensee, [Switzerland]: Verein zur Förderung der Missionswissenschaft, etc., 1945– . 4 issues per year. NZM, Fritz Folmli, Missionshaus Bethlehem, 6405 Immensee, Switzerland.

Norsk Tidsskrift for Misjon. Oslo, Norway: Egede Institute in cooperation with Tapir Publishers, 1948– . 4 issues per year. NTM, Tapir Forlag, Nardovn. 14, 7005 Trondheim, Norway. E-mail: tapir.forlag@tapir.ntnu.no

South-Pacific Journal of Mission Studies. North Turramurra, NSW, Australia: South Pacific Association of Mission Studies, 1989– . Irregular. SPJMS, Jim Mulroney, SPAMS, Columban Mission Institute, 420 Bobbin Head Road, North Turramurra, NSW 2074, Australia. E-mail: cmi@columban.org.au

Svensk Missionstidskrift/Swedish Missiological Themes. Uppsala, Sweden: Swedish Institute of Missionary Research, 1913– . 4 issues per year. SMT, c/o Swedish Institute of Missionary Research, P.O. Box 1526, 751 45 Uppsala, Sweden. E-mail: gustafbjorck@teol.uu.se; Web: www.teol.uu.se/hemsidor/simeng/index.html.

Theology in Context: Information on Theological Contributions from Africa, Asia, Oceania and Latin America. Aachen, Germany: Institute of Missiology, 1984– . 2 issues per year. Institute of Missiology Missio, P.O. Box 11 10, 52012 Aachen, Germany. E-mail: Marieluise.herzog@missio-aachen.de or dokumentation@missio-aachen.de

Third Millennium: Indian Journal of Evangelization. Gujarat, India: Third Millennium, 1998– . Quarterly. The Managing Editor, *Third Millennium,* Bishop's House, P.B. No. 1, Kalavad Road, Rajkot 360005, Gujarat, India. E-mail: bprajkot@wilnetonline.net

Tidskriften Missionsforum: Utges Av Svenska Missionsradet. Stockholm, Sweden: Svenska Missionsradet, 1995– . 4 issues per year. Svenska Missionsradet, Box 1767, 111 87 Stockholm, Sweden. E-mail: smr@ekuc.se

Transformation: An International Evangelical Dialogue on Mission and Ethics. Oxford, England: Oxford Centre for Mission Studies, 1984– . 4 issues per year. *Transformation,* Paternoster Press, P. O. Box 300, Carlisle, Cumbria, CA3 0QR, UK. E-mail: pp@stl.org; Web: www.paternoster-publishing.com; E-mail: ocms@ocms.ac.uk.

Wereld en Zending: Oecumenisch tijdschrift voor missiologie en missionaire Praktijk, voor Nederland en Belgie. Kampen, The Netherlands: Uitgeverij Kok, [1972]– . 4 issues per year. Uitgeverij Kok, Postbus 130, 8260 AC, Kampen, The Netherlands.

Zeitschrift für Mission. Stuttgart, Germany; Basel, Switzerland: Deutschen Gesellschaft für Missionswissenschaft und der Basler Mission, 1975– . 4 issues per year. ZM, Evangelischer Missionsverlag im Christlichen Verlagshaus GmbH, Postfach 31 11 41, 70471 Stuttgart, Germany.

Zeitschrift für Missionswissenschaft und Religionswissenschaft. Münster, Germany: Internationales Institut für missionswissenschaftliche Forschungen e. V., 1911– . 4 issues per year. ZMR, Institut für Missionswissenschaft, Hufferstr. 27, 48189 Münster, Germany.

Survey Questionnaire

Shown on these pages is the full questionnaire used for this version of the *Handbook*. For agencies that had previously appeared in the *Handbook*, their name, address, etc., and information covered by questions 1-8 was printed with an option to review it and make any needed updates or fill in questions 1-8. Every agency was asked to fill in questions 9-16 with their current statistical information (for the calendar or fiscal year 1998) as applicable. The questionnaire for Canadian agencies had "Canada" or "Canadian" instead of "USA" in the relevant places. EFMA member missions receive an annual questionnaire from EFMA which includes additional questions relevant only to EFMA members.

MISSION HANDBOOK
USA Protestant Ministries Overseas Questionnaire

1. What is your organization's name as you are known and would like to be listed in the *Mission Handbook?*

   ____

2. Mailing Address:

   ____

   (P.O. Box or Street) (City) (State) (Zip)

3. Telephone number: (__________) ______________________

   Fax number: (__________) ______________________

   E-Mail ______________________

   Web Site ______________________

4. Chief Executive Officer in the USA:

   ____

   (Name) (Title of Position)

5. Year organization founded in USA: ____________

6. Which **one** of the following is most used in describing your organization's denominational orientation?

❏ Denominational ❏ Interdenominational ❏ Nondenominational ❏ Transdenominational

❏ Prefer that denominational orientation not be used Other ____________

7. Which **one** (or two if needed) of the following terms describes the traditional doctrinal and/or ecclesiastical stance of your organization?

❑ Adventist
❑ Baptist
❑ Brethren
❑ Christian (Restoration Movement)
❑ Christian/Plymouth Brethren
❑ Charismatic
❑ Congregational
❑ Ecumenical
❑ Episcopal
❑ Evangelical
❑ Friends
❑ Fundamentalist
❑ Holiness
❑ Independent
❑ Lutheran
❑ Mennonite
❑ Methodist
❑ Pentecostal
❑ Presbyterian
❑ Reformed
❑ Wesleyan
Other: ______________
____
____

8. Select **up to six** descriptors from the following list which are **primary activities** of your organization. If actively involved in more than six, please indicate only the six for which the most resources are currently committed.

❑ Agricultural programs
❑ Audio recording/distribution
❑ Aviation services
❑ Bible distribution
❑ Broadcasting, radio and/or TV
❑ Camping programs
❑ Childcare/orphanage
❑ Children's programs
❑ Church construction/financing
❑ Church establishing/planting
❑ Correspondence courses
❑ Development, community/other
❑ Disability assistance programs
❑ Education,church/sch. gen. Christian
❑ Education, missionary (certificate)
❑ Education, theological by extension
❑ Education, extension (other)
❑ Education, theological
❑ Evangelism, mass
❑ Evangelism, personal & small group
❑ Evangelism, student
❑ Funds transmission
❑ Furloughed missionary support
❑ Information service (mission related)
❑ Leadership development
❑ Linguistics
❑ Literacy
❑ Literature distribution
❑ Literature production
❑ Management consulting/training
❑ Medical supplies
❑ Medicine, incl. dental & public health
❑ National church nurture/support
❑ National worker support
❑ Psychological counseling
❑ Purchasing services
❑ Recruiting/mobilizing
❑ Relief and/or rehabilitation
❑ Research (missions related)
❑ Services for other agencies
❑ Short-terms programs coord.
❑ Supplying equipment
❑ Technical assistance
❑ Training/orientation, msny.
❑ Training, other
❑ Translation, Bible
❑ Translation, other
❑ Video/film production/dist.
❑ Youth programs
❑ Other: ______________
____

Which **one** of the above activities above is most commonly associated with your organization? ______________________________

Please fill in items 9-16 as applicable for your organization.

FINANCIAL DATA (Note: if some of the following categories do not apply, please indicate "NA" for not applicable.)

9. What was your organization's **grand total income for all ministries in the USA and overseas,** raised in the USA in calendar or fiscal 1998? (Denominations should report their board total) $ ______________

10. Of the grand total for all ministries reported in Question 9, what was the amount of **income for overseas ministries?** $ ______________

11. Of the amount reported in Question 10, what, if any, was the **dollar amount of gifts-in-kind** commodities and/or services that were donated for overseas activities to your organization? ______________

12. **COUNTRIES OF SERVICE AND FIELD PERSONNEL**

For personnel from USA: Include those engaged in **cross-cultural ministry and fully supported** under your organization as of Jan. 1, 1999. Include those on furlough and those on loan to another organization if they are fully supported by your organization. Include those on loan to your organization only if fully supported by you. Include spouses, even if they don't have "official" ministry status but serve in a ministry or support role.

For personnel from non-USA countries: Include personnel with specific mission/ministry duties who are fully or partially supported by/through your organization from funds raised in the USA.

Please make additional copies of this page if needed.

Note: Indicate a region only if a specific country is not suitable:	Year Work Began	From USA: Fully supported personnel with length of service expected to be:			From non-USA countries: Fully or partially supported personnel. Show the number on the appropriate country of service line.	
Country of Service		1 up to 2 years	2 to 4 years	More than 4 years	Citizens of their country of service	Not citizens of their country of service

OTHER PERSONNEL (Categories other than those reported in Question 12)

13. Number of **nonresidential mission personnel** from the USA (persons not residing in the country(s) of their ministry focus but assigned to overseas duties and traveling overseas at least 12 weeks per year on operational aspects of the ministry) who are supported by your organization.
__________ Fully supported by your organization __________ Partially supported

14. Number of **short-term personnel** from the USA who went on overseas service projects or mission trips **less than 1 year, but at least 2 weeks,** in 1998 through your organization, either fully or partially supported including those raising their own support:
____

If you have a short-term program, where are **initial contacts** usually made with potential participants:
__ Churches __ Conferences (other than in churches) __ Individually Other: ___

How many of your **regular staff** in the USA and overseas have **duties related to short-term programs?**
__ Full time S-T program Partial duties S-T program: __ 50% of total time __10-49%

15. Number of USA **bi-vocational or "tentmaker" personnel sponsored or supervised by your organization** (persons who support themselves partially or fully through non-church/mission vocations and live overseas for the purpose of Christian witness, evangelism, and/or encouraging believers). __________

If you relate to "tentmakers," do you have staff assigned to maintain such contacts?
_____ Yes _____ No

Note: If countries of service for personnel in Items 13–15 are not already listed in the table in Item 12, add those countries. Also list countries with no personnel but with regular ongoing programs you support.

16. Number of **staff** and/or other employees assigned to ministry and/or office duties **in the USA.**

__ Full-time paid staff __ Part-time paid staff/associates __Volunteer (ongoing) helpers

If your organization has a board-adopted short **purpose or mission statement, please enclose a copy** from a brochure, letterhead, newsletter, or other copy that you share with others.

If you have **additional comments** about your organization or this survey that you would like us to be aware of, please indicate here or enclose an additional sheet.

THANK YOU for responding to this survey! We appreciate it.

Submitted by: ______________________________ Date: ____________

Mission handbook 2001-2003